Elements of Neurophysiology

Elements
of
NEUROPHYSIOLOGY

Sidney Ochs

Department of Physiology
Indiana University School of Medicine
Indianapolis, Indiana, USA

1965
John Wiley & Sons, Inc.
New York – London – Sydney

Preface

This text grew out of the need for a relatively simple yet comprehensive and modern introduction to the field of neurophysiology for medical and graduate students in physiology. Neurophysiology has grown rapidly within the last 15 years. Application of new physical and chemical techniques has permitted an insight into the ionic nature of nerve impulses in single cells. With the use of the electron microscope the fine structure of neurons may be observed almost at molecular dimensions, and the newly recognized subcellular entities have been related to neuronal function. The relation of emotion and consciousness to the activity of the brain is under active investigation and in the near future sophisticated computer techniques promise to help unravel the complex flow of information within the nervous system. These advances have created an interest in neurophysiology among students in allied fields of study—in biochemistry, anatomy and psychology. By taking a broad biological point of view, it is hoped that this book will meet their needs.

Keeping in mind the need for coherence in an elementary text, the basic functional concepts are introduced step-by-step. Those introduced in early chapters are given in most detail as they form the groundwork for later discussions. The experimental evidence used was selected for its generality, the aim being to subordinate the variety of information to the development of the concepts involved. Where instructive, an historical approach was used to show the continuity of present-day concepts with classical information.

In dealing with the wide range of published neurophysiological material, it was impossible to include a number of excellent studies and yet keep within the framework of an elementary introduction. Consequently, it is hoped that the reviews, monographs and reference works cited will serve as a guide to that large store of knowledge.

The author wishes to take this opportunity to thank the many persons who in one way or another helped bring this book about. First and foremost especial thanks are due Professor A. van Harreveld who read the whole of two drafts of this book, and whose encouragement and criticisms have been invaluable. Professor H. McIlwain helped greatly in his comments dealing with the neurochemical sections and in catching errors in other sections. The encouraging overall comments of Professor R. W. Gerard are also very much appreciated.   Thanks are also due to M. Aprison, C. Ferster, M. Matsunaga, H. Suzuki and R. Werman who read parts of the early drafts and to other colleagues and my students who by their discussion or response to lectures helped shape the evolution of this book.   Appreciation and thanks are also due to Professor B. Katz, J. L. de C. Downer, A. Grinnell, E. J. Harris, R. Orkand, I. S. Russell and C. Slater all at University College, London, for reading sections of the final galleys and supplying valuable corrections and comments.

The author assumes responsibility for what appears in this book. In a work of this nature there are bound to be errors of omission and commission, and suggestions and criticisms from the reader are invited.

The laborious task of typing and retyping has been patiently borne over the years by Mrs. Helen Granger, Mrs. Lois Baker, Mrs. Beatrice Leap and Miss Carol Hidy.   The assistance of the editorial staff of Wiley & Sons, London, in the translation of the manuscript to the printed page is very much appreciated.

Finally, without the innumerable assistances of my wife, Bess, the preparation of this work would not have been possible.

May, 1964   Sidney Ochs

Contents

1

Introduction

Historical notes

Neurophysiology may be defined as the study of those special mechanisms which control and underlie behavior. In this broad sense it probably has always been of interest to man. Deviations from normal behavior must have some explanation, and early medicine and theology supplied the first frameworks and guided primitive attempts at treatment. Trephine holes with rounded edges, showing that they were made during life, have been found in the skulls of prehistoric man and probably represent attempts to cure neurological disorders. Burton (1628) speaks of ancient authorities prescribing trephination as a cure for melancholy. Although we do not know what prehistoric man thought, some of his ideas are found in the earliest written speculations of the ancient Greeks. Such writings concerned themselves with a *pneuma* or *vital spirit* which gives life and thought to the body. It is remarkable that this theory served as an explanation of neural function for more than 2000 years, to be supplanted only little more than 100 years ago.

Briefly, the theory was that the vital pneuma entered the body from the air upon inspiration during breathing. The blood acted as the conveyance to distribute pneuma throughout the body, the heart being the means of blood movement (Keele, 1957). Though mainly limited to directly observable phenomena, the physiological facts available to the ancient observer were dramatic. When breathing is prevented death occurs; therefore, breathing appeared to be necessary for the abstraction of the intangible vital principle from the air. If passage of blood to a limb is prevented, then before long that limb will die; this was considered to result from the loss of pneuma conveyed to the limb by the blood. Cutting large vessels or stopping the heart prevents the flow of the vital principle.

Further facts which were considered were related to the special functions of the head. Blows or other damage to regions of the head where the major sensory organs, eye, ear and nose, are located cause alterations of senses. This was taken into account by Hippocrates (460–377 B.C.) in his discussion of epilepsy, the 'sacred

1

disease': A blockade of the vital spirit within the head produced overactivity there while the rest of the body remained insensible. The froth sometimes seen on the lips of the epileptic was considered to be evidence of the vital spirit leaking out under excessive pressure. The body spasms were taken as the sign of vital spirits being forced under pressure, first in one and then in another of some remaining (neural) channels leading from the brain into the body.

Galen (A.D. 130–200) believed that the pneuma brought by the blood to the brain was further refined by that organ. The finer animal spirit which was separated in the brain then flowed down nerves to the muscles to control movements. Galen's contributions qualify him as the founder of experimental neurophysiology. He found, for example, when he cut the nerves to the larynx of a pig that its vocalization was interrupted, showing that the larynx was controlled by its nerve supply. Some would give this honor to Erasistratus (310–250 B.C.) who much earlier had described some nerves as sensory, others motor. However, this discovery was forgotten until in the 19th century Bell and Magendie discovered the sensory and motor functions of the dorsal and ventral spinal roots (Fulton, 1930).

Descartes (A.D. 1595–1650) further elaborated the pneuma theory. He concluded that at a common center within the brain sensations converged, i.e. at a *sensus commune*. To effect motion, the vital fluid flowed out of the brain ventricles and into motor nerves. The outward movement into the various motor nerve channels leading to the appropriate portion of the musculature was controlled by the pineal gland. His ideas had some relation to those curious concepts of Islamic thinkers in the Middle Ages concerning the ventricles of the brain and categories of higher mental function. The medievalists regarded the anterior ventricle as the residence of the sensus commune, the middle ventricle of intellect, and the posterior ventricle the reservoir for outflow of animal spirits (Magoun, 1963).

If, as Descartes supposed, animal spirits flowing from the nerves into the muscles caused them to expand and contract, their volume should increase upon contraction. In the 17th century Swammerdam failed to find an increase in muscle volume upon contraction, and this finding was ominous for the pneuma theory. The long history of spirits and animal fluids finally came to a close with the renewed interest in experimental evidence. The stage was set for a truer insight into neural mechanisms and behavior.

The discovery of electricity in animal tissues by Galvani in the late 18th century ushered in a new principle of nerve function (Brazier,

1958).   At first 'animal electricity' merely supplanted 'pneuma' as an agent in nerve activity.   The present era of electrical studies of the nervous system began when it was clearly shown by Du Bois-Reymond that electrical currents were associated with the nerve impulse (Brazier, 1959).

In the past the material substance of the nervous system was considered to be a homogeneous mass.   This impeded a consideration of the relation of structure to function except for the obvious large masses of grey and white tissue and the ventricles visible to the eye.   It was probably by the use of the early spherical magnifying lenses which permitted Descartes in the 17th century to report nerve as composed of 'tubes' and 'filaments,' though at this time Leeuwenhoek and others had looked for nerve tubes without success. Aberrations produced by the simple lenses then in use prevented sufficient resolution of small structures.   After the practical physical problem of making parabolic lenses was solved, and achromatic lenses became available, further advances of fundamental significance became possible; and with the work of Schwann and Schleiden the cell became recognized as the fundamental unit of living tissue (Nordenskiöld, 1942).

Techniques for hardening the soft tissues of the nervous system (fixation) so that thin sections could be cut and stained were developed in the 19th century (Liddell, 1960).   Eventually it was recognized that the fibers of peripheral nerves were extensions of the cell bodies located in the central nervous system (CNS) or in the peripheral ganglionic masses.   Much of our knowledge of the structure of the neuron came about with the discovery of the silver impregnation methods of Golgi.   By this means the detailed structure of various neurons could be observed.

The demonstration of the individuality of the neurons in the nervous system is associated with the name of Ramón y Cajal. Using the Golgi silver stain as well as other neuronal stains, he studied the form of nerve cells and the related cells found in the central and peripheral nervous system (Ramón y Cajal, 1909, 1911). This remarkable body of work, much of it still of value, showed clearly that the neurons of the nervous system like other cells are individual entities.   Ramón y Cajal strongly supported the *neuron doctrine* which was opposed to the idea of a syncytium, where the cytoplasm of one cell merges with that of other cells (Ramón y Cajal, 1954). The concept that the functions of the nervous system are to be explained by an integration of neurons was the basis of Sherrington's (1906) classic studies and of present-day neurophysiology.

The neuron

As mentioned, the neuron is the basic unit of neural function, and it will be well to note its general features at this time.   In a thin section through the cell body or perikaryon stained with an analine dye, the *nucleolus* within the *nucleus* has a dark blue color (Fig. 1.1).   The pale cytoplasm around the nucleus contains smaller clumped particles

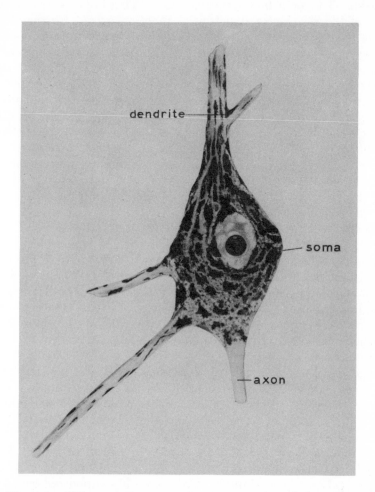

Fig. 1.1. This semi-diagrammatic representation of the neuron soma shows the lightly stained nucleus with a central intensely stained nucleolus. Around the nucleus are the Nissl bodies in the cytoplasm seen as dark staining clumped particles. Nissl particles are found in dendrites but not in the axon. (Spielmeyer, *Histopathologie des Nervensystems*, Springer, 1922.)

staining deep blue, and these are called *Nissl particles* or *Nissl bodies* after their discoverer. Another less well-defined subcellular particulate material in the cell is the *Golgi structure*, described by Golgi as reticulated or rod-shaped particles. The nucleus together with the cytoplasm around it is referred to as the *soma* (Greek: body), the *cell body* or *perikaryon*.

From the perikaryon, tree-like processes arise which branch into finer and finer divisions. These are the *dendrites* (Greek: tree) which in some types of neurons are very extensive and contain Nissl particles (Fig. 1.2). In addition to the dendrites, a relatively long extension arises from the perikaryon, the *axon*, which does not contain Nissl substance. A consequence of the neuron doctrine is that the functions of the organism comes about by interactions between the individual cells. In the case of the neuron this means transfer of activity via the axons. An enlargement known as the *bouton* is found at the terminal ending of an axon in contact with the membrane surface of the soma or dendrites of other neurons. The term *synapse* (Greek: joining) was introduced by Sherrington to express the concept of transfer of neuronal activity between neurons at this region of contiguity. Even such lowly forms as coelenterata, which have been thought until recent times to operate by means of syncytial *nerve nets* with the merging of cytoplasm between cells, have been shown to have synapses at the junctions between the fibers composing such neural networks (Pantin, 1950).

A whole new insight into the finer structure of the neuron down to molecular dimensions has been afforded in recent years by the use of the electron microscope (Zworykin *et al.*, 1945; Kay, 1961). Electrons accelerated in an electrical field have smaller wavelengths than light and the ability to resolve objects very much smaller. Tissues impregnated with osmium tetroxide or other heavy atom 'stains' are embedded in such plastic materials as Methycrylate, Epon, etc., cut into fine sections and placed in the path of focused electrons inside the evacuated column of the electron microscope (Pease, 1960). Structural differences are revealed as the beam is either scattered or passes through regions of different atomic density. The osmium or other relatively heavy atoms adhering differentially to molecular structures enhances the density differences. A comparison of a neuron cell body treated in the ordinary way with a section examined with the electron microscope is shown in Fig. 1.3. A more scattered distribution of the Nissl material is apparent in the electron micrograph. The cytoplasmic particle is composed in part of a fine canaliculate structure which has been found within the

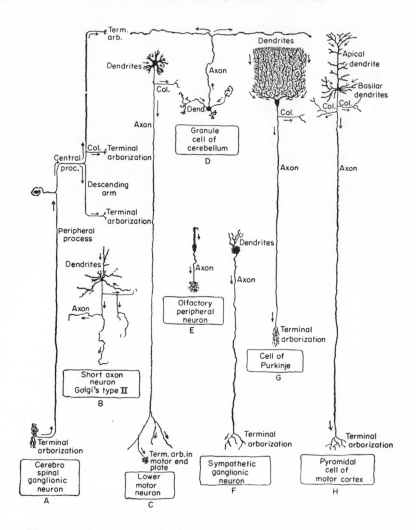

Fig. 1.2. Axonic and dendritic extensions of various types of sensory and motor neurons (A–H) are shown. The direction of conduction shown by arrows. Col, collateral branch; proc, process; term. arb, terminal arborization. (Bailey's *Textbook of Histology*, 11th Ed., Williams and Wilkins, 1944.)

cytoplasm of neurons and other cells and known as the *endoplasmic reticulum* (Fig. 1.4).   Associated with these cannulae are small dense particles, the *ribosomes*, which contain ribonucleic acid (RNA) and are related to the protein synthesizing capabilities of neuron cell bodies (Chapter 8).   The ribosomes clumping together with the endo-

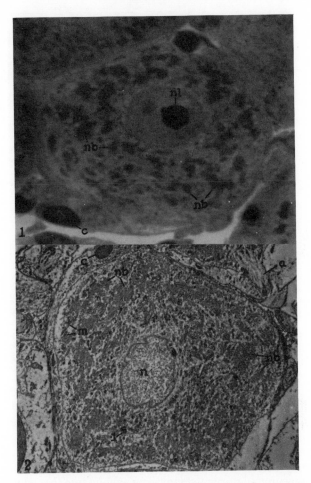

Fig. 1.3. (1). Photomicrograph through a dorsal root ganglion cell. The cytoplasm contains Nissl bodies (nb), some fine granules and unstained matrix. Nucleus (n) appears clear except for dense nucleolus (nl) and weakly stained chromatin. Capsule cells (c) surround perikaryon. (2). Electron micrograph from same cell as shown above. This section does not show the nucleolus. Small irregular Nissl bodies, mitochondria (m), and lipid droplets (l) are seen in cytoplasm. At c is the nucleus of a capsule cell and at a, an axon leaving a neighboring perikaryon. (Courtesy S. L. Palay; Palay and Palade, *J. Biophys. Biochem. Cytol.* **1**, 69, 1959.)

plasmic reticulum constitute the Nissl bodies seen in the ordinary stained preparation under the light microscope. The nucleus contains deoxyribonucleic acid (DNA), the genetic material. It controls

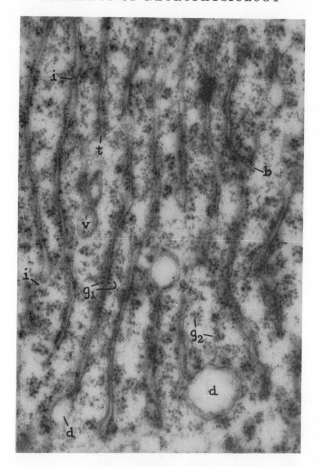

Fig. 1.4.   Electron micrograph of a section through a Nissl body of a motoneuron.   Elongated profiles predominate in the endoplasmic reticulum of the Nissl body disposed in rows that show a few narrow interruptions (i).   Some rows terminate (t), others branch (b).   Most end in relation to large dilations (d).   A few vesicles (v) are found between profiles.   The outer membranes of the profiles have disposed on them dense granules at regular intervals in rows (g_1), other granules are scattered in the cytoplasmic matrix (g_2).   (Courtesy S. L. Palay; Palay and Palade, *J. Biophys. Biochem. Cytol.* **1**, 69, 1959.)

the composition of the RNA present in the perikaryon and, in turn, the type and amount of protein produced in the neuron.

Perhaps the most remarkable achievement made with the electron microscope has been the actual demonstration of a membrane, approximately 75 A thick, completely enclosing the contents of the cell.   For many years the presence of a membrane around the cyto-plasm of the cell was inferred from osmotic behavior.   Furthermore, electrical excitation and conduction have long been believed to involve special reactions of a cell membrane (Chapter 4).   It was particularly satisfactory to resolve such a membrane around the neuron and its processes.   Further details concerning this membrane and its composition and a discussion of the fine structure of neurons will be dealt with in subsequent chapters.

Electron microscopy has also revealed that the detailed structure of the CNS is much more complex than was conceived of by means of the light microscope.   Structures below the resolution of the light microscope were not seen and the spaces between the optically visible elements were believed to be filled with a 'ground substance'. Since the studies of Wyckoff and Young (1956) this is known not to be the case.   Fine branches of dendrites and of the neuroglial cells fill much of this apparent space.   At present the size of the true *extracellular space* existing between the cells of the CNS is not resolved.   The physiological evidence for an extracellular space larger than appears in electron microscope sections will be presented in Chapter 19.

It is possible to study isolated parts of the nerve outside the body, most easily the nerve fibers.   In order to keep these *in vitro* preparations functioning, the fluids in which they are immersed or with which they are kept moist must have a composition similar to that normally found in the extracellular spaces.   Following the earlier studies of Sidney Ringer, various *Ringer solutions* have been devised.   A simple frog–Ringer solution commonly used has the following concentrations of salts: 115 mM NaCl, 2 mM KCl, and 1.8 mM $CaCl_2$.   Phosphate or carbonate buffers and glucose may be added to the Ringer solution.   The composition of salts required is also somewhat different for tissues from different species.

Divisions of neurophysiology

Neurophysiology deals with functional aspects of the nervous system, with transmission of nerve impulses, motor control, reflexes, and even with perception, emotion and mentation.   How, then, do the neurons and their synaptic interconnections give rise to these varied and abstract activities ?   For purposes of our study we may consider the subject as composed of three levels of increasing complexity.   The first level of study is that of excitation and propagation of an impulse, which is conveniently studied in isolated peripheral nerves.   Frog nerves can survive after isolation for hours and days in a moist environment and have long been favored for studies of excitation. These are nerve trunks composed of a large number of individual nerve fibers. We shall use the term 'nerve' to refer to a nerve trunk or nerve bundle, and 'fiber' to refer to a single nerve fiber. Within the last several decades isolated single giant nerve fibers of the squid have been used to reveal fundamental principles of the membrane potential and of excitation, relating these phenomena to ionic composition and transfer. As these fibers have diameters of 0.5 mm and greater, direct measurement of the membrane changes have been made with electrodes inserted inside them allowing for a detailed physical-chemical and biochemical analysis of excitation (Chapters 4–7). Studies of excitability and the conducting properties of different parts of the neuron have revealed differences in the nature of excitation and conduction between the axon, cell body, and the dendrites of the cell. One of the differences encountered in considering the peripheral part of the sensory fiber is the *transduction* by sensory receptors and nerves of the various physical stimuli from the environment acting on the organism. The nerve impulses resulting from stimulation of the sensory nerve terminals form a *code* which is related to the stimulus, a code whose 'meaning' is assessed by the CNS (Chapters 11, 12).

The second level of our study of the nervous system is of events which take place at the synapse between two cells where new properties are found. Most synaptic junctions operate by release of special *transmitter substances* from the *pre-synaptic* endings of axons which effect excitation of the *post-synaptic* cell. The most accessible synapse is the neuromuscular junction where motor nerves innervate muscles. At this junction in the vertebrate *acetylcholine* (*ACh*) has been identified as the transmitter substance. It is released by the nerve endings to produce a special local reaction of the muscle membrane and in turn this excites an action potential which causes muscle contraction (Chapter 9). Synaptic transmission between neurons within the CNS is more difficult to study. The chemical nature of the synaptic transmitter substances involved is lacking except in one case, that of the *Renshaw cell* which is excited by ACh (Chapter 16). Other transmitter substances are known for the peripheral nervous system (Chapter 10). Some of them may operate similarly in the CNS.

The third level in our study of neurophysiology is concerned with the pattern of connections between neurons and groups of neurons related to a known function. It is within the CNS that the number of synapses between cells achieves monumental proportions. It has been estimated that there are ten billion neurons within the brain of man, and on many of these neurons there may be thousands of synaptic endings. In turn, the axons of each cell may have hundreds of collateral branches synapsing with other cells. The number of possible permutations of the neuronal interconnections in even a small part of the CNS is astronomical. This level of study is the most difficult and challenging. Large numbers of cell bodies within the CNS, the *nuclear groups*, are readily distinguished in stained histological sections. Nuclear groups and tracts of axons connecting them can be traced from place to place in the CNS. It is to such relatively complex nuclear regions that we relate various functions of the CNS. For example, we consider respiratory and cardiovascular 'centers' in the brain stem and motor reflexes to be regulated by spinal cord nuclear groups. However, such functions appear in many cases to require a number of relatively far-spaced nuclear groups and interconnecting tracts working harmoniously. The problem of the localization of functions within groups of neurons found in various parts of the nervous system will occupy our attention in most of the later chapters of this book.

A few electrical and instrumental considerations

Modern neurophysiology has become characterized by the use of electrical techniques for eliciting and recording neuronal responses. This is because the means of propagation of the nerve signal itself is electrical in nature. The reader is referred to the book on instrumentation by Dickinson (1950) and the larger one by Donaldson (1958). For an elementary presentation Suckling's (1961) book is useful. The recent book by Bureš *et al.* (1960) on electrophysiological methods has, in addition to a fairly large section on electronic instrumentation, a valuable presentation of experimental procedures in neurophysiology.

It will be well to mention a few of the special electrical terms and practices which are continually used and referred to in the literature of neurophysiology. It should be recognized that the terminology used to indicate the direction of current flow is an arbitrary convention; the current is considered to flow from the positive pole or *anode* of a battery through the tissue to the *cathode*. Actually electrons are known to flow toward the positive pole in metallic conductors. However, and this cannot be stressed too much, the flow of current in electrolyte solutions (e.g. cells and tissues) is carried by *ions*. In general, *cations* and *anions* are moving in both directions at once, toward cathode and anode respectively. Lines of current are commonly used to show the flow of current between cells or across the membrane of cells, but these should be considered as a convenient abstraction of the real physical situation.

Electrochemical reactions occurring at the surfaces of electrodes introducing current into tissues can be complex and give rise to a phenomenon known as *polarization*. That the electrodes are polarized is shown when after the voltage source is switched on the current flow becomes gradually reduced. The result is much as if a resistance increase had occurred at the electrode surface or as if an opposing voltage had been introduced in opposition to the flow of current, a *voltage of polarization*. Electrode polarization is diminished by the use of *non-polarizable electrodes*. Calomel electrodes and silver chloride electrodes *reversible* to one or the other ion species present in the electrolyte solution are non-polarizable electrodes in common use. Even with their use current levels must be low or polarization will still occur. Non-polarizable electrodes are required when recording steady or slow-changing potentials arising from cells and tissues and where polarization voltages of the electrodes would obscure the true voltages present in the cell or tissues.

Voltage measurements must often be made from cells which are immersed in a conducting electrolyte solution, the Na^+ and Cl^- of the extracellular space, which acts as an electrical shunting path of current. The current flow around electrically active cells reduces and changes the recorded voltages in characteristic ways. The principle of voltage measurements in such *volume conductors* may be demonstrated by the use of a two-dimensional conductor made of a large sheet of blotter paper moistened with NaCl solution as a conductor. Current is introduced by applying electrodes at two points on the surface and the resulting lines of current flow and potentials are distributed as shown in Fig. 1.5. The current enters the sheet via the *source* electrode (anode) and is led out through the *sink* (cathode) electrode. The probe electrode records different potentials, depending on its position with relation to the source and sink. The other, or *indifferent*, electrode is placed at a point so remote from the source and sink as to be effectively zero with regard to them. Current and voltage are related by Ohm's law in any unit length and width of this two-dimensional current field. The dotted lines at right angles to the current lines are *isopotential* lines. All along the isopotential lines the probe electrode will record the same voltage. The three-dimensional conducting volume of a tissue can be considered as an extension of the two-dimensional case presented.

A more detailed discussion of volume conductor principles is given by Wilson *et al.* (1933) and Woodbury (1960).

Some familiarity with the instrumentation commonly used is necessary and only the most important aspects can be noted here. The electrical changes produced by nerve tissue are small and rapid.

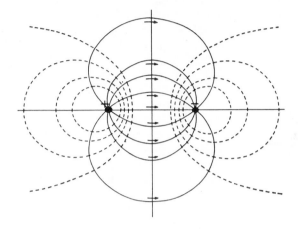

Fig. 1.5. Potential and current fields in a two-dimensional conductor arise from a current flow at the anode (+) and a sink at the cathode (−). Solid line indicates current flow. Voltage drops occur along these paths. Isopotential lines where voltages are the same are shown in dotted lines at right angles to the current lines.
(Fulton, *Textbook of Physiology*, 1955.)

Therefore, amplifiers are required to increase voltage and current changes to measurable amounts. A *direct-coupled* (d.c.) vacuum tube amplifier is used to measure *steady potentials* or slowly varying potentials. By connecting single stages of amplification together, the required large amplifications are obtained. For example, if each stage has a gain of 10 (i.e. increases the voltage 10 times), then a second stage connected to the first also with a gain of 10 gives rise to a resulting gain of 100. A further stage gain of 10 gives a total amplification of 1000, and so on. A limit to the amplification obtained by such cascading of single stages is soon reached because of the electrical noise and instability which results in a drifting of the original or *baseline* level. To obviate this difficulty, *alternating current* (a.c.) or *capacitance-coupled* amplifiers are commonly used. Condensers prevent the steady voltages between the stages of amplification from affecting each other. Alternating currents may be amplified by capacitance-coupled amplifiers down to a lower limit of frequencies of 1 cycle per second (cps) or less.   Because many neurophysiological studies involve only the rapidly changing action potentials, a.c. amplifiers are often adequate.   However, the limitation of passage of low frequencies by a.c. amplifiers must be taken into account when measuring slow-changing voltages.   A useful measure of an a.c. amplifier's lower frequency response is its *time-constant*.   This is the time taken by a *step-function* of voltage, an indefinitely long pulse of voltage, applied at the input of the amplifier to fall to 1/e of its value at the output as shown in Fig. 1.6.   An amplifier must

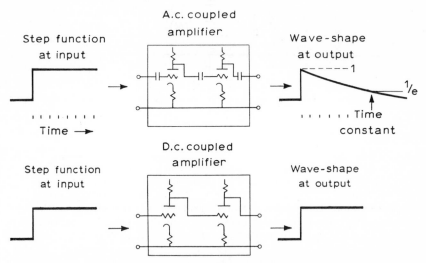

Fig. 1.6.   The stages of an a.c. amplifier are shown in the upper diagram coupled with condensers; the stages of the d.c. amplifier are directly coupled.   A step-function of current at the input falls at the output of the a.c. amplifier with a time-constant determined by the values of the condensers and resistances of the amplifier. The time constant is given by the time taken for the voltage to fall to 1/e of its amplitude at the onset of the step-function.

have a longer time-constant when slower changing voltages are being recorded.   As already noted, a d.c. amplifier is required for very slowly changing or steady potential measurements.   Short time-constants are occasionally desirable when only fast voltage changes are to be observed.   A short time-constant is used, for example, when action potentials to be recorded are found superimposed on steady or slower-changing voltages which need not be taken into account.

A *cathode follower* pre-amplifier circuit is sometimes required. The virtue of the cathode follower circuit is that voltages of tissues and cells can be measured with only a minute drain of current from the cells measured. This is of great value when the drain of current from the cell being measured would change the value of the voltage to be determined. It is necessary in particular when microelectrodes with very fine tips are placed inside cells to record potentials. The higher resistance through the tip and the electrical capacitance along the wall of these microelectrodes makes a cathode-follower input necessary to compensate for the distortions of recording which would otherwise result.

The *cathode ray oscilloscope* is commonly used to display the voltage change of an action potential. This device has been of inestimable value in the development of modern neurophysiology. The movement of a beam of electrons can faithfully display the fastest electrical

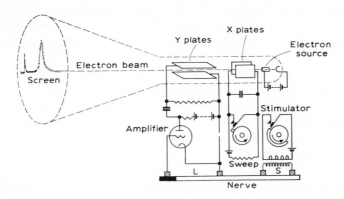

Fig. 1.7.   A beam of electrons is emitted from the electron source at one end of the cathode ray and the electron beam passes between the two sets of X and Y deflecting plates before striking the fluorescent screen at the inner face of the tube. Voltages are applied to the horizontal X-plates to sweep the beam horizontally and the signal of the amplified action potential is applied to the vertical Y-set of deflection plates to move the beam vertically. (Erlanger and Gasser, *Electrical Signs of Nervous Activity*, 1937.)

changes which have been led off from nerve. Its operation may be clarified by referring to the diagram of Fig. 1.7. A beam of electrons is emitted from a heated cathode at one end of the tube and these electrons are accelerated toward the other end of the cathode ray tube where the beam becomes visible when it strikes a screen with phosphorescent coating. Electrodes placed along the trajectory of the electron beam are used to focus the beam to a point on the screen. Sets of horizontal and vertical plates are also placed along the path of the beam to deflect it. When a voltage difference is applied between a set of plates, the beam is deflected from the negative plate and attracted toward the positive plate. Voltages to be measured are usually applied to a set of such plates in the vertical axis. The beam of the cathode ray tube is deflected upward or downward to a degree proportionate to the voltage across the plates. Small voltages such as those present in nerve must first be properly amplified before they are applied to the vertical set of deflection plates. The oscilloscope can be made to show the temporal changes of these voltages by deflecting the beam horizontally at the same time at a determined velocity. This horizontal *sweep* movement is usually set so that the beam is moved from the left to the right side of the tube screen as the observer faces the front of the tube. With the beam sweeping at a constant speed in the horizontal direction (X-axis), a voltage change from the nerve which has been amplified and simultaneously applied to the vertical plates (Y-axis) will cause the electron beam to trace out a *voltage–time pattern*. These displays are observed directly by the fluorescence of the screen excited by the beam or they are photographed from the screen for later examination. In modern oscilloscopes a single X–Y tracing may be observed. The electron beam is shut off (blanked) and then rapidly returned to the left-hand position to await the next cycle of display (Chapter 2).

In some applications where voltage changes in the tissue are not so fast, galvanometers are connected to the output of the amplifier so that ink tracings may be continuously recorded on a moving strip of paper. This is common practice in the recording of brain wave potentials, *electroencephalography* (Chapter 18).

REFERENCES

Brazier, M. A. B. (1958). The evolution of concepts relating to the electrical activity of the nervous system 1600 to 1800. *The Brain and its Functions*. Pp. 191–222. Wellcome Foundation Symposium. Blackwell, Oxford.

Brazier, M. A. B. (1959). The historical development of neurophysiology. *Handbook of Physiology—Neurophysiology*. Vol. 1, pp. 1–58. American Physiological Society, Washington, D.C.

Bureš, J., Petrain, M. and Zachár, J. (1960). *Electrophysiological Methods in Biological Research*. Translated by P. Hahn. Academic Press, New York.

Burton, R. (1628). *The Anatomy of Melancholy*. Republished 1941. Edited by F. Dell and P. Jordan-Smith. Tudor Publishing Co., New York.

Dickinson, C. J. (1950). *Electrophysiological Technique*. Electronic Engineering, London.

Donaldson, P. E. K. (1958). *Electronic Apparatus for Biological Research*. Butterworths, London.

Fulton, J. F. (1930). *Selected Readings in the History of Physiology*. Charles C. Thomas, Springfield.

Kay, D. (1961). *Techniques for Electron Microscopy*. Blackwell, Oxford.

Keele, K. D. (1957). *Anatomies of Pain*. Charles C. Thomas, Springfield.

Liddell, E. G. T. (1960). *Discovery of Reflexes*. Oxford Univ. Press, Oxford.

Magoun, H. W. (1963). *The Waking Brain*. 2nd Ed. Charles C. Thomas, Springfield.

Nordenskiöld, E. (1942). *The History of Biology. A Survey*. Translated by L. Bucknall Eyre. Tudor Publishing Co., New York.

Pantin, C. F. A. (1950). Behavior patterns in lower vertebrates. *Soc. Exptl. Biol. Symp.* **4**: 175–195.

Pease, D. C. (1960). *Histological Techniques for Electron Microscopy*. Academic Press, New York.

Ramón y Cajal, S. (1909). *Histologie du système nerveaux de l'homme et des vertébrés*. Vol. 1. Maloine, Paris. Republished 1952. Instituto Ramón y Cajal, Madrid.

Ramón y Cajal, S. (1911). *Histologie du système nerveaux de l'homme et des vertébrés*. Vol. 2. Maloine, Paris. Republished 1955. Instituto Ramón y Cajal, Madrid.

Ramón y Cajal, S. (1954). *Neuron Theory or Reticular Theory*. Translated by U. Purkiss and C. A. Fox. Consejo Superior de Investigaciones Cientificas. Instituto Ramón y Cajal, Madrid.

Sherrington, C. S. (1906). *The Integrative Action of the Nervous System*. Yale University Press, New Haven. Revised Ed. 1947. Cambridge University Press, Cambridge.

Suckling, E. E. (1961). *Bioelectricity*. McGraw-Hill, New York.

Wilson, F. N., MacLeod, A. G. and Barker, P. S. (1933). *The Distribution of Currents of Action and Injury Displayed by Heart Muscle and Other Excitable Tissues*. University of Michigan Press, Ann Arbor.

Woodbury, J. W. (1960). Potentials in a volume conductor. *Neurophysiology*. Edited by T. C. Ruch, H. D. Patton, J. W. Woodbury, and A. L. Towe. Pp. 83–91. Saunders, Philadelphia.

Wyckoff, R. W. and Young, J. Z. (1956). The motoneuron surface. *Proc. Roy. Soc. B*. **144**: 440–450.

Zworykin, V. K., Morton, G. A., Ramberg, E. G., Hillier, J. and Vance, A. W. (1945). *Electron Optics and the Electron Microscope*. John Wiley & Sons, New York.

2

Stimulation and Recording of
the Action Potential

For many years the isolated sciatic nerve–gastrocnemius muscle preparation of the frog (Fig. 2.1) was used to study the fundamental nerve properties of excitability and conduction. It will be convenient to use it here to introduce the most basic notions of excitation and response. The twitch of the muscle indicates that the nerve has been adequately excited either by electrical currents, mechanical stimulation (e.g. a light tap), or by chemicals applied to the nerve. If muscle twitches are elicited through stimulation of its nerve, the responses are referred to as *indirectly* excited. If the muscle itself is stimulated to respond, these are *directly* excited responses. Electrical stimulation has been used almost universally to study the excitation of nerve because it easily excites the nerve and, within limits, does so without apparent damage to the tissue. Furthermore, as will be discussed further on, electrical currents are the natural means by which the action potential is propagated along nerve and muscle fibers. We shall, therefore, discuss the excitation of nerve by electrical means, though other modes of stimulation show similar properties of excitation.

The muscle twitch is a relatively long-lasting phenomenon, approximately 100 milliseconds (1 msec = 1/1000 sec), compared to the action potential which has a duration of approximately 1 msec. This and the release of the transmitter substance which takes place at the synapse between nerve and muscle (Chapter 9) whereby the muscle becomes indirectly excited, make an exact study of excitation difficult. After an introduction to the study of excitation with the nerve–muscle preparation, the recording of action potentials will be described, then to be used as an index of excitation (Chapter 3).

Stimulation and the strength–duration curve

A simple way to stimulate the nerve is by the use of a step-function of current. This is done by the closure of a switch in the circuit passing current into the nerve via electrodes (Fig. 2.1). The intensity of the current flowing through the nerve is increased in successive trials by advancing the tap on the potentiometer. This is done until the first sign of excitation is seen, a muscle *twitch* or *contraction*. The minimal intensity of current which excites a response is a

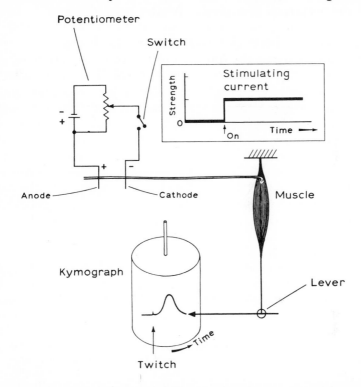

Fig. 2.1. A potentiometer controls the strength of the current passing from anode through the nerve and out through the cathode of the nerve–muscle preparation when the switch is closed. The muscle twitch recorded on the kymograph indicates adequate nerve excitation. The form of the step-function of current produced by closing the switch is shown in the insert.

measure of the *threshold*. Using the nerve–muscle preparation, stimulation of motor nerve fibers causes action potentials to propagate down the motor nerve fibers which excite the muscle cells and give rise to the visible twitch of the muscle fibers innervated by those motor nerve fibers. The threshold intensity of current which excites the motor nerve by a step pulse of indefinitely long duration is termed the *rheobase*.

With electronic techniques now available, brief *square wave pulses* of precise duration and current strength can be readily produced. By using successively shorter pulse durations, a rheobasic current is found to be effective until it is shortened to less than about one msec. When still shorter pulse durations are used, threshold is not attained unless more current is applied. As the pulse duration is further shortened, the intensity of the current must be increased still further. The relationship found between the strength of current required to excite and the duration of the pulse of current applied is described by the *strength–duration curve* (Fig. 2.2). Plotting

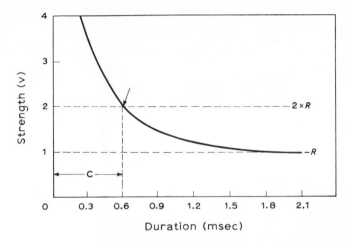

Fig. 2.2.   The strength–duration curve is shown as a curved solid line and it is determined by the strength of stimulation (ordinate) required for each duration of stimulus (abscissa). In this example, after approximately 1.8 msec, further increases in duration do not result in a lowering of the strength of the stimulation required. This is the rheobase (R). Chronaxie (C) is determined (arrow) as that duration along the strength–duration curve at a strength twice the rheobase ($2 \times R$).

logarithmically the strength required, in terms of voltage or current, against the required duration is useful so that the excitability of various tissues may be compared with the standard curves determined by Hill (1936).

When a rheobasic current is used, the nerve actually becomes excited a short time after the onset of the step pulse of current. This time is called the *utilization time*. A utilization or *utilized time* also occurs during the still shorter times of excitation found when using stimulating pulses stronger than rheobase. The strength–duration curves differ when comparing two different tissues or when comparing the same tissue in different physiological states. The excitability of a tissue may be conveniently expressed by a single defined point on the curve. At a point along this curve at twice the rheobase current, the duration of stimulus required to excite is called the *chronaxie* (Lapique, 1926). The theoretical significance once attached to chronaxie by Lapique is no longer considered important (Rushton, 1935; Davis and Forbes, 1936), but the experimental basis for its original construction is instructive. Lapique believed that transmission between nerve and muscle was electrical rather than via the neurohumoral mediator, acetylcholine, as we now know to be the case (Chapter 9). The electrical theory required the close matching of strength–duration curves (*isochronism*)

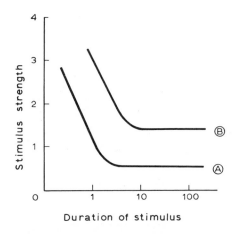

Fig. 2.3. Strength–duration curves before (A) and after (B) curare. The shift in the strength–duration curve is due to a change from stimulation of nerve endings in A to stimulation of muscle fibers in B.

between nerve and muscle. The substance *curare* (Chapter 9) was supposed to block neuromuscular transmission by shifting the chronaxie of the muscle sufficiently from that of nerve to prevent isochronism. However, it has been convincingly shown by Lucas (1906), Rushton (1935), and others that nerves and muscles have different strength–duration curves and are not normally isochronic. The shift in the strength–duration curves from the more excitable curve A in Fig. 2.3 to the less excitable curve B is due to the fact that curare blocks excitation between the nerve and the muscle, and the nerve is normally more excitable with short duration pulses than muscle. Unless special arrangements are employed, or parts of the muscle used where nerves are not present, the strength–duration curve of muscle which is measured is actually that of nerve. Therefore, when curare blocks nerve transmission, the strength–duration curve of muscle with its longer chronaxie appears.

The difference between the strength–duration curves of nerve and muscle is useful in the clinical evaluation of the presence or lack of normal innervation of muscle. An electrode is placed on the *motor point* of a muscle, that is, on the point of the skin surface over the

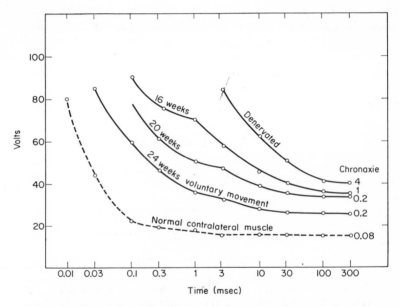

Fig. 2.4. The normal strength–duration curve from a motor point of the muscle (abductor) is shown by the dashed line with the other curves from the denervated muscle of the other hand. Determinations at different times during reinervation show the return of the strength–duration curve towards normal. (After Ritchie in Wright, *Applied Physiology*, 10th Ed., Oxford, 1954.)

muscle where nerves are most easily excited and a normal strength–duration curve for nerve can be obtained. If the nerve has been damaged and has degenerated (Chapter 8), that motor point will give a strength–duration curve characteristic of muscle (Fig. 2.4). As time goes on the nerve regenerates (Chapter 8) and reinnervates the muscle.

As it makes functional union, the measured strength–duration changes back to the normally innervated type as indicated by Fig. 2.4. Chronaxie, which is a measure of the strength–duration curve, is therefore used clinically as an index of nerve degeneration and of recovery of muscle function after regeneration and reinnervation.

The effectiveness of stimulating currents depends upon the fraction of the applied current which enters and then leaves the nerve fibers. For analytic purposes, the excised nerve trunk of a nerve-muscle preparation may be thought of as a single nerve cylinder and the electrical path of current between fibers and inside the fibers represented by the model shown in Fig. 2.5. The part of the current

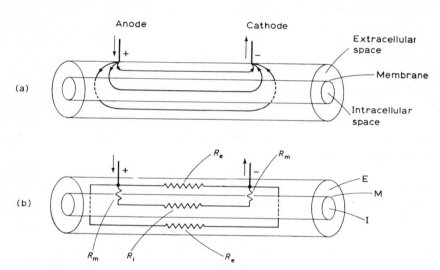

Fig. 2.5. The fibers of a nerve are represented in the diagram by a single nerve fiber. In the upper diagram (a) the extrapolar flow of current between the anode and cathode outside the membrane is ineffective for excitation. The effective path of current flow is the one passing through the membrane into the fiber and then out through the membrane at the cathode where excitation takes place. The lower diagram (b) shows resistance symbols which represent the electrical equivalents of the extracellular spaces (R_e), the path through the membrane (R_m), and the intracellular space (R_i).

which passes between fibers is called the *shunted* current, with the *effective* current passing across the membrane of the nerve fiber. Shunting, therefore, is a factor which expresses the reduction in the effectiveness of applied stimulating currents. Shunting is increased when an extra volume of conducting fluid is placed between the stimulating electrodes. In this case unless an increase in current is not employed, more current passes in that part of the circuit (R_e) external to the nerve membrane. Shunting is reduced when a non-conductor (e.g. sucrose solution) replaces Ringer fluid in the inter-electrode region and the resistivity of the fluid around the nerve becomes larger. Therefore with a higher external resistance more current passes into the nerve if all else remains the same. Another factor which changes the effectiveness of an applied stimulating current is the spatial separation between the two stimulating electrodes. Because of the relatively high electrical resistance of the nerve membrane (Chapter 4), current enters the fibers over a rela-tively long stretch of nerve. Therefore, the effectiveness of a given strength of stimulating current increases as the separation between the electrodes is increased. The proportion of current passing into fibers with respect to that between the fibers increases. However, this takes place with electrode separation only up to a certain dis-tance; further increases in separation of the stimulating electrodes require more applied voltage due to the increased longitudinal resistances inside the nerve fibers as the inter-electrode paths are made longer (Katz, 1939).

The direction of the stimulating current led through the nerve is another important factor in excitation. The nerve is excited at the *cathode* where current leaves the fibers as shown in Fig. 2.5. A considerable amount of indirect evidence obtained in the past has been supported by more recent direct investigations with internal electrodes (Chapter 4) in showing that excitation does indeed occur in the nerve membrane where current is passing from inside the fibers through the membranes to the outside, i.e. outward across the membrane at the cathode.

To demonstrate excitation at the cathodal region, the stimulating electrodes are placed far enough apart so that the nerve between the two stimulating electrodes can be crushed with a fine forceps. If the cathode of the stimulating electrode is between the muscle and the crush (A of Fig. 2.6), then stimulating pulses which were effective before crushing still remain so. If the polarity of stimulation is reversed as in B, then the stimulation is ineffective. In the latter case, because it damages nerve fibers, the crush will *block* the con-duction of the action potential excited at the cathode. It should be noted that, unlike the action potential, the passage of electrical current in the stimulation circuit will not be hindered by such a crush. Instead of mechanical crush an equally effective block to conduction could have been produced by applying a concentrated solution of KCl, a narcotic agent, or very cold temperatures, or, in general, by using any agent which would destroy the nerve properties required for propagation (Chapter 6).

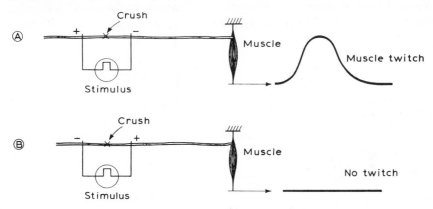

Fig. 2.6.   The crush of the nerve between anode and cathode (A) does not block excitation from the cathode as shown by the remaining twitch.   In B with polarity of stimulation reversed the crush prevents the passage of excitation from the cathode.

Recording the action potential

The study of nerve excitability was rapidly advanced when the nerve action potential could be easily and reliably recorded.   That a wave of electrical disturbance passes outward from the stimulating site along the nerve fibers was known from the work of Du Bois-Reymond and Helmholtz in the nineteenth century (Brazier, 1959).   In ingenious experiments the *conduction velocity* of the nerve impulse was shown by Helmholtz to be very much slower than the speed of electricity conducted in electrolyte solutions, and even its approximate rate of propagation was estimated.   However, as those early studies were obtained with the muscle response used as an index of excitation, the results were uncertain until vacuum tube amplifiers and the cathode ray oscilloscope were used to record the action potential of nerves.   In Fig. 2.7 the stimulating electrodes are shown at one end of the nerve and the recording electrodes at the other.   A diagrammatic plan of the stimulator, amplifier and oscilloscope used to display the action potential is shown. The stimulator has a control for stimulus strength analogous to the potentiometer shown in Fig. 2.1.   Another control determines the duration of the stimulus pulse.   Yet another control is for the initiation of a train of stimulating pulses—referred to as *tetanic stimulation*.

The voltage change developed by nerve during an action potential is quite small, and considerable amplification must be employed for oscilloscope display. As noted in Chapter 1, the amplified voltages are applied to the vertical plates of the oscilloscope tube, with the

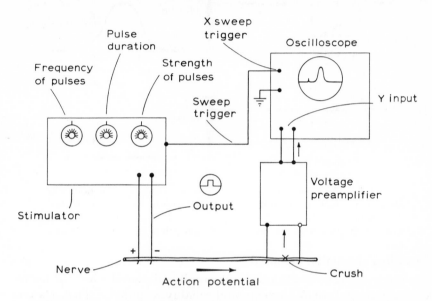

Fig. 2.7. A trigger impulse from the stimulator initiates the horizontal sweep (X) of the beam of the oscilloscope. After an interval an impulse from the stimulator is delivered to the nerve. The resulting action potential is amplified and applied to the vertical plates (Y) of the oscilloscope. The controls of the stimulator allow selection of stimulating pulses of different durations, strengths, repetition rates. (Cf. Fig. 1.7.)

horizontal plates controlled by a sweep generator moving the beam from the left to the right side of the screen at a predetermined rate of speed. The horizontal sweep movement is usually started by a *trigger impulse* from the stimulator, and a short time later (a control for this is available) a brief stimulating pulse is delivered to the nerve through the stimulating electrodes. The nerve action potential initiated by the stimulus pulse propagates along the nerve to the recording electrodes. The region of the nerve where the impulse is located is negative in potential with respect to the rest of the nerve. This area of negativity moves along the nerve. Therefore, as the action potential propagates into the region of the first electrode, that electrode becomes negative relative to the second electrode (Fig. 2.8). Following the usual convention, a negative deflection is displayed upward on the oscilloscope screen. Then, as the action potential passes by the first electrode the potential decreases and

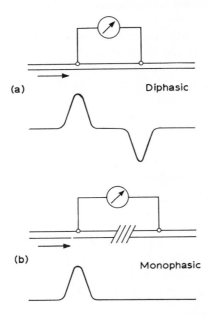

Fig. 2.8. The action potential appearing first under the nearest recording electrode and then the other gives rise to a diphasic action potential (a). (A negative change appearing under each electrode is shown as an upward deflection.) In b a crush blocks passage of the action potential to the far electrode resulting in the monophasic action potential.

returns to the baseline. Continuing in its propagation, the action potential arrives at the second recording electrode, and that electrode in turn becomes negative relative to the first electrode. This causes a potential difference of the same magnitude between the two recording electrodes, but because the action potential is now present under the second recording electrode, making it negative relative to the first, the oscilloscope beam is deflected in the opposite direction. This swing of potential first one way and then the other is called the *diphasic action potential* (Fig. 2.8(a)).

When propagation is prevented by crushing or applying KCl to the nerve between the two recording electrodes, conduction beyond the first electrode is blocked and the second part of the diphasic action potential does not appear. The simplified action potential remaining is called the *monophasic action potential* (Fig. 2.8(b)). In most studies of the properties of the action potential it is convenient to use the monophasic action potential which, because of its shape, is often referred to as the *spike*.

Returning to the display of the action potential we note several important points with regard to its properties. First, a brief deflection appears at the time when the stimulating current pulse is applied to the nerve. This electrical disturbance is called the *stimulus artifact* (Fig. 2.9). The stimulus artifact is caused for the most

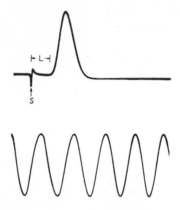

Fig. 2.9. In the upper trace, the small deflection at the left is the artifact disturbance when a brief shock (S) is delivered to the nerve. The latency (L) is the time between artifact and the beginning of the action potential. The interval of 1 msec between peaks of the 1000 cps sine wave shown below is used to calibrate the sweep velocity.

part by adventitious capacitative coupling between the stimulator and the amplifier input. With modern electronic techniques of stimulation and recording this artifact, is sometimes so small that a signal mark has to be introduced to show when the stimulus is introduced. Using the stimulus artifact, the period of time elapsing between stimulation and the beginning of the action potential can be determined if the sweep speed is known. This period of time is referred to as the *shock-response latency*, or briefly termed the *latency*. It represents the time taken for the action potential to be propagated from its origin at the cathode to the first recording electrode (Fig. 2.9). This time varies according to the speed or *conduction velocity* of the propagated action potential.

Conduction velocity is determined by the following equation:

$$V = D/T \qquad (2.1)$$

where V is the velocity of the action potential, D is the distance between the stimulating cathode and the first recording electrode, and T is the time elapsing between the stimulus artifact and the beginning of the action potential. Time is usually given in seconds and distance in meters, hence conduction velocity is given in meters per second (m/sec).

The time is determined by measuring the speed of the beam sweeping horizontally across the face of the oscilloscope tube. A common method of determining the beam speed is to use a calibrated sine-wave oscillator. If the frequency of the oscillator is known, the distance between wave peaks of the calibrator wave (Fig. 2.9) gives the time it takes the beam to move a given distance horizontally on the screen. To give an example, if the shock-response latency turned out to be 1 msec and the distance between the stimulating and the recording electrodes measured 4 cm, the computed conduction velocity would be 40 m/sec, a velocity common for the larger fibers in frog sciatic nerve (*vide infra*).

The action potential is referred to as an 'explosive' or as an *all-or-none* reaction (Hill, 1932). It acts much as a gunpowder fuse which once lit burns steadily along its length, the burning portion igniting its adjoining segment. The nerve action potential also when once excited to conduct is then no longer related to the strength of the stimulating current, and it continually regenerates itself by exciting the next stretch of membrane, etc. Extending the analogy of nerve conduction to a burning fuse somewhat further, a damp region may cause the fuse to sputter; however, if that region is successfully passed by, the fuse then recovers its usual rate of burning. A region of the nerve may be treated with narcotic agents such as ether or alcohol to depress its excitability and reduce the size of the nerve action potential. Once past that affected region, normal propagation is recovered. This was convincingly shown by Kato (1926) who used this and other evidence to overthrow an earlier supposition that nerve propagates in *decrementing* fashion, i.e. that the action potential continually decreases in size with increasing distance from the stimulated site. Decrementing conduction occurs only under special circumstances, namely, within narcotized regions of nerve (Lorente de Nó and Condouris, 1959), and possibly it may occur normally in dendritic portions of the neuron (Chapter 18).

The shape of the action potential and fiber groups

The individual nerve fibers found in a nerve are not of equal size. There is, in fact, a wide range of fiber diameters. A further distinction among fibers is made on the basis of the myelin sheath which is present around some nerve axons but not on others—the *myelinated* and *nonmyelinated* fibers respectively. A cross-section of a nerve

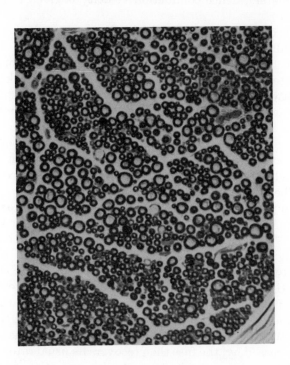

Fig. 2.10.   The myelin sheath of nerve fibers cut in cross-section are shown.   The largest diameters measure approximately 16 μ in this nerve bundle.   Nonmyelinated fibers less than 2 μ are not visible.

stained with a special stain (osmium tetroxide) which is taken up by the myelin shows the different sizes of myelinated nerve present (Fig. 2.10).   Details of myelination will be discussed in Chapter 6.

The various fiber diameters are related to differences in the action potentials.   When the stimulus to a nerve is gradually increased, the action potential increases in size to a maximum amplitude. As will be discussed in Chapter 3, this apparently 'graded' response is brought about by the summation of the all-or-none responses of the individual nerve fibers contained in the nerve. Further increase in stimulus strength does not increase the amplitude of this response, but instead brings about a change in the shape of the action potential —the *compound action potential*. When using higher stimulating strengths the falling phase of the simple action potential becomes broader and humped. The later-appearing potentials are due to other nerve groups successively adding their responses to the total (Fig. 2.11). The groups giving rise to these later action

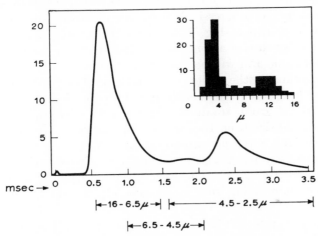

Fig. 2.11. Subgroups of the *A* group fall into the following ranges of fiber diameters, as estimated from their conduction velocities: α and β, 16.5–6.5 μ; γ, 6.5–4.5 μ; δ, 4.5–2.5 μ. Inset shows the measured diameters, and the number of fibers of each diameter present. Note that the larger number of smaller diametered fibers does not give as large a response as the larger diameter subgroup. (From Gasser, 1943.)

potentials are subgroups of the *A* group of myelinated fibers. They are labelled with Greek letters α, β, γ and δ, ranging in discontinuous groups from the α group (which appears with the lowest threshold) to the δ group. At still higher stimulus strengths, a much later-appearing and smaller potential is added by the nonmyelinated *C* fibers. An intermediate *B* group of myelinated fibers is found present only in autonomic nerves (Chapter 11).

The relation of different parts of a compound action potential response to the different sized groups of fibers was elucidated by

Erlanger and Gasser (1937).   The various subgroups α, β, γ, δ of
the A fibers, and the C group have not only successively higher
thresholds to stimulation, but also lower conduction velocities.
This accounts for their appearing later.   The slower conducting
responses should be more apparent with a greater separation between
stimulating and recording electrodes.   The analogy may be made to
a race where at the beginning of the race all runners are in line and
with increasing distance the faster ones outstrip the slower, until as
more time elapses the racers become strung out along the track.
Erlanger and Gasser took advantage of the long lengths of bullfrog
sciatic nerve to show the separate origins of the α and β subgroups of
a compound response.   These responses become clearly separated
when recorded at progressively increased distances from the stimulating site as shown in Fig. 2.12.   Another technique for separating
different subgroups of a compound response makes use of the *double-
shock* technique and will be described in Chapter 3.

The maxima in the action potential are related to populations of
fibers with different diameters found in nerve.   The myelinated
fibers of the A group are divided by size into subgroups α through δ.
They range in size from 16 μ to 2.5 μ in diameter.   A reconstruction
of the various potential subgroups correlated with the number of
fibers in these different sized groups shows a reasonably close fit, as
indicated in Fig. 2.11.   The assumptions regarding potential and
nerve size underlying such a correspondence will be discussed in
Chapter 6.

Velocity is also related to nerve fiber size.   The A group has
conduction velocities ranging from 15–90 m/sec.   The B group
composed of small myelinated fibers in autonomic nerves in the range
of 3 μ has a velocity ranging from 10–20 m/sec.   The C group
corresponds to the nonmyelinated fibers ranging from approximately
2.0 to 0.5 μ or less in size, and these have a much lower range of
conduction velocities—from 1–2 m/sec.

There have been differences of opinion with regard to the presence
of myelin in the C fibers.   X-ray diffraction studies suggested the
presence of a small amount of myelin and the question arose as to
whether they should be called nonmyelinated fibers.   Electron
microscope studies have resolved the problem: the smaller fibers
have a single myelin membrane around the nerve membrane proper
while myelinated fibers have many more such myelin layers comprising its myelin sheath (cf. Chapter 6).   With this small reservation the
terms myelinated and nonmyelinated fibers are used to distinguish
the two main types of nerve fibers.

Physical and chemical agents have shown selective effects on the various nerve fiber types. The larger myelinated fibers are particularly sensitive to mechanical trauma. Local anesthetics such as *cocaine* or *procaine* infiltrated into a region of nerve fibers causes a block of conduction of the smaller fibers before that of the larger

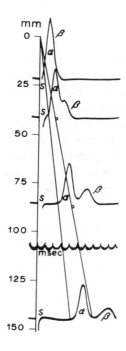

Fig. 2.12. The compound action potential is shown recorded at different distances from the stimulating electrode, the numbers giving recording electrode distances in millimeters. Latency from the shock artifact S increases and at the same time the α and β subgroups become separated as indicated by the slope of the lines drawn to the foot of the two subgroups. (Erlanger and Gasser, 1937.)

fibers. Asphyxiation of the nerve produced by cuffing an arm to stop circulation blocks conduction of the larger myelinated fibers carrying touch sensation before that of the small fibers carrying pain (Zotterman, 1933). However, in spite of many efforts to show a possible relation of sensory modalities with action potential responses characteristic of a given range of fiber sizes, there is little evidence for such a connection (Gasser, 1943). As an example, pain (cf.

Chapter 11) is carried by the smaller myelinated fibers as well as by the nonmyelinated C fibers (Zotterman, 1959). In general, while sensory function is not related to fiber size, there may be some special biochemical differences between fibers of different sizes or type, e.g. between sensory or motor nerves or the B fibers found in autonomic nerves although these differences are not revealed by their action potentials.

After-potentials

The term *after-potential* was first used with respect to phenomena observed in the frog sciatic nerve, a tissue which is much more complex than earlier appeared to be the case. After-potentials are those variations in potential appearing after the termination of the action potential. Instead of a return to the baseline after an action potential, a slower decline or residual potential may appear. This is known as the *negative after-potential* which is often followed by a smaller swing in the opposite direction giving rise to the *positive after-potential* (Fig. 2.13). Variations in the experimental conditions

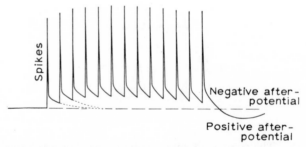

Fig. 2.13. A series of action potential responses shown in diagrammatic fashion is followed by the negative and positive after-potentials. These are drawn disproportionately large with respect to the spikes. (Erlanger and Gasser, 1937.)

markedly affect the appearance of after-potentials. The after-potentials of the frog sciatic nerve are exaggerated after a period of tetanic stimulation, particularly the positive after-potential. Other factors causing variations in the after-potentials are the length of time the nerve has been removed from the animal, the presence or absence of CO_2 and other metabolic factors, and the type of nerve examined (Erlanger and Gasser, 1937; Graham, 1942). Studies of a relationship between the after-potential in the nerve and metabolism are complicated by the diffusion barrier presented by the *perineural* and *epineural sheath* surrounding the nerve fibers (Chapter 6).   The after-potentials found in single giant axons are more amenable to analysis, and these will be discussed in Chapter 6.

Polarization

By replacing one recording electrode on a crushed portion of nerve or muscle and the other electrode further away on an intact part, a constant difference in potential can be recorded with the use of a d.c. amplifier.   These potentials are referred to as *injury* or *demarcation potentials*.   The voltages found may measure as high as 30 mv (1 mv = 1/1000 volt), depending upon the amount of electrical shunting present between the fibers.   The injured portion is electrically negative in polarity with respect to the intact parts (Fig. 2.14).

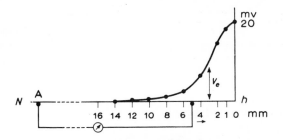

Fig. 2.14.   The nerve N has been injured at the point h becoming negative with respect to uninjured nerve.   This negative demarcation potential falls off with distance from the injured region. V_e is the length constant.   (After Lorente de Nó, *Harvey Lectures* **42**: 43, 1947.)

An analysis made of these injury potentials indicated that the inside of the fibers are negatively charged with respect to the outside, a voltage difference exists across the membrane.   Upon injury, current flows from the outside of the intact membranes through the injured parts of the membrane producing the injury voltages recorded with external electrodes (Lorente de Nó, 1947).

Historically, this was taken to mean that there is a reduced movement of ions across the membrane of nerve and muscle, i.e., a *semipermeability* to ions, and this was related to the voltages recorded.   It will be useful to describe the earlier concept because some of its essential aspects are retained in the present-day theory of nerve and muscle properties.

The voltage difference across the nerve axon or muscle membrane which constitutes the *polarized state* of the normal fiber was believed by Ostwald to be due to a *Nernst potential* (Chapter 4) caused by the greater concentration of K^+ present within the cells (Katz, 1939). The injury voltage was lower than the theoretical value of 60 mv expected on that basis, but the smaller values found were believed (and rightly so) to be due to the shunting of the injury currents in the conducting medium between the fibers.   With one electrode on the injured region, the other on intact portions of the nerve at successively greater distances from it, the voltage difference reached a maximum within several millimeters.

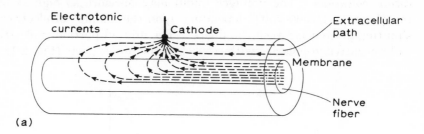

(a)

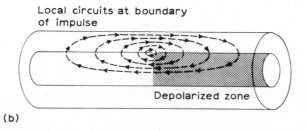

(b)

Fig. 2.15.   The nerve fibers are diagrammatically represented as a single fiber.   In (a) an imposed flow of current is shown passing through the membrane, the extracellular compartment and back to the cathode.   In (b) the flow of local current is shown passing through the membrane and extracellular compartment between a region occupied by the action potential and a nearby region of nerve which is being invaded.   The outward flow of current through the nerve membrane depolarizes the membrane to the critical level necessary for excitation.   (From Hodgkin, *J. Physiol.* **90**: 183, 1937.)

Bernstein's (1912) theory of nerve excitation and conduction was based on these observations of the charged electrical state of fibers. This theory has survived until recent times and in a modified form is part of the modern theory of nerve excitation (Chapters 4, 5).

In the Bernstein hypothesis the fiber becomes excited when its resting membrane potential is decreased or *depolarized* under the cathode of a stimulating electrode. The impermeability to ions other than K$^+$ is locally lost in the depolarized region, resulting in a further fall in the resting membrane voltage at that site. The polarized portions of the membrane to the side of the depolarized region discharge through this 'leak' in the membrane. A negative potential change is then recorded with an external electrode placed at this region. The current flowing from the sides which are normally polarized constitute the *local currents* (Fig. 2.15). The local currents are directed outward in the nearby regions of the membrane. This acts like a cathodal stimulating electrode to depolarize those membranes to the critical level and in turn cause them to lose their semipermeability and potential. This, then, repeated indefinitely along the nerve fiber is the action potential. To use Sherrington's picturesque phrase: 'the action potential constitutes a traveling leak moving down the nerve.' We shall replace these ideas with more precise concepts to be developed in Chapters 4 and 5.

REFERENCES

Bernstein, J. (1912). *Elektrobiologie.* Vieweg, Braunschweig.

Brazier, M. A. B. (1959). The historical development of neurophysiology. *Handbook of Physiology–Neurophysiology.* Vol. 1, pp. 1–58. American Physiological Society, Washington, D.C.

Davis, H. and Forbes, A. (1936). Chronaxie. *Physiol. Rev.* **16**: 407–441.

Erlanger, J. and Gasser, H. S. (1937). *Electrical Signs of Nervous Activity.* University of Pennsylvania Press, Philadelphia.

Gasser, H. S. (1943). Pain-producing impulses in peripheral nerves. *Res. Assoc. Nervous Mental Disease,* **23**: 44–62.

Graham, H. T. (1942). The effects of polarization on nerve action potentials. *J. Neurophysiol.* **5**: 137–152.

Hill, A. V. (1932). *Chemical Wave Transmission in Nerve.* MacMillan, New York.

Hill, A. V. (1936). The strength-duration relation for electric excitation of medullated nerve. *Proc. Roy. Soc. B.* **119**: 440–453.

Kato, G. (1926). *The Theory of Decrementless Conduction in Narcotized Region of Nerve.* Nankodo, Japan.

Katz, B. (1939). *Electrical Excitation of Nerve.* Oxford University Press, London.

Lapique, L. (1926). *L'excitabilité en fonction du temps; La chronaxie, sa signification et sa mesure.* Presses Univ. de France, Paris.

Lorente de Nó, R. (1947). *A Study of Nerve Physiology.* Vols. 131, 132: Studies from the Rockefeller Institute of Medical Research. Rockefeller Institute, New York.

Lorente de Nó, R. and Condouris, G. A. (1959). Decremental conduction in peripheral nerve. Integration of stimuli in the neuron. *Proc. Natl. Acad. Sci. U.S.* **45**: 592–617.

Lucas, K. (1906). The excitable substance of amphibian muscle. *J. Physiol.* **36**: 113–135.

Rushton, W. A. H. (1935). The time factor in electrical excitation. *Biol. Rev.* **10**: 1–17.

Zotterman, Y. (1933). Studies in the peripheral nervous mechanism of pain. *Acta Med. Scand.* **80**: 185–242.

Zotterman, Y. (1959). *The Peripheral Nervous Mechanism of Pain: A Brief Review in Pain and Itch Nervous Mechanisms.* Edited by G. E. W. Wolstenholme and M. O'Connor, Ciba Foundation Study Group I. Little, Brown and Company, Boston.

3

Excitability

The term *excitability* refers to a characteristic property of nervous tissue. It replaces the older term *irritability* generally used to describe the fact that a characteristic response occurs when an organism is adequately stimulated (cf. the stimulus–response behavior studied by the psychologist). In this chapter fundamental properties of excitation will be described, and in later chapters these will be related to the actual physical-chemical processes which are thought to underlie excitation and conduction.

The population of fibers and excitability

The relation of stimulus strength to response was discussed in the preceding chapter so that the basic phenomenon of the action potential could be discussed. We now wish to look more closely at the relation between the stimulus and the response which defines excitability. For a single nerve fiber, isolated from the others and separately recorded from, excitation is a function of the strength of stimulation when the duration of a brief pulse is kept fixed. The individual fiber either will or will not be fired, i.e. threshold will or will not be reached. In a mixed nerve such as the sciatic nerve of the frog where many fibers are recorded from at once, the most excitable fibers are fired first as the strength of stimulation is gradually increased. These fibers can be seen to give rise to irregularly occurring action potentials due to small random changes of excitability at near-threshold strengths. As the strength of stimulation is increased further, more fibers are excited and the amplitude of the nerve action potential becomes regular and increases in size.

The responses shown in Fig. 3.1 represent a range of excitabilities of the individual nerve fibers within the responding group, the α group of A fibers. This fiber group is the most excitable and fired by the lowest stimulating strengths. As stimulus strength is successively increased, threshold is attained for those fibers of the α group with somewhat lesser excitability and these become *recruited* into the response. With further increase in strength, recruitment continues as the fibers with the higher thresholds are successively added to the responding population until finally all the fibers of the α group are fired.   This is the *maximal response* and is defined as that amplitude of the action potential which is not further increased by increasing the stimulus strength.   The actual position of the maximal response point is indefinite as the amplitude gradually approaches

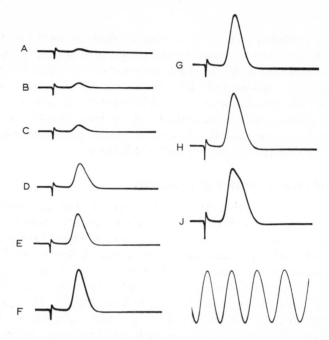

Fig. 3.1.   Increased strengths of stimulation are shown in traces A–J.   The monophasic action potential response in A is just above threshold for the alpha group.   It attains a maximum in G.   With increased strengths of stimulation (H, J) the addition of the beta group lengthens the potential response but does not increase the amplitude of the alpha response.   Sine wave at 1000 cps for time calibration.

maximal height.   To assure a maximal response the strength of the stimulus is usually increased 10 to 20% above that required for a maximal response, namely, a *supramaximal* stimulus is employed. This results (H, J of Fig. 3.1) in the addition of the β group, the amplitude of the α group remaining unchanged.   A further increase in current strength excites other subgroups of the A group of fibers with smaller diameters and higher threshold, the γ through δ subgroups and eventually the C groups.

Double-shock technique

Excitability changes occur in the nerve fibers following a stimulus or response. They are revealed by the use of paired electrical stimulations, i.e. the *double-shock* technique. This double-shock procedure will be described in some detail because it is useful in excitability studies made not only on peripheral nerve but also on muscle, spinal cord, cerebral cortex, reticular formation, etc. The essential idea of the double-shock technique is represented in Fig. 3.2.

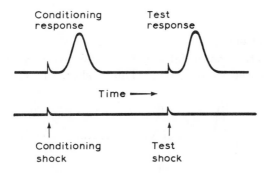

Fig. 3.2. Double-shock technique is shown: a conditioning shock elicits a conditioning response, followed by a test shock giving rise to a test response. The interval between the conditioning and test shocks is varied and also the strength of the conditioning shock causing changes in excitability and the test response.

The line indicates the sweep of the cathode ray beam moving steadily across the oscilloscope tube from left to right. Shock 1 is delivered at the selected time indicated by the first arrow; shock 2 at the selected time indicated by the second arrow. The first shock is often called the *conditioning shock*; the second, the *test shock*. The responses to these shocks are also referred to as *conditioning* and *test responses*. Excitability may be measured in the following way when dealing with a multi-fibered nerve: the strength of a test pulse of current is adjusted so that the test response is less than maximal (e.g. one-half the maximal action potential amplitude). Then, any ensuing changes in the excitability of this population would result in either the addition of previously non-responding fibers, or the removal of some of the fibers from the responding group with, respectively, a corresponding increase or decrease in the amplitude of the test response.

In dealing with the response of a single fiber which responds in all-or-none fashion, a different technique must be used to determine changes in excitability. In this case, the measure of excitability is the strength of stimulation required to reach threshold and excite the fiber in half the number of stimulation trials. This is a *firing index* and may, for example, be taken as 5 if 5 out of 10 trials are successful. An alteration in excitability is revealed by the changed probability of firing of the cell; in this case the firing index changes toward 0 or 10. Another technique to assess excitability change is to measure the change in stimulation strength required to maintain a given firing index.

Refractory periods

During an action potential and for a short time afterwards nerves show a decreased excitability. This is shown in Fig. 3.3 using the

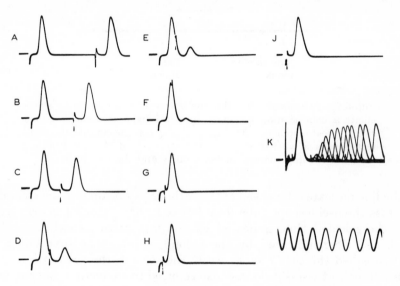

Fig. 3.3.   Two monophasic responses at decreasing time intervals from A–J give rise to a decrease of the second test response in C–F and its absence in G–J (relative and absolute refractoriness). In K, a series of double-shock traces is overlayed to show in a more compact form the decreasing amplitude of the test response during refractoriness.   1000 cps calibration in the lowermost trace.

double-shock procedure in a multi-fibered nerve preparation with the time between the two shocks being gradually reduced. With the shortest intervals (G–J of Fig. 3.3), no response can be elicited to the second test shock regardless of the strength of the stimulus. The nerve is said to be *absolutely refractory*, or in the *absolute refractory period*. At greater intervals of time between the two shocks, the second stimulation excites a response of less than maximal size. During this period of reduced response amplitude, when some of the fibers have recovered and are firing, the nerve is said to be in the *relative refractory period*. During the phase of *relative refractoriness* those nerve fibers not firing can be made to do so in response to an increased strength of stimulation. The recovery occurs first in the most excitable fibers of the population, their thresholds returning faster to pre-stimulus values than the other fibers of the group.

Refractoriness in the case of a single fiber is measured by the strength of the test stimulus required to excite after a first conditioning response. During the absolute refractory period, the fiber is inexcitable. During the relative refractory period, the excitability rises, i.e. the threshold gradually falls to its normal level.

The duration of the refractory period is conveniently shown by overlaying a series of these double shocks at different periods (K of Fig. 3.3) and is seen to last approximately 3–5 msec. The duration of the refractory period may be changed by various procedures. For example, the refractory period may be doubled by a period of tetanic stimulation (Brink *et al.*, 1952).

The double-shock technique was used in an elegant way by Erlanger and Gasser (1937) to separate the α and β subgroups of the A group. A conditioning shock was produced which was maximal for α fibers, but did not attain threshold for β fibers. A stronger shock was used for the test shock, such that both α and β groups were fired. Then, as the test shock was brought closer in time to the conditioning shock, the α group of the test shock fell into the refractory phase of the preceding α conditioning response leaving the β group of the test response remaining in isolation. This may be seen in Fig. 3.4.

Supernormal and subnormal periods

Smaller and longer-lasting changes in nerve excitability are known to occur after the refractory period, and these are referred to as periods of *supernormality* and *subnormality*. After the relative refractory period the test response may become a little larger than control size during such a supernormal period. The phase of supernormality is followed by a smaller decrease in excitability, the phase of subnormality, and afterwards still smaller increases and decreases in excitability may be seen.   The phenomenon appears to have a relationship to the inherent oscillatory nature of nerve excitability which will be discussed in a later section.   These slow swings in excitability following a response have some obscure relationship to the

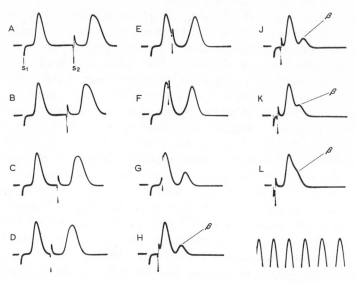

Fig. 3.4.   The second test response of a double-shock pair (A) is made stronger to include a β group (cf. J of Fig. 3.1).   The α group of the test response becomes refractory as it is brought closer to the conditioning response (A–G) but the β wave remains. 1000 cps calibration peaks at lower right.

time the nerve has been isolated from the animal, the ionic environment of the nerve, or the amount of preceding stimulation as when stimulating at different frequencies (Erlanger and Gasser, 1937). However, the presence of these excitability changes can be demonstrated in nerve in a normal environment.   It is possible to excite nerves in the living animal, or in man, through the skin or via electrodes inserted below the skin, and record the resulting action potentials further along the nerve.   Stimulating the median nerve with paired shocks at the wrist and recording at the elbow in humans, an absolute refractory period of 0.6 msec was found, with a relative absolute period of between 2.5 and 3.0 msec.   This was followed by a supernormal phase of 10–15 msec, where threshold fell 8–15% below resting levels (Gilliatt and Willison, 1962).

Subliminal excitability changes

By the use of the double-shock arrangement, excitability changes may be found in a single nerve fiber after a subliminal conditioning shock set just below threshold to excite an action potential. In the example given by Erlanger and Gasser (1937) and shown in Fig. 3.5, a brief subliminal conditioning shock which was just below

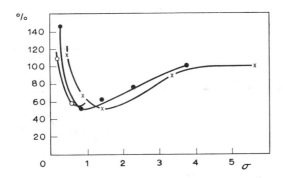

Fig. 3.5. Subliminal changes in excitability of a single fiber induced by an electrical shock just submaximal for excitation of an action potential is shown by the curves obtained from three different experiments. Excitability is determined by the stimulus strength required for the second test shock to reach threshold (100%). A brief increase in excitability lasting a fraction of a millisecond is seen soon after the conditioning shock followed by a longer period of depressed excitability (σ, msec). (Erlanger and Gasser, 1937.)

threshold was delivered to a nerve. This was followed by a test shock at various times afterwards, and the strength required of the test stimulus to reach threshold was determined at each time interval. Excitability was shown by this method to rise and then to fall after the subliminal shock.

The excitability increase is localized at the cathodally-stimulated region, giving rise to the term *local excitatory change*, and it shows a graduation in its size which depends on the strength of the conditioning stimulus. It is therefore spoken of as a *graded response* in contradistinction to the all-or-none propagated action potential response. The terms *latent addition, summation interval*, or *summation period*, as used by Lucas (1917), refer to the fact that two such graded responses readily summate to reach threshold and excite an all-or-none action potential. The subliminal increase of excitability is brief; it is over within 0.2–0.5 msec and is followed by a *hypoexcitability* lasting 3–4 msec (Erlanger and Gasser, 1937).

A similar brief period of excitability increase caused by subliminal stimulation can also be seen in a multi-fibered nerve trunk. As two subliminal stimulating pulses are gradually brought closer together in time, the local excitatory changes summate to bring about a large action potential (Fig. 3.6). The summation period extends from coincidence to approximately 0.3–0.5 msec.

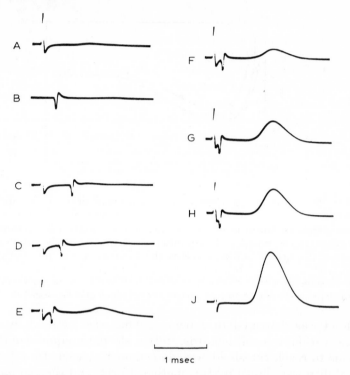

Fig. 3.6. Two just-threshold stimuli giving hardly visible responses are shown in A, B. In C–J the two shocks are presented at successively closer intervals. Summation of excitability and large responses are seen at intervals of 0–0.5. Time calibration, 1 msec.

Electrotonus and local potential

When an electrical current is applied to nerve or muscle, a lateral spread of current takes place in the tissue because of the high electrical resistivity of the cell membranes. The lateral spread of current and resulting distribution of voltage is referred to as *physical electrotonus*. The spread of injury currents and the resulting demarcation potentials near damaged regions already referred to

(Chapter 2) are brought about by this same property. Lorente de Nó (1947) showed that narcotic drugs and other agents which change excitability also change the spread of electrotonic currents of frog sciatic nerve. However, much of the electrotonus in a multi-fibered nerve such as the frog sciatic nerve is due to the electrical properties of the dense fibrous epineurium found around the nerve trunk. A relatively high electrical impedance of the epineural sheath was shown by Cole and Curtis (1936) when they compared the electrical impedance of intact and desheathed nerves. Rashbass and Rushton (1949) showed by inserting stimulating electrodes under the epineurium that much of the electrotonus found in frog nerve trunks was due to this structural component. The spread of current in the epineural sheath causes the site of excitation to be displaced from the vicinity of the cathode, as much as 3 mm away from it (Rushton, 1949; Rashbass and Rushton, 1949). This result is of importance with regard to the true estimation of conduction velocity where, in our elementary treatment, this factor was disregarded.

A clearer picture of the relation of electrotonus to excitability was obtained by study of the single giant nerve of the crab (Hodgkin and Rushton, 1945). With a recording electrode placed on the nerve at various distances from an electrode in which current was introduced, the resulting electrical changes were found to spread beyond a region of conduction block (Fig. 3.7). The electrical properties of the nerve membrane determines the extent of these potential spreads. In the next several chapters we will discuss those electrical properties and their ionic basis in detail. For present purposes it is sufficient to recognize that these are *passive* spreads of current to be distinguished from *active* electrical responses of the nerve membrane. Active electrical changes occur in the near vicinity of an electrode which is cathodal, i.e. where the applied current is moving outward across the cell membranes. The active electrical potential produced by the membrane is a depolarization with a time course and amplitude which is related to the local increases in excitability following brief subliminal shocks which we have mentioned in the previous section. These *local potentials*, as they are referred to, are shown in Fig. 3.8. Brief weak cathodal pulses of current were introduced into the single crab nerve fiber and a passive catelectrotonus observed. As the cathodal pulse of current was increased in strength, an additional hump of voltage was recorded, superimposed on the passive electrotonic potentials (Hodgkin, 1938). This is the electrical sign of an active local response. It becomes larger as the stimulating current is still further increased, the local potential increasing in size until the critical level of depolarization and threshold is reached. Then, the all-or-none action potential is excited which is propagated along the fibers. The local response is better seen when the passive electrotonic portions of the curves have been subtracted (insert of

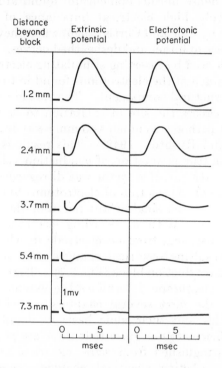

Fig. 3.7. The extrinsic (local) potentials of action potentials recorded at different distances beyond a nerve block are shown at left. A similar spatial extent of electronic potentials is shown following an imposed current at right. (Hodgkin, *J. Physiol.* **90:** 183, 1937.)

Fig. 3.8). Increasing pulses of anodal current do not excite an action potential but merely gives rise to larger and larger anelectrotonic potentials.

Oscillatory behavior and repetitive firing

After a brief stimulus, a nerve usually gives rise to a single action potential but under certain conditions a repetitive series of action

potential discharges may be observed.   This is particularly striking
when the Ca^{2+} concentration has been lowered either *in vivo* or in the
in vitro Ringer solution bathing the nerve (Arvanitaki, 1938).   If
Ca^{2+} is still further reduced, these fibers may fail to fire propagated
action potentials and a series of smaller depolarizations may be seen
at the time of the expected spike discharge.   These *oscillatory
potentials* look like a series of local potential changes.
  In the case of a mixed nerve such as the frog sciatic which has been

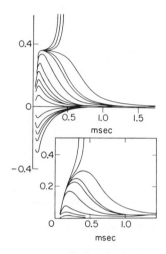

Fig. 3.8.   In the region of the cathode, electrotonic potentials
increase in size with increasing strengths of stimulation until, near
threshold, an additional voltage is actively produced by the nerve.
These local potentials are seen better after subtracting the electrotonic potential (insert).   Local potentials grow until threshold
is reached when an all-or-none action potential is produced.
Only the leading edge of the action potential is visible.   (Hodgkin,
1938).

bathed in citrate to reduce Ca^{2+} levels, oscillatory behavior and
repetitive firing is shown by a series of spike-like discharges following
the action potential elicited by a shock to the nerve.   These eventually disappear as the individual fibers fall out of phase in their rate of
firing.   Records taken from single isolated nerve fibers show a long-
maintained repetitive discharge after bathing in citrate solution
(Brink *et al.*, 1946).
  Monnier (1952) has emphasized the essentially rhythmic character
of nerve activity.   In his view, the action potential is a highly

damped oscillation with usually only the first wave of the train appearing.   He speaks of the normal action potential as a 'damped wave' and of a 'damping factor' normally present in nerve which keeps them from firing repetitively.   The concept of an inherent rhythmicity of the nerve, an *autorhythmicity*, has derived support (Huxley, 1959) from recent considerations of the ionic mechanisms of the giant nerve fiber which will be discussed in Chapter 5.   An inherent though suppressed tendency of axons to show rhythmic discharge is of interest with respect to the normal property of afferent nerve terminations of sensory receptors to discharge rhythmically when excited by the stimuli to which they are selectively sensitive (Chapter 11).

A concept often expressed, following Adrian's (1928) suggestion, is that the rate at which fibers fire repetitively is determined by its refractory period.   On this hypothesis an action potential occurs when the threshold of the fiber returns to its original level.   This, however, cannot generally be true, for Hodgkin (1948) has shown that the repetition rate observed in single giant nerve fibers during a long pulse of depolarization is in general much slower than would correspond to the refractory period (Fig. 3.9).   However, the

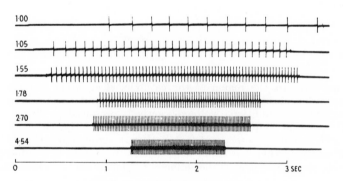

Fig. 3.9.   The application of long-lasting depolarizing currents to a single fiber gives rise to repetitive action potential discharges. Numbers indicate the applied current strength relative to the rheobase.   (Hodgkin, 1948.)

absolute refractory period sets an upper limit to the rate at which a nerve can repetitively respond.   If a nerve has an absolute refractory period of one msec, then it cannot respond at rates greater than 1000/sec.   Nerve fibers usually respond repetitively at much lower rates, although in some situations a firing rate of 1500/sec has been found in some types of neurons in the central nervous system.

Accommodation

We have been discussing the excitation of a nerve by a step-function current or by brief square wave pulses of current. The stimulating current used to excite may not be abrupt as in a square pulse but instead rise with a gradually increasing leading edge, e.g., with a *sawtooth* or *linearly rising* wave form. In this case, the nerve may not be excited at all if the slope is too low (Katz, 1939). This phenomenon of a lack of excitation with too gradually an increasing passage of stimulating current is called *accommodation*. The term implies that the excitable membrane can somehow, if given enough time, adjust or accommodate itself to the exciting current so that its threshold is never reached. Accommodation can be considered as a process which tends to gradually elevate the threshold.

Differences in accommodation are seen in different types of nerves or changes in accommodation may be produced by changing its state of excitability (Skoglund, 1942). As has been mentioned, decreased levels of Ca^{2+} favor oscillatory nerve activity and a decrease in Ca^{2+} also lowers accommodation.

Formal theories of excitation

Formal theories of nerve excitation were developed by Rashevsky, Monnier and Hill (see Katz, 1939). The various treatments, however, were shown to be essentially similar, representing mathematically the notion that local excitability summates to reach threshold while accommodation as a counter-process causes threshold to become elevated (Rashevsky, 1960). Formalistic approaches have been of much value in clarifying concepts and initiating new experimental studies. Lillie's (1932) use of the iron wire phenomenon discovered by Ostwald is an example of a physical model showing a striking analogy to excitation and conduction of the nerve. Putting an iron wire into nitric acid and touching it with another wire causes a visible surface change which then propagates along the surface much as an action potential. This curious phenomenon served to direct attention to the nerve membrane. A comprehensive treatment of formal theories and models used to describe excitation was recently given by Franck (1956). However, much as such analogies are of value, an understanding of the actual physical-chemical events underlying the process of excitation has long been desired (Hill, 1932). Within recent years such an insight has become available with the modern theory of the action potential which we will examine in detail in subsequent chapters.

REFERENCES

Adrian, E. D. (1928). *The Basis of Sensation.* Christophers, London.

Arvanitaki, A. (1938). *Les variations graduées de la polarisation des systèmes excitables.* Hermann and Cie., Paris.

Brink, F., Jr., Bronk, D. W. and Larrabee, M. G. (1946). Chemical excitation of nerve. *Ann. N. Y. Acad. Sci.* **47**: 457–485.

Brink, F., Jr., Bronk, D. W., Carlson, F. D. and Connelly, C. M. (1952). The oxygen uptake of active axons. *Cold Spring Harbor Symp. Quant. Biol.* **17**: 53–67.

Cole, K. S. and Curtis, H. J. (1936). Electric impedance of nerve and muscle. *Cold Spring Harbor Symp. Quant. Biol.* **4**: 73–96.

Erlanger, J. and Gasser, H. S. (1937). *Electrical Signs of Nervous Activity.* University of Pennsylvania Press, Philadelphia.

Franck, U. F. (1956). Models for biological excitation phenomena. *Progr. Biophys.* **6**: 171–206.

Gilliatt, R. W. and Willison, R. G. (1962). Refractoriness and supernormality in human peripheral nerve. *J. Physiol.* **161**: 29–30 P.

Hill, A. V. (1932). *Chemical Wave Transmission in Nerve.* MacMillan, New York.

Hodgkin, A. L. (1938). The subthreshold potentials in a crustacean nerve fiber. *Proc. Roy. Soc. B.* **126**: 87–121.

Hodgkin, A. L. (1948). The local electric changes associated with repetitive action in a non-medullated axon. *J. Physiol.* **107**: 165–181.

Hodgkin, A. L. and Rushton, W. A. H. (1945). The electrical constants of a crustacean nerve fiber. *Proc. Roy. Soc. B.* **133**: 444–479.

Huxley, A. F. (1959). Ion movements during nerve activity. *Ann. N. Y. Acad. Sci.* **81**: 221–246.

Katz, B. (1939). *Electric Excitation of Nerve.* Oxford University Press, Oxford.

Lillie, R. S. (1932). *Protoplasmic Action and Nervous Action.* 2nd Ed. University of Chicago Press, Chicago.

Lorente de Nó, R. (1947). *A Study of Nerve Physiology.* Vols. 131, 132 of Studies from the Rockefeller Institute of Medical Research. Rockefeller Institute, New York.

Lucas, K. (1917). *The Conduction of the Nervous Impulse.* Longmans, Green and Co., London.

Monnier, A. M. (1952). The damping factor as a functional criterion in nerve physiology. *Cold Spring Harbor Symp. Quant. Biol.* **17**: 69–95.

Rashbass, C. and Rushton, W. A. H. (1949). The relation of structure to the spread of excitation in the frog's sciatic trunk. *J. Physiol.* **110**: 110–135.

Rashevsky, N. (1960). *Mathematical Biophysics: Physico-Mathematical Foundations of Biology.* Revised Ed. Dover Publ., New York.

Rushton, W. A. H. (1949). The site of excitation in the nerve trunk of the frog. *J. Physiol.* **109**: 314–326.

Skoglund, C. R. (1942). The response to linearly increasing currents in mammalian motor and sensory nerves. *Acta Physiol. Scand.* **4**: *Suppl.* 12, 75 pages.

4

Membrane Potential

Ions and potentials

Bernstein (1902) and Nernst (1908) provided the earliest physical-chemical theories relating the ionic composition of nerve to its bioelectric potential. A semipermeable membrane is defined as one which imposes a restriction on the movement of some ion species through the membrane. While certain ions can pass through the membrane, others are left behind. The resulting asymmetrical distribution of charged ions across the membrane is the cause of the potential difference. Using physical models with semipermeable membranes Nernst was able to derive a relationship between the differences in concentration of an ion species on the two sides of a membrane and the resulting membrane potential:

$$E = \frac{RT}{znF} \ln \frac{C_1}{C_2} \tag{4.1}$$

where E = potential in volts, R = the gas constant, T = temperature, n = number of moles, z = valency of ions, F = Faraday, C_1 and C_2 = concentrations of a given ion species on the two sides of the membrane.

When constants and conversion factor for natural logarithms to logarithms with base 10 are combined, the equation at 20°C has the following simplified form for univalent ions:

$$E = 58 \log \frac{C_1}{C_2} \tag{4.2}$$

where E = potential in millivolts.

In the earliest ionic theories relating to the potentials found in muscle and nerve, selective permeability only to K^+ was believed to account for the membrane potential because of its higher concentration in the cell. The electrical potential differences between the inside and outside of the cells was given by the demarcation potential of nerve or muscle (Chapter 3). The demarcation potential measured as high as 30 mv and from estimates of the amount of shunting, the actual voltage across the membrane was estimated to be 50 to 60 mv

(Lillie, 1932). This value is close to that expected on the basis of the Nernst equation from the chemical determinations of the K^+ concentration in the cell and in the extracellular medium (cf. Eq. 4.1).

The concentration of K^+ is greater inside the nerve fibers than outside, and the K^+ can be considered to have a *chemical driving force* making it tend to leave the fibers. With some of the K^+ leaving the fiber, the inside becomes relatively negative in electrical charge, the degree of the negativity related to the number of K^+ ions passing out across the membrane. The movement of K^+ stops when the difference of potential across the membrane increases to the extent that the inside becomes sufficiently negatively charged to attract the positive K^+ back into the cell. This electrical attraction or *electrical driving force* 'pulling' K^+ back into the cell equals at equilibrium the tendency of K^+ to leave because of the concentration difference, i.e. the chemical driving force.

The *electrochemical potential* can be expressed as the sum of chemical and electrical potentials as follows (see for example Teorell, 1953):

$$n_j = \mu_j + zF\psi \qquad (4.3)$$

where n = electrochemical potential, μ = chemical potential, ψ = electrical potential, z = valence, F = Faraday, and j = the species of ion to which the relationship is applied. It is the gradient of the electrochemical potential which determines the flux of an ion.

The Nernst equation and Eq. 4.3 may be considered as showing the balance between electrical and chemical potentials. The chemical potential term ($\ln C_1/C_2$) on one side of the Nernst equation balances the electrical potential on the other side. A consequence of this balance of chemical and electrical potentials is that if an electrical potential is imposed across the membrane there will eventually be a change in the ion ratio which at equilibrium will correspond to the expected total electrochemical potential of the Nernst equation. However, this ionic redistribution may take a considerable period of time because of the relatively low permeability to ions across the cell membranes.

Crucial to the understanding of the relation of ions to potential is the realization that only a very small number of ions need be displaced across the membrane to give rise to changes in the membrane potential. The actual number of ions which can cause the voltage changes observed across the membrane is too small to be measured chemically. We may calculate the ionic difference of charge from elementary electrostatic principles if simplifying assumptions are made. The relationship in electrical theory between capacitance, voltage and electrical charge is given as follows:

$$CV = Q \qquad (4.4)$$

where C = capacitance in farads/cm^2, Q = charge in coulombs and V = volts. If we assume a potential difference across the membrane of 100 mv and a capacitance of 1 mfd/cm^2 (Chapter 6), we have:

$$10^{-6} \times 10^{-1} = 10^{-7} \text{ coulombs of charge.}$$

A Faraday equals 96,500 coulombs per mole and, therefore, the molar quantity of ions displaced is approximately:

$$10^{-7}/10^5 = 10^{-12} \text{ M} = 1 \text{ pM} \qquad (\text{p} = \text{pica} = 1 \times 10^{-12}).$$

Donnan theory of membrane potential

In their classical study of muscle with respect to the ion permeability and potential across the membrane, Boyle and Conway (1941) demonstrated that not only K^+ but also Cl^- can enter muscle fibers when increased amounts of K^+ are present in the external solution. Their results removed a key presumption of the earlier theory that only K^+ can penetrate the membrane. Some other basis for the membrane potential had to be considered. Boyle and Conway found that the behavior of the muscle with respect to the entry of K^+ and Cl^- and water closely followed the predictions made from the Donnan theory of membrane potential. Donnan had experimentally verified the earlier prediction of Gibbs that an asymmetrical distribution of ions can be produced by the presence of a charged non-permeable molecular species on one side of a membrane which is freely permeable to other ions (Davson, 1964). A typical case would be a protein or amino acid acting as a non-permeant molecule, and K^+ and Cl^- as the permeating ions. The dotted lines of Fig. 4.1 represent a membrane separating the ionic species of compartments 1 and 2 through which K^+ and Cl^- can diffuse but not the larger anion present in compartment 1 which may be considered to be a protein. At the start KCl is present in a greater concentration in compartment 2. A quantity X of both K^+ and Cl^- moves across the membrane until with the passage of time, equilibrium is reached. A condition of the Donnan distribution is that the products of the concentrations of ions on each side of the

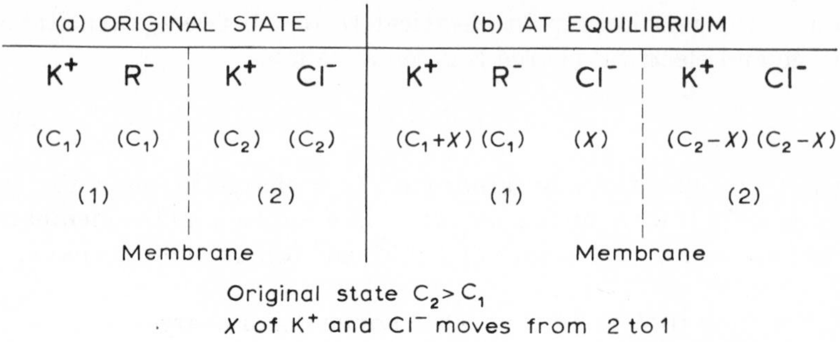

(a) ORIGINAL STATE				(b) AT EQUILIBRIUM				
K^+	R^-	K^+	Cl^-	K^+	R^-	Cl^-	K^+	Cl^-
(C_1)	(C_1)	(C_2)	(C_2)	(C_1+X)	(C_1)	(X)	(C_2-X)	(C_2-X)
(1)		(2)		(1)			(2)	
Membrane				Membrane				

Original state $C_2 > C_1$
X of K^+ and Cl^- moves from 2 to 1

Fig. 4.1. The Donnan distribution is shown before equilibrium (a) with K^+ and Cl^- present in the two compartments on either side of a semipermeable membrane at concentrations C_1 and C_2. An impermeant species R^- is present in compartment 1. After equilibrium (b) some amount X of K^+ and Cl^- has moved from compartment 1 to compartment 2.

membrane which can cross the membrane are equal. At equilibrium the concentrations will appear as follows:

$$[K^+]_1 \times [Cl^-]_1 = [K^+]_2 \times [Cl^-]_2 \tag{4.5}$$

or

$$\frac{[K^+]_1}{[K^+]_2} = \frac{[Cl^-]_2}{[Cl^-]_1}.$$

Using relatively simple algebraic equations, Donnan showed how the ratio of ions transferred can be calculated (Gortner and Gortner, 1949). The presence of the non-diffusible anion on one side has a considerable effect on the ratio of cations pertaining at equilibrium.

The Nernst relationship (Eq. 4.1) is applied to the ratio of each of the ion species at equilibrium as indicated:

$$E = \frac{RT}{nF} \ln \frac{[K^+]_1}{[K^+]_2} = \frac{RT}{nF} \frac{[Cl^-]_2}{[Cl^-]_1}. \tag{4.6}$$

We shall discuss the measurement of membrane potential in detail in the next section, but note should be taken that the ratios of K^+ and Cl^- appearing in Eq. 4.6 are inverted because of their difference in charge. The voltages they would produce across the membrane therefore is oriented in the same direction instead of in opposition and can be considered as two 'batteries' connected together in parallel.

The non-diffusible ion species which could give rise to a Donnan distribution found in muscle were listed by Boyle and Conway as phosphocreatine, magnesium, carnosine, sodium, adenylpyro-phosphoric acid, calcium, hexose monophosphate, and protein. Aspartic acid in crustacean nerve and isethionic acid and arginine in giant nerve fibers of squid have been considered important as non-diffusing species giving rise to a Donnan equilibrium. (Phospho-creatine and arginine as arginine phosphate have special properties, as will be described in Chapter 7.)

Trans-membrane voltages and the Donnan hypothesis

Changing the external concentration of K^+ should result in a changed membrane voltage in accordance with the Nernst equation (Eq. 4.1). Techniques for obtaining the true trans-membrane potential have been developed and a confirmation with theoretical expectations found. Young (1936) pointed out that lower forms such as squid and cuttlefish have giant nerve fibers with diameters of 0.5 mm or more. This interested investigators in the possibility of directly measuring the resting potential across the membrane of these giant nerve fibers. Electrodes were placed directly inside such giant nerve fibers by Hodgkin and Huxley (1939) and Curtis and Cole (1940).

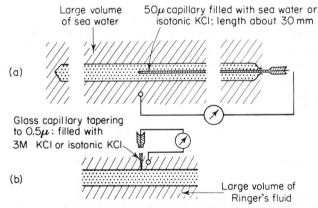

Fig. 4.2. (a) Glass capillary electrode inserted inside giant fiber to measure membrane potential with the other electrode present in the medium outside. (b) Microelectrode inserted through the membrane to measure potential. (From Hodgkin, 1951.)

The internal recording electrode used was a fine pipette inserted down the middle of the axon through one open end of the nerve with the other electrode placed in the bath (Fig. 4.2). The resting membrane potential found for the squid measured approximately 60 mv with the inside of the axon negative in charge.

Another approach to recording trans-membrane potentials was

the use of ultra-fine microelectrodes passed directly through the surface membrane of nerve fibers and muscle cells (Fig. 4.2). This was successfully accomplished in the technique developed by Ling and Gerard (1949). In the production of microelectrodes suitable for this purpose, glass capillary tubing is heated until soft, and then rapidly drawn out so that the resulting tip diameters are approximately 0.5 μ. These micro-capillaries are then filled with liquid conducting solutions (usually with 3M KCl) to help overcome the very high electrical resistances due to the small tip, and to reduce the junctional potential found between solutions of dissimilar composition and the *tip potential* in these electrodes (Adrian, 1956). A cathode-follower input (Chapter 1) is employed to compensate for the high electrical resistance and capacitance of the tips. These microelectrodes are so small that they produce but a small amount of damage upon passage through the membrane; the cell membrane apparently seals around the microelectrode after entry.

External K^+ concentrations were altered while trans-membrane potentials were directly measured to see if the resulting changes in the membrane potentials conformed to the Nernst equation. A correspondence of membrane potential with the ratio of K^+ concentration across the membrane over a wide range of variation in external K^+ was found for different tissues (Hodgkin, 1951). The changes of muscle membrane potentials with different levels of external K^+ concentration found by Adrian (1956) are plotted in Fig. 4.3. Notice that at higher external K^+ concentrations, the relation between the logarithm of the K^+ concentration and the membrane potential can be fitted by a straight line close to a 58 mv change for a ten-fold change in external K^+ concentration, as expected from the Nernst equation (Eq. 4.2). The deviation from the Nernst relationship found with K^+ concentrations of 2–3 mM normally present in the external media could reflect different mechanisms controlling permeability of K^+ in that range. One such explanation relating to Na^+ will be mentioned in a later section of this chapter.

In some studies discrepancies have been seen between the potentials and K^+ concentrations which appear to be due to diffusion rates. Hodgkin and Horowicz (1959) measured trans-membrane potential during changed levels of external K^+ using isolated single muscle fibers to permit ionic equilibrium to be more rapidly attained. The external concentration of K^+ was varied keeping the product of K^+ and Cl^- constant (Eq. 4.5). In other cases K^+ alone was varied. Their results were consistent with the expectations of the Boyle–Conway hypothesis.

Recently it was found possible by means of a small roller to gently extrude the cytoplasm from a giant squid nerve axon and to reinflate the axon by perfusing the inside with solutions of different compositions (Oikawa *et al.*, 1961; Baker *et al.*, 1962a, b). With isotonic K_2SO_4 placed inside the axon the resting membrane potential was

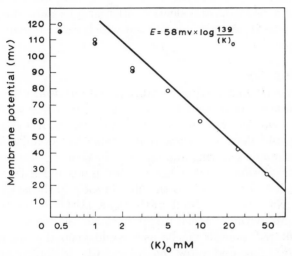

Fig. 4.3. With the different external concentrations of potassium $(K)_0$ shown on the abscissa (chloride as anion o, sulfate ⊙), the corresponding membrane potentials E calculated on the basis of an internal potassium concentration of 139 mM are shown. A deviation of potentials from the theoretical Nernst potential is indicated at lower concentrations of external potassium. (From Adrian, 1956.)

similar to that found for the intact axon. Such reinflated axons can give rise to action potentials (Chapter 5). With NaCl placed inside to equal the concentration of NaCl in the external medium, the resting membrane potential was zero. For that matter with the same concentration of solutions of K_2SO_4, KCl, Na_2SO_4 or sea water placed on each side of the membrane, the potential was zero. The lack of effect of Cl^- on the resting membrane potential was shown by comparing the effect of isotonic solutions of K_2SO_4 and KCl placed inside the axon. The membrane potential did not differ by more than a few millivolts indicating that the Cl^- ion makes very little contribution to the resting membrane potential of the giant nerve axon.

Replacing the internal solution with different proportions of KCl and NaCl (the latter relatively inert with respect to the resting potential) gave rise to the variations in potential expected of the Nernst equation. At the higher internal K^+ concentrations there was a deviation due to an effect of K^+ on membrane permeability and another deviation was found at low internal K^+ concentrations. Only approximately 4% of the original cytoplasm was left remaining in these perfused axons and electron micrographs showed a thickness of the cytoplasm near the membrane which ranged from 1 to 12 μ and averaged 7 μ.

The sodium pump

While it appears that resting membrane potentials are controlled by K^+ (and in the case of muscle also by Cl^-) according to the expectations of a Donnan equilibrium, radioisotope studies showed soon after Boyle and Conway's work that a small but definite amount of Na^+ is continually entering and leaving the cells.

The contradiction between the results indicating a Donnan equilibrium for K^+ and Cl^- across the membrane and the isotope studies showing a Na^+ entry existed until Dean (1941) suggested that a special 'pump' within the cell might eject Na^+ at the same rate with which it entered; such a mechanism could keep the inside concentration of Na^+ low and allow the K^+ and Cl^- to control the resting membrane potential. This *sodium pump*, as the mechanism has come to be known, would require a source of energy to move Na^+ back out of the cell against the high electrochemical gradient which causes it to enter the cells. The sodium pump is a type of *active transport* present in a variety, if not in all, cell types and related to metabolism (Krogh, 1946). The term active transport has been variously used. Ussing (1949) defined active transport as the movement of a substance requiring an expenditure of energy from some additional (metabolic) source. A number of different pump models have been devised. For our purposes the sodium pump may be visualized as a special carrier molecule in the membrane with which Na^+ can combine. The carrier after combining with Na^+ on the inside surface moves to the outside surface of the membrane where Na^+ is released and the carrier then returns to the inside surface to be combined with more internal Na^+, etc. Metabolic changes could alter the reactivity of the carrier and its ability to take up and release Na^+ (Chapter 7).

Active transport was quantitatively measured in the frog skin studies of Ussing and Zerahn (1951). Frog skin is mounted between two compartments of a chamber containing Ringer solution on each side. Tracer ions can be placed in the compartment facing either the outside or inside surface of the skin. Electrodes are placed close to the skin on either side to measure the potential difference existing across the membrane and another set of electrodes is placed at the ends of each compartment in order to pass current through the skin. The normal potential difference across the skin is approximately 100 mv with the inside surface found to be positive. Ussing and Zerahn showed that this voltage is due to an active transport of Na^+ from the outside solution through the skin to the compartment facing the inside surface. The active transport of Na^+ through the frog skin was measured by reducing the voltage across the skin to zero by passing a current from the electrodes at the ends of the chambers. In practice this is done by adjusting the current until the potential difference measured with electrodes placed close on either side of the skin becomes zero. This procedure effectively reduces the electrochemical gradient across the skin to zero because the concentrations of ions on each side are equal and the voltage gradient is reduced to zero by the imposed current. The sodium pump mechanism continues to move Na^+ from the outside to the inside compartment in such *short-circuited* preparations as shown when Na^+ isotopes are added to the inside and to the outside chambers. The isotope studies showed a greater Na^+ flux from the outside to the inside compartment than in the reverse direction. The measurements of Na^+ flux in the short-circuited skin also showed that the current required to reduce the potential across the skin to zero was a good indirect measure of the amount of Na^+ moved across the skin by the Na^+ pump. (To be differentiated from this sodium pumping action, where there is a *net* transfer of ions from one compartment to the other (or from the inside of a cell to the outside), is the phenomenon of *exchange*. When an isotope of an ion is added to the medium, then an exchange of unlabeled for labeled isotope occurs and there is an apparent influx or efflux although there is no net movement.)

If metabolic poisons are added to either one or both of the chambers on either side of the frog skin, then metabolism is blocked and so also is the sodium pump and eventually the potential falls (Chapter 7).

The frog skin is a rather complex tissue. However, there appears to be only a single layer of cells in the stratum germinativum which are active in transport (Ussing, 1959). The cells appear to be functionally polarized with the sodium pump present on the surface of the cell membrane facing the inner surface of the skin. Sodium ions combine with the pump carrier to be ejected from the cell to the inner chamber. It was found that K^+ was required in the chamber facing the inner surface of the skin for the operation of the sodium pump. As Na^+ is ejected, the carrier appears to pick up K^+ in its return back inside the cell where K^+ is released and more Na^+ taken up. By this means the concentration of K^+ is maintained high inside the cell while at the same time Na^+ is ejected.

A model of how such a sodium pump could work has been suggested by Davies and Keynes (1961): A lipoprotein carrier present in the membrane combines at different sites with either Na^+ or K^+. At the Na^+-channel Na^+ combines with the carrier. The carrier rotates bringing Na^+ to the outside surface where it is released and K^+ is attached. On rotating back again K^+ is released to the inside of the cell and Na^+ attached, etc. Such models are not to be considered real but rather as attempts to visualize the working of a sodium pump which is coupled to an uptake of K^+.

It has been known for many years that isolated muscle and nerve fibers tend to leak K^+ and gain Na^+ unless the external concentration of K^+ is raised above the level normally found in the extracellular fluid of the animal's body (Fenn, 1940). This indicates that the sodium pump may be altered *in vitro*. Possibly some substance present *in vivo* is required to maintain the sodium pump in normal operation. Carey and Conway (1954) found that an addition of blood serum to the external medium decreased the leakage of K^+ and the gain of Na^+ suggesting that some serum factor may be at least in part responsible for its maintenance.

Membrane pores and ionic movements

Permeation of ions through membranes focuses attention on the nature of the structures of the membrane which control permeability. The membrane around nerve and muscle responsible for resting potential and excitability has been identified in electron micrographs as a 75–80 A membrane. With the greater resolution possible with permanganate staining this membrane has been resolved into outer and inner dense staining layers and a middle light staining zone (Robertson, 1960). This is the *unit membrane* present in electron micrographs of the membranes of a wide variety of cells. On the basis of chemical analysis and physical-chemical measurements the membrane is known to contain lipid and protein. These are considered to be arranged as shown in Fig. 4.4. This representation of the unit membrane was first inferred by Davson and Danielli (1952) from the fact that the lipid extracted from cell membranes spreads out over a water surface in a monomolecular thickness to cover an area twice that determined for the membrane surface area. The presence of protein on the surfaces of the cell membrane was indicated by measurements of the surface tension of cells showing them to be hydrophilic.

extracellular substance

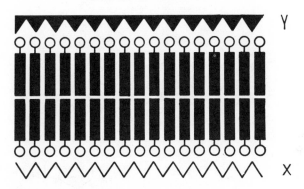

cytoplasm

Fig. 4.4. The membrane is diagrammatically shown composed of lipid centrally with their hydophilic ends facing protein layers X and Y. (Robertson, *Assoc. Res. Nervous Mental Disease* **40**: 1962.)

Until recently it had been considered that osmium tetroxide is a lipid stain. The denser staining of the outer and inner surfaces of the unit membrane was puzzling if these are protein. However, it has been shown that osmium tetroxide reacts with sulfhydryl groups, terminal amino groups, and other functional groups occurring in protein (Schmitt and Geschwind, 1957). The staining of the outer protein layers and the lack of staining of the internal lipid part of the unit membrane is, therefore, in line with present evidence.

The nature of the lipids present in the membrane has been derived from studies of the myelin sheath of nerve which are considered to be composed of a number of unit membranes. (We shall reserve discussion of the myelin sheath until Chapter 6.) Based on that analysis of myelin, the manner in which the various molecular constituents are considered to be arranged in the membrane is shown in Fig. 4.5. The phosphatidylserine molecule would have to be folded in order for its length to fit into the space one-half the membrane thickness. The phosphate at the end confers a hydrophilic character to the outer and inner parts of the membrane where the protein layers are present. The cholesterol molecule fits into the remaining space. The importance of the integrity of phospholipids in the membrane is suggested by the rapid block of

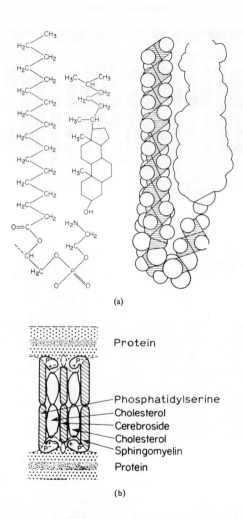

(a)

Protein

Phosphatidylserine
Cholesterol
Cerebroside
Cholesterol
Sphingomyelin
Protein

(b)

Fig. 4.5. The phosphatidylserine molecule (a) is folded in the membrane with the phosphate end facing the protein layers on the outer and inner surfaces (b). Cholesterol is fitted into the remaining space alternating with sphingomyelin. (From Finean, 1953 and 1957; after Robertson, 1960.)

excitation found when nerve fibers are exposed to a phospholipase (Tobias, 1958).

Both water-soluble and lipid-soluble molecules penetrate cell membranes. Overton considered that the lipid-soluble molecules first dissolve in a lipid phase of the membrane before penetration. The mixed structure of the membrane is usually considered to account for permeability properties—lipid-soluble substances dissolving in the lipid, with *pores* or *channels* for the passage of ions and other water-soluble substances (Davson and Danielli, 1952). Considering the pores as narrow tubes to which Poiseuille's law of diffusion could be applied, movement of labeled water molecules through nerve membrane by diffusion and also under conditions of an osmotic gradient across the membrane was compared (Nevis, 1958). The studies of Villegas, Caputo and Villegas (1962) indicated a pore size of the order of 4 A in radius, a size similar to that found in various other cells (Solomon, 1961).

The pore size in some theoretical treatments has been considered to be a critical factor in explaining membrane properties. Mullins (1961) taking a pore radius size of approximately 4 A and the available physical data on the hydrated and unhydrated sizes of K^+ and Na^+ considers that the accumulation of K^+ inside the cell may be accounted for on a selection basis—the smaller hydrated K^+ would be able to enter but not the larger hydrated Na^+. Such rather close fitting between ions and pore sizes may not explain all the known phenomena, but a close relation between pore size and ions has been used to explain differences in transient permeability increases caused by excitatory and inhibitory transmitters at synapses (Chapter 16).

Most of the discussions of the relationship of pores to potential across the membrane rests on the presupposition that the pore size and ion permeation are passive properties of the membrane. The *constant field theory* of Goldman (1943) makes this assumption explicit. The electrical difference across the membrane imposes an electrical gradient across the thickness of the membrane and its channels. A charged particle such as an ion then moves through the pore or channel according to this gradient. For the ions commonly concerned, the resting membrane potential was related to ionic composition by Hodgkin and Katz (1949) shown in the following modified form of the Nernst equation:

$$V = \frac{RT}{F} \ln \frac{P_K[K^+]_o + P_{Na}[Na^+]_o + P_{Cl}[Cl^-]_i}{P_K[K^+]_i + P_{Na}[Na^+]_i + P_{Cl}[Cl^-]_o} \qquad (4.7)$$

where P_K, P_{Na}, P_{Cl} are the permeability coefficients for the corresponding ion species.

The permeability coefficients are defined in the equation by the measured passage of a given species per unit time across a known area of membrane under a given concentration gradient (Davson and Danielli, 1952). A marked transient change in the permeability coefficient of Na^+ occurs during activity, a subject which will be discussed in Chapter 5. The equation shows that in the resting membrane the permeability coefficient for Na^+ though small will allow a small amount of Na^+ to leak into the fiber. In their study of single muscle fibers exposed to rapid changes in K^+ and Cl^- Hodgkin and Horowicz (1959) found that the deviation from the expectations of the Nernst equation at the lower external concentrations of K^+ previously referred to could be approximated by an equation that included a contribution of Na^+ to that overall ion permeability. The modification of the Nernst equation to take into account a partial effect of Na^+ at low K^+ levels is shown in the following equation:

$$V = \frac{RT}{F} \ln \frac{[K^+]_o + \alpha[Na^+]_o}{[K^+]_i + \alpha[Na^+]_i} \qquad (4.8)$$

where α has a value of 0.01 and is equal to the permeability ratio P_{Na}/P_K. At low external K^+ the permeability of Na^+ becomes appreciable, thereby explaining the deviation from expectation of the Nernst equation. At higher values of external K^+, the membrane potential is controlled by K^+ and Cl^- as earlier indicated.

We would like to examine the electrical correlate of permeability, namely, the electrical resistivity of the resting membrane. A variety of cells were shown by the Wheatstone bridge measurements of Cole and his co-workers to be characterized as having both a high resistivity and capacitance (Cole, 1962). This was shown by measuring resistances at different frequencies with a Wheatstone bridge.

The capacitance is related to the lipid present in the membrane and is relatively unchanged upon excitation. Considering the probable value for the dielectric constant of the lipids present in the membrane, the thickness of the membrane was calculated as 33 A, a value surprisingly close to the thickness of the inner zone of the unit membrane derived from the electron microscope measurement (*vide supra*).

The membrane resistance measures 1000 ohm-cm² for the giant nerve fiber and is related to passage of ions in the pores and, as will be described (Chapter 5), a transient conductance increase occurs with excitation. (Resistance is the reciprocal of conductance.) The resistance of 1000 ohm cm^2 for the resting state of the membrane is of interest with regard to the thickness of the membrane. Resistivity is given in ohms by the value found for a piece of material 1 cm^2 in cross-section and 1 cm in length. If the thickness is decreased, then the resistance should decrease correspondingly. A membrane resistance of 1000 ohm-cm^2 with a thickness of 75 A, therefore, indicates a very high resistivity of the membrane material, approaching that of good electrical insulators such as glass. We would expect that the number of pores present in an area of one cm^2 would be relatively few to account for the high resistance of the membrane. Isotopic measurements of the permeabilities of nerve membrane conform with the low values indicated by impedance measurements (Hodgkin, 1951).

The movement of K$^+$ through the channels has also been described by Katz and by Hodgkin and Horowicz as showing a *rectifying action* with an easier transfer found for the passage of K$^+$ from the external medium into the cell than for passage outward. This may be 100 times greater in the inward direction even though the internal concentration of K$^+$ inside the cell is so much greater than that outside and a greater flux in the outward direction might be expected. Anomalous movements of K$^+$ through the pores of the membrane of giant nerve fibers were previously reported by Hodgkin and Keynes (1955) and the ions were considered to move through the channels in a single fiber rather than individually to account for deviation from a simple flux (cf. Harris, 1960).

Other views on the origin of the membrane potential

In his *fixed-charge* hypothesis Ling (1952) has argued against the pores of the membrane controlling the entry of the various ions into the cell and against the Donnan hypothesis. He has considered the accumulation of K$^+$ in the cell on the basis of the smaller size of its hydrated atomic radius which allows a closer approach to sites on the protein molecules in the cytoplasm than does the larger hydrated Na$^+$ atom (cf. Eisenman, 1961). According to this theory the internal concentration of K$^+$ is regulated by the cytoplasm operating somewhat like an ion-exchange substance. However, electrical conductivity measurements of the axoplasm shows a conductivity expected of freely mobile ions (Cole and Hodgkin, 1939; Hodgkin and Keynes, 1953). Also, as already indicated the region controlling membrane potential is at the surface and certainly only a few microns in thickness at most. The channels or pores of the membrane or a thin region near it could have fixed-charged properties (Harris, 1960). Teorell (1953) on the basis of a study of artificial membranes concluded that the membrane could be regarded as having both a Donnan distribution at the inter-faces and fixed-charge properties present within its pores.

Isolated muscles when exposed to K^+-free solutions slowly lose K^+ and gain Na^+; this change is reversed when sufficient K^+ (about 10 mM) is added to the medium (Steinbach, 1951; Conway, Kernan and Zadunaisky, 1961). This phase of Na^+ extrusion from the muscle appears to be associated with a membrane potential approximately 9 mv above that calculated from the K^+ ratio, and the Nernst equation (Kernan, 1962a; Keynes and Rybová, 1963). Substances such as lactate and insulin having stimulating effects on metabolism will also give rise to Na^+ extrusion even when the external K^+ is as low as 2.5 mM (Kernan, 1962b). The mechanism of this *electrogenic* action of the sodium pump is not yet understood, but it does appear to contribute, to a small extent, to the maintenance of resting membrane potential.

REFERENCES

Adrian, R. H. (1956). The effect of internal and external potassium concentration on the membrane potential of frog muscle. *J. Physiol.* **133**: 631–658.

Baker, P. F., Hodgkin, A. L. and Shaw, T. I. (1962a). Replacement of the axoplasm of giant nerve fibres with artificial solutions. *J. Physiol.* **164**: 330–354.

Baker, P. F., Hodgkin, A. L. and Shaw, T. I. (1962b). The effects of changes in internal ionic concentrations on the electrical properties of perfused giant axons. *J. Physiol.* **164**: 355–374.

Bernstein, J. (1902). Untersuchungen zur Thermodynamic der bioelecktrischen Ströme. *Pfluger's Arch. Physiol.* **92**: 521–562.

Boyle, P. J. and Conway, E. J. (1941). Potassium accumulation in muscle and associated changes. *J. Physiol.* **101**: 1–63.

Carey, M. J. and Conway, E. J. (1954). Comparison of various media for immersing frog sartorii at room temperature, and evidence for the regional distribution of fibre Na^+. *J. Physiol.* **125**: 232–250.

Cole, K. S. and Hodgkin, A. L. (1939). Membrane and protoplasm resistance in the squid giant axon. *J. Gen. Physiol.* **22**: 671–687.

Cole, K. S. (1962). The advance of electrical models for cells and axons. *Proc. Intern. Biophys. Congr., Biophys. J.* **2**: *Suppl.* 101–119.

Conway, E. J., Kernan, R. P. and Zadunaisky, J. A. (1961). The sodium pump in skeletal muscle in relation to energy barriers. *J. Physiol.* **155**: 263–279.

Curtis, H. J. and Cole, K. S. (1940). Membrane action potentials from squid giant axon. *J. Cell. Comp. Physiol.* **15**: 147–157.

Davies, R. E. and Keynes, R. D. (1961). A coupled sodium–potassium pump. *Membrane Transport and Metabolism.* Edited by A. Kleinzeller and A. Kotyk. Pp. 336–340. Academic Press, New York.

Davson, H. (1964). *A Textbook of General Physiology.* 3rd Ed. Little, Brown and Co., Boston.

Davson, H. and Danielli, J. F. (1952). *The Permeability of Natural Membranes.* 2nd Ed. Cambridge University Press, Cambridge.

Dean, R. B. (1941). Theories of electrolyte equilibrium in muscle. *Biol. Symp.* **3**: 331–348.

Eisenman, G. (1961). On the elementary origin of equilibrium ionic specificity. *Membrane Transport and Metabolism.* Edited by A. Kleinzeller and A. Kotyk. Academic Press, New York.

Fenn, W. O. (1940). The role of potassium in physiologic processes. *Physiol. Rev.* **20**: 377–415.

Finean, J. B. (1953). Further observations on the structure of myelin. *Exptl. Cell. Res.* **5**: 202–215.

Finean, J. B. (1957). The molecular organization of nerve myelin. *Acta Neurol. Psychiat. Belg.* **5**: 462–471.

Goldman, D. E. (1943). Potential, impedance and rectification in membranes. *J. Gen. Physiol.* **27**: 37–60.

Gortner, R. A. Jr. and Gortner, W. A. (1949). *Outlines of Biochemistry.* 3rd Ed. John Wiley & Sons, Inc., New York.

Harris, E. J. (1960). *Transport and Accumulation in Biological Systems.* 2nd Ed. Butterworths Scientific Publications, London.

Hodgkin, A. L. (1951). The ionic basis of electrical activity in nerve and muscle. *Biol. Rev.* **26**: 339–409.

Hodgkin, A. L. and Horowicz, P. (1959). The influence of potassium and chloride on the membrane potential of single muscle fibers. *J. Physiol.* **148**: 127–160.

Hodgkin, A. L. and Huxley, A. F. (1939). Action potentials from inside a nerve fibre. *Nature* **144**: 710–711.

Hodgkin, A. L. and Katz, B. (1949). The effect of sodium ions on the electrical activity of the giant axon of the squid. *J. Physiol.* **108**: 37–77.

Hodgkin, A. L. and Keynes, R. D. (1953). The mobility and diffusion coefficients of potassium in giant axons from *Sepia. J. Physiol.* **119**: 513–528.

Hodgkin, A. L. and Keynes, R. D. (1955). The potassium permeability of a giant nerve fibre. *J. Physiol.* **128**: 61–88.

Kernan, R. P. (1962a). Membrane potential changes during sodium transport in frog sartorius muscle. *Nature* **193**: 986–987.

Kernan, R. P. (1962b). The role of lactate in the active secretion of sodium by frog muscle. *J. Physiol.* **162**: 129–137.

Keynes, R. D. and Rybová, R. (1963). The coupling between sodium and potassium fluxes in frog sartorius muscle. *J. Physiol.* **168**: 58P.

Krogh, A. (1946). The active and passive exchanges of inorganic ions through the surfaces of living cells and through living membranes generally. *Proc. Roy. Soc. B.* **133**: 140–200.

Lillie, R. S. (1932). *Protoplasmic Action and Nervous Action.* 2nd Ed. University Chicago Press, Chicago.

Ling, G. (1952). The role of phosphate in the maintenance of the resting potential and selective ionic accumulation in muscle. *Phosphorus Metabolism*. Edited by McElroy and Glass. Vol. II. Johns Hopkins University Press, Baltimore.

Ling, G. and Gerard, R. W. (1949). The normal membrane potential of frog sartorius fibres. *J. Cell. Comp. Physiol.* **34**: 382–396.

Mullins, L. J. (1961). The macromolecular properties of excitable membranes. *Ann. N.Y. Acad. Sci.* **94**: 390–404.

Nernst, W. (1908). Zur Theorie das elektrischen Reizes. *Pfluger's Arch. Physiol.* **122**: 275–314.

Nevis, A. H. (1958). Water transport in invertebrate peripheral nerve fibers. *J. Gen. Physiol.* **41**: 927–958.

Oikawa, T., Spyropoulos, C. S., Tasaki, I. and Teorell, T. (1961). Methods for perfusing the giant axon of *Loligo pealii*. *Acta Physiol. Scand.* **52**: 195–196.

Robertson, J. D. (1960). The molecular structure and contact relationship of cell membranes. *Progr. Biophys.* **10**: 343–418.

Schmitt, F. O. and Geschwind, N. (1957). The axon surface. *Progr. Biophys.* **8**: 165–215.

Solomon, A. K. (1961). Measurement of the equivalent pore radius in cell membranes. *Membrane Transport and Metabolism*. Edited by A. Kleinzeller and A. Kotyk. Pp. 94–113. Academic Press, New York.

Steinbach, H. B. (1951). Sodium extrusion from isolated frog muscle. *Am. J. Physiol*, **167**: 284-287.

Teorell, T. (1953). Transport processes and electrical phenomena in ionic membranes. *Progr. Biophys.* **3**: 305–369.

Tobias, J. M. (1958). Experimentally altered structure related to function in the lobster axon with an extrapolation to molecular mechanism in excitation. *J. Cell. Comp. Physiol.* **52**: 89–107.

Ussing, H. H. (1949). Transport of ions across cellular membranes. *Physiol. Rev.* **29**: 127–155.

Ussing, H. H. (1959). Ionic movements in cell membranes in relation to the activity of the nervous system. *Ergeb. Physiol.* **50**: 159–173.

Ussing, H. H. and Zerahn, K. (1951). Active transport of sodium as the source of electric current in the short circuited isolated frog skin. *Acta Physiol. Scand.* **23**: 110–127.

Villegas, R., Caputo, C. and Villegas, L. (1962). Diffusion barriers in the squid nerve fiber. *J. Gen. Physiol.* **46**: 245–255.

Young, J. Z. (1936). Structure of nerve fibers and synapses in some invertebrates. *Cold Spring Harbor Symp. Quant. Biol.* **4**: 1–6.

5

Analysis of the Action Potential

The sodium hypothesis

With a capillary recording electrode inserted into a giant nerve fiber
(Fig. 4.2) and the fiber stimulated at one end, a propagated action
potential is recorded when it passes over the membrane in the
vicinity of the tip of the internal electrode (Hodgkin and Huxley,
1939; Curtis and Cole, 1940). The potential changes from its
resting level of 60 mv to give rise to an action potential of approximately 90 mv (Fig. 5.1). An action potential larger than the

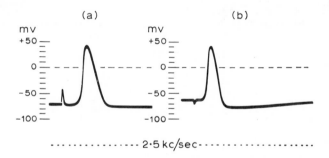

Fig. 5.1.   In (a) the action potential is taken *in vivo* from the axon
with a microelectrode inserted through the membrane.   In (b) in the
in vitro case an internal electrode measures a lower resting membrane potential and a greater after-positivity.   (Hodgkin, 1958.)

resting membrane potential is also shown, recorded *in vivo* with
a microelectrode.   This result cannot be explained simply as a
reduction of the membrane potential to zero as would be expected
from the Bernstein hypothesis (Chapter 3), and another explanation
is required.   The portion of the spike which exceeds the zero of
the membrane potential is called the *overshoot* and requires
the inside of the fiber to become positively charged by approximately
30 mv during the peak of the action potential.   The later studies of
this overshoot and of the flow of currents during an action potential
(Hodgkin and Katz, 1949; Hodgkin and Huxley, 1952a–d; Hodgkin,

Huxley and Katz, 1952) resulted in the now classic *sodium hypothesis* (Hodgkin, 1951, 1958). It will be of advantage to present the main points of the sodium hypothesis in this section and then in subsequent sections to discuss the basis for the hypothesis in more detail.

According to the hypothesis, when on stimulation the threshold is reached, the relatively low permeability of the membrane to Na$^+$ changes to a higher permeability. The electrochemical gradient for Na$^+$ which is directed into the cell can now transport Na$^+$ into

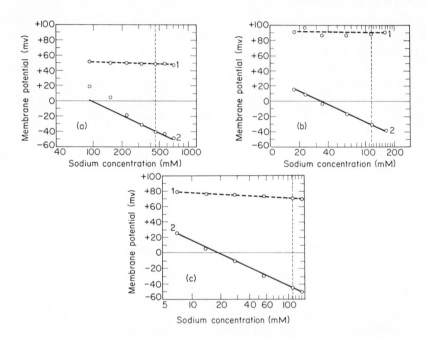

Fig. 5.2. In each case at the different external Na$^+$ concentrations shown on the abscissa a small or negligible effect on resting membrane potential is indicated by the dashed line (1), and pronounced effect is found on the action potential as shown by the solid line (2); a decrease in the amplitude of the action potential occurs with decreased Na$^+$; (a) squid, (b) frog sartorius muscle, (c) frog myelinated nerve. (From Hodgkin, 1951.)

the interior of the cell. By bringing the positive charge of Na$^+$ into the cell the interior becomes positive, thereby accounting for the overshoot of the action potential. After a few milliseconds the Na$^+$ permeability decreases and the permeability to K$^+$ increases. The positive charge which has been brought into the cell by Na$^+$ in conjunction with the high concentration of K^+ already present constitute the driving forces which move K^+ out of the cell to return the potential toward its original level and bring about the end of the action potential. The amount of K^+ leaving the cell is equivalent to the amount of Na^+ which has entered, and as both Na^+ and K^+ have equal positive charges there is a zero net change of charge across the membrane at the end of the action potential. However, a minute amount of Na^+ has been gained by the fiber and a similar amount of K^+ lost from the axoplasm. Complete recovery is accomplished at a later time by subsidiary mechanisms, i.e., by a compensating increased operation of the sodium pump to eject the excess Na^+ and to recover K^+ (Chapter 7).

The difference between the electrical properties of the resting membrane and the active membrane during an action potential is to be especially noted. As pointed out in Chapter 4, in this theory the resting membrane potential of the giant axon is controlled by the ratio of the concentrations of K^+ across the nerve membrane, as expected from the Nernst equation. On the other hand, the amplitude of the action potential is related to the ratio of Na^+ across the membrane. This is shown in Fig. 5.2 where the concentration of Na^+ in the external medium was decreased and the action potential amplitude was correspondingly reduced without much effect on the resting membrane potential. The effect of Na^+-deficient medium to reduce action potentials and Na^+-free solution to reduce and block action potentials of myelinated and nonmyelinated mammalian nerve fibers has been shown for a number of different cells (Hodgkin, 1951).

Membrane currents

The ingenious technique of stimulating and recording from a large area the whole of the membrane of a giant nerve fiber was first devised by Marmont (1949) and it opened the way to the elucidation of the sodium hypothesis. A long metal electrode was inserted down the middle of a giant nerve fiber and electrodes placed in the medium outside the nerve to complete the circuit across the membrane. By means of these electrodes and guard rings, a uniform exposure of the central portion of the axon membrane to stimulating currents is accomplished and the resultant current flow or voltage change across this area of nerve membrane can be measured. In the arrangement of Hodgkin, Huxley and Katz (1952) shown in Fig. 5.3, two separate electrodes are placed inside the axon: one for passing current and the other for measurement of potential. A brief pulse of outward electrical current passed through the membrane via one internal electrode gave rise to an apparently typical action potential which was recorded by the other electrode (Fig. 5.4). The potential arising from the whole surface of the membrane is termed a *membrane*

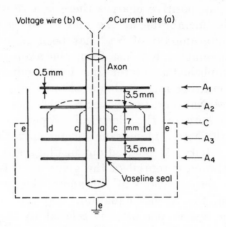

Fig. 5.3. The electrode system to measure membrane current is shown with two electrodes inserted inside the giant nerve fiber (one electrode to apply current (a), the other to measure voltage changes (b) and to hold constant the voltage across the membrane, i.e. clamping). Electrodes (c, d) are placed outside the membrane to measure the current flow to the applied voltage change (e). Insulators (A_1–A_4) placed along the length of the nerve restrict current flow to a uniform portion in the central (C) part of the membrane. (Hodgkin, Huxley and Katz, 1952.)

action potential, to be distinguished from the propagated action potentials arising in successive portions of the membrane; propagation is eliminated with this technique. The membrane action potentials which are recorded are similar in form to propagated action potentials and also show an overshoot. The overshoot, therefore, cannot be ascribed to complications taking place during propagation.

A greater insight into the nature of ionic events taking place during the action potential came about when the current flows brought about by ion movements were studied. In order to study current movements, a step-function or long-lasting pulse of voltage was introduced across the membrane and this voltage change was held at a constant level by an electronic feedback circuit and the resulting current flows across the membrane measured. Holding a voltage change across the membrane at a constant predetermined level is referred to as *voltage clamping*. Using voltage clamping, a quick surge of current is found early after the onset of the voltage step due to the capacitance of the membrane (Chapter 6). Fortunately this surge is over within a very brief time and is then followed

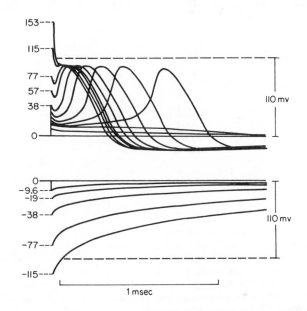

Fig. 5.4. Increasing strengths of outward current using the system of Fig. 5.3 (numbers are mμcoulombs/cm²) excite action potentials with decreasing latencies as the strength is increased. Inward currents shown in the lower part are ineffective to excite.
(Hodgkin, Huxley and Katz, 1952.)

by the flow of relatively large currents. These larger currents which move through the membrane during the time of the action potential are brought about by the various ions present across the membrane. These *membrane currents* should conform to the following general formula:

$$I = C\frac{dv}{dt} + I_{\mathrm{K}} + I_{\mathrm{Na}} + I_{\mathrm{Cl}} \qquad (5.1)$$

where I = the total current flow; I_{Na}, I_{K} and I_{Cl} are the ionic species flowing, and $C\dfrac{dv}{dt}$ = capacitance current.

What is stated in the above equation is that the total current is the result of the individual ionic currents plus a capacitative component. Because the voltage across the membrane is held constant, the capacitative current is effectively equal to zero after its brief surge and can therefore be discounted during the later ionic current flows. Column A of Fig. 5.5(a) shows the effect of de-

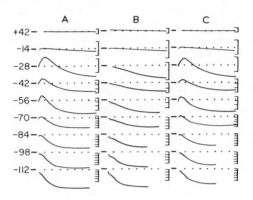

Fig. 5.5(a).   Using the membrane electrode of Fig. 5.3, membrane currents in sea water (column A) show a reduction in the inward component flow (upward deflection) as the membrane is clamped at successively lower levels (depolarization).   In column B at these same levels of depolarization with the nerve in a sodium-deficient medium, the inward component of current flow is absent.   Upon return to sea water (C) a recovery of the inward component is seen.   Time dots in msec.   (From Hodgkin and Huxley, 1952a.)

polarizing the membrane to different potentials as indicated in each trace.   Hyperpolarizing voltage is ineffective, other than giving rise to the brief surge of capacitative current.   When depolarizing voltages of sufficient degree are imposed on the membrane, large flows of current are found, of the order of several mA/cm^2 of axonal membrane.   The direction of the current flow was first inward into the axon (shown in this figure as an upward deflection) followed by a longer-lasting outward flow of current.   This is in accordance with the sodium hypothesis where the inward current flow would be due to Na^+ moving into the axon.   It should be noted that this inward movement of current is in the direction opposite to that of the imposed clamping potential which stimulates the membrane and is directed outward across the membrane.   The inward ionic flow following excitation is in the direction of the electrochemical gradient for Na^+ as required of the sodium hypothesis.

This inward current soon becomes reversed and is followed by a current in the outward direction. This later outward current flow is in the same direction as that of the depolarizing pulse imposed across the membrane by the voltage clamp, but it is much larger than the passive current due to the clamping voltage. We would expect from the sodium hypothesis that K^+ is the ion moving outward across the membrane to give rise to this later outward current.

Excitation and the inward membrane current

The identification of Na^+ as the ion entering during the inward current phase was made by replacing Na^+ in the external medium in equimolar amounts with an inactive substance such as sucrose. When the concentration of Na^+ was made low in the external medium by this means, the inward phase of current was much reduced as shown in column B of Fig. 5.5(a) where different degrees of depolarization were imposed. Upon returning the amount of Na^+ present in the external medium to its usual level, a recovery of the

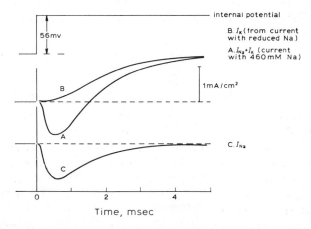

Fig. 5.5(b). Curve A shows the inward component of current flow (downward direction) followed by an outward current in response to a depolarization of -56 mv. In a sodium-deficient medium (B) the inward component is absent while the potassium current (I_K) remains. Subtraction of curves B from A gives in C the sodium current (I_{Na}). (After Hodgkin and Huxley, 1952a.)

amplitude of inward current was found. Therefore, this phase of inward current is considered to be due to the entry of Na^+ into the cell. The later outward current was unaffected. This is the rationale for a separation of the inward and outward currents into

Na$^+$ and K$^+$ currents respectively (Hodgkin and Huxley, 1952b). (Cf. Fig. 5.5(b).)

With the usual concentration of Na$^+$ in the external medium (column C, Fig. 5.5(a)) and increasing degrees of depolarizing clamping voltages applied, Na$^+$ entry was decreased as shown by smaller inward currents. Depolarization was carried to the point where the inside of the axon was made positive relative to the external solution. The inward Na$^+$ current (I_{Na}) was eliminated at a voltage clamp level of approximately 110 mv and if increased still more, the phase of early inward current was even reversed. The voltage across the membrane at which the inward current was reduced to zero is called the *equilibrium potential* for sodium (E_{Na}). At this point the voltage across the membrane equals and opposes the chemical potential driving Na$^+$ inward, i.e. electrochemical equilibrium for Na$^+$ is attained. The equilibrium potential for Na$^+$ is determined by the concentration difference of sodium on either side of the membrane (Chapter 4). By varying the concentration of Na$^+$ in the external medium, E_{Na} should change in accordance with the Nernst equation for Na$^+$ during the time of increased Na$^+$ permeability:

$$E_{Na} = \frac{RT}{F} \ln \frac{[Na^+]_i}{[Na^+]_o} \qquad (5.2)$$

This was found to be the case (Hodgkin and Huxley, 1952b).

The permeability change to Na$^+$ should be distinguished from the actual flow of Na$^+$ ions, namely I_{Na}, the Na$^+$ current. The sodium permeability may be high while no current or very little current flow is taking place as is the case for Na$^+$ at its equilibrium potential (E_{Na}). While the permeability to ion passage is high at E_{Na}, the electrochemical driving force is zero. Using a form of Ohm's law, and noting that the reciprocal of resistance is conductance (g), Na$^+$ conductance (g_{Na}) can be derived from the electrical driving force across the membrane clamped to a given voltage level and the resulting Na$^+$ current:

$$g_{Na} = \frac{I_{Na}}{E - E_{Na}} \qquad (5.3)$$

where g_{Na} = sodium conductance, I_{Na} = Na$^+$ current and $E - E_{Na}$ = the voltage difference between membrane potential and equilibrium potential for Na$^+$, i.e. the electrical driving force.

As noted above, the currents due to Na$^+$ and to K$^+$ are separated by replacing Na$^+$ in the external medium with a non-permeant

constituent such as sucrose.   The computation of Na$^+$ and K$^+$
conductances affords a clear representation of the changes occurring
during an action potential (Fig. 5.6).   As can be seen in this figure,
an early Na$^+$ conductance increase is followed by a K$^+$ conductance

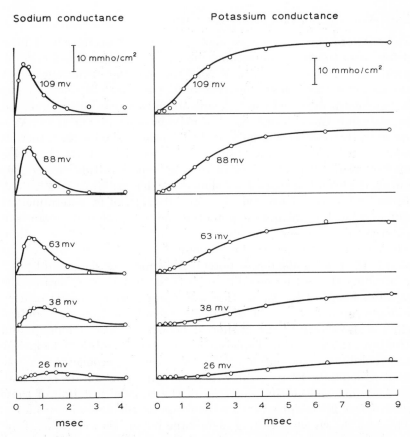

Fig. 5.6.   Conductances are shown for sodium and potassium
determined from the ratio of their respective current flows and
membrane voltages.   The conductances are shown for different
degrees of depolarization.   (After Hodgkin and Huxley, 1952a.)

increase.   Notice the brevity of the Na$^+$ conductance increase with
a quick return to its usual low level during a continued depolarization.   The process by which Na$^+$ conductance is reduced and ter-
minated is called *inactivation*.   The inactivation of Na$^+$ conductance
was studied by use of brief pulses of depolarization and shown to be

much more rapid than the return of K^+ conductance to its original lower level. Special mechanisms appear to be involved in the inactivation of the permeability increase of Na^+ which serves to terminate the action potential (Hodgkin and Huxley, 1952c).

Excitation and outward membrane current

The outward current which is mainly due to K^+ begins with a brief delay, after the Na^+ conductance increase following excitation of the membrane. The movement of Na^+ through the membrane is not the cause of this delayed increase of K^+ permeability because the K^+ current is observed when the inward current has been eliminated by reducing the external Na^+ as may be seen in Fig. 5.6. As a result of the positive charge brought into the nerve by Na^+, there is a greater tendency for the positively charged K^+ to leave the inside of the axon. Therefore, at increasing depolarization levels, the outward current increases as shown in the example of Fig. 5.6. From such experiments, the K^+ current (I_K) can be determined at different levels of membrane potential and with different amounts of external K^+ present and shown to follow the Nernst equation. The equilibrium potential for potassium (E_K) cannot be taken as simply the resting membrane potential, as might be suggested by K^+ controlling the resting membrane potential (Chapter 4) because the steady leakage of K^+ shows that these preparations are not exactly in equilibrium. The deviation of the membrane from K^+ equilibrium is also shown by use of short depolarizing pulses (Hodgkin and Huxley, 1952c). The displacement of the membrane from the true equilibrium potential for K^+ and the hyperpolarization was determined to be 13 mv greater than the resting membrane potential. The trauma and cutting involved in the surgical isolation of these giant nerve fibers appears to be the cause for the deviation from E_K. This was shown when resting membrane potentials were taken from a giant nerve fiber *in vivo* with a microelectrode inserted into the axon radially through the surface. The resting potential by this means was found to be approximately 10 mv higher than usual for the *in vitro* preparation as indicated in Fig. 5.1.

Another interesting phenomenon related to the condition of the fiber is the positive after-potential seen after the action potential in the isolated nerve preparation (Fig. 5.1). Positive after-potentials are either diminished in amplitude or not seen at all when the action potential is obtained via microelectrodes from the nerve *in vivo*. The after-potential appears to be related to the difference between the membrane potential and E_K. This subject will be discussed in a later section.

The equation used to compute K^+ conductance (g_K) has the same form as that given for Na^+:

$$g_K = \frac{I_K}{E - E_K} \tag{5.4}$$

where $I_K = K^+$ current and E_K = equilibrium potential for K^+.

Near the potassium equilibrium potential the total resting current flow was computed to have a very low value. On that basis it was considered that Cl^- and other ions contribute only a small amount to the resting 'leakage.' This is not the case for the muscle membrane where the Cl^- contribution to the conductance is relatively large (Chapters 4, 9).

Measurement of ionic exchanges across the active membrane

When isotopes of Na^+ or K^+ are added to the external medium in *in vitro* studies of isolated nerves or muscles, the influx of these ions can be measured by the uptake of isotopes in the cells at measured time intervals. Similarly, after uptake of isotope into the cell interiors, the efflux of tracer back out into the external medium can be found by measuring at various time intervals the activity remaining in the cells or the activity of the isotope which has passed into the external medium (Keynes, 1951, 1954). Study of the influx and efflux rates of K^+ and Na^+ shows that the isolated nerves and muscles are not exactly in equilibrium. These cells are continually gaining a small amount of Na^+ and losing a comparable amount of K^+. This deviation has already been mentioned with regard to the equilibrium for K^+. Discounting this small deviation from equilibrium, the isotope technique has been of great value in showing that the trans-membrane movements of Na^+ and K^+ during action potential activity conform to the sodium hypothesis. The flux of tracer ions was determined in giant nerve fibers before, during, and after a period of tetanic stimulation. During such a period of activity the rate of radioactive Na^+ uptake was increased (Fig. 5.7) and as well the rate of K^+ influx (Fig. 5.8). Both the inward and outward flux of Na^+ and K^+ were increased but more Na^+ was gained than lost and more K^+ lost than gained by the cells. The calculated net gain of Na^+ per action potential was 6.6 pM/cm^2 and the loss of K^+, 4.7 pM/cm^2. Using more exact figures for the relation between charge and voltage across the membrane than those given in the discussion of Eq. 4.4, the ionic exchange per action

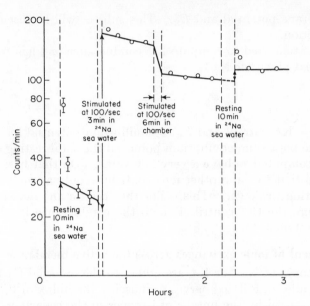

Fig. 5.7.   The gain and loss of Na⁺ on immersion of *Sepia* axon in Na⁺ isotope solution is shown with repetitive stimulation used to augment the entry of Na⁺.   (1 count/min is equivalent to 4.25×10^{-11} M Na⁺/cm axon.)   (Keynes, 1951.)

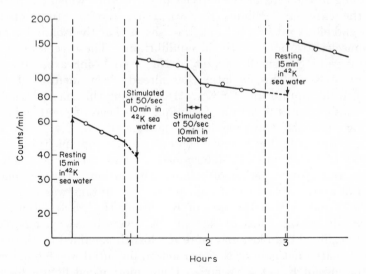

Fig. 5.8.   Movement of K⁺ as in Fig. 5.7 using K⁺ isotope.   (1 count/min is equivalent to 1.17×10^{-11} M K⁺/cm axon.)   (Keynes, 1951.)

potential found from isotope tracer studies is somewhat larger but of the expected order to account for the ionic movements estimated from electrical current flow studies. The extra number of ions found transferred by isotope measurement may be due to additional changes caused by the repetitive stimulation of the nerve. It would be of great advantage to be able to study the effect of a single response on ion movements, but the amount of Na^+ gained and K^+ lost during a single action potential is too small to be readily studied with present techniques.

Hinke (1961) was able to measure the concentrations (activities) of Na^+ and K^+ inside the axon by means of cation-selective micro-electrodes. Special glasses present at the tips of the electrodes inserted into giant axons could selectively measure the activity of either Na^+ or of K^+. The net changes of these ions found after nerve stimulation also conforms with the sodium hypothesis. The net gain of Na^+ per impulse was 3.8 pM/cm^2; the net loss of K^+, 5.6 pM/cm^2. The values found by this technique appear to be experimentally close enough so that we can consider that the same amounts of Na^+ and K^+ are exchanged across the membrane during each action potential.

Axons with axoplasmic replacement and active responses

As noted in Chapter 4, the axoplasm of squid giant axon may be extruded and replaced with isotopic K^+ solutions and yet still give rise to apparently normal action potentials (Baker et al., 1962a, b). When an axon prepared in this way is excited at one end these action potentials conduct in the usual fashion to be recorded from the other end of the axon (A, C, D of Fig. 5.9). The resting potential in these axons is controlled by the ratio of K^+ present on the two sides of the membrane (Chapter 4). With decreased amounts of Na^+ present in the outside medium the size of the action potential was reduced. Increasing the internal concentration of Na^+ decreased the height of the action potential as expected from the decrease in the electrochemical driving force moving Na^+ into the interior of the axon upon excitation. By calculating the effects of changed K^+ and Na^+ the following modified Nernst equation was shown to account for the behavior of the axon:

$$V = \frac{RT}{F} \ln \frac{[K^+]_o + b[Na^+]_o}{[K^+]_i + b[Na^+]_i} \tag{5.5}$$

where V is the amplitude of the action potential, b is the ratio of

Na$^+$ and K$^+$ permeabilities, and the other symbols have their usual significance. (This equation is equivalent to Eq. 4.8.)

In the resting membrane the permeability of Na$^+$ is low compared to K$^+$ and the value of b is low; a factor of 0.06 was found. Upon excitation Na$^+$ permeability increases and b increases accordingly (to a factor of 7 for the excited membrane).

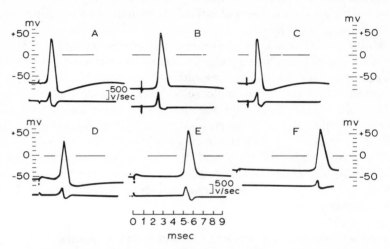

Fig. 5.9. Axoplasmic replacement and action potentials. The nerve axoplasm is extruded and replaced with isotonic K$_2$SO$_4$, or various proportions of isotonic K$_2$SO$_4$ and isotonic glucose: A, C and D with isotonic K$_2$SO$_4$; B, 0.33 K$_2$SO$_4$, 0.67 glucose; E, 0.17 K$_2$SO$_4$, 0.83 glucose; F, 0.083 K$_2$SO$_4$, 0.917 glucose. With a decrease in internal K$^+$ the conduction velocity decreases as shown by the increased latency of the responses on the upper trace. The lower traces show rate of change of potential. (Baker, Hodgkin and Shaw, 1962b.)

When the internal concentration of Na$^+$ is zero and the Na$^+$ present in the external medium very much higher than the K$^+$ present, Eq. 5.5 can be simplified as follows:

$$V = \frac{RT}{F} \ln \frac{b[\text{Na}^+]_o}{[\text{K}^+]_i} \tag{5.6}$$

In this case reduction of the internal concentration of K$^+$ should increase the amplitude of the spike (V). Replacing part of the internal K$^+$ with glucose was found by Baker *et al.* (1962b) to increase the spike overshoot as shown in B, E, F, of Fig. 5.9. The effect of increasing internal glucose is also to increase the internal resistivity of the axon and therefore to decrease conduction velocity. This is seen in the lengthened latencies of B, E, F, Fig. 5.9 and will be discussed in Chapter 6.

Electrical model of the membrane

A current flow through the membrane occurs when the membrane permeability increases greatly during the action potential. This result confirms the earlier work of Cole and Curtis (1939) who showed that the electrical impedance of the membrane of nerve undergoes a reduction to less than 1/40 of its original level during the action potential. An a.c. oscillator and a bridge circuit were used to measure the impedance drop in a giant nerve fiber in the region of the axon where an action potential was also recorded (Fig. 5.10).

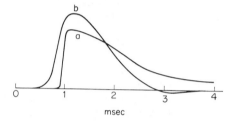

msec

Fig. 5.10. An increase of membrane conductance (a) is seen to occur concommitantly with the monophasic action potential (b) measured in the same region of the giant nerve axon. (After Cole and Curtis, 1939.)

When the action potential occupied this region the membrane resistance was shown by the bridge measurement to drop to a low level while membrane capacitance showed no change. This increase in electrical conductivity during the action potential would be expected to correspond with the measurements of the Na^+ and K^+ conductances and are seen to do so in the reconstruction shown in Fig. 5.11. The electrical model of the membrane of Hodgkin and Huxley (1952d) summarizes the behavior of the membrane derived from their studies. In the diagram of Fig. 5.12 current may flow either into the capacitance element or through the ionic channels. Three ionic 'batteries' are figured, each in series with resistance representing the permeabilities. Variable resistance symbols are given for the Na^+ and K^+ channels to indicate an independent change of permeability for each of the ion species. A 'leak' battery and resistance represents the small exchange of other ions which

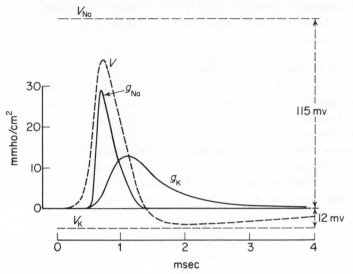

Fig. 5.11. The computed conductances for sodium (g_{Na}), and potassium (g_K) are shown in relation to the action potential (V). Equilibrium potential levels for sodium (V_{Na}) and for potassium (V_K) are indicated by the upper and lower dashed lines, respectively. (Hodgkin and Huxley, 1952d.)

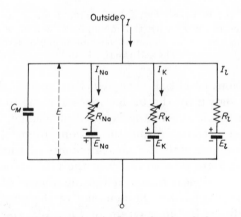

Fig. 5.12. An electrical equivalent circuit of the membrane is shown with sodium and potassium and 'leakage' currents $(I_{Na}, I_K$ and $I_l)$ flowing from their ionic 'batteries' E_{Na}, E_K and E_l, the amount of current depending on the conductance through sodium and potassium channels shown as variable resistance elements R_{Na}, R_K and R_l. The capacitance of the membrane (C) does not enter into the slower ionic currents of the clamped membrane. (After Hodgkin and Huxley, 1952d.)

contributes only a small conductance in the resting state of the giant nerve membrane. The K^+ and the leak batteries are shown with their positive poles facing the outside of the membrane. The Na^+ battery faces in the reverse direction. When the Na^+ resistance drops during excitation it allows the Na^+ battery to bring positive charge (Na^+) into the cell; this in effect is a battery making the inside of the cell positive when it is allowed to act.

The mechanisms controlling these permeability changes, in our model an opening of one or other of these channels, are, as yet, unknown. Presumably it is the effect of the potential change caused by the stimulus moving charged elements in the membrane which opens up the Na^+ channel. Alternatively there may be special biochemical mechanisms associated with the permeability change (Chapter 7). In any case, an abrupt voltage change across the membrane of sufficient size to reach the *critical level* of depolarization is required for excitation. If this voltage does not change at a sufficiently rapid rate, Na^+ inactivation is initiated and this mechanism, by closing down the Na^+ channels as fast or faster than the mechanism opening it, accounts for the phenomenon of accommodation (Chapter 3). While there is reason to consider that there might be a connection between the conductance changes for Na^+ and K^+, these have been formally described by separate sets of kinetic rate constants and equations (Hodgkin and Huxley, 1952d). The equations derived by Hodgkin and Huxley involve sophisticated mathematical treatment, and appear to match the real behavior of the nerve membrane for the shape and velocity of the action potential, sub-threshold excitatory phenomena and refractoriness. For example, the nerve action potentials at different temperatures could be computed from the derived equations and these resemble closely the actual action potentials (Fig. 5.13). The equations have non-linear properties which can give rise to a rhythmicity. A decrease in calcium in the external medium is known to cause rhythmicities in the real nerve as has been mentioned (Chapter 2). These appear in the recordings from low-calcium nerves as small local potential oscillations of membrane potential which, when sufficiently large, set off the propagated action potentials. Huxley (1959) found that the oscillatory behavior computed from the kinetic equations agreed with that of the actual nerve behavior.

After-effects of activity

Alterations in ionic movements after an action potential gives rise to *after-potentials*. Frankenhaeuser and Hodgkin (1956) stimulated the isolated axons of squid at a rate of 50 pulses/sec and found that the *positive after-potentials* declined in height whereas the *negative after-potentials* increased in size.   Changes in ionic composition and various drugs can bring about large after-potentials (Fig. 5.14).

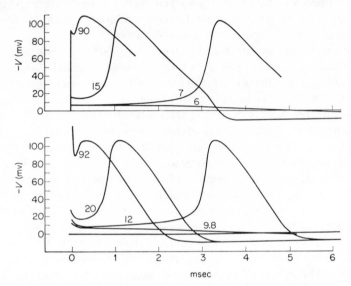

Fig. 5.13. The upper family of action potential curves as a function of temperature were obtained from the equations of a model of the membrane and correspond to the actual nerve membrane potential changes shown in the lower group.   (Hodgkin and Huxley, 1952d.)

The after-potentials are sensitive to small changes in the level of K^+ in the external medium, being reduced when greater concentrations of K^+ are present.   Increasing the frequency of stimulation increases the degree of after-effect.   Temperature variations were studied and found to change the after-effects with a Q_{10} of 1.3 which is considered to be indicative of a non-metabolic process. In order to explain the increase of the negative after-potential with repetitive activity, Frankenhaeuser and Hodgkin postulated that the K^+ moving out of the cell after an action potential is temporarily constrained by a thin barrier at the surface.   A similar conclusion was earlier reached by Shanes (1951) to explain increases in the negative after-potential under various conditions.

The nature of this barrier was indicated by electron microscope studies of the surface of the giant axon.   Around the nerve membrane there is an overlapping of several layers of sheet-like Schwann cells with clefts between them leading from the axon membrane surface out to the external medium (Fig. 5.15). The clefts can be considered as irregular sheet-like channels 60 A thick and 4.3 μ long (Villegas and Villegas, 1960).

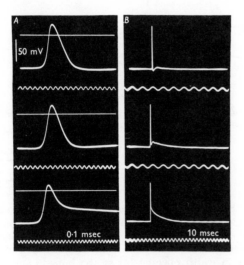

Fig. 5.14.   In column A at fast sweep speeds and in column B at slower ones, the action potential of a single giant cockroach axon is shown.   Top, response with no treatment; middle, 38 min, and lower, 90 min after DDT shows the appearance of negative after-potentials.   (Narahashi and Yamasaki, *J. Physiol.* **152**: 122, 1960.)

However, the after-negativity observed cannot entirely be explained in this way.   Treatment with some types of veratrine alkaloids leads to very large negative after-potentials (Shanes, 1958). Presumably these agents delay the onset of K^+ permeability increase and efflux after the onset of the action potential and thereby produce large negative after-potentials.

A similar mechanism has been used to account for the prolonged action potentials found in heart muscle.   Microelectrode recording of the heart action potential shows, instead of the usual rapid repolarization, a prolonged phase of depolarization, i.e. a *plateau* is seen before repolarization (Fig. 5.16).   Similar appearing potentials can be produced in squid giant axons which have been injected with tetraethylammonium ion (Tasaki and Hagiwara, 1957).   Figure 5.17 shows the rapid development of such plateaus following injection

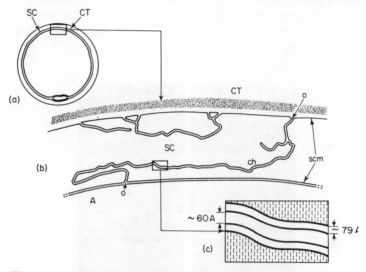

Fig. 5.15.   Schwann cell (SC) channels in giant nerve axon (a) are shown by clefts from one Schwann cell membrane (scm) to the other leading from the nerve membrane to the connective tissue (CT) and the external medium (b).   The channels (ch) are estimated to be 60 A in width opening (o) at the outside and inside and approximately 4.3 μ in length (c).   (Villegas and Villegas, 1960.)

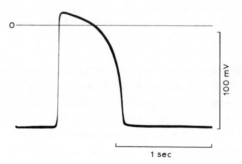

Fig. 5.16.   Intracellular action potential of frog ventrical heart cell shows the rising phase with overshoot followed by a slower maintained phase (plateau) before the repolarization to the baseline.   (Courtesy of R. Orkand and R. Niedergerke.)

of tetraethylammonium ion. Such plateaus can be curtailed or *abolished* by a sufficiently large brief pulse of anodal current through the membrane. A theoretical model was used by Tasaki and Hagiwara to explain these plateaus. They consider that the

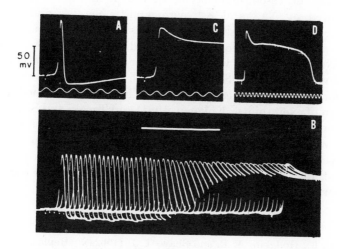

Fig. 5.17. The action potential of a giant nerve axon before (A) and after (C, D) internal injection of tetraethylammonium chloride. The development of prolonged action potentials is shown in B. Responses were elicited at 1 sec intervals and tetraethylammonium ion injected at the time of the horizontal bar. (Tasaki and Hagiwara, 1957.)

potential's remaining at a plateau level and the process of abolishment with return to normal resting potentials indicate that the membrane can exist in *two stable states*. During the transition between the two states, two species of 'patches' are distributed over the surface of the membrane and this is considered to result in a 'mixed' state in the membrane. Current will rapidly flow from one of these regions to the other to bring about a transfer of all the membrane to one or the other of the two stable states. In support of this concept Segal (1958) has shown that the giant axon depolarized by immersion in potassium acetate could be excited to give rise to an 'inverted spike' by a pulse of anodal current. Such a reversed spike is explainable on the two-stable-states hypothesis when with high K^+ solutions the membrane was brought to the 'upper' stable state, and then when excited anodally the spike-like response is a transitory return toward the 'lower' stable state (Tasaki, 1959). However, Fitzhugh (1960) was able to reproduce the principal qualitative features of the two-stable-states behavior with some modifications of the parameters of the Hodgkin–Huxley equations. It would appear therefore that the Hodgkin–Huxley formulation represents the essential behavior of the membrane which can be represented by Na^+ and K^+ permeability changes and rate constants controlling these permeabilities. Yet there is evidence not at present reconciled with the sodium hypothesis. In some cases, Na^+ *per se* was found not to be crucial for the excitation of action potentials. Substances such as the tetraethylammonium ion and hydrazine can replace Na^+ in the external medium with retention of excitability (Koketsu, 1961) and Tasaki and Spyropoulos (1961) consider that an excitable membrane having a *permselective* nature with fixed-charge properties of the pores (Chapter 4) best explains these and other such findings. We should expect that future studies directed to the nature of the mechanisms controlling ionic permeability will help resolve this problem.

REFERENCES

Baker, P. F., Hodgkin, A. L. and Shaw, T. I. (1962a).   Replacement of the axoplasm of giant nerve fibres with artificial solutions.   *J. Physiol.* **164**: 330–354.
Baker, P. F., Hodgkin, A. L. and Shaw, T. I. (1962b).   The effects of changes in internal ionic concentrations on the electrical properties of perfused giant axons.   *J. Physiol.* **164**: 355–374.
Cole, K. S. and Curtis, H. J. (1939).   Electric impedance of the squid giant axon during activity.   *J. Gen. Physiol.* **22**: 649–670.
Curtis, H. H. and Cole, K. S. (1940).   Membrane action potentials from the squid giant axon.   *J. Cell. Comp. Physiol.* **15**: 147–157.
Fitzhugh, R. (1960).   Thresholds and plateaus in the Hodgkin–Huxley equations.   *J. Gen. Physiol.* **43**: 867–896.
Frankenhaeuser, B. and Hodgkin, A. L. (1956).   The after-effects of impulses in the giant nerve fibres of *Loligo*.   *J. Physiol.* **131**: 341–376.
Hinke, J. A. M. (1961).   The measurements of sodium and potassium activities in the squid axon by means of cation-selective glass micro-electrodes.   *J. Physiol.* **156**: 314–335.
Hodgkin, A. L. (1951).   The ionic basis of electrical activity in nerve and muscle.   *Biol. Rev.* **26**: 339–409.
Hodgkin, A. L. (1958).   Ionic movements and electrical activity in giant nerve fibres.   *Proc. Roy. Soc. B.* **148**: 1–37.
Hodgkin, A. L. and Huxley, A. F. (1939).   Action potentials recorded from inside a nerve fibre.   *Nature*, **144**: 710–711.
Hodgkin, A. L. and Huxley, A. F. (1952a).   Currents carried by sodium and potassium ions through the membranes of the giant axon of *Loligo*.   *J. Physiol.* **116**: 449–472.

Hodgkin, A. L. and Huxley, A. F. (1952b). The components of membrane conductance in the giant axon of *Loligo*. *J. Physiol.* **116**: 473–496.

Hodgkin, A. L. and Huxley, A. F. (1952c). The dual effect of membrane potential on sodium conductance in the giant axon of *Loligo*. *J. Physiol.* **116**: 497–506.

Hodgkin, A. L. and Huxley, A. F. (1952d). A quantitative description of membrane current and its application to conduction and excitation in nerve. *J. Physiol.* **117**: 500–544.

Hodgkin, A. L., Huxley, A. F. and Katz, B. (1952). Measurements of current-voltage relations in the membrane of the giant axon of *Loligo*. *J. Physiol.* **116**: 424–448.

Hodgkin, A. F. and Katz, B. (1949). The effect of sodium ions on the electrical activity of the giant axon of the squid. *J. Physiol.* **108**: 37–77.

Huxley, A. F. (1959). Ion movements during nerve activity. *Ann. N.Y. Acad. Sci.* **81**: 221–246.

Keynes, R. D. (1951). The ionic movements during nervous activity. *J. Physiol.* **114**: 119–150.

Keynes, R. D. (1954). The ionic fluxes in frog muscle. *Proc. Roy. Soc. B.* **142**: 359–382.

Koketsu, K. (1961). Mechanism of active depolarization. Dispensability of sodium. *Biophysics of Physiological and Pharmacological Actions*. Edited by A. M. Shanes. Pp. 145–163. American Association for the Advancement of Science, Washington, D.C.

Marmont, G. (1949). Studies on the axon membrane. I. A new method. *J. Cell. Comp. Physiol.* **34**: 351–382.

Segal, J. (1958). An anodal threshold phenomenon in the squid giant axon. *Nature*, **182**: 1370.

Shanes, A. M. (1951). Potassium movements in relation to nerve activity. *J. Gen. Physiol.* **34**: 795–807.

Shanes, A. M. (1958). Electrochemical aspects of physiological and pharmacological action in excitable cells. *Pharm. Rev.* **10**: Part I, 59–164; Part II, 165–273.

Tasaki, I. (1959). Demonstration of two stable states of the nerve membrane in potassium-rich media. *J. Physiol.* **148**: 306–331.

Tasaki, I. and Hagiwara, S. (1957). Demonstration of two stable potential states in the squid giant axon and tetraethylammonium chloride. *J. Gen. Physiol.* **40**: 859–885.

Tasaki, I. and Spyropoulos, C. S. (1961). Permeability of the squid axons membrane to several organic molecules. *Am. J. Physiol.* **201**: 413–419.

Villegas R. and Villegas, G. M. (1960). Characterization of the membranes in the giant nerve fiber of the squid. *J. Gen. Physiol.* **43**: 73–103.

6

Conduction of the Action Potential

Our purpose in this chapter is to examine the mechanism of conduction of the action potential. In the giant nerve fiber and in the thin nonmyelinated fibers of vertebrates, propagation is *continuous*, corresponding with the apparently homogeneous nature of the membrane. This is not the case with myelinated nerve where *discontinuous* propagation is found. We shall first discuss continuous conduction, and then myelinated nerve and discontinuous conduction.

The mechanism of conduction by local currents is based on the electrical nature of the membrane and the ionic mechanisms of excitation. When a region of the membrane is excited and the permeability to Na^+ is increased in that area, Na^+ enters the fiber and the presence of the added positive charge inside the fiber causes a lateral redistribution of the ions present in its environment. Positively charged ions are repelled and negative ions attracted, the resulting movement of ions in the nearby membrane constituting the local currents mentioned in Chapters 2 and 3. Note should be taken that the ion distribution of local currents is non-specific in so far as these currents are constituted by whatever ions are present along the lines of current. The relevant property is the electrical charge of the ions present, these moving in relation to the electrical potential difference created by the entrance of Na^+ during an action potential. The local current spreading laterally depolarizes the nearby section of membrane and generally is more than sufficient to bring about the critical level of depolarization required to excite the membrane. The *safety factor* is the ratio of the depolarization produced by these local currents to the critical level of depolarization required for excitation. When the adjoining membrane is excited by the local currents, the specific increase of Na^+ permeability takes place with an entrance of Na^+ and local currents which excite the next region, etc. The lateral extent of the spread of the local currents can be seen to control the propagation velocity. If the local currents reach out further from the region of Na^+ entry, the critical level of depolarization is attained more quickly in a more distant region of membrane and, therefore, the propagation velocity is greater. The factors which control the spread of local currents have been shown to be adequately defined by the electrical characteristics of the fiber, especially of its membrane.

Electrical properties of the membrane

Each small part of the membrane is considered to contain the electrical elements described in Chapter 5 repeated in the form which is shown in Fig. 6.1. An estimate of the values of the

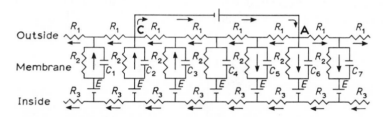

Fig. 6.1. Resistance (R), capacitance (C) and voltage (E) elements of the membrane (2) are shown distributed along the length of the fiber. Current impressed on the membrane at the anode (**A**) passes outward at the cathode (**C**). External medium (1), internal (3). (From Fulton, *A Textbook of General Physiology*, 17th Ed., Saunders, 1955.)

electrical components can be made by applying sub-threshold polarizing currents at one point on a nerve and observing the electrotonic potentials lateral to the polarizing electrode (Chapter 3). The strength of these polarizing currents must be small if they are cathodal, or else the active local responses described in Chapter 3 will be initiated. Figure 6.2 shows the arrangement of electrodes used to introduce a step-pulse of current and the position of the recording electrodes at the polarizing electrode and at various distances from it in the *extrapolar* length of nerve. The voltages recorded extrapolarly decline in height as the recording electrode is placed further from the polarizing current electrode (Fig. 6.3). This holds whether the polarizing electrode near the recording electrode is the cathode (as in this figure and a *catelectrotonus* produced) or the anode (and an *anelectrotonus* produced which is similar in shape but opposite in polarity). The steady-state height of the electrotonic potentials attained at greater distances from the polarizing electrode undergoes a gradual decrease in amplitude which can be represented approximately by an exponential curve. This curve in turn, whether falling rapidly or slowly, is characterized by a constant, the *space constant* or *length constant*, λ. The length constant λ is determined by the distance along the nerve where the extrapolar electrotonic potential decays to $1/e$ of its original level at the polarizing electrode where the pulse or step-function of current is introduced. This relationship is expressed by the following equation:

$$\frac{V}{V_0} = e^{-(x/\lambda)} \tag{6.1}$$

where V = the measured voltage at different distances x from the source voltage V_0. (Note that when $\lambda = x$, $V = 1/e \cdot V_0$.)

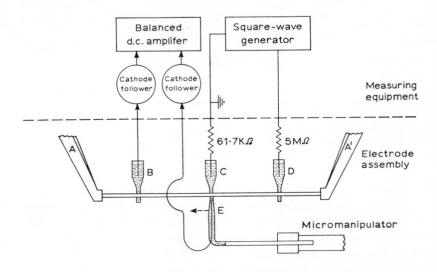

Fig. 6.2. Current passed through the giant nerve between electrodes C and D results in electrotonic voltages measured between electrodes B and E. The position of E relative to C can be adjusted with a micromanipulator. A and A′, clamps holding the nerve. (Hodgkin and Rushton, 1946.)

The same spatial spread and λ is found whatever the original source of current flow, whether induced by electrical current or produced by injury, where demarcation currents flow from the polarized to the damaged depolarized regions (Fig. 2.14).

The spread of electrotonic potential characterized by λ is a

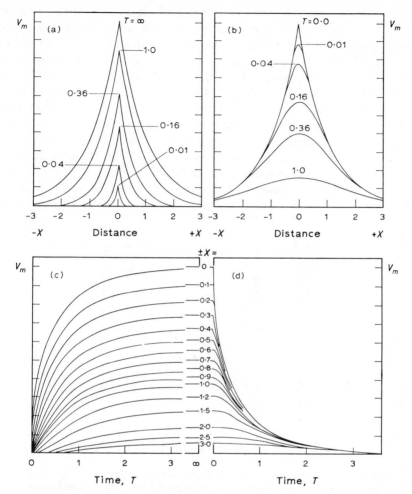

Fig. 6.3. The theoretical distribution of electrotonic potential (V_m) shown at various distances along the nerve on the abscissa at the relative times (T) given. The electrotonic potentials are shown following the onset of current (a) and after it is broken (b). The time course of potential at different distances (X) from the electrode after making the current is shown below at the left (c) and after breaking it (d). (Hodgkin and Rushton, 1946.)

function of the membrane resistance and the internal and external resistivities are related by the following equation:

$$\lambda = \sqrt{\frac{R_m}{R_o + R_i}} \qquad (6.2)$$

where R_m = resistance of membrane/cm², R_i = resistivity of inside axoplasm/cm, R_o = resistivity of outside medium/cm, λ = the length constant. With the value of λ found and R_o and R_i either measured directly or estimated, the resistance of the membrane, R_m, may be determined. The values found by this means or by the use of an internal electrode and direct measure (Chapter 5) or that obtained by means of the Wheatstone bridge technique (Cole and Curtis, 1939) all give approximately the same value for the giant axon, a membrane resistance of approximately 1000 ohm-cm².

The capacitance of the membrane found by the bridge technique used by Cole and Curtis showed a value of approximately 1 mfd/cm² for the giant nerve axon. The capacitance can also be determined by the *time constant* of the membrane if the membrane resistance R_m

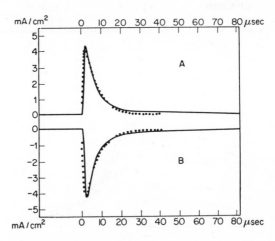

Fig. 6.4. At the onset of a voltage clamp a surge with respect to inward (A) and outward (B) current through the capacitative element may be seen with fast sweep speeds. Abscissa in μsec; ordinate, milliamps/cm². Continuous curves experimentally derived; dotted curves exponential. (Hodgkin, Huxley and Katz, 1952.)

is known. The time constant is determined by the time it takes the leading edge of the electrotonic potential (Fig. 6.3) to rise after applying an anodal step-pulse to 83% of its steady state value, or to fall after a cathodal step-pulse of current. The time constant is related to the capacitance and membrane resistance as follows:

$$T_m = C_m R_m \qquad (6.3)$$

where T_m = time constant, C_m = membrane capacitance (mfd/cm^2), R_m = membrane resistance (ohms-cm^2).

The capacitance of the giant axon is also found by the brief surge of current preceding the slower ionic currents when membrane currents are measured (Chapter 5). A faster sweep speed of the oscilloscope is required to show this surge of current at the onset of a clamping voltage displacement (Fig. 6.4). The direction of this surge is directly related to the direction of the applied voltage step, as would be expected from a passive electrical capacitance element in the membrane. The total amount of charge (the ions moving into or out of this capacitance) is equal to the area under the curves of Fig. 6.4. On integration the total charge displaced was found to be 35 mμcoulombs/cm^2 for an imposed voltage change of 40 mv. From the relationship $CV = Q$ (Eq. 4.6), the capacitance of the squid membrane was calculated to be approximately 1 mfd/cm^2 (Hodgkin and Huxley, 1952). This value is similar to that found with the Wheatstone bridge technique (Cole and Curtis, 1939).

Continuous conduction

The characteristics of electrotonic spread in nerve are similar to the leakage of electrical currents in long, insulated telegraph cables laid down in sea water. Although the electrical insulation around such cables is high, the presence of a small leakage current over a sufficiently great length adds up and results in the passage of large currents. The nerve membrane can be considered as similar since it also has a high membrane resistance, and leakage currents due to spreads of current over relatively long distances add up to a sizeable transmembrane flow of current (Fig. 6.1). The equation governing the distribution of currents in the nerve is therefore called the *cable equation*. Discussion of the cable equation may be found elsewhere (Lorente de Nó, 1947; Hodgkin and Rushton, 1946; Katz, 1939). For our purposes it will be sufficient to discuss the concept of the spread of local current controlling conduction velocity with respect to Eq. 6.1, which shows the electrotonic potential resulting from an applied current. It can be seen from this equation, and from Eq. 6.2 that the lateral spread of current in a fiber, and therefore conduction velocity, is closely related to λ. As has been previously noted, the distance, short or long, which the local currents reach to bring the membrane to the critical level is the factor determining conduction velocity. The spread of local currents is practically instantaneous although capacitance introduces a more gradual increase in a far part of the network. As a first approximation only the resistive elements will be considered.

If λ is large, then the term $e^{-(x/\lambda)}$ becomes larger and thus, from Eq. 6.1, the term V/V_0. In other words the voltage reaches out further and velocity is greater. Variation in external and internal resistivity can change λ. We can show this dependence of conduction velocity on resistivities contained in λ by considering in Eq. 6.2 that R_m is a constant and velocity varies as λ:

$$Q = (R_o + R_i)^{-1/2} \tag{6.4}$$

where Q = conduction velocity.

Both the external and internal resistivity have been experimentally altered and the results with respect to conduction velocity are in accordance with Eq. 6.4. The resistance of the external medium was increased by immersing a crab nerve fiber in oil, leaving only a thin layer of external conducting medium around the axon. The conduction velocity was decreased (Hodgkin, 1939). Decreasing the external resistance with metal strips increased velocity. The recent new technique of replacing the internal axoplasm of the squid giant axon with various solutions (Chapters 4, 5) has given a direct verification of the relationships between internal resistivity and conduction velocity. With the axon filled with K_2SO_4 (which has lower resistivity than axoplasm), the conduction velocity is greater than that of intact axon (Baker et al., 1962a). When glucose with its much greater resistivity was used to replace part of the internal conducting fluid (Baker et al., 1962b), the conduction velocity was decreased (Fig. 5.9).

The effect of experimental modification of the membrane resistivity on velocity has been investigated in various ways. It might be expected that stretching fibers would open pores and perhaps decrease the membrane resistance and, from Eq. 6-1, conduction velocity. Skeletal muscle can be changed with different degrees of stretch from 67 to 122% of its resting length. When the muscle length is changed, however, conduction velocity is unchanged, a result accounted for by the fact that the membrane is pleated; the stretch simply smooths out these pleats without actually changing the overall length of the membrane (Hodgkin, 1954). As pointed out by Hodgkin, it is the electrical properties of the membranes which control conduction velocity and the actual length of the membrane, whether pleated or stretched out.

If the basic electrical properties of nerve and muscle fibers do not change with size, then on the basis of the cable equation conduction velocity will be related to the square root of the fiber diameter; the amount of surface area remains the constant factor (Hodgkin, 1954). Such a square-root relationship has been found for the giant fibers (Pumphrey and Young, 1938). However, though the report has not gone unchallenged, Gasser (1950) found a linear relationship of diameter and velocity for the nonmyelinated nerve fibers. Håkansson (1956) reported conduction velocity of frog sartorius muscle fibers to vary with circumference. Variations in the velocity–size relationships would at least leave open the possibility that membrane characteristics do change to some extent with fiber size.

The structure of myelinated nerve

As will be discussed, myelinated nerve has a high conduction velocity compared to nonmyelinated nerve of similar size. The fast conduction velocity was early associated with the myelin covering the fiber which is interrupted at intervals of approximately 0.5–1.5 mm along the fiber, at the *nodes of Ranvier*. The distances between the nodes, the *internodal lengths* vary with the size of the fiber, its age, and with species (Hiscoe, 1947; Tasaki, 1953). An electrical insulation property of the myelin was inferred from its fatty nature and a lower electrical resistivity would be expected at the nodes. Lillie (1925) showed by use of his iron-wire model that short segments of glass threaded along the wire to represent myelin, with spaces left at intervals, caused a speeding up of the conduction velocity. The surface changes then occurred only at the open spaces of the iron-wire between the glass pieces. The analogy to myelinated nerve is apparent. Instead of local currents spreading out in the membrane in a continuous and decrementing fashion, the high electrical resistivity of the myelin sheath constrains the local currents to flow through and excite only at the nodes. The discontinuous excitation taking place at the nodes is usually spoken of as *saltatory conduction*, from the Latin *per saltum* (by leaps).

Investigation of the structure of myelin by means of X-ray diffraction by Schmitt, Bear and Palmer (1941), and by Elkes and Finean (1949) revealed an ordered radial molecular structure of the myelin having a *fundamental period* (spacing) of 171 A. This led to the suggestion that long chains of lipoproteins are radially oriented in the membrane in association with protein layers, the whole structure repeating at intervals of 171 A. A 4.7 A spacing found in the X-ray diffraction studies was taken to be the lateral distance between the radially oriented lipid chains.

Electron microscope studies of the myelin sheath (Fernández-Morán, 1950; Robertson, 1960) show that it is ordered into a series of lamellae with alternate dark and light layers in osmium-impregnated preparations with a spacing of approximately 150 A (Fig. 6.5). Considering the very different techniques involved, this is a

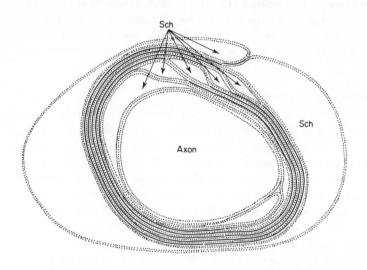

Fig. 6.5.   Diagram of myelin layers in cross-section taken from an electron micrograph. Open spaces between the lamellae represent cytoplasm of Schwann (Sch) cell in the region of the Schmidt–Lantermann incisure. (Robertson, 1960.)

quite good match with the fundamental spacing of the lamellae given by X-ray diffraction. With high resolution it was revealed that each lamella was actually composed of two membranes, each similar to the unit membrane of approximately 75–80 A in thickness, previously discussed in Chapter 4. The composition of the myelin lamellae from unit membranes became clearer after the discovery of how the nerve axon comes to be myelinated by the Schwann cells. Geren (1954), studying the different stages of embryonic development of nerve myelination, found that the Schwann cells first came in contact with, and then engulfed, the axon (Fig. 6.6(a)). The edges of the Schwann cell membrane, meeting around the axon, forms a double-unit membrane known as the *mesaxon*. The cytoplasm of the Schwann cell on one side of the mesaxon increases in amount and the mesaxon then is laid down in jelly-roll fashion around the axon. The adult myelin sheath therefore is a continuous spiral of mesaxon of the Schwann cell membrane wrapped many times around the axon. In support of this view of myelination, it was shown upon careful

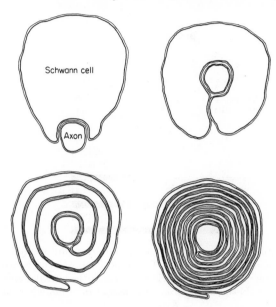

Fig. 6.6(a).   Genesis of myelin sheath around the nerve axon shown with the earliest stage at the upper left when a Schwann cell just invests an axon.   Later (upper right), the axon is engulfed with a double layer of connected Schwann membranes referred to as the mesaxon.   The mesaxon becomes wrapped around and around the axon to form the multilayered myelin sheath.   The representation of the final stage (lower right) shows a much thicker myelin sheath relative to the axon diameter than is normally the case.   (Geren, 1954.)

observation of adult myelinated nerves that an outer mesaxon is present at the outer surface of the myelin connecting to the Schwann cell membrane and an inner mesaxon passing to the sheath from the layer of membrane wrapped around the axon.   Each Schwann cell forms an independent myelin sheath.   One Schwann cell body is found along each of the internodal lengths of axon.   The nodes represent the open space between adjoining Schwann cells and their myelin sheaths.

Apparently there is a difference between the proteins of the Schwann cell membrane on the outside and inside surfaces.   When the mesaxon is formed, the outside surfaces come together to form the lamellae (Fig. 6.6(b)). This protein between the two unit-membranes of the lamella is either weakly impregnated with osmium or not impregnated at all. The other, inner surfaces in apposition are

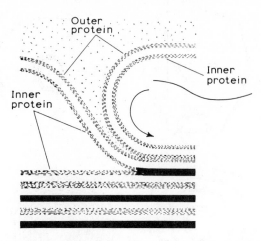

Fig. 6.6(b). Formation of lamellae of myelin sheath from a joining of unit membranes. The apposition of proteins from the inner surfaces produces a darker layer and the lamellar spacings of 171 A. (Robertson, *Electron Microscopy in Anatomy*, Chapter 7, Arnold, 1961.)

more densely impregnated and this is the dark line seen repeated at approximately 150 A between the lamellae of the myelin sheath in electron micrographs. The difference in protein at these contacts is termed the *difference factor* by Finean (1961).

The water present in myelin appears to be associated with the protein and is relatively low in amount, approximately 30% as compared to 70–80% of water in other cell areas. Changes in water content were shown in X-ray diffraction studies by comparing the fundamental period before and after drying. In the frog the fundamental period was changed from 171 A to 144 A, mammalian fibers from 184 A to 158 A (Schmitt *et al.*, 1941). A change from 180 A to 130 A was found in rat sciatic nerve on dehydration by Finean (1961). Changes were also found produced by fixation with osmium and then subsequent embedding in plastic, from 164 A to 145 A.

During the spiraling of the myelin an extensive proliferation of the endoplasmic reticulum is found in the Schwann cell cytoplasm and of ribosome granules near the lamellae, evidence of a notable synthetic activity to be expected as new membrane is being formed (Robertson, 1961). The presence of augmented endoplasmic reticulum and ribosomes distinguishes the embryonic myelinated nerve from nonmyelinated nerve fibers. These were shown by Gasser (1958) to have Schwann cell investments similar to the earliest stage of myelin formation of layer fibers (Fig. 6.7). Often, a single Schwann cell may be found investing a group of nonmyelinated fibers.

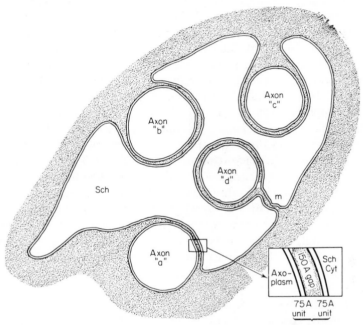

Fig. 6.7. Single *C* axons ("a"–"d") have an investment of one layer of Schwann (Sch) cell myelin which may partially or completely invest an axon. The apposition in the completely surrounded axon is the mesaxon (m). Insert shows detail of unit membranes of axon and Schwann cell. (Robertson, 1960.)

The myelinated fibers of the central nervous system have very much the same appearance as peripheral nerve fibers, but there exists a difference of opinion with regard to the formation of myelin around CNS fibers. Instead of this jelly-roll wrapping type of myelin sheath development, some investigators believe that myelin is laid down by a coalescence of small cytoplasmic vesicles found in glia cells (Luse, 1961). In a variant of this hypothesis glia cells are described as overlapping the axons, laying down myelin in sheets.

However, studies of myelination of central axons showed the same wrap-around course of development as found in peripheral nerve (Bunge, Bunge and Ris, 1961). One special difference found in CNS myelination is that one glial cell may have cytoplasmic extensions to several axons, giving rise over each axon to a jelly-roll layering of myelin.

A longitudinal section through the nodes shows the terraced appearance of the lamellae and membrane uncovered by myelin at the nodes (Fig. 6.8(a)). The Schwann cell membranes from either side may partially interdigitate at the node but open spaces of comparatively large size remain so that no structural hindrance to ionic flow appears to be present at this site. Nodes are also present in myel-inated fibers of the CNS, a point which for a time was disputed.

A structural feature of the internodal portion of the sheath deserves comment. In osmium-fixed nerve and in nerves stained in other ways an apparent slit in the myelin has been observed which is referred to as *clefts* or *incisures of Schmidt–Lantermann*. These occur at closer intervals in the larger fiber, at an average of 32 μ for 11.5 μ fibers, compared to a separation of 92 μ in fibers 3.5 μ in diameter (Hiscoe, 1947). The incisures are subject to marked fixation changes but they are seen in the freshly isolated fiber and in freeze-substituted nerve preparations and are therefore not artifacts of fixation. In the early era of electron microscopy they appeared to be true clefts leading through the myelin between the nerve membrane and the external medium. Because as many as 20 or so of such clefts may be found along an internode of a large fiber, a considerable amount of ionic current could pass through the incisures if these are openings. However, it has been shown that the lamellae of the myelin sheath are all present within the incisure though with a separation between the lamellae due to interposed Schwann cell cytoplasm. In electron microscope pictures with good resolution the separate individual lamellae within the incisure are readily seen (Fig. 6.5).

Saltatory conduction and nodal properties

Because of the electrical resistance of myelin, action currents more readily enter and leave at the nodes accounting for the faster con-duction velocity (Fig. 6.8(b)). The proof of saltatory transmission required the patient and delicate isolation of single myelinated nerve fibers. This technique has been developed by Kato (1934) and his students, and the procedure of isolation is described in detail by Tasaki (1953). A higher excitability of the nodes was shown by bringing a stimulating microelectrode to various points along the length of an isolated single motor nerve fiber. The threshold for excitation was lower at the nodes than at the internodal lengths of the nerve fiber axon (Fig. 6.9).

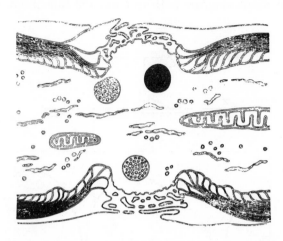

Fig. 6.8(a). Diagrammatic representation of a node. The lamellae at the sides have a terraced appearance and do not cover the node. Shown within the axon are mitochondria, vesicles and other unknown structures—'the dark bodies'. (Robertson, 1960.)

In the theory of saltatory conduction a high resistivity is required of the myelin sheath. The measured resistance is 0.16 megohm-cm^2 and the measured capacitance is 0.0025 mfd/cm^2 (Hodgkin, 1951). These values are of the right order if we consider that the unit

Fig. 6.8(b). Passage of current through the nodal region during saltatory propagation of an action potential is shown in diagrammatic fashion. Excitation takes place at the node.

membranes comprising the lamellae have similar electronic properties to those of the nerve membrane (1000 ohm/cm^2 and 1 mfd/cm^2). Electrically, the myelin lamellae are in series and would add their resistances while the capacitance should decrease for that same reason. Therefore, the resistivity of the internodal myelin sheath is very high as required by the theory and as shown by direct measurement.

Currents passing across the node must return via the external medium between the nodes to complete the electrical circuit. The requirement of an external path to complete the circuit was shown

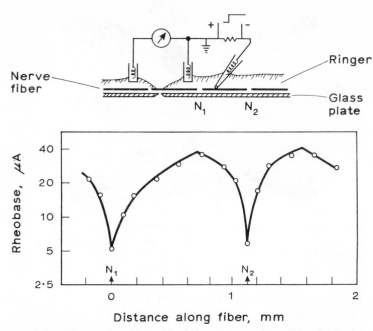

Fig. 6.9. Variation of excitability along a fiber is determined by cathodal stimulation with a microelectrode placed at successive points along the nerve fiber. Excitability is greatest at the nodes, N_1 and N_2, as shown by the lower rheobase values. (After Tasaki, 1953.)

with the use of a *gap technique* (Tasaki, 1953). The myelinated internodal portion of a single fiber is placed over an air gap measuring approximately 0.5–1.0 mm between two sheets of glass. Ringer solution is placed on each sheet of glass and a single nerve fiber placed on them so that the internode portion stretches across the gap with the nodes present in each of the pools of Ringer (Fig. 6.10). The Ringer fluid which adheres to the internodal portion of the fiber bridging the gap is washed away with a sucrose solution and dried so that this path for electrical conduction is reduced. When the electrical resistance becomes so high that current cannot return from one node to the next to complete the circuit, a block of conduction occurs (Huxley and Stämpfli, 1949).   This seemingly direct experiment, however, is complicated by the electrical capacitance between the glass plates on either side of the gap which may allow a capacitative flow of current.   It is also difficult to adequately wash away all the conducting electrolyte from the internodal portion of the

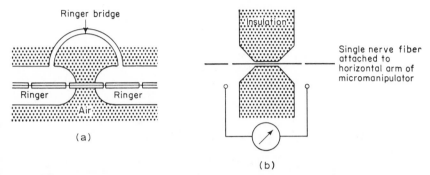

(a)

(b)

Fig. 6.10.   An air gap technique of investigating single fibers is shown (a) with the internode exposed to air and a Ringer bridge completing the circuit.   Conduction is blocked when the Ringer bridge is removed.   A single fiber is passed through a narrow channel of an insulator (b) and by this technique longitudinal currents passing in the external medium between the nodes may be measured.   (From Huxley and Stämpfli, 1949; after Hodgkin, 1951.)

fiber bridging the gap.   Some of this conductance is contributed by the Schwann cell cytoplasm.   However, under favorable experimental conditions it can be shown by this means that conduction requires a completion of the path of electrical current outside the myelin sheath (Tasaki, 1959).

The current flowing in the external medium as a result of excitation may be measured by a resistance inserted in that path.   The action current was shown by this means to be biphasic.   Current enters first the one node when it is excited and this flows out through the second node.   Subsequently, that node is excited and as a result current flows inward and the direction of current in the external circuit becomes reversed to produce the biphasic or *binodal* action current.   The current flow is largely inward at the nodes as shown in Fig. 6.11.

A node may be made inexcitable by treating it with a solution of 0.2% cocaine.   Cocaine has the virtue of not depolarizing the nodal membrane while permitting passive flows of current through the inexcitable nodal membrane.   By placing cocaine in the pool containing one node, the node of the fiber on the other side of the gap now gives rise to a longer lasting *monodal* action current when it is excited (Tasaki, 1953).

Besides measuring the nodal currents, a *nodal action potential* may be recorded. For this purpose the external path resistance across

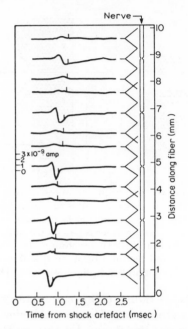

Fig. 6.11. Membrane currents of single fibers measured with the arrangement b of Fig. 6.10. Membrane current determined by the voltage difference found between two points along the nerve resulting from the flow of longitudinal current. Membrane current is shown relative to the position of the nodes. Currents are directed into the nodes (downward) during activation. (Huxley and Stämpfli, 1949.)

the gap is made very high and a cathode follower is used for recording the potential from the node. When a single node so recorded from is adequately excited, an all-or-none action potential response of the node is developed (Fig. 6.12). The amplitude of the nodal action potential is greater than the resting membrane potential, i.e. it has an overshoot as is found in nonmyelinated nerve and muscle (Chapter 5).

Local responses of the node are also found upon subliminal stimulation (del Castillo and Stark, 1952). As sub-threshold depolarizing pulses of current are made larger, the local responses increase until threshold is reached and an all-or-none action potential is excited. Subliminal excitatory changes in myelinated nerve were previously shown by indirect means by Katz (1939).

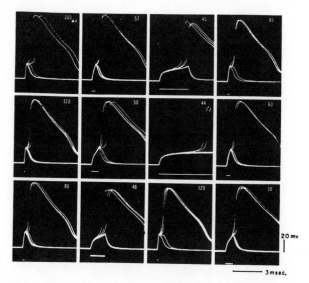

Fig. 6.12. Stimulation at different strengths (numbers in milli-volts) and durations (bar lengths) are shown. An all-or-none monophasic response of the node arises with different latencies from a smaller local potential when threshold is reached. (Tasaki, *J. Gen. Physiol.*, **39**: 377, 1956.)

During a nodal action potential a reduction of resistance is found in the node similar to that described for the giant axon (Chapter 5) (Tasaki, 1953, 1959). The conductance increase starts at the time the action potential arises and outlasts the action potential for a short time. Decreasing Na^+ in the external medium causes a reduction in the height of the action potential (Huxley and Stämpfli, 1951). Therefore, the similarity of behavior of the node to that of the giant nerve axon suggests that the sodium hypothesis applies also to the node. The small area of the node creates some difficulties in the measurement of some of its properties. Hodgkin (1951) calcu-lated that approximately 1/300 the amount of Na^+ enters the node per action potential as compared to a nonmyelinated fiber of similar size. However, it has been found possible to apply clamping techniques to a single node (Dodge and Frankenhaeuser, 1959;

Dodge, 1961). Instead of electrodes threaded inside as in the giant fiber, the assumption is made that the conductance of the axoplasm is very much greater than that of the nodal membrane and that all the surface of the node is involved in ionic transport (Fig. 6.13).

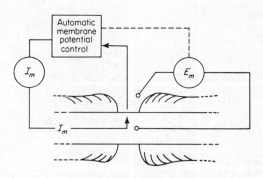

Voltage clamp on the node of Ranvier

Fig. 6.13. The technique of voltage clamping of a single node is shown. The voltage is measured (E_m) and used to control the clamping circuit (the automatic membrane potential control) so that the resulting currents (I_m) may be measured. (Dodge, 1961.)

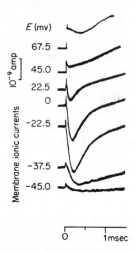

Fig. 6.14. The current flowing as a result of different levels of depolarization of the node (given by numbers in millivolts at the left of the traces) show a large early inward current (downward) when threshold is reached. (Dodge, 1961.)

As in the giant axon, a step-pulse of voltage is introduced across this nodal membrane and held clamped at a constant predetermined level. The resulting membrane currents consist of capacitative and ionic components. After the brief capacitative surge the remaining curve represents ionic flow and resembles that found for the giant axon. Depolarization of the membrane by clamping pulses of different amplitudes is shown in Fig. 6.14. An inward phase of current is seen (followed by a delayed phase of outward current). Excitation and an inward current occurs when the resting membrane potential has been depolarized to about -45 mv. The inward phase is maximal when the membrane has been depolarized to approximately -15 mv. As the inside of the fiber is changed and clamped at still more positive voltages, the inward current becomes smaller as would be expected from a reduced electrochemical driving force for Na^+ into the node. As in the case of the giant nerve, a point is reached when there is no more inward movement of Na^+, that is when the sodium equilibrium potential (E_{Na}) is reached.

The separation of an early current due to a Na^+ movement into the node from a delayed outward current was shown by methods similar to those used for the giant nerve fiber. When Na^+ was reduced in the external media, the inward phase of current was reduced or eliminated while the delayed current remained present. The delayed outward current was further analysed by Frankenhaeuser (1962a, b, c) and shown to behave as expected if it is brought about by an outward movement of K^+. Changes in the K^+ present in the external medium resulted in the changes in the delayed current expected from the Nernst equation. On the other hand, changes in the level of Cl^- in the external medium had no effect, showing that the node acts like the giant nerve fiber and has no large Cl^- component as does muscle.

However, not all studies have shown this close similarity of the node to the giant axon. Stämpfli (1959) measured the resting membrane potential of a node while varying the external concentrations of ions. The membrane behaved in a fashion which depended on the level of K^+ present in the external medium. At low levels of K^+ the node behaved as expected. When high levels of K^+ were present in the medium, a contribution of Cl^- to conductance was revealed. Further studies of nodal behavior with isotopes should be helpful in resolving the fundamental properties of the node.

We might expect a faster conduction velocity the further apart the nodes are in a fiber. Rushton (1951) examined the problem from a theoretical view and considered that if all properties of a nerve fiber were to remain unchanged except for size, the length of the internode should be the main factor controlling velocity. Internodal distance was found to vary directly with diameter. Therefore conduction velocity should vary directly with diameter. This is shown in Fig. 6.15 where the relationship between conduction and fiber diameter follows more closely a linear rather than a square-root or square function.

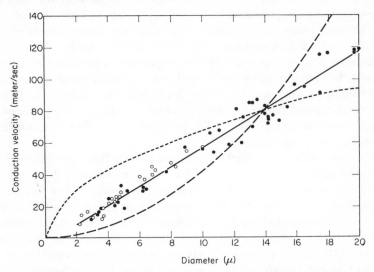

Fig. 6.15.   The conduction velocity determined for myelinated nerves of different fiber diameters is shown related to fiber diameter for the adult cat (•) and for kittens (○).   These follow a straight-line relationship (solid line) more closely than a square-root or square relationship given by the dotted and dashed lines respectively.   (After Hursh, 1939.)

However, not all investigators have found this relationship to hold. Sanders and Witteridge (1946) in a study of regenerating nerves found that although the fibres had a closer internodal spacing than normal fibers, their conduction velocities were the same as normal fibers.   More recently a 25% reduction in velocity of regenerating fibers was reported by Cragg and Thomas (1964).   A consideration not always taken into account is the inherent difficulty in determining true fiber size.   It is known that in the process of fixation and sectioning of tissues, various degrees of shrinking or swelling may occur (Bahr et al., 1957; Williams, P. L. and Wendell-Smith, 1960).   Sunderland and Roche (1958) found a considerable variation in diameter along the length of fibers. Narrowing, for example, occurs at the incisures and at the nodes. Some of these size variations, and the indeterminate degree of shrinking of the different-sized fibers, could affect the relationships drawn between size and velocity.

Below a fiber size of approximately 1 μ, the surface area relative to the diameter increases rapidly and nonmyelinated fibers should conduct faster than the myelinated fibers (Rushton, 1951). Myelination is usually found in fibers larger than 1–2 μ (Duncan, 1934), although some myelinated fibers of smaller size have been observed in electron microscope preparations. Mention has been made of the small amount of Na^+ entering the node per action potential, an amount computed to be 1/300 that required for an action potential in nonmyelinated fibers of similar size. Myelinated fibers would therefore need a very much lower expenditure of energy to extrude the smaller amount of Na^+ gained per action potential. Considering the number of myelinated nerve fibers in the white matter tracts of the mammalian nervous system, the reduction of metabolic requirements afforded by myelination appears to have been essential to the evolutionary development of higher organisms with complex nervous systems packed into a relatively small space.

The increase in nerve velocity with myelination has ontogenetic significance. Correlations have been made between the appearance of myelin and the early development of reflex behavior in various species, particularly in the human, where myelination may take months or years to develop in certain fiber tracts. The increased velocity incident on myelination should bring about changes in CNS function, most likely as part of an orderly sequence of growth. The full understanding of such a relationship of myelination to functional development is not yet known.

REFERENCES

Bahr, G. F., Bloom, G. and Friberg, U. (1957). Volume changes of tissues in physiological fluids during fixation in osmium tetroxide or formaldehyde and during subsequent treatment. *Exptl. Cell Res.* 12: 342–355.
Baker, P. F., Hodgkin, A. L. and Shaw, T. I. (1962a). Replacement of the axoplasm of giant nerve fibres with artificial solutions. *J. Physiol.* 164: 330–354.
Baker, P. F., Hodgkin, A. L. and Shaw, T. I. (1962b). The effects of changes in internal ionic concentrations on the electrical properties of perfused giant axons. *J. Physiol.* 164: 335–374.
Bunge, M. B., Bunge, R. P. and Ris, H. (1961). Ultrastructural study of remyelination in an experimental lesion in adult cat spinal cord. *J. Biophys. Biochem. Cytol.* 10: 67–94.

Cole, K. S. and Curtis, H. J. (1939). Electric impedance of the squid giant axon during activity. *J. Gen. Physiol.* **22**: 649–670.

Cragg, B. G. and Thomas, P. K. (1964). The conduction velocity of regenerated peripheral nerve fibres. *J. Physiol.* **171**: 164–175.

del Castillo, J. and Stark, L. (1952). Local responses in single medullated nerve fibres. *J. Physiol.* **118**: 207–215.

Dodge, F. A., Jr. (1961). Ionic permeability changes underlying nerve excitation. *Biophysics of Physiological and Pharmacological Actions.* Edited by A. M. Shanes. Pp. 119–143. American Association for the Advancement of Science, Washington, D.C.

Dodge, F. A. and Frankenhaeuser, B. (1959). Sodium currents in the myelinated nerve fibre of *Xenopus laevis* investigated with the voltage clamp technique. *J. Physiol.* **148**: 188–200.

Duncan, D. A. (1934). A relation between axon diameter and myelination determined by measurement of myelinated spinal root fibres. *J. Comp. Neurol.* **60**: 437–471.

Elkes, J. and Finean, J. B. (1949). The effect of drying upon the structure of myelin in the sciatic nerve of the frog. *Disc. Faraday Soc.* **6**: 134–143.

Fatt, P. (1964). An analysis of transverse electrical impedance of striated muscle. *Proc. Roy. Soc. B.* **159**: 606–651.

Fernández-Morán, H. (1950). Sheath and axon structure in the internode portion of vertebrate myelinated nerve fibres. An electron microscope study of rat and frog sciatic nerves. *Exptl. Cell Res.* **1**: 309–337.

Finean, J. B. (1961). The nature and stability of nerve myelin. *Intern. Rev. Cytol.* **12**: 303–336.

Frankenhaeuser, B. (1962a). Delayed currents in myelinated nerve fibres of *Xenopus laevis* investigated with voltage clamp technique. *J. Physiol.* **160**: 40–45.

Frankenhaeuser, B. (1962b). Instantaneous potassium currents in myelinated nerve fibres of *Xenopus laevis*. *J. Physiol.* **160**: 46–53.

Frankenhaeuser, B. (1962c). Potassium permeability in myelinated nerve fibres of *Xenopus laevis*. *J. Physiol.* **156**: 54–61.

Gasser H. S. (1950). Unmedullated fibers originating in dorsal root ganglia. *J. Gen. Physiol.* **33**: 651–690

Gasser, H. S. (1958). Comparison of the structure, as revealed with the electron microscope, and the physiology of the unmedullated fibers in the skin nerves in the olfactory nerves. *Exptl. Cell Res. Suppl.* **5**: 3–17.

Geren, B. B. (1954). The formation from the Schwann cell surface of myelin in the peripheral nerves of chick embryos. *Exptl. Cell Res.* **7**: 558–562.

Håkansson, C. H. (1956). Conduction velocity and amplitude of the action potential as related to circumference in the isolated fibre of frog muscle. *Acta Physiol. Scand.* **37**: 14–34.

Hiscoe, H. B. (1947). Distribution of nodes and incisures in normal and regenerated nerve fibers. *Anat. Rec.* **99**: 447–475.

Hodgkin, A. L. (1939). The relation between conduction velocity and the electrical resistance outside a nerve fibre. *J. Physiol.* **94**: 560–570.

Hodgkin, A. L. (1951). The ionic basis of electrical activity in nerve and muscle. *Biol. Rev.* **26**: 339–409.

Hodgkin, A. L. (1954). A note on conduction velocity. *J. Physiol.* **125**: 221–224.

Hodgkin, A. L. and Huxley, A. F. (1952). A quantitative description of membrane current and its application to conduction and excitation in nerve. *J. Physiol.* **117**: 500–544.

Hodgkin, A. L. and Rushton, W. A. H. (1946). The electrical constants of a crustacean nerve fibre. *Proc. Roy. Soc. B.* **133**: 444–479.

Hursh, J. B. (1939). Conduction velocity and diameter of nerve fibers. *Am. J. Physiol.* **127**: 131–139.

Huxley, A. F. and Stämpfli, R. (1949). Evidence for saltatory conduction in peripheral myelinated nerve fibres. *J. Physiol.* **108**: 315–339.

Huxley, A. F. and Stämpfli, R. (1951). Effect of potassium and sodium on resting and action potentials of single myelinated nerve fibers. *J. Physiol.* **112**: 496–508.

Kato, G. (1934). *The Microphysiology of Nerve.* (2nd Ed., 1950.) Nakayama, Tokyo.

Katz, B. (1939). *Electric Excitation of Nerve.* Oxford Univ. Press, Oxford.

Katz, B. (1948). The electrical properties of the muscle fibre membrane. *Proc. Roy. Soc. B.* **135**: 506–534.

Lillie, R. S. (1925). Factors affecting transmission and recovery in the passive iron nerve model. *J. Gen. Physiol.* **7**: 473–507.

Lorente de Nó, R. (1947). A study of nerve physiology. *Studies from the Rockefeller Institute for Medical Research.* Vols. 131 and 132. Rockefeller Institute, New York.

Luse, S. A. (1961). Membrane and myelin. *Properties of Membranes and Diseases of the Nervous System.* Pp. 55–70. Springer, New York.

Pumphrey, R. J. and Young, J. Z. (1938). The rates of conduction of nerve fibres of various diameters in cephalopods. *J. Exptl. Biol.* **15**: 453–466.

Robertson, J. D. (1960). The molecular structure and contact relationships of cell membranes. *Progr. Biophys.* **10**: 344–418.

Robertson, J. D. (1961). New unit membrane organelle of Schwann cells. *Biophysics of Physiological and Pharmacological Actions.* Edited by A. M. Shanes. Pp. 63–96. American Association for the Advancement of Science, Washington, D.C.

Rushton, W. A. H. (1951). A theory of the effects of fibre size in medullated nerve. *J. Physiol.* **115**: 101–122.

Sanders, F. K. and Witteridge, D. (1946). Conduction velocity and myelin thickness in regenerating nerve fibres. *J. Physiol.* **105**: 152–174.

Schmitt, F. O., Bear, R. S. and Palmer, K. J. (1941). X-ray diffraction studies on the structure of the nerve myelin sheath. *J. Cell. Comp. Physiol.* **18**: 31–42.

Stämpfli, R. (1959). Is the resting potential of a Ranvier node a potassium potential? *Ann. N.Y. Acad. Sci.* **81**: 265–284.

Sunderland, S. and Roche, A. F. (1958). Axon–myelin relationships in peripheral nerve fibres. *Acta Anat.* **33**: 1–37.

Tasaki, I. (1953). *Nervous Transmission.* Charles C. Thomas. Springfield.

Tasaki, I. (1959). Conduction of the nerve impulse. *Handbook of Physiology—Neurophysiology.* Vol. 1, pp. 75–121. American Physiological Society, Washington, D.C.

Williams, P. L. and Wendell-Smith, C. P. (1960). The use of fixed and stained sections in quantitative studies of peripheral nerve. *Quant. J. Microsc. Sci.* **101**: 43–54.

7

Metabolism related to Excitation and Conduction

The relation of metabolic function to other cell functions and to electrical potential across the membrane has been touched on in earlier chapters. It is necessary to consider neurochemical aspects in more detail. We can consider three general functions which may have different associated metabolic processes: (1) excitation and conduction, (2) synaptic transmission, and (3) the formation of materials in the cell body and the movement of those materials down the axon, a mechanism called *axoplasmic flow*. In this chapter the metabolism relating to excitation and conduction will be discussed, essentially the metabolism of isolated peripheral nerve. Metabolism relating to axoplasmic flow will be discussed in Chapter 8 and metabolism of CNS tissue where synapses are abundant will be treated in Chapter 19.

Heat production

From an overall thermodynamic point of view, a net heat increase should be produced as a result of nerve activity. Techniques used early in this century were inadequate to detect the very small heat changes occurring. It was a commonly held opinion that the nerve action potential was a 'physical' phenomenon rather than a 'chemical' one. Therefore, an important advance in our understanding occurred when nerve was shown to have a measurable heat output and an increase in heat output during and following activity (Hill, 1932). Those measurements were obtained by using a large number of thermocouples wired in series and a sensitive galvanometer (Downing, Gerard and Hill, 1926).

More recently Abbott, Hill and Howarth (1958) using improved measuring techniques for a better resolution of the early heat changes showed that previous values given for heat output were too low. The *early* or *initial heat* produced by stimulation of a non-myelinated nerve of the spider crab (*Maia*) at 0°C is shown in Fig. 7.1. The *positive phase* of this initial heat output is followed by a more prolonged *negative phase* of cooling. This diphasic initial heat component is in turn followed by the *delayed* or *recovery* heat. Although the action potential is prolonged at the low temperatures used, the course of these initial heat changes is still slower and cannot be directly correlated with the action potential. However, it seems

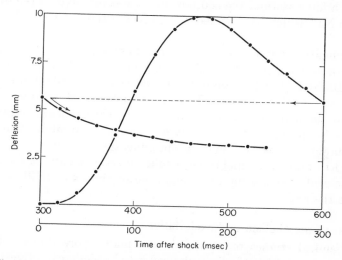

Fig. 7.1. *Maia* (crab) nerve at 0°C. The heat output is shown to rise to a maximum at approximately 160 msec after the shock and then to fall more slowly. The curve is continued back at the left following the arrow for a period of 540 msec (note double abscissa time marks). (After Abbott, Hill and Howarth, 1958.)

clear that the positive phase of the initial heat is more closely related to the action potential while the negative phase which lasts for a much longer time is not. Analysis of the thermocouple data shows the positive phase to amount to the release of 14×10^{-6} cal/g/impulse. The possibility was suggested that the positive phase of initial heat is related to chemical reactions of the membrane connected with excitation. The probable thickness of the membrane is approximately 75 A; therefore, the positive heat would represent a much larger figure if the heat output is calculated in relation to the volume of the membrane involved in heat production (Hill, 1960). On that basis, an estimate of 2.8×10^{-3} cal/g of surface material/impulse was made for the positive heat during the action potential. This is a large heat figure and at present support for such a calculation is not available.

While it is attractive to consider that the initial heat may be connected with special chemical events underlying the action potential, the Na^+ and K^+ ionic currents flowing during the impulse discharge could contribute either part or most of the initial heat (Abbott, 1960). The still longer-lasting delayed heat may be associated with the increased operation of the sodium pump mechanism. As we shall see in a later section, the sodium pump is considered to remove the excess Na^+ which has entered and to regain the K^+ which has been lost.

Myelinated nerve has a smaller metabolic requirement, and positive and negative heat phases are not so easily resolved. Hill and Howarth (1958) estimate the initial heat of myelinated nerve at 0.8×10^{-6} cal/g/impulse. If it is assumed that activity occurs only at the nodes, on a membrane volume basis this amounts to the relatively enormous heat output of 0.05 cal/g/impulse. This type of computation is too much a simplification and it can be interpreted to mean that metabolism takes place not only at the nodes, but as well in the adjoining membrane of the axon (Hill, 1960) or inside the axon.

Oxidative metabolism and excitability

Biochemical studies of nerve, though made more difficult by the very low rate of metabolism, showed it to be similar to other tissues: glucose is utilized, O_2 taken up and CO_2 given off, and lactate accumulates during anoxia (Gerard, 1932; Brink, 1957). Upon exposure of anoxic nerve to oxygen the accumulated excess of lactate becomes utilized. Glycolysis furnishes pyruvate (Fig. 7.2) which is then oxidatively metabolized via the *Krebs cycle* (Fig. 7.3). Some energy is derived by the breakdown of glucose to pyruvate, but this is not sufficient and anoxic nerve eventually fails to be excited and to conduct. Metabolic inhibitors or poisons which act at various steps in the metabolic chain will block excitability. The available evidence is that the failure of nerve function produced by anoxia, lack of glucose, or the application of metabolic inhibitors is an indirect one. These alterations of metabolism bring about their effect through an interference with the normal asymmetric ion distribution across the membrane responsible for resting and active potentials (Chapters 4, 5) and not through a direct linkage of metabolic reactions with potential (Shanes, 1958).

Oxygen uptake and the main production of useful energy is associated with the presence of mitochondria in cells. These subcellular organelles are more abundant in some parts of the nerve, i.e. in the dendrites and at the terminals of axons synapsing on other cells and

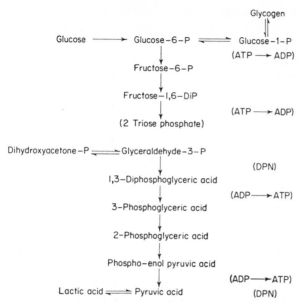

Fig. 7.2. The general scheme of glycolytic metabolism with glucose broken down in stepwise fashion to 3-carbon (triose) molecules. From this step, there is a further breakdown to pyruvic acid. P = phosphate, ADP = adenosine diphosphate, ATP = adenosine triphosphate, DPN = diphosphopyridine nucleotide (NAD). (From Tower in Harlow and Woolsey, *Biological and Biochemical Basis of Behavior*, Univ. Wisconsin Press, 1958.)

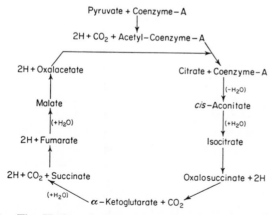

Fig. 7.3. The Krebs tricarboxylic acid cycle whereby pyruvate becomes oxidized and its energy utilized. (From Tower in Harlow and Woolsey, *Biological and Biochemical Basis of Behavior*, Univ. Wisconsin Press, 1958.)

at nodes of myelinated nerve. Mitochondria contain the necessary enzymes required for the breakdown of pyruvate and utilization of its energy via the Krebs cycle. The series of enzymes by which energy is gained from the Krebs cycle is present in some organized array in the mitochondrion. The resulting energy is transferred to the *energy-rich phosphate bonds* ($\sim$ P) of creatine phosphate and adenosine triphosphate (ATP). Transfer of energy from the Krebs cycle to these high-energy phosphate bonds apparently occurs in the electron transfer system leading from nicotinamide nucleotide to oxygen. The term *uncoupling* is used in reference to chemical agents such as azide or dinitrophenol which appear to block those reactions leading to the formation of the energy-rich phosphate bonds; other metabolic steps involved in the uptake of oxygen remain unblocked (Brink *et al.*, 1952). A difference in metabolism between the resting and active metabolism of nerve was suggested by an oxygen uptake of active nerve which is roughly twice that of resting nerve (Gerard, 1932) and the finding that the uncoupling agent, azide, depressed the extra oxygen uptake of active nerve while the resting oxygen uptake was left unaffected (Doty and Gerard, 1950). Brink (1957) considers that this may be explainable by differential levels of sensitivity of the nerve to azide. In his view, the higher rate of oxygen utilization seen during activity is a simple speeding up of the respiratory rate and not due to a qualitatively different mechanism. Because metabolic inhibitors do not have single specific actions, and generally act on a number of systems, the interpretation of their effects with regard to underlying mechanisms is difficult. At present the possibility of a special metabolism of activity, one involving a special set of chemical reactions, remains unresolved.

The level of $\sim$ P compounds such as ATP and creatine phosphate in nerve varies with the state of activity or metabolism. A fall in creatine phosphate is found in anoxia, and activity will decrease the level of creatine phosphate present in normally oxygenated or in anoxic nerve. One way of interpreting such findings is that the $\sim$ P bonds are connected with restorative metabolic processes in the nerve. If the supply of oxygen is diminished, the constant metabolic requirements lead to a fall in the storage level of $\sim$ P in creatine phosphate. With increased nerve activity there is an increased metabolic demand and a further fall. In another view, activity of the nerve is associated with a diversion of metabolic activity from the production of $\sim$ P. Further details may be found elsewhere (McIlwain, 1959; Abood, 1960).

Metabolism and the sodium pump

The high-energy phosphate bonds present in ATP play an important role in the sodium pump mechanism. This was shown in a series of investigations on the giant nerve axon. The metabolic blocking agents cyanide (CN), 2:4 dinitrophenol (DNP) or azide when present in the external medium were found to inhibit the operation of the sodium pump (Hodgkin and Keynes, 1955). The output of Na^+ from axons previously loaded with the radioactive tracer was used as the measure of the pump operation. As shown in Fig. 7.4, when the axon was immersed in a solution containing

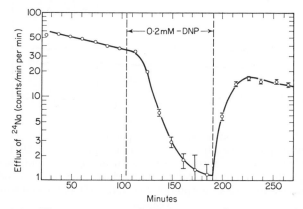

Fig. 7.4. The movement of Na^+ tracer from nerve before, during the presence of dinitrophenol (DNP), and after its removal. The movement of Na^+ from the nerve is decreased during the presence of the inhibitor with a recovery after its removal. (Hodgkin and Keynes, 1955b.)

DNP, the output of Na^+ dropped over a period of 100 minutes and when the axon was returned to its normal medium, Na^+ output was resumed. A similar blocking effect of Na^+ output was found with CN and azide.

It is important to notice in this experiment that while the metabolic blocking agents interfered with the sodium pump and Na^+ output, the resting membrane potential and action potentials remained relatively unchanged for over an hour (Fig. 7.5). This is strong evidence for the lack of a direct connection between metabolism and the mechanisms giving rise to the resting and action potentials. In other words, the purpose of the metabolic mechanisms is to bring about those asymmetric distributions of ions on which resting potentials (Chapter 4) and action potentials (Chapter 5) depend.

Metabolic processes supply the energy requirements of the sodium pump which actively operates against the passive electrochemical gradient of Na^+ across the membrane. Therefore, the metabolic

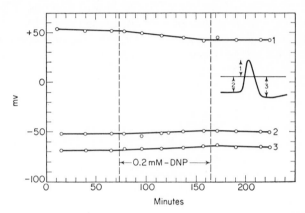

Fig. 7.5. The resting membrane potential (2), overshoot (1), and after-positivity (3) before, during the presence of DNP, and after its removal. Little effect is seen on these potentials even though this amount of DNP has a marked effect on the sodium pump to decrease Na^+ output (cf. Fig. 7.4). (Hodgkin and Keynes, 1955b.)

blocking agents which interfere with the output of Na^+ should have little effect on the passive entry of Na^+. This was found to be the case when the uptake of Na^+ was studied with giant nerve axon in a medium containing DNP (Fig. 7.6).

With CN, DNP, or azide present in the external medium, not only is Na^+ output blocked, but so also is the uptake of K^+. This is understandable if the membrane of the giant nerve axon works in similar fashion to that of the frog skin (Chapter 4) where a coupling of Na^+ output from the cell to K^+ uptake into the cell was described. This type of coupling between Na^+ output and K^+ uptake was shown for the giant axon when the K^+ concentration outside the fiber was reduced and the Na^+ output accordingly became reduced to about one-third its value (Fig. 7.7). This figure also shows a rapid drop in Na^+ output in a K^+-free medium as compared to the slow onset with a metabolic inhibitor present (Fig. 7.4).

A connection between $\sim P$ compounds and the sodium pump of

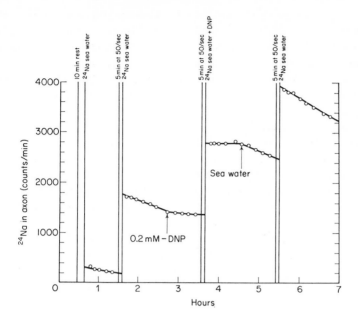

Fig. 7.6. The movement of Na$^+$ into the nerve fiber is not affected by the presence of DNP (cf. Fig. 7.4). (Hodgkin and Keynes, 1955b.)

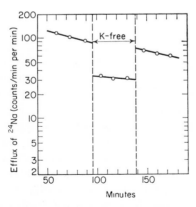

Fig. 7.7. The movement of Na$^+$ from nerve before and during the removal of K$^+$ from the external medium, and after its replacement. A decrease of outward Na$^+$ movement is seen to occur with the decreased external K$^+$. (Hodgkin and Keynes, 1955b.)

giant nerve axon has been found (Keynes, 1960; Caldwell, 1960; Caldwell *et al.*, 1960a, b). When giant nerve axons were placed in a medium containing 2 mM CN or 0.2 mM DNP, the content of arginine phosphate and ATP within the fiber fell, coincident with the block of the sodium pump and fall of Na$^+$ output. (Arginine phosphate serves as a store of $\sim$ P in the cephalopod tissue as creatine phosphate does in the mammal.) The decrease of ATP and arginine phosphate produced by the metabolic inhibitors was, therefore, connected with a decrease in Na$^+$ output. When the sodium pump was depressed by poisoning the nerve with CN or DNP, injection of ATP or arginine phosphate into the fiber caused a return of Na$^+$ output back toward normal levels, the effect lasting for several hours (Fig. 7.8). Arginine phosphate was particularly effective in aug-

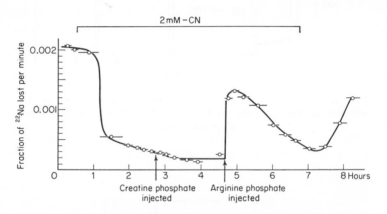

Fig. 7.8. Outward Na$^+$ movement is shown to be decreased by cyanide (CN). Creatine phosphate injected into the poisoned axon was ineffective in changing Na$^+$ movement. Arginine phosphate injected into the axon caused a long-lasting increased outward movement of Na$^+$. (Caldwell, Hodgkin, Keynes and Shaw, 1960a.)

menting Na$^+$ output in CN-poisoned nerves. Other $\sim$ P compounds such as creatine phosphate were ineffective. External application of arginine phosphate was ineffective as was arginine phosphate which had been hydrolysed in order to break the high-energy phosphate bonds before injecting it into the axon. The results indicate that the $\sim$ P bonds in arginine phosphate are transferred to ATP which is closely related to the sodium pump mechanism in the membrane of the giant axon (*vide infra*). Potassium must be present in the external environment for the sodium pump efflux to be activated by the injected arginine phosphate; the pump action is therefore considered to be K^+-*sensitive*. A K^+-*insensitive* type of sodium movement was found when ATP was injected in the poison-depleted nerves. In that case, Na^+ output was increased, but, unlike normal sodium pumping action, the increase occurred even when K^+ had been removed from the external medium (Keynes, 1960). Injection of arginine phosphate increases the level of ATP with an energy level sufficiently high to drive the sodium pump which is K^+-sensitive (Caldwell *et al.*, 1964). With ATP injection there is a more rapid transfer to ADP with a lower total energy level, insufficient to overcome the energy gradient (or barrier) for sodium pumping. What remains is an outward movement of ions due to exchange (Chapter 4) which is insensitive to external K^+.

At its point of action the $\sim P$ bond of ATP must be enzymatically broken before it can perform useful work. Libet (1948) had shown that ATPase is localized in the sheath of the giant nerve axon, and Abood and Gerard (1954) found ATPase activity in sub-microscopic particles isolated from homogenates of the nerve sheath. This enzyme is activated by Mg^{2+} and it readily hydrolyses ATP to ADP releasing the $\sim P$. It is of interest that the enzymatic activity of isolated ATPase is increased by Na^+ and not so readily by K^+ (Skou, 1961). However, K^+ has a stimulating effect on the enzyme which depends on the presence of Na^+. At low concentrations of Na^+, the addition of a small amount of K^+ increases enzymatic activity while more K^+ decreases the activity of the enzyme. Such behavior of this enzyme with respect to Na^+ and K^+ ions has been taken to indicate that the ATPase could be the hypothetical Na^+ carrier or at least closely related to Na^+ transport mechanisms (Skou, 1961; McIlwain, 1963).

An alternative view has been presented by Conway (1960) who has attempted to relate the sodium pump to a *redox* mechanism. According to his hypothesis a carrier in the membrane releases Na^+ to the outside surface where specific oxidation-reduction reactions take place to overcome the energy barrier to its transfer. The pump could operate by electrons changing the electrical charge on a carrier with which Na^+ is combined. From the redox equation used by Conway, 4 protons or electrons are transferred for every O_2 utilized. If oxygen is directly coupled to Na^+ transport, then at 100% efficiency, 4 sodium ions at most can be transported for every O_2 molecule taken up. While for giant nerve axon Hodgkin and Keynes (1954) found that one sodium ion was transported for every oxygen molecule, the concept of a redox pump cannot be generally valid.   In the frog skin 18 sodium ions or more are transported per oxygen molecule utilized (Zerahn, 1956).   However, frog skin is a fairly complex tissue (Chapter 4) and it is not certain if Na^+/O_2 ratios have the same significance as in nerve and muscle. In an interesting theory of Harris (1960) metabolic activity is considered to change the charge on the wall of pores and in this fashion have an effect on ion flux.   Models relating metabolism to ion movement are discussed by McIlwain (1963).

Is there a specific metabolism of excitation?

The metabolic events so far discussed have been concerned with the operation of a sodium pump, i.e., with mechanisms which bring about the asymmetrical distribution of ions on which membrane potentials depend.   This concept is diagrammed in Fig. 7.9.   Metab-

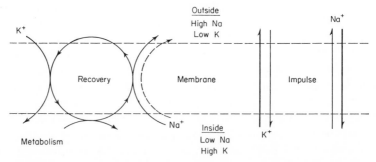

Fig. 7.9.   As indicated diagrammatically, metabolism brings about an asymmetrical ionic distribution.   The rapid Na^+ and K^+ movements occurring during a nerve impulse are not directly connected to metabolism.   (Hodgkin and Keynes, 1955b.)

olism is shown as a process which is remote from the ionic events underlying potentials.   Can there be another type of metabolic process more closely associated with those fast permeability changes which have been discussed in Chapter 5 as underlying excitation and the action potential?

A simple hypothesis of the increased Na^+ permeability which occurs as an early step during excitation is that the depolarizing potential either from a cathode or local currents can move some charged element in the membrane thereby opening a Na^+ channel or freeing a Na^+ carrier to bring Na^+ into the cell.   Alternatively it is possible that a more complex system is involved, one which may require enzymatic systems of control. The positive initial heat described in an earlier section could be the result of such biochemical activity. Nachmansohn (1959) has constructed one type of enzymatic theory in which a crucial role is played by acetylcholine (ACh) and the enzymes related to it. According to this theory, an imposed depolarization or the depolarization of the membrane produced by local currents releases ACh from a bound state in the membrane. In turn the free ACh acts to bring about the specific increase in Na^+ permeability. Acetylcholinesterase present in the membrane then hydrolyses the free ACh to terminate its action allowing Na^+ permeability to return to its original low level. The enzyme choline-acetylase later rebuilds ACh back into its bound form. In support of the theory, ACh and the enzymes cholinesterase and choline-acetylase are found in nerve tissues. However, not all the available evidence supports this theory (Burgen and MacIntosh, 1955; Hebb, 1957; Hebb and Krnjevic, 1962). For example, it is known that the amount of cholinesterase is quite low in the dorsal roots, although Nachmansohn supposed that such lower levels of activity could still be consistent with its postulated action if uniformly distributed. However, by means of histochemical techniques it was shown that a few fibers have high acetylcholinesterase activity, while most of the sensory fibers of mammalian dorsal roots are entirely devoid of this key ACh enzyme (Giacombini, 1959). This and other evidence cited in the reviews of Burgen and MacIntosh, Hebb, and Hebb and Krnjevic, argue against the universality of the ACh system.

While it does not appear that ACh is crucial in the process of excitation, it plays some important but as yet little understood role in nerve. The ability of some quaternary ammonium compounds related to acetylcholine to substitute for Na^+ and maintain the excitability of nerve has been referred to (Chapter 5). The presence of the ACh enzymes cholinesterase and choline-acetylase in the motor fibers may possibly be related to a movement of these materials from a site of synthesis in the cell bodies down along the fiber to the neuromuscular junctions by an axoplasmic flow mechanism (Chapter 8).

Nerve-sheath barrier

The epineural sheaths around the whole nerve trunk and the perineural sheaths found around nerve bundles appears to have a controlling influence on entry of various ions and metabolites. This was shown by the low permeability of the nerve trunk to various agents which block excitation and conduction compared with their speed of action when the sheath has been slit lengthwise to allow penetration directly to the fibers (Feng and Gerard, 1930; Crescitelli, 1951).

An analysis of the ionic composition of the endoneural fluid with respect to external body fluids showed that its Na^+ and Cl^- concentrations differed from that of the external body fluids (Krnjevic, 1955) suggesting that the interfiber ionic composition is regulated by the sheath. Wide variations occur in the ionic content of the body fluids of insects (Tobias, 1947) and if the sheath were not present as a regulating barrier, depolarization and loss of excitability would occur (Hoyle, 1953). The flat sheet-like 'satellite' cells found around the axolemma of the giant nerve axon may also have a similar ion-regulating function (Schmitt and Geschwind, 1957).

REFERENCES

Abbott, B. C. (1960). Heat production in nerve and electric organ. *J. Gen. Physiol. Suppl.* **43**: 119–127.

Abbott, B. C., Hill, A. V. and Howarth, J. V. (1958). The positive and negative heat production associated with a nerve impulse *Proc. Roy. Soc. B*. **148**: 149–187.

Abood, L. G. (1960). Neuronal metabolism. *Handbook of Physiology—Neurophysiology*. Vol. 3, pp. 1815–1826. American Physiological Society, Washington, D.C.

Abood, L. G. and Gerard, R. W. (1954). Enzyme distribution in isolated particulates of rat peripheral nerve. *J. Cell. Comp. Physiol.* **43**: 379–392.

Brink, F. Jr. (1957). Nerve metabolism. *Metabolism of the Nervous System*. Pp. 187–207. Edited by D. Richter. Pergamon Press, New York.

Brink, F. Jr., Bronk, D. W., Carlson, F. D. and Connelly, C. M. (1952). The oxygen uptake of active axons. *Cold Spring Harbor Symp. Quant. Biol.* **17**: 53–67.

Burgen, A. S. V. and MacIntosh, F. C. (1955). The physiological significance of acetylcholine. *Neurochemistry*. Edited by K. A. C. Elliot, I. H. Page and J. H. Quastel. Pp. 311–389. Charles C. Thomas, Springfield.

Caldwell, P. C. (1960). The phosphorus metabolism of squid axons and its relationship to the active transport of sodium. *J. Physiol.* **152**: 545–560.

Caldwell, P. C., Hodgkin, A. L., Keynes, R. D. and Shaw, T. I. (1960a). The effects of injecting 'energy-rich' phosphate compounds on the active transport of ions in the giant axons of *Loligo*. *J. Physiol.* **152**: 561–590.

Caldwell, P. C., Hodgkin, A. L., Keynes, R. D. and Shaw, T. I. (1960b). Partial inhibition of the active transport of cations in the giant axons of *Loligo*. *J. Physiol.* **152**: 591–600.

Caldwell, P. C., Hodgkin, A. L., Keynes, R. D. and Shaw, T. I. (1964). The rate of formation and turnover of phosphorus compounds in squid giant axons. *J. Physiol.* **171**: 119–131.

Conway, E. J. (1960). Critical energy barriers to active transport in muscle and the redox pump theory. *Regulation of the Inorganic Ion Content of Cells.* Ciba Foundation Study Group 5. Pp. 2–20. Little, Brown and Co., Boston.

Crescitelli, F. (1951). Nerve sheath as a barrier to the action of certain substances. *Am. J. Physiol.* **166**: 229–240.

Doty, R. W. and Gerard, R. W. (1950). Nerve conduction without increased oxygen consumption. Action of azide and fluroacetate. *Am. J. Physiol.* **162**: 458–468.

Downing, A. C., Gerard, R. W. and Hill, A. V. (1926). The heat production of nerve. *Proc. Roy. Soc. B.* **100**: 223–251.

Feng, T. P. and Gerard, R. W. (1930). Mechanism of nerve asphyxiation: with a note on the nerve sheath as a diffusion barrier. *Proc. Soc. Exptl. Biol. Med.* **27**: 1073–1076.

Gerard, R. W. (1932). Nerve metabolism. *Physiol. Rev.* **12**: 469–592.

Giacombini, E. (1959). The distribution and localization of cholinesterases in nerve cells. *Acta Physiol. Scand.* **45**: *Suppl.* **156**: 1–45.

Harris, E. J. (1960). *Accumulation and Transport in Cells.* 2nd. Ed. Butterworths, London.

Hebb, C. O. (1957). Biochemical evidence for the neural function of acetylcholine. *Physiol. Rev.* **37**: 196–220.

Hebb, C. O. and Krnjevic, K. (1962). The physiological significance of acetylcholine. *Neurochemistry.* 2nd Ed. Edited by K. A. C. Elliot, I. H. Page and J. H. Quastel. Pp. 452–521. Charles C. Thomas, Springfield.

Hill, A. V. (1932). *Chemical Wave Transmission in Nerve.* Cambridge University Press, London.

Hill, A. V. (1960). The heat production of nerve. *Molecular Biology.* Edited by D. Nachmansohn. Pp. 153–162. Academic Press, New York.

Hill, A. V. and Howarth, J. V. (1958). The initial heat production of stimulated nerve. *Proc. Roy. Soc. B.* **149**: 167–175.

Hodgkin, A. L. and Keynes, R. D. (1954). Movement of cations during recovery in nerve. *Symp. Soc. Exptl. Biol.* **8**: 423–437.

Hodgkin, A. L. and Keynes, R. D. (1955). Active transport of cations in giant axons from *Sepia* and *Loligo.* *J. Physiol.* **128**: 28–60.

Hoyle, G. (1953). Potassium ions and insect nerve muscle. *J. Exptl. Biol.* **30**: 121–135.

Keynes, R. D. (1960). The effect of complete and partial inhibition of metabolism on active transport in nerve and muscle. *Regulation of the Inorganic Ion Content of Cells.* Ciba Foundation Study Group 5. Pp. 77–88. Little, Brown and Co., Boston.

Krnjevic, K. (1955). The distribution of Na^+ and K^+ in cat nerves. *J. Physiol.* **128**: 473–488.

Libet, B. (1948). Adenosinetriphosphatase (ATPase) in nerve. *Federation Proc.* **7**: 72.

McIlwain, H. (1959). *Biochemistry and the Central Nervous System.* 2nd Ed. Little, Brown and Co., Boston.

McIlwain, H. (1963). *Chemical Exploration of the Brain.* Elsevier, Amsterdam.

Nachmansohn, D. (1959). *Chemical and Molecular Basis of Nerve Activity.* Academic Press, New York.

Schmitt, F. O. and Geschwind, N. (1957). The axon surface. *Progr. Biophys.* **8**: 165–215.

Shanes, A. (1958). Electrochemical aspects of physiological and pharmacological action in excitable cells. *Pharmacol. Rev.* **10**: Part 1, 59–164 and Part 2, 165–272.

Skou, J. C. (1961). The relationship of a $(Mg^{2+} + Na^+)$–activated, K^+–stimulated enzyme or enzyme system to the active, linked transport of Na^+ and K^+ across the membrane. *Membrane Transport and Metabolism.* Edited by A. Kleinzeller and A. Kotyk. Pp. 228–236. Academic Press, New York.

Tobias, J. M. (1947). The high potassium and low sodium in the body fluid and tissues of a phytophagous insect, the silkworm *Bombyxmori* and the change before pupation. *J. Cell. Comp. Physiol.* **31**: 143–148.

Zerahn, K. (1956). Oxygen consumption and active sodium transport in the isolated and short-circuited frog skin. *Acta Physiol. Scand.* **36**: 300–318.

8

Nerve Growth and Maintenance

Neurotropism

During embryonic development growing nerve fibers find their right 'addresses,' that is, they make proper termination upon other neurons and peripheral effector organs. The overall pattern of these connections is genetically determined. The growing fibers must extend in some cases for a relatively long distance to make the proper connection. The agency or force controlling the direction of growth taken by the fibers is referred to as *neurotropism*.

At one time electrical fields were postulated to have a neurotropic influence. In order to test this, nerves were grown outside the body in tissue culture and the influence of electrical fields on the direction of their growth studied. Such experiments did not support the theory of an electrical neurotropic influence (Weiss, 1941). A surface must be present in tissue culture for the nerve fibers to grow on, and Weiss' studies indicated the importance of mechanical factors for the direction of the growth of fibers. If the supporting medium of the nerve culture is stretched, the fibers tend to grow along the direction of elongation of the medium. Presumably, the molecular alignment produced by stretching underlies this directive influence (Weiss, 1941). Chemical factors or a *chemotactic* type of neurotropism has been invoked. As we shall see, there is evidence against a specific long-range chemotaxis, although chemical directing forces may act at close range (*vide infra*). Possibly a start in the identification of chemotactic agents has been initiated by the isolation of specific proteins which are able to stimulate 'growth of ganglion cells to abnormal size (Levi-Montalcini and Angeletti, 1961).

The growth of nerve fibers within the body has been observed microscopically in the tail of the tadpole by taking advantage of the translucency of the skin of the animal (Speidel, 1941). Growth of nerve fibers appears to be random to some degree with those branches developing in the 'wrong' direction regressing, and those fibers in the 'right' direction continuing in their growth. The term *saturation* has been used to describe the fact that once inner-vated, the target cell no longer stimulates further growth of nerve fibers toward it (Sperry, 1951).

The existence of a neurotropic influence and also a saturation mechanism can be demonstrated in the mature vertebrate organism where peripheral nerves retain the power of regrowth after interruption (*vide infra*). If a portion of muscle is deprived of its innervation, nerves near the denervated portion send collaterals to reinnervate those muscles (Edds, 1953; van Harreveld, 1952). Similarly, for sensory endings, if a skin area is denervated, collaterals from nearby sensory nerves sprout out to enter into and innervate that region (Weddell, Guttmann and Gutmann, 1941).

The study of neurotropic influences in individual cells and their processes in the CNS is made difficult by the tangled appearance of the dendrites and axons, referred to as the *neuropil*. Comparative studies afford some simplification in showing the evolution of the simple ganglionic centers of the lowest species into the complex *nuclear formations* and the corresponding growth of their connecting tracts of fibers—the *white matter* of the higher forms (Ariëns-Kappers, Huber and Crosby, 1936). The term *neurobiotaxis* (Ariëns-Kappers, 1917) refers to the growth and development of analogous CNS structures in successively higher forms. In Ariëns-Kappers' view the dendritic processes become oriented toward the region of greatest activity. In successive evolutionary developments this growth of dendrites is followed by the elaboration of synaptic connections to them, and then the neuron cell bodies eventually become displaced in the direction of the dendrites. We would have to suppose that an individual's experiences can result in a species change, a position which is not accepted today.

For the most part the connections between neurons within the CNS are stable as shown by the stability of reflex behavior. However, some neurons are considered to retain a degree of pliancy throughout life. The processes of learning and memory suggest that new synaptic connections or other neuronal changes can be made in order to retain the experiences of the individual organism (Chapter 25).

Regeneration

To a large measure lower vertebrates such as the urodele amphibia (newts and salamanders) and the anuran amphibia (frogs and toads) have the ability to regenerate tissues. For example, if amputated, a whole limb may be regenerated. Also, in the early stages of development of these lower vertebrates if a limb bud is implanted next to the normal limb bud, it will grow out as an additional or a *supernumerary* limb and it will become functional. The individual muscles of the supernumerary limb contract synchronously with those corresponding in the normal limb, a phenomenon called *myotopy* (muscle-specificity) by Weiss (1950). The various nerve fibers of the normal nerve plexus branch off to innervate the same muscles of the supernumerary limb as ordinarily innervated in the normal limb. Some kind of neurotropic influence is at work in the supernumerary limb for the nerve fibers to be directed to the appropriate muscles. The limb muscles become active in sequence to move the animal forward. If a limb bud is grafted onto an animal in the reverse anteroposterior direction, the resulting grown limb becomes active in the same sequence. However, because the supernumerary limb is connected in the reverse direction, the limbs will move the animal backwards when it attempts to move forward. The animal does not learn to compensate for this peripheral change. In other words, the animal's behavior does not show *plasticity*, i.e., there is no rearrangement of the organization of its CNS with respect to a changed peripheral input.

Regeneration of central tracts such as the optic nerve is also possible in these lower vertebrates. After section of the optic nerve, the axons of the retinal cells grow out and reinnervate the optic lobe which in these forms is the CNS receptor area. The more complex visual connections present in the mammal will be discussed in Chapters 12 and 21. The regeneration of the retinal fibers to their usual positions in the optic lobe is indicated by the subsequent behavior of the animal (Sperry, 1943). Upon presentation of a small food object as a lure, the normal animal can accurately leap at it and capture it. This type of visual–motor performance shown by animals with regenerated optic nerves indicates that the fibers have regenerated in sufficiently accurate fashion to allow for *pattern vision* of the visual field. This requires a correspondence between points in the visual field and points in the visual receptor area in the optic lobe (Chapter 21). The recovery of such a *topological correspondence* suggests that the axons of the retinal cells in each small region of the retina in the course of its regeneration find their way to that small region of neurons of the optic lobe with which they are normally synaptically associated. Regeneration also will occur after the optic nerve has been cut and the eyeball rotated 180° (Sperry, 1943). In this case, the direction in which the animal strikes at a lure becomes reversed, e.g., in the downward direction when the lure is presented above (Fig. 8.1). This would follow if the axons of the regenerating retinal cells originate from the same retinal points as do

the normal retinal cells and end in the same place in the optic lobe as
their normal counterparts, the difference being that in the case of the
rotated eye the visual scene is now projected onto an upside down
retina and the animal perforce interprets its visual information in
inverse fashion.   Electrical recording of the responses has confirmed

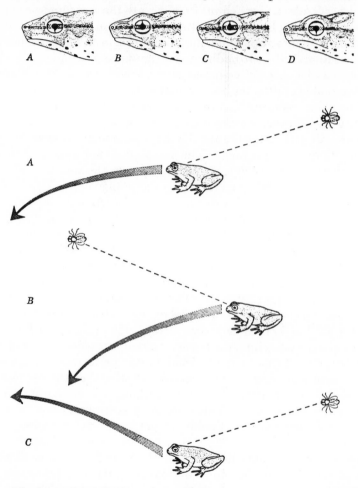

Fig. 8.1.   *Top:* Optic nerve cut and eye rotated.   A, normal;
B, 180° rotation; C, dorsoventral inversion; D, nasotemporal
inversion.   *Bottom:* Eye rotated 180° and frog strikes at a point
diametrically opposite to the position of the fly used as a lure (A).
Dorsoventral inversion of the eye and frog strikes inversely in the
dorsoventral direction (B).   Nasotemporal inversion of the eye and
frog strikes inversely with respect to the nasotemporal direction (C).
(Sperry, 1951.)

these behavioral studies in showing that the regenerated retinal fibers end in their determined points on the optic lobe (Gaze, 1960).

To explain this phenomenon, it was suggested that fibers grow in random fashion toward their terminus at the optic lobe. When close to their final termination specific neurotropic influences from each small part of the optic lobe act on corresponding fibers so that proper termination is made. This assumes that a high degree of biochemical specificity exists between the fibers and the neurons on which

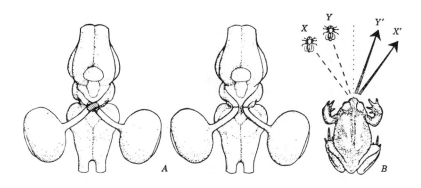

Fig. 8.2. Optic chiasm cut and regeneration of fibers occurs to the eye of the same side (A) instead of to the contralateral side. After regeneration (B), the frog strikes at the lure at X' or Y' as though it were presented at Y or X. (Sperry, 1951.)

they terminate. However, the connections made do not appear to be entirely specific. Some generality extends to the neuronal termini in the opposite optic lobe. This was shown by cutting the optic nerve at the chiasm (Fig. 8.2) and rechanneling the regenerating nerves to the optic lobes of the same (*ipsilateral*) side instead of the usual situation where nerves cross at the chiasm to innervate the opposite (*contralateral*) side. With this type of cross-channeling to the ipsilateral side, the retinal neurons of each eye after regeneration reinnervates the 'foreign' optic lobe. Function returns, but because these lobes now receive different parts of the visual field from each retina, the animal interprets the lure as coming from the wrong side and strikes to the side in the opposite direction to the one on which the lure is presented.

Degeneration and regeneration of nerve in the mammal

In the higher vertebrates the power of regeneration is retained to some extent. If a nerve trunk such as the sciatic nerve is cut, the amputated distal part of the nerve undergoes a dissolution first described by Waller (1850) and known as *Wallerian degeneration*

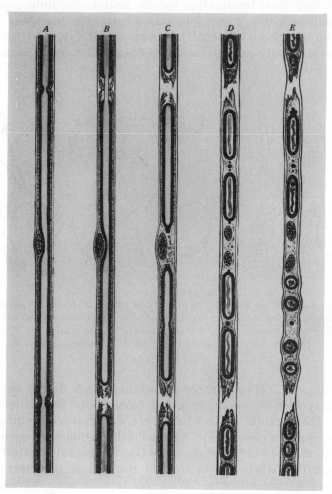

Fig. 8.3.   Stages of Wallerian degeneration of an amputated part of myelinated nerve fiber shown after periods of days and weeks. Normal fiber (A).   Early in degeneration (B) there is a retraction of myelin from the nodes.   Later (C) long ovoids are formed which still later (D, E) become smaller and round up into vesicular structures.   (Courtesy of J. Z. Young; from Young, *Advan. Surg.*, **1**: 165, 1949.)

(Ramón y Cajal, 1928; Young, 1942).   The distal amputated nerve fibers show irregularities of form within a day.   The myelin of the peripheral fibers begins to retract from the nodes and over the next few days the myelin rounds into ellipsoids and spheres (Fig. 8.3) and then later becomes gathered together into droplets until after several weeks or months the axons are phagocytized and resorbed.   The narrowed tube-like Schwann sheaths remaining are filled with cytoplasmic material formed by the Schwann cells.

The isolated distal portion of the nerve becomes inexcitable within a few days after interruption.   The loss of excitation differs for the various nerve fiber groups.   In the visceral afferents of the monkey conduction was lost within 50–60 hours, followed 5–10 hours later by the somatic nerves.   Later the myelinated autonomic fibers became inexcitable and finally the nonmyelinated fibers lose their excitability 90 hours after amputation (Heinbecker, Bishop and O'Leary, 1932).   In the peroneal nerves of rabbits, excitability was lost in 70–80 hours (Gutmann and Holubar, 1950).   The nerve loses its excitability throughout its whole length at the same time (Gerard, 1932; Young, 1942; Gutmann and Holubar, 1950).   If nerves are repetitively stimulated during degeneration, they fail sooner.   The survival time is presumably related to metabolic stores present in the axon.   The dependence of the peripheral axon on its continuity with the cell body implies that some continual supply of necessary substances from the cell body is required for maintenance of the peripheral portions of the nerve membrane, a concept which will be discussed more fully in the next section.

Within a few days after nerve interruption the process of *regeneration* begins.   The ends of the fibers just proximal to the lesion begin to develop buds or sprouts.   This sprouting is analogous to the protrusions of the cell membrane in various directions such as seen in normal growth of nerve in the tadpole tail or in tissue culture. The sprouts grow out into thin fibers from the proximal end of the cut nerve (Fig. 8.4) and more or less find their way into the sheaths of the distal degenerated part of the nerve (Ramón y Cajal, 1928; Young, 1949).   Further growth occurs down the distal degenerated sheath and reinnervation of the effector structure takes place by the regenerated fiber.   Afterwards the regenerated nerve axon gradually increases in diameter over a period of 4–12 months (Weiss, Edds and Cavanaugh, 1945), a process referred to as *maturation*.

The outgrowth and maturation of the nerve fiber is related to the production of new axoplasm by the cell body, and the volume of protoplasm produced must be quite large as can be assessed from the

measurement of fiber diameter and rate of growth.   For sensory
nerves (Fig. 8.5) the rate of growth was determined by the furthest
point along the nerve distal to the original interruption at which the
animal will respond to a small pinch of the nerve (Gutmann, Guttmann,
Medawar and Young, 1942).   For motor nerves (Fig. 8.6) the rate

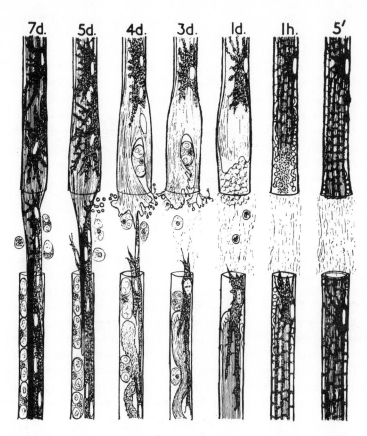

Fig. 8.4. Distal part of nerve fiber 5 minutes after cutting
shown at the right. Retraction of the central end of the cut
axon 1 hour later. Budding at third and fourth day. Slender
axon grows into the distal degenerated stumps at days 5 and 7.
(Courtesy, J. Z. Young; from Young, *Advan. Surgery*, 1: 165, 1949.)

was determined by the time it took for recovery of reflex toe-spreading
after interruption of nerves at various distances from the muscle in
different animals.   These studies show that the nerve grows 3.5–4.5
mm/day, a rate which coincided with measurements of growth rate

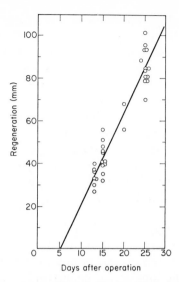

Fig. 8.5. Rate of growth of fibers after nerve interruption determined by the farthest point of response to pinching of a small part of the exposed nerve. The measured rate is approximately 4 to 5.5 mm per day. (Gutmann *et al.*, 1942.)

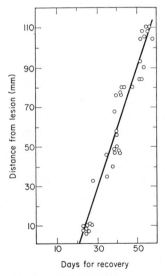

Fig. 8.6. The rate of regrowth as determined by the time for recovery of a reflex toe-spreading after interrupting the motor nerve at various distances from the muscle. (Gutmann *et al.*, 1942.)

based on histological examination of the tips of regenerating nerve fibers.

The fact that fibers find their way into the distal stumps was considered by Ramón y Cajal (1928) to be an expression of a chemotropic effect exerted by the degenerated nerve. While fibers which are destined for a given muscle will usually regenerate into the distal part of degenerated nerve to reinnervate that muscle, those nerve fibers may also innervate other denervated muscles. The innervation of muscles by 'foreign' nerves was shown by cutting a nerve and suturing it to the distal stump of the foreign nerve to be innervated. The regenerating fibers are then directed in their growth via the degenerated sheaths to which they are sutured to innervate the foreign muscle. For example, the central end of a cut peroneal nerve will grow out into the distal end of a tibial nerve to innervate that muscle and vice versa. This shows that the power of specificity between nerve fiber and stump is not over-riding. However, the presence of a specific long-range neurotropic effect could be better judged if two nerves were exposed to the presumed neurotropic effect on an equal basis. If such a neurotropic effect is present then a nerve should reinnervate its own stump rather than a 'foreign' one. This hypothesis was tested by Weiss and Hoag (1946). The peroneal and tibial nerves of rats were cut and the nerves allowed to reinnervate the plantar extensor muscle which is normally innervated by the tibial nerve. If a specific neurotropic influence is present more tibial nerve fibers will find their way to the plantar muscle. The plan of the experiment is shown in Fig. 8.7. The proximal ends of the cut nerves were inserted in a Y-shaped sleeve of blood vessel serving as an indifferent guide for nerve growth. After regeneration was accomplished, the central ends of the two nerves were cut and then stimulated so that the maximal tension developed by the reinnervated plantar muscle was determined. No difference was found in the tensions produced by stimulating each nerve, indicating that the regenerating fibers showed no selective growth in their reinnervation of the muscle. Bernstein and Guth (1961) performed an even simpler experiment. In the rat more ventral root fibers of the lumbar 4th spinal segment will innervate the plantaris muscle than the soleus muscle. The relative amounts of innervation were first determined by the muscle tension developed in the two muscles in response to repetitive stimulation of the exposed roots. If after interruption of the sciatic nerve and subsequent reinnervation this differential pattern persisted, this would be evidence for a neurotropic effect. The result of this experiment was that the muscle responses to stimulation of the 4th ventral root changed so that the responses to stimulation of the roots were now similar, a result indicating a chance reinnervation of the two muscles by the regenerated fibers. Therefore, it would appear from these two sets of experiments that there is no long-range specific neurotropic effect exerted by the denervated muscle which acts on the adult regenerating fibers. Once the muscle becomes innervated by either its own or a 'foreign' nerve the receptor sites are saturated and the muscle will reject additional innervation. Which nerve will inner-

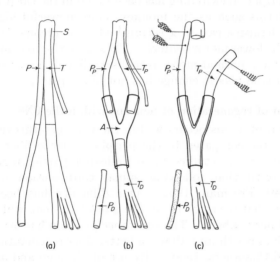

(a) (b) (c)

Fig. 8.7. In (a) the peroneal (P) and tibial (T) branches of the sciatic nerve (S) are cut, and inserted (b) into a Y-shaped segment of artery (A) as a guide. After regeneration into the tibial end, the proximal ends of the peroneal (P_P) and tibial (T_P) nerves are stimulated to determine if there has been a preference in reinnervation of the tibial nerve (T_D) and its muscle. (Weiss and Hoag, 1946.)

vate any given muscle is apparently determined by which nerve will reach it first. A specific short-range neurotropic influence near the termination is not excluded by these experiments and, as noted above, serves to explain the patterned reinnervation of the frog optic lobe. The possibility of a longer-range neurotropism has been indicated for optic nerve by Sperry (1963).

The nerves innervating extensor and flexor muscles when cut and cross-sutured will regrow to innervate those foreign muscles. This was used for a study of possible CNS plasticity. The question at issue was whether control from the CNS then becomes reversed from the animal's ordinary use of those muscles to compensate for the peripheral switch (Sperry, 1945).   The muscles continue to operate according to the usual pattern of discharge from the CNS. Because of the reversed connections of nerves to the muscles, they contract oppositely and the limb movement is inappropriate for the animal's attempted responses.   Species as advanced as the rat or cat do not show this kind of CNS plasticity, although recently statistical evidence of some degree of central neuronal changes following peripheral switching has been found in the cat (Chapter 22). In higher forms such as the monkey, more powerful higher motor control mechanisms can to a certain extent overcome the changed pattern of the lower motor centers.   These give rise to compensations with apparently normal motor responses, though occasional failures show that a true plastic change has not taken place.

The problem of regeneration of neurons within the CNS

Regeneration of axons occurs within the CNS but this regenerative growth is feeble compared to the peripheral nerve fiber (Ramón y Cajal, 1928).   Some studies have indicated partial regrowth and functional restitution following spinal cord section (Sugar and Gerard, 1940; Freeman, 1952).   One difficulty has been the formation of a glial overgrowth at the site of the cut which inhibits regrowth of nerve fibers.   The substance piromen has been found to suppress glial growth and allows a better fiber regeneration to occur (Windle and Chambers, 1950).   By use of piromen and a technique of inserting a millipore filter between the cut ends to reduce glial formation, a regrowth of nerve fibers of the lateral columns beyond a complete cut of the spinal cord of cats was demonstrated by the recording of electrical responses transmitted across the line of the cut (Thulin, 1961).   While some fibers may grow again after transection, one of the unresolved difficulties is to assess the degree of restitution of function after regeneration.   Some of the apparent recovery is due to the high level of reflex activity present later in the caudal part of the spinal cord (Chapters 14, 22).

Chromatolysis and regeneration

After interruption of a peripheral nerve the cell bodies of those axons change in their reaction to the Nissl stains.   Instead of the cells staining their usual deep-blue color, the Nissl bodies do not stain so deeply and the cells appear paler and swollen (Fig. 8.8). This *chromatolysis*, as it is called, appears in the motoneurons of the cat spinal cord 4–5 days after interruption of the sciatic nerve and reaches a peak within two weeks (Barr and Hamilton, 1948). Thereafter recovery of normal staining takes place over a period of several months, during which time a reinnervation of muscle occurs and the regenerated fibers attain their normal thickness. Earlier

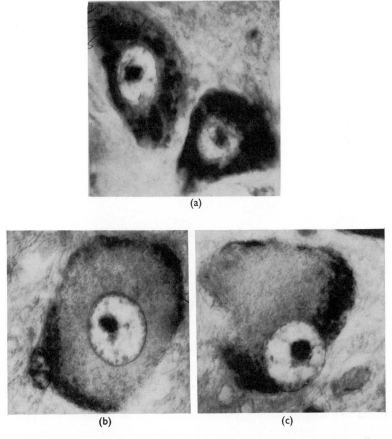

(a)

(b) (c)

Fig. 8.8. Normal hypoglossal cell bodies (a) are contrasted to cell bodies (b) and (c) 1 week after transection of the axon. The Nissl material of the chromatolysed cell is dispersed and the cell is swollen. (Courtesy, S. O. Brattgård; from Brattgård, Edström, and Hydén, 1957.)

studies of single cells made with an ultraviolet spectrophotometric technique seemed to show that the amount of nucleic acid in the cell bodies falls during the first 10 days after nerve interruption (Hydén, 1943). However, later studies showed that the total content of nucleic acid in the cell body was actually unchanged; the neurons became swollen during this early 'outflow' period (Gersh and Bodian, 1943) and the increase in volume results in a relative decrease in the concentration of nucleic acid in the cell (Brattgård, Edström and Hydén, 1957; Hyden, 1960) (Fig. 8.9). After this

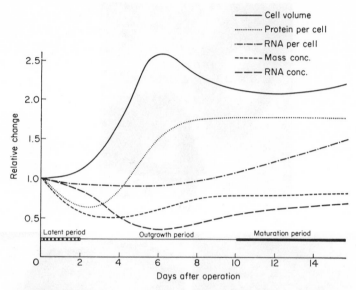

Fig. 8.9.   Changes in amounts of cell constituents in the soma at different times after section of axons and during regeneration. Note large increase of cell volume (swelling) during 'outgrowth' period.   (Brattgård, Edström and Hydén, 1957.)

stage there is an actual increase in the amount of nucleic acid present in the cell bodies (Fig. 8.10).

What is the 'signal' to the cell body that the axon has been cut leading to these chromatolytic changes?   One possibility is that the degenerating nerve or its denervated muscle releases some specific chemical substance or substances into the blood which are carried to those cell bodies in the CNS which undergo the chromatolytic changes.   However, removal of the entire limb, including all the muscular field along with the distal portions of the transected nerves does not prevent the usual chromatolytic changes from occurring (Ochs, Booker and DeMyer, 1961).   The removal of sensory inflow may be the signal as shown when the dorsal roots of cats and rabbits were cut and some chromatolysis was induced.   However, this does not appear to be the case in the monkey.   Perhaps a clue to the mechanism lies in the fact that chromatolysis is usually much greater when the nerve is interrupted closer to the cell body than when the interruptions are made more distally. Another puzzling feature is that not all the motoneurons having their peripheral fibers cut

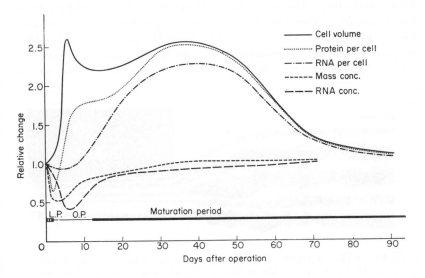

Fig. 8.10. In the later stages of regeneration (up to 90 days) a large increase in RNA and protein of the cell body is observed. Brattgård, Edström and Hydén, 1957.)

show the same degree of chromatolysis. Some motoneurons are severely affected and die while others appear indistinguishable from normal cells. Neurons which have a number of axon branches may show little chromatolysis when part of the axon termination is cut.

Axoplasmic flow

The relatively high content of RNA in the cell body of motoneurons shows that these cells are involved in a high rate of protein synthesis. Proteins (including the specific enzymes necessary for metabolism) are constantly being turned over and it would appear that the level of synthesis occurring in the cell body is high because of a constant replenishment of the contents of the axon. The concept that there is a constant supply of axoplasmic material from the cell body was earlier arrived at from the study of Wallerian degeneration where a trophic substance was inferred to be necessary to prevent degeneration. Such a supply requires a continual peripheral movement of axoplasmic substance, i.e. an *axoplasmic flow* moving down the nerve fibers (Gerard, 1932). Evidence for such an axoplasmic flow was obtained by Weiss and Hiscoe (1948). A constriction was placed around a nerve trunk tight enough to compress but not enough to completely interrupt the continuity of the individual nerve fibers, and after some weeks the nerves were removed and examined histologically. The fibers were bulged and tortuous a few millimeters proximal to the constriction, while the diameters of the fibers at and below the constriction site were much reduced in size (Fig. 8.11). The evidence indicated that a constant movement of axo-

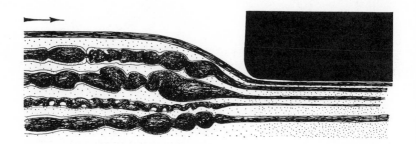

Fig. 8.11. A region of partial constriction of the nerve is shown at the right by the black block, with the fibers proximal to the constricted region at the left. After several weeks of damming, the fibers proximal to the dam are swollen, tortuous, convoluted, and beaded. The fibers in the constricted region are thinner than normal. (Courtesy, P. Weiss; from Weiss and Hiscoe, 1948.)

plasmic material toward the periphery of the axon was taking place with a *damming* of the flow at the partial obstruction. A rate of movement of axoplasm of several millimeters per day was estimated. Friede (1959) found in applying histochemical techniques to sections taken through the nerves above and below such a constriction that an increased content of succinic acid dehydrogenase activity was present several millimeters above the constriction with little of the enzyme present at and below the constriction. Other enzymes present in nerve did not show an accumulation above the dammed region, suggesting a differential flow of some constituents moving down the axon and not of others. This enzyme is closely associated with mitochondria and in electron micrographs taken in Weiss's laboratory the bulged regions of the axons above a constriction showed a great accumulation of mitochondria. Evidence for a differential movement of some of the axon constituents was also indicated in the work of Samuels *et al.* (1951). In those studies radioactive phosphorus (^{32}P) was injected into guinea pigs, and after different periods of time their sciatic nerves were removed and divided into proximal and distal portions. A larger amount of labeled phosphorus was found in some of the phosphorus fractions (most likely the diphosphoinositide fraction) extracted from the portions of the sciatic nerve closer to the cord than in the distal portions. This gradient changed gradually until at later times the distal part contained more than the proximal portions. Their evidence indicated that the labeled phosphorus was taken up from the circulation by the motoneuron cell bodies of the spinal cord, synthesized into phosphate compounds, and then some of these phosphorous compounds were slowly moved outward down the inside of the axons of the peripheral nerve fibers.

The blood-brain barrier (Chapter 18) considerably slows the uptake of labeled phosphate into the spinal cord. To bypass the barrier it was found feasible to inject small quantities of the labeled phosphorus directly into the spinal cord in the vicinity of the motoneurons (Ochs *et al.*, 1962). On subsequent days the ventral roots were removed and a gradient of activity in the roots was found with higher activity closer to the cord than in the distal parts. The proportion of activity found distally increased with time as expected from an axoplasmic flow. The rate of axoplasmic flow is at present not well established; it may depend on the type of labeled material which is being transported. Koenig (1958) used the labeled amino acids methionine or glycine which are readily incorporated into protein by the neurons of the CNS. These substances injected into either the cisterna magna or lumbar cistern of cats gained access to the cell bodies, and after incorporation into protein an outward flow of labeled material was found in the nerve fibers with an estimated rate of 4–11 mm per day. Waelsch (1958) also used labeled amino acids and a similar route of injection and found a similar proximodistal gradient. Miani (1963) found a higher rate for phospholipid.

Droz and Leblond (1964) used an autoradiographic technique to show more directly that substances are actually being transported outward inside the axon. After injecting the labeled amino acid leucine into animals, the sciatic nerves were removed at various times after injection and cross-sections of the nerves were coated with photographic emulsion. The radioactivity in the labeled protein present in the nerve produced dark silver grains in the photographic emulsion over that point in the tissue. The silver grains were found present over the region of the axoplasm of the fibers

(Fig. 8.12). From sections taken at different distances from the spinal cord and at different times after injection, an outward movement of the labeled material was shown.

The relatively high content of enzymes of the ACh system in motor fibers mentioned in Chapter 7 has suggested the possibility that these substances are *in transit* in the motor nerve fibers from a

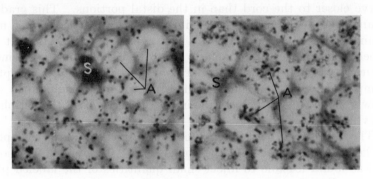

Fig. 8.12. Animals were injected with radioisotopically tagged leucine; the amino acid is incorporated into protein in the motoneurons. Some weeks later, after axoplasmic flow carries the tagged protein outward in the fibers, the radioactive particles are localized inside the axons (A) as shown by cross-sections of nerves (right). In regions of nerve where axoplasmic flow has not yet carried tracer to the site, radioactive particles are not present (left). Some particles are present over the Schwann cells (S) outside the myelin of the fibers. (Courtesy, C. P. Leblond; from Droz and Leblond, *Science*, **137**: 1047, 1962.)

synthetic site in cell bodies to the nerve terminations on muscle fibers. Evidence supporting this concept is the accumulation of choline-acetylase in a region above a transection of nerve (Hebb, 1957; Hebb and Silver, 1961). An accumulation of choline-acetylase and of cholinesterase was also found present above a transection by Lubinska *et al.* (1961). These accumulations would be expected of a continual movement of the enzyme and a damming at the obstruction created by the cut. A normally occurring linearly decreasing gradient of acetylcholinesterase was recently found present in nerve (Lubinska *et al.*, 1962), but its relation to axoplasmic flow is not understood.

Some of the evidence is against ACh enzyme transport. Koenig and Koelle (1961) injected animals with an anticholinesterase which combines irreversibly with cholinesterase. If new enzyme replacing the axon enzyme is formed in the cell bodies, activity should first reappear in those parts of the nerve closest to the CNS. Sections were taken at various times after injection of the anticholinesterase. It was found that the enzyme reappeared at approximately the same time along the nerve, i.e., no proximo-distal gradient was found. Clouet and Waelsch (1961) actually found a reversed gradient after anticholinesterase injections with more of the enzyme appearing first in the distal rather than in the proximal portions of the nerves. To explain these discrepancies it could be assumed that a precursor of the enzyme remains present in the axon. These enzymes may be present in subcellular particles such as those containing ACh and cholinesterase (Hebb and Whittaker, 1958). A number of subcellular entities are found present in electron micrographs of the nerve axon. Among these are vesicles 200–500 A in diameter and dense particles which may be filled vesicles (Vial, 1958). Similar appearing vesicles and dense particles are packed in the terminal endings of axons at their synaptic sites. As will be discussed in Chapters 9, 10 and 19, these vesicles and particles appear to contain transmitter substances involved in synaptic transmission. Some of the vesicles and particles in the axon could be such packets of transmitter substance in transit along its length. Van Breeman, Anderson and Reger (1958) studied electron micrograph sections of regions of the nerve fibers above a nerve constriction and found an increase in the number of vesicular bodies as would be expected if these vesicles were being transported down the axon and dammed up at the obstruction.

Movement of secretory material along fibers has been recognized for some time with regard to the *hypothalamic–hypophysial system*, and will be discussed more fully in Chapter 23. Large pale-staining neuronal cell bodies are found within the hypothalamus, having the morphological properties of secretory cells (Scharrer and Scharrer, 1940). These cells produce hormones which flow down nerve fibers of the hypophysial stalk. The transport of hormonal substances down these fibers was shown by cutting the pituitary stalk and finding an accumulation of the hormone above the interruption and a depletion of hormone below that level (Hild, 1956). The electron microscope studies of de Robertis (1958) and his colleagues show that the neurosecretory material is likely to be present within vesicles found in the nerve fibers of the stalk. These vesicles, averaging 620 A at the hypothalamus, fill to become dense homogeneous granules and appear to become larger in size as they reach their terminations in the infundibular region of the neurohypophysis, where they average 1150 A. Therefore we must not only consider an initial synthesis in the cell bodies, but, as the vesicles are moved along in the axoplasm, a progressive accumulation, or further synthesis, can also take place.

An axoplasmic flow of trophic materials has been invoked to explain changes in muscle after severing the motor nerve. This subject will be discussed in Chapter 9.

Transport mechanisms in the axon

At the present time the mechanism, or mechanisms, underlying axoplasmic flow are little understood. Vesicular or particulate structures containing various substances may be moved down the axon by some special means. Possibly some of the subcellular structures found in nerve may be part of a transport system. *Neurofilaments* 100–200 A wide and indefinitely long form a loose network oriented lengthwise inside the axon (Schmitt, 1957). *Neurotubules* are also seen present in the axon. A movement along these linear elements, or even the separate movement or a growth of these elements down the inside of the axon, is a possibility.

The damming experiments suggest another type of transport, a movement of the fluid portions of the axoplasm (Young, 1945). A continuous pressure exerted by the cell body seems ruled out as does simple diffusion. These mechanisms would not appear to have effects over the long distances involved (Weiss, 1958). Changes in the diameter of the axon passing along the fiber could produce an axoplasmic flow. Such a *peristalsis* was indicated by time-lapse cinematography of nerve fibers *in vitro* in a tissue culture by Weiss *et al.* (1962). A series of dilations and constrictions can be excited in living nerve fibers by a slight stretch (Ochs, 1963). This type of *beading* may have a relation to a peristaltic mechanism of flow. Constriction would permit some material to move in a distal-proximal, as well as in a proximo-distal, direction. For many years the possibility that tetanus toxin gains access to the CNS from peripheral tissue by progressing up the inside of motor nerves has been considered. The evidence on which this theory was based was the appearance of *local tetanus*, a reflex spasm of muscles occurring after a muscle was injected with tetanus toxin. Local tetanus could also be produced if the nerve trunk itself was injected with a small amount of the toxin, the higher the injection was made into the nerve trunk, the sooner the local tetanus appeared. A participation of the CNS is required, the tetanus toxin apparently ascending into the spinal end to produce the reflex-like local tetanus by blocking inhibitory action of the motoneurons (Brooks, Curtis and Eccles,

1957), a subject to be discussed more fully in Chapter 16.   Wright (1955) and his colleagues showed that the actual conduit by which the toxin moved upward was within the rather large tissue spaces present in the nerve trunk between the nerve fibers—the *endoneural spaces*.   Ethanolamine oleate and other sclerosing agents were used to block this channel by the fibrous reaction they produce around the nerve fibers while leaving the fibers themselves functionally intact. When, after such a sclerosis had been produced, tetanus toxin was injected into the nerve trunk below the site of sclerosis, it did not gain access to the nervous system and local tetanus did not develop. The propulsion of the toxin up endoneural spaces of the nerve trunk is most likely brought about by the lateral pressures of the contracting muscles around the nerve trunk.   This can account for the appearance of symptoms of local tetanus as soon as 18–20 hours after injecting the sciatic nerve with a small volume of the tetanus toxin at such relatively great distances of 10–30 cm from the CNS. Such experiments, however, do not exclude an intra-axonal path by which tetanus toxin or other substances can enter the CNS.   As has been indicated, there is still much to be known concerning the mechanism of axoplasmic flow.

REFERENCES

Ariëns-Kappers, C. U. (1917).   Further contributions on neurobiotaxis, IX. An attempt to compare the phenomena of neurobiotaxis with other phenomena of taxis and tropism.   The dynamic polarization of the neurons.   *J. Comp. Neurol.* **27**: 261–298.
Ariëns-Kappers, C. U., Huber, G. C. and Crosby, E. C. (1936).   *The Comparative Anatomy of the Nervous System of Vertebrates, Including Man.* MacMillan Co., New York.
Barr, M. S. and Hamilton, J. D. (1948).   A quantitative study of certain morphological changes in spinal motor neurons during axon reaction. *J. Comp. Neurol.* **89**: 93–121.
Bernstein, J. J. and Guth, L. (1961).   Nonselectivity in establishment of neuromuscular connections following nerve regeneration in the rat. *Exptl. Neurol.* **4**: 262–275.
Brattgård, S. O., Edström, J. E. and Hydén, H. (1957).   The chemical changes in regenerating neurons.   *J. Neurochem.* **1**: 316–325.
Brooks, V. B., Curtis, D. R. and Eccles, J. C. (1957).   The action of tetanus toxin on the inhibition of motoneurones.   *J. Physiol.* **135**: 655–672.
Clouet, D. H. and Waelsch, H. (1961).   Amino acid and protein metabolism of the brain—VII.   The penetration of cholinesterase inhibitors into the nervous system of the frog.   *J. Neurochem.* **8**: 201–215.
de Robertis, E. (1961).   Morphological basis of synaptic processes and neurosecretion.   *Regional Neurochemistry.*   Edited by S. S. Kety and J. Elkes.   Pp. 248–258.   Pergamon Press, New York.

Droz, B. and Leblond, C. P. (1964). Axonal migration of proteins in the central nervous system and peripheral nerves as shown by radioautography. *J. Comp. Neurol.* **121**: 325–346.

Edds, M. V. (1953). Collateral nerve regeneration. *Quart. Rev. Biol.* **28**: 260–276.

Freeman, L. W. (1952). Return of function after complete transection of the spinal cord of the rat, cat and dog. *Ann. Surg.* **136**: 193–205.

Friede, R. L. (1959). Transport of oxidative enzymes in nerve fibers; a histochemical investigation of the regenerative cycle in neurons. *Exptl. Neurol.* **1**: 441–466.

Gaze, R. M. (1960). Regeneration of the optic nerve in amphibia. *Intern. Rev. Neurobiol.* **2**: 1–40.

Gerard, R. W. (1932). Nerve metabolism. *Physiol. Rev.* **12**: 469–592.

Gersh, I. and Bodian, D. (1943). Some chemical mechanisms in chromatolysis. *J. Cell. Comp. Physiol.* **21**: 253–279.

Gutmann, E., Guttmann, L., Medawar, P. B. and Young, J. Z. (1942). The rate of regeneration of nerve. *J. Exptl. Biol.* **19**: 14–44.

Gutmann, E. and Holubář, J. (1950). The degeneration of peripheral nerve fibres. *J. Neurol. Neurosurg. Psychiat.* **13**: 89–105.

Hebb, C. O. (1957). Biochemical evidence for the neural function of acetylcholine. *Physiol. Rev.* **37**: 196–220.

Hebb, C. O. and Silver, A. (1961). Gradient of choline-acetylase activity. *Nature* **189**: 123–125.

Hebb, C. O. and Whittaker, V. P. (1958). Intracellular distributions of acetylcholine and choline-acetylase. *J. Physiol.* **142**: 187–196.

Heinbecker, P., Bishop, G. H. and O'Leary, J. (1932). Nerve degeneration in poliomyelitis. *Arch. Neurol. Psychiat.* **27**: 1421–1435.

Hild, W. (1956). Neurosecretion in the central nervous system. *Hypothalamic–Hypophysial Inter-relationships.* Edited by W. S. Fields. Charles C. Thomas, Springfield.

Hydén, H. (1943). Protein metabolism in the nerve cell during growth and function. *Acta Physiol. Scand.* **17**: *Suppl.* **6**: 1–136.

Hydén, H. (1960). The neuron. *The Cell; Biochemistry, Physiology, Morphology.* Edited by J. Brachet and A. E. Mirsky. Vol. 4, Chapter 5. Academic Press, New York.

Koenig, H. (1958). The synthesis and peripheral flow of axoplasm. *Trans. Am. Neurol. Assoc.* **83**: 162–164.

Koenig, E. and Koelle, G. B. (1961). Mode of regeneration of acetylcholinesterase in cholinergic neurons following irreversible inactivation. *J. Neurochem.* **8**: 169–188.

Levi-Montalcini, R. and Angeletti, P. U. (1961). Biological properties of a nerve growth-promoting protein and its antiserum. *Regional Neurochemistry.* Edited by S. S. Ketty and J. Elkes. Pp. 362–377. Pergamon Press, New York.

Lubinska, L., Niemierko, S. and Oderfeld, B. (1961). Gradient of cholinesterase activity and of choline-acetylase activity in nerve fibres. *Nature* **189**: 122–123.

Lubinska, L., Niemierko, S., Oderfeld, B. and Szwarc, L. (1962). Decrease of acetylcholinesterase activity along peripheral nerves. *Science* **135**: 368–370.

Miani, N. (1963).   Analysis of the somato-axonal movement of phospholipids in the vagus and hypoglossal nerves. *J. Neurochem.* **10**: 859–874.

Ochs, S. (1963).   Beading phenomena of mammalian myelinated nerve fibers. *Science* **139**: 599–600.

Ochs, S., Booker, H. and DeMyer, W. (1961).   Note on signal for chromatolysis after nerve interruption. *Exptl. Neurol.* **3**: 206–208.

Ochs, S., Dalrymple, D. and Richards, G. (1962).   Axoplasmic flow in ventral root nerve fibers of the cat. *Exptl. Neurol.* **5**: 349–363.

Palay, S. L. and Palade, G. E. (1955).   The fine structure of neurons. *J. Biophys. Biochem. Cytol.* **1**: 69–88.

Ramón y Cajal, S. (1928).   *Degeneration and Regeneration of the Nervous System.*   Translated by R. M. May.   Oxford University Press, London.

Samuels, A. J., Boyarsky, L. L., Gerard, R. W., Libet, B. and Brust, M. (1951). Distribution exchange and migration of phosphate compounds in the nervous system. *Am. J. Physiol.* **164**: 1–15.

Scharrer, E. and Scharrer, B. (1940).   Secretory cells within the hypothalmus. *Assoc. Res. Nervous Mental Disease Proc.* **20**: 170–194.

Schmitt, F. O. (1957).   The fibrous protein of the nerve axon. *J. Cell. Comp. Physiol.* **49**: 165–174.

Speidel, C. C. (1941).   Adjustments of nerve endings. *Harvey Lectures* **36**: 126–158.

Sperry, R. W. (1943).   Effect of 180 degree rotation of the retinal field on visuomotor coordination. *J. Exptl. Zool.* **92**: 263–279.

Sperry, R. W. (1945).   The problem of central nervous reorganization after nerve regeneration and muscle transposition. *Quart. Rev. Biol.* **20**: 311–369.

Sperry, R. W. (1951).   Mechanisms of neural maturation. *Handbook of Experimental Psychology.*   Edited by S. S. Stevens.   Pp. 236–280. John Wiley & Sons, New York.

Sperry, R. W. (1963).   Chemoaffinity in the orderly growth of nerve fiber patterns and connections. *Proc. Natl. Acad. Sci. U.S.* **50**: 703–710.

Sugar, O. and Gerard, R. W. (1940).   Spinal cord regeneration in the rat. *J. Neurophysiol.* **3**: 1–19

Thulin, C. A. (1961).   Bioelectric characteristics of regenerated fibers in the feline spinal cord. *Exptl. Neurol.* **2**: 533–546.

van Breemen, V. L., Anderson, E. and Reger, J. F. (1955).   An attempt to determine the origin of synaptic vesicles. *Exptl. Cell Res. Suppl.* **5**: 153–167.

van Harreveld, A. (1952).   Reinnervation of paretic muscle by collateral branching of the residual motor innervation. *J. Comp. Neurol.* **97**: 385–407.

Vial, J. D. (1958).   The early changes in the axoplasm during Wallerian degeneration. *J. Biophy. Biochem. Cytol.* **4**: 551–556.

Waelsch, H. (1958).   Some aspects of amino acid and protein metabolism of the nervous system. *J. Nervous Mental Disease* **126**: 33–39.

Waller, A. V. (1850).   Experiments on the section of the glossopharyngeal and hypoglossal nerves of the frog, and observations of the alterations produced thereby in the structure of their primitive fibres. *Phil. Trans. Roy. Soc. London* **140**: 423–429.

Wedell, G., Guttmann, L. and Gutmann, E. (1941).   The local extension of nerve fibers into denervated areas of skin.   J. Neurol. Psychiat. 4: 206–225.

Weiss, P. (1941).   Nerve patterns: the mechanics of nerve growth. Growth, Suppl. 5: 163–203.

Weiss, P. (1950).   Experimental analysis of co-ordination by the disarrangement of central–peripheral relations.   Symp. Soc. Exptl. Biol. 4: 92–111.

Weiss, P. (1958).   The concept of perpetual neuronal growth and proximodistal substance convection.   Regional Neurochemistry.   Edited by S. S. Kety and J. Elkes.   Pp. 220–242.   Pergamon Press, New York.

Weiss, P. and Hiscoe, H. B. (1948).   Experiments on the mechanism of nerve growth.   J. Exptl. Zool. 107: 315–395.

Weiss, P. and Hoag, A. (1946).   Competitive reinnervation of rat muscles by their own and foreign nerves.   J. Neurophysiol. 9: 413–418.

Weiss, P., Taylor, A. C. and Pillai, P. A. (1962).   The nerve fiber as a system in continuous flow: microcinematographic and electromicroscopic demonstrations.   Science 136: 330.

Weiss, P., Edds, Mc V., Jr. and Cavanaugh, M. (1945).   The effect of terminal connections on the caliber of nerve fibers.   Anat. Rec. 92: 215–233.

Windle, W. F. and Chambers, W. W. (1950).   Regeneration in the spinal cord of the cat and dog.   J. Comp. Neurol. 93: 241–257.

Wright, G. P. (1955).   The neurotoxins of Clostridium botulinum and Clostridium tetani.   Pharm. Rev. 7: 413–465.

Young, J. Z. (1942).   The functional repair of nervous tissue.   Physiol. Rev. 22: 318–374.

Young, J. Z. (1945).   The history of the shape of a nerve fibre.   Essays on Growth and Form.   Edited by W. E. LeGros Clark and P. B. Medawar.   Pp. 41–94.   Oxford University Press, Oxford.

Young, J. Z. (1949).   Factors influencing the regeneration of nerves.   Advan. Surg. 1: 165–220.

9

Neuromuscular Transmission

Ultimately, transactions of the nervous system with the outside world take place by the contraction of muscles in appropriate temporal and spatial patterns. The events which take place from motor nerve excitation through muscle contraction will be analysed in this chapter. We will be concerned mainly with striated muscles acting on the vertebrate skeletal system. Crustacean muscles will be discussed as another type of neuromuscular system; also, mechanisms in this muscle have similarities to CNS synaptic systems. Smooth muscle, which is the characteristic effector of the autonomic nervous system, will be discussed in Chapter 10.

The motor unit

The vertebrate pattern of innervation typically has a number of separate muscle fibers excited by the branches of a single motor nerve fiber. The motor nerves branch and rebranch within the nerve trunk and muscle, and eventually terminate on muscle fibers (Fig. 9.1). The *motor unit* is defined as those muscle fibers which are excited by a single motoneuron. The number of muscle fibers in a unit may range from a few, as in extra-occular muscles of the eye, to several hundred as in the postular muscles of the limb. In general, motor units controlling fine movements have a smaller number of muscle fibers allowing for a finer *gradation,* i.e. a finer variation in the degree of muscle control. Upon excitation of a motor nerve, the muscle fibers are excited to contract in all-or-none fashion. Different degrees of contraction come about by changes in the number of motor units put into operation at any given time or by changes in the rate of motor nerve discharge (*vide infra*).

The individual fibers of large muscles found in the vertebrate are grouped anatomically by their wrapping of connective tissue into bundles, the *fasciculi.* These fasciculi contain hundreds of muscle fibers but these are not complete motor units. The individual fibers of a motor unit are found present in a number of fasciculi and may be widely dispersed in the muscle. This is shown when upon interruption of the nerve fiber of a motor unit only a portion

of the muscle fibers of a fasciculus will *atrophy* or, at a later
stage, *degenerate*.   Degenerative changes of muscle occurring after
denervation will be discussed later in this chapter.

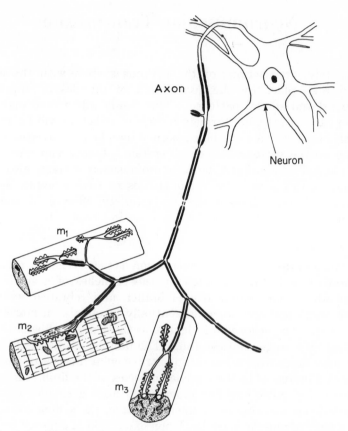

Fig. 9.1.   The axon branches of a motoneuron are shown terminating on several muscle fibers (m_1, m_2 and m_3).   (Courtesy,
R. Miledi; from Miledi, *Discovery*, Oct. 1962.)

Besides the branching and rebranching of motor nerves within the
nerve trunk, the most extensive branching of the nerve fiber occurs
when the motor nerve axon is close to its terminus.   At this point,
lateral branches have small final terminals ending on a number of
muscle fibers scattered through the muscle.

Are the muscle fibers innervated by one or more nerve terminals
derived from a single motor axon or by several nerve fibers?

The latter case is spoken of as *multiple* or *polyneuronal* innervation. One technique of investigating this question physiologically is to stimulate two different branches of motor nerves leading to the muscle and record the amplitude of the muscle action potentials or their contractions in response to nerve excitation. Because the principle involved is also important in other contexts where it is referred to as *occlusion,* this technique will be presented in some detail. If each muscle fiber gets its motor nerve supply from a single nerve fiber, then stimulation of separate nerve branches or trunks innervating those muscles should give rise to independent muscle contractions. The amplitude of the response to the activation of each nerve separately should upon their algebraic summation be

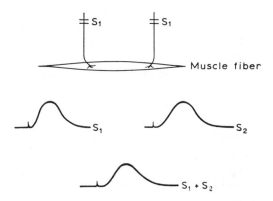

Fig. 9.2. A single muscle fiber shown innervated by two nerves. Stimulation of either nerve S_1 or of S_2 gives rise to a twitch. Stimulation of both nerves at the same time would give rise to a muscle twitch of the same size.

equal to the amplitude of the response produced when both motor nerve groups are excited together. If there is an extensive polyneuronal innervation, this would be revealed by a *deficit* in the contraction responses developed by simultaneous stimulation as compared to the algebraic summation of the response to each nerve stimulated separately (Fig. 9.2). The contraction deficit comes about by the occlusion of the response and is a measure of the degree of polyneuronal innervation.

The frog sartorius muscle is a particularly good preparation to study for the presence of single or polyneuronal innervation. The muscle is a flat sheet approximately 4 cm long with most of its individual fibers running the whole length of the muscle. Two nerve branches enter the muscle. Upon stimulating each of these branches separately and recording the action potentials propagated along the fibers, Katz and Kuffler (1941) found a *collision* of the responses, i.e., a relatively large number of the fibers were innervated by each of these two nerve sources, and the response of the muscle to the stimulation of one nerve occluded the response to the other. However, there are differences in single or multiple innervation in the muscles of different species. This was indicated by the studies of Brown and Mathews (1960) who showed that an apparent twitch deficit of hind limb muscles of the cat when its two nerve supplies were excited was not brought about by polyneuronal innervation, but was caused by the elastic component of the muscle response. The use of tetanic contractions obviated that factor, and stimulation of nerves separately or together showed, by the lack of a deficit, that for the most part those mammalian skeletal muscle fibers are singly innervated. One apparent exception was long considered to be the cricothyroid muscle.

The cricothyroid muscle has two nerves innervating it, the laryngius superior and the laryngius medius, and the fibers of the muscle were considered to be multiply innervated because cutting one nerve did not result in a degeneration of muscle fibers. However, van Harreveld and Tachibana (1961) used a gold stain and found that nearly all the muscle fibers had only single end-plates. Also, microelectrode recordings taken from individual muscle fibers showed upon excitation of one or the other nerve that only a small percentage of the fibers were multiply innervated. Upon cutting one nerve to the cricothyroid muscle, the other nerve fiber was found to send branches to reinnervate those muscle fibers deprived of their usual nerve supply (Chapter 8), accounting for the lack of muscle degeneration.

The fact that the discharge of a motor axon causes a relatively large number of muscle fibers in the motor unit to discharge together makes the electrical recording of muscle activity, *electromyography*, a relatively easy procedure. Electromyographic records may be taken via electrodes placed on the skin over the muscle or from within the muscle tissue by means of electrodes inserted into the muscle. Electrodes used for recording from within muscles are commonly made of needles which are electrically insulated except at the tips. Normally muscles do not show electrical activity at rest. When motor units are excited to discharge in response to a reflex or voluntary contraction, an irregular discharge is seen with the use of gross electrodes. This is due to the recording of a number of individual motor units which are firing asynchronously, although each at a regular rate.   To demonstrate this, the tip of the recording needle is made so small that when it is inserted into the mass of the muscle it picks up only the potentials of nearby fibers, while others even a short distance away are attenuated in amplitude.   The needle is moved about inside the muscle until only one or a few such motor units are picked up.   The regular, repetitive muscle action potentials which can then be recorded (Fig. 9.3) represent the

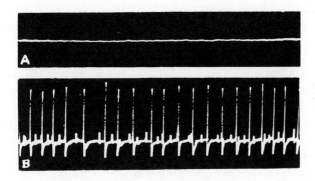

Fig. 9.3.   Electromyographic recording of a single motor unit: A, no activity in relaxed biceps muscle; B, repetitive discharge in the muscle during contraction.   One motor unit is giving rise to the larger discharge.   Two smaller sized responses of different motor units are also seen.   (From Kaada and Gelfan in Fulton, *A Textbook of Physiology*, 16th Ed., 1949.)

discharge of the muscle fibers of a motor unit.   The relatively large potentials are due to the fact that a number of muscle fibers are synchronously discharged in response to the nerve volleys causing relatively large flows of current in the immediate vicinity of its muscle fibers.

As muscle tension is increased, i.e. by a voluntary muscle contraction, the rate of discharge of a single unit increases from approximately 5–6/sec to a maximum of 30–40/sec and occasionally 50/sec (Adrian and Bronk, 1929).   The strength of contraction is related to the rate of motor nerve discharge.   The rate of discharge and the number of motor units responding are the means by which muscle control is graded in its degree of tension.   In the case of a delicate manipulation produced by the muscles controlling the fingers or the larynx in the production of sound, such gradation can be exceedingly fine.

Transmission at the neuromuscular junction

The muscle fiber directly stimulated by a current pulse or indirectly excited via its nerve gives rise to the usual type of conducted action potential with overshoot (Hodgkin and Nastuck, 1950). The muscle membrane potential is approximately 88 mv and, except for the higher contribution of Cl^- to the membrane potential, the ion mechanisms are similar to those of other excitable tissues (Chapter 4). The action potential arises by an increased Na^+ influx followed by a delayed K^+ efflux. A Cl^- permeability increase contributes to the repolarization phase (Hodgkin and Horowicz, 1959).

Before discussing the special physiological aspects of neuromuscular transmission, examination of its structure will be helpful. The termination of a single nerve fiber at the *end-plate* region of the muscle can be observed by special staining and cytochemical means (Couteaux, 1958) and in much greater detail by means of electron microscopy (Robertson, 1956, 1960; Birks *et al.*, 1960a). In the electron microscope picture of the myoneural junction (Fig. 9.4) the nerve is seen to sit in a trough or gutter in the muscle with an extracellular space between nerve and muscle membranes; this space or *synaptic cleft* is approximately 500 A wide. The transverse folds of the muscle membrane in the gutter around the nerve are a striking feature of the junction; possibly they serve to increase the surface area of the muscle membrane at the junction. Within the nerve ending synaptic vesicles are evident. These appear as clear round structures approximately 500 A in diameter surrounded by a single dense membrane. There is evidence suggesting that these vesicles contain acetylcholine which is the transmitter substance in neuromuscular transmission. Mitochondria are also seen in the nerve terminals in relatively great number, presumably because of metabolic activity at the nerve ending related to the release and reconstitution of the synaptic mediator substance as will be discussed later.

If curare, or preferably its active purified form D-*tubocurarine* is injected into an animal's vascular system, transmission between nerve and muscle is rapidly blocked when it reaches the neuromuscular junctions. In an animal so paralysed, stimulation of a motor nerve no longer excites twitch responses in the skeletal muscle it innervates. Curare does not block the conduction of nerve impulses in the nerve fibers, and direct electrical or mechanical excitation of the muscle can still give rise to a muscle twitch. In the 19th century, Claude Bernard correctly concluded that the site of curare block is at the junction between nerve and muscle. There is a difference in the effectiveness of curare in blocking neuromuscular transmission in the various muscles.   First, skeletal limb muscles are blocked; then at a higher level of curare, the diaphragmatic muscles.   Death ensues in curare-poisoned animals from asphyxiation when the muscles of respiration no longer respond to respiratory discharges in the phrenic nerve.

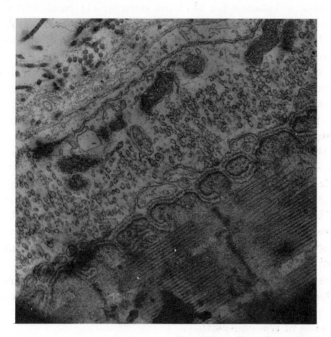

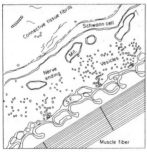

Fig. 9.4. In the nerve terminal of this electron micrograph of the neuromuscular junction a large number of small vesicles are seen in addition to the larger mitochondria.   In   the muscle membrane around the nerve axon, folds are present and below this the filaments of muscle. (Birks, Huxley and Katz, 1960.)

The fact that a specific substance such as curare has an action at the neuromuscular junction suggests that a special receptor substance able to react with curare exists there.   Such a receptor substance would be able to respond to substances released from the nerve endings to bring about muscle excitation. This concept of a neurotransmitter substance acting on a receptor was first proposed by Elliott (1940) in terms of the action of adrenalin on autonomic muscle effectors (Chapter 10) and later for neuromuscular transmission in skeletal muscle by Langley (1909). Dale *et al.* (1936) gave the following evidence that acetylcholine (ACh) is the neurotransmitter substance for skeletal muscle: (1) Stimulation of the motor nerve to the muscle caused ACh to appear in the fluid perfusing the muscle (Ringer solution containing the anticholinesterase substance *eserine* to prevent hydrolysis of acetylcholine). (2) ACh did not appear in the perfusing medium following direct stimulation of denervated muscle. (3) Curare prevented transmission, but ACh was still released from the nerve. And finally (4), after nerve stimulation which was repeated until the response was diminished, ACh was no longer released into the medium.

The special sensitivity of the end-plate region was shown by the use of micropipettes to release ACh at various places along the length of single muscle fibers (Kuffler, 1943; del Castillo and Katz, 1956) and a much greater sensitivity to ACh was found in the end-plate region than elsewhere. An amount as small as 10^{-16}M of ACh could excite reponses when applied to the end-plate region (Katz, 1958). The amount of ACh released by nerve stimulation was found to be of a similar order, 10^{-17} M (Krnjevic and Mitchell, 1961). Also, the presence of curare in the medium of the nerve–muscle preparation did not interfere with the release of ACh as would be expected if curare acts by blocking the action of ACh on the receptor in the muscle side of the end-plate.

Recently an action of D-tubocurarine on the presynaptic terminals to block release of the transmitter has been reported. However, such an action could only be of secondary importance relative to the main effect on the muscle part of the end-plate. This is more easily seen after the discussion of the following section.

The end-plate potential (EPP)

Closer examination of the electrical changes taking place at the end-plate during transmission has won almost universal support for the concept of a chemical mediator. If suitable amounts of D-tubocurarine are added to the medium in which an isolated sartorius nerve–muscle preparation is placed, a block to indirect stimulation through the nerve is produced (Eccles *et al.*, 1941). When the nerve is excited in such curare-blocked preparations a brief electrical depolarization can be recorded in the end-plate region. This potential is smaller than the muscle action potential and, unlike the all-or-none action potential, the response was found to decrease in amplitude when recordings were taken at successively increased distances from the end-plate. This end-plate potential (EPP) was first shown by Gopfert and Schaefer (1938) and clearly established by the use of microelectrodes placed in the muscle fiber close to or at a short distance from an end-plate (Fatt and Katz, 1951). To perform such experiments the isolated muscle is placed in a chamber containing frog–Ringer solution with its fascia-free underside facing

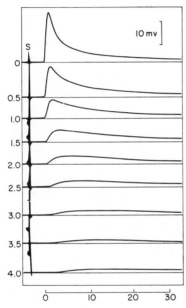

Fig. 9.5. In curarized muscle, the end plate potential (EPP) is seen following nerve stimulation (S) after a latency of several milliseconds. The EPP has a decreased amplitude at increased recording distances from the junction (numbers give millimeters). Time scale in milliseconds. (From Fatt and Katz, 1951.)

upward. The individual muscle fibers can readily be penetrated with little apparent injury potential by microelectrodes with tip diameters of 0.5 μ and less. The tips may be placed inside the cell close to the end-plate region. Upon stimulation of the nerve supplying that fiber, the EPP seen after a latency of 0.6–0.9 msec rises rapidly and then decays more slowly (Fig. 9.5). Not only does the amplitude of the EPP vary with distance from the end-plate as shown in Fig. 9.7, but its size is related to the amount of

D-tubocurarine present.   D-Tubocurarine can be washed away from
a curarized muscle by replacing the medium with fresh frog–Ringer.
As the D-tubocurarine is removed from the end-plate the EPP
increases in size.   When the depolarization reaches a critical level
of approximately 40–50 mv, a propagated action potential is
excited in the surrounding muscle membrane.   This can be seen in
Fig. 9.6 as a break in the curvature of the rising phase of the depolarization where the EPP initiates the propagated action potential.

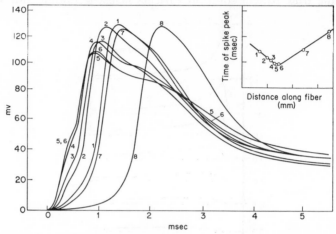

Fig. 9.6.   At the end-plate region (shown by the numbers in
the insert with the end-plate centered at 5), the action potential
has a break in the rising phase where the EPP is followed by the
action potential.   The amplitude of the action potential is also
smaller and a hump on the falling phase is found.   In regions far
from the end-plate the latency is greater.   (Fatt and Katz, 1951.)

It is not seen when recording further from the end-plate.   The spike
originating from an EPP is seen in Fig. 9.7 where external electrodes
were used.

The EPP comes about when the ACh released by the nerve
terminals depolarizes the muscle membrane at the end-plate (the
postsynaptic membrane).   A similar depolarization was shown when
releasing small amounts of ACh from a micropipette in the vicinity
of the end-plate gave rise to a depolarization, which if large enough
could excite propagated action potentials in the muscle (Fig. 9.8).

When the micropipette containing ACh was inserted in the muscle
fibre below the end-plate, ACh was ineffective in exciting propagated
response.   The receptor then can be activated by ACh only at the
surface of the muscle membrane facing the nerve terminal.

The electrical resistivity of the end-plate region drops to a low value during an EPP, as low as 1 ohm-cm (Katz, 1958). This indicates that ACh causes the ionic permeability to become high. It appears that the cations usually present in the external medium and inside the muscle move across the end-plate to bring about the EPP. When Na$^+$ in the external medium was removed and replaced by

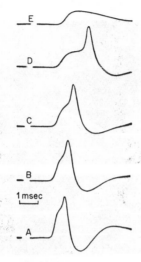

Fig. 9.7. Records taken from the end-plate region of a single muscle fiber with an external electrode (A). From B to E the effect of progressive curarization is shown with the spike elicited at later and later times until failure of the spike occurs and only the EPP remains (E). There is a relative reduction of spike amplitude compared to the EPP with this type of recording. (From Kuffler, *J. Neurophysiol.* **5**: 18, 1943.)

sucrose, the EPP was diminished in amplitude showing that Na$^+$ is an ion moving into the end-plate when permeability has been increased. However, the permeability change at the end-plate produced by ACh is not due to a selective increase of Na$^+$ permeability such as occurs in a propagated action potential (del Castillo and Katz, 1956). Takeuchi and Takeuchi (1959, 1960) clamped the end-plate region so that the end-plate current (e.p.c.) flowing during the time of an EPP could be studied. The e.p.c. had a total duration of 4–5 msec, though it mainly lasted for only two milliseconds. By changing the ions present in the medium, they showed that the e.p.c. is due mainly to the movement of Na$^+$ and K$^+$ through the end-plate.

Most of the EPP after the first 2 msec is due to the passive spread of the electrical currents in the surrounding muscle membrane, similar to the spread of local currents in the membrane of nerve fibers previously discussed (Chapter 6). This is shown by calculations of the electrical charge transferred during the EPP at different distances from the end-plate (Fatt and Katz, 1951).

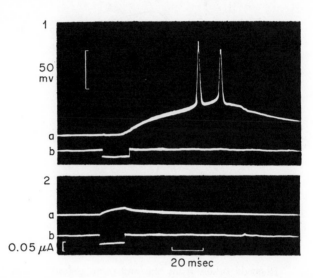

Fig. 9.8. Acetylcholine depolarization and spike production is shown (1) with a microelectrode placed in the end-plate region (a) while ACh is released at the time of the pulse signal from a nearby micropipette (b). A depolarization occurs which reaches sufficient amplitude to excite action potentials. The same release of ACh below the surface (2) is ineffective in producing depolarization and spike discharge. (From del Castillo and Katz, 1956.)

The end-plate region contains a relatively high concentration of acetylcholine esterase which within a few msec hydrolyses ACh and terminates its activity. Several anticholinesterases are known, among them *eserine* and *prostigmine* which when administered give rise to prolonged EPPs of much larger size. This appears to be the basis for the efficacy of anticholinesterases in the treatment of *myasthenia gravis*. In this disease the muscle response to nerve stimulation is weakened. The prolongation of EPP activity by anticholinesterase substances probably compensates for deficiencies of a smaller output of ACh or possibly the partial block brought about by some circulating curare-like substance in this disease.

A complexity of the mechanisms giving rise to the EPP is shown by temporal interaction studies. Summation of EPPs is shown in Fig. 9.9. In a moderately curarized preparation the summation

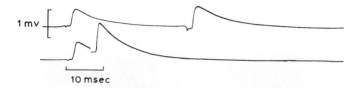

1 mv

10 msec

Fig. 9.9. In a curarized frog, two EPPs are excited by successive nerve impulses and recorded with an external recording electrode near the neuromuscular junction. If the second EPP is produced within approximately 50 msec of the first, summation occurs. (Eccles, Katz and Kuffler, *Biol. Symp.* **3**: 349, 1941.)

of the EPPs may be sufficient to reach critical level and excite a propagated action potential. Repetitive stimulation may cause the EPPs to be increased in size, i.e. to be *facilitated*. Repetitive stimulation may in other muscles result in a series of diminished responses (Fig. 9.10). A decrease in the amplitude of EPPs during a tetanic

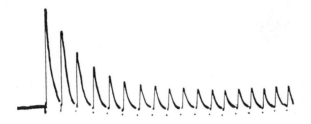

Fig. 9.10. EPPs recorded from muscle fiber of rat diaphragm upon repetitive nerve stimulation. A progressive decrease in the amplitude of the EPPs is shown. (From Liley and North, *J. Neurophysiol.* **16**: 509, 1953.)

response may be due to a reduced mobilization or depletion of ACh in the nerve terminals (Eccles, 1964). The continued presence of transmitter substance at the end-plate can lead to an unresponsiveness to the transmitter agent which is called *desensitization*. This is shown when test pulses of ACh are used which give rise to depolarizations. A continuous application of ACh during the administration of the test pulses reduces the amplitude of these depolarizations.

Miniature EPPs and the mechanism of ACh release

In the region of the end-plate, small depolarizations which look like miniature end-plate potentials (MEPPs) appear in records taken with microelectrodes from the resting membrane (Fig. 9.11). These

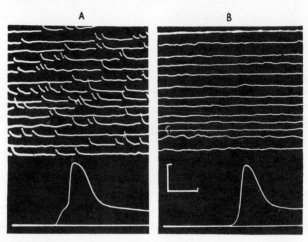

Fig. 9.11. Microelectrode placed inside a fiber in the end-plate region shows in the upper traces (A) a random spontaneous discharge of miniature end-plate potentials (MEPPs). The shape of the muscle action potential in response to nerve stimulation is shown in the lower part of the figure. With the microelectrode in the fiber further from the end-plate region (B), MEPPs are not seen and the action potential elicited by nerve stimulation is not preceded by an EPP. Calibrations 50 mv and 2 msec. (del Castillo and Katz, 1956.)

MEPPs appear to represent small *quantal* releases of the transmitter ACh which are apparently spontaneously discharged in a random fashion from the nerve endings. This is suggested by the fact that their amplitude remains the same, and a summation is seen when two MEPPs occur at the same time. Probability studies of their occurrence is fitted by a Poisson distribution indicating that each MEPP is an individual event (del Castillo and Katz, 1956). The frequency of the MEPP quantal discharge is increased by depolarization of the nerve ending as shown with isotonic K_2SO_4 or by use of electrical currents. Therefore, action potentials which invade the nerve termination could be the effective agent for the simultaneous release of a large number of MEPPs; these quanta add together to give the EPP (Katz, 1958). Some computations indicate that approximately 100–300 MEPPs constitute an EPP (Eccles, 1964).

The vesicles within the nerve endings seen in electron micrographs could contain a packet of ACh molecules constituting a quantum which brings about a single MEPP. Judging from the depolarization produced by known quantities of ACh, each vesicle would contain several thousand ACh molecules. The size of the MEPP remains the same suggesting that the vesicle discharges its entire contents into the cleft facing the muscle membrane of the end-plate.

When an action potential invades the nerve terminal it could change the reactivity of the membrane. The vesicles which are presumably continually colliding with the internal side of the membrane would then be able to release their contents of ACh through the membrane (Katz, 1962). On this hypothesis a change in collision rate need not be invoked. The nature of the postulated reactivity of the terminal membrane and the mechanism of release remain unknown. That Ca^{2+} is involved in the mechanism of release was shown by the increased rate of MEPPs with increased Ca^{2+} levels during depolarization, either imposed or during nerve activity. The closely related divalent ion Mg^{2+} has an opposite, inhibitory effect on the release of MEPPs.

Another aspect of vesicles related to transmitter action was revealed by an electron microscope study of the nerve terminals at different stages after nerve interruption (Birks, Katz and Miledi, 1960). In the first 3 days after nerve section transmission seemed normal but the mitochondria in the terminals appeared swollen. Later the vesicles were clumped together into large honeycomb structures and then they disintegrated. The Schwann cells persisted as did the folds in the muscle membrane at the site of the end-plate, allowing comparison to be made between degenerated and normal end-plates. Of great interest was the decrease in the rate of MEPP discharge after a few days and then the resumption of a low-level discharge (Fig. 9.12). The distribution of the amplitudes of the MEPPs seen near denervated end-plates differs from that of the normally innervated end-plate where the MEPPs discharge with amplitudes distributed statistically in a bell-shaped curve ranging from 0.5–0.75 mv, while the degenerated end-plates have amplitudes of MEPPs falling into the low end of the scale (Fig. 9.13). The MEPPs found in degenerated end-plates could possibly arise from Schwann cells which in this condition are seen to contain inclusions and have synaptic-like contact with the muscle cell membrane.

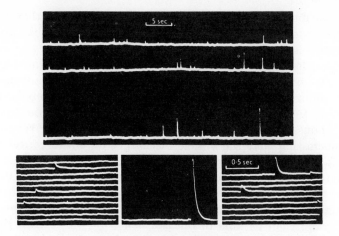

Fig. 9.12. In the upper part of the figure a low level of MEPP activity is seen in the end-plate region 9 days after denervation. Time calibration, 5 sec. In the lower part of the figure MEPP activity 5 days after denervation is shown outside the end-plate regions. No response to nerve stimulation was seen (center). (Birks, Katz and Miledi, 1960.)

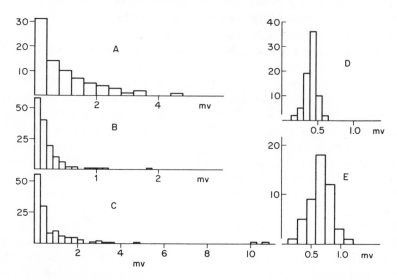

Fig. 9.13. The amplitude distribution of spontaneous MEPPs is taken from denervated muscle (A, B) 15 days, and (C) 9 days after nerve section showing no EPP response to nerve stimulation. Amplitudes of an innervated control muscle (D). Example of one junction still found transmitting in a fiber 7 days after denervation (E). (Birks, Katz and Miledi, 1960.)

The receptor substance and the action of blocking agents

Reference was made to the qualitative aspects of curare block indicating its attachment to a special receptor site or substance which is also selectively acted on by ACh. Fitting with this similarity of action is the fact that ACh and D-tubocurarine are similar in their chemical structures. When D-tubocurarine is present at that site, ACh cannot attach to it to produce its effect. This then would explain the blocking action of curare. If the block is *competitive* more curare will be required to block the muscle when an increased amount of ACh is present at that site. When this was tested experimentally, the block was shown to be competitive (Jenkinson, 1960). Another group of blocking agents is known. These are the *depolarizing blocking* agents: decamethonium, acetylcholine in high concentrations and succinylcholine. The depolarizing blocking agents, unlike curare, are associated with decreases in the resting membrane potential which are mainly located near the end-plates (Burns and Paton, 1951). The persistent depolarization present was considered by Burns and Paton to be the cause of transmission block brought about by this group. However, the depolarization produced in the end-plate region may only last a short time while transmission block persists for a much longer time (Thesleff, 1955a, b). As shown by Thesleff, the depolarization brought about by these agents may spread beyond the end-plate region. These agents apparently have a dual blocking action: a temporary phase with depolarization followed by repolarization and a more persistent 'curariform' block.

Membrane-contractile link

The presence of an action potential in the membrane will bring about a mechanical contraction by a mechanism as yet unknown. It will be useful to outline the present concept of the molecular basis of muscle contraction as given by Huxley (1960). The individual fibers of a muscle and its bands are shown in Fig. 9.14. In electron micrographs the fibrils were found to be composed of thick and thin filaments arranged in parallel (Fig. 9.15). The thin filaments are attached to the *Z-lines* with the thick filaments found between them. The unit of the muscle is the *sarcomere* stretching from Z-line to Z-line and is approximately 2.3 μ long. According to the sliding filament theory, it is the relative position of the thick and thin filaments moving along one another in each sarcomere which produces a contraction (Huxley, 1960). The specific muscle proteins actin and myosin (which as isolated biochemical entities show contractile properties) appear to be present in the thin and thick filaments respectively.

Under a special optical system, a microelectrode was moved transversely along the edge so that different parts of a sarcomere could be selectively stimulated. By this means, Huxley and Taylor (1958) found that depolarizing currents excited a local contrac-

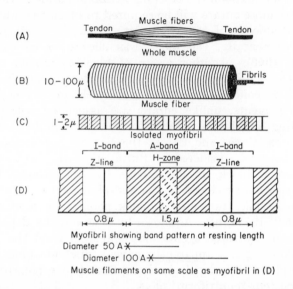

Fig. 9.14. The muscle (A) is composed of fibers (B) 10–100 μ in diameter. Fibers are in turn composed of myofibrils (C) which have a striated appearance brought about by the neurofilaments (Fig. 9.15). The I-band appears lighter than the A-band (D). Within the I-band are found Z-lines and the unit of the muscle (sarcomere) is considered to be the distance between two Z-lines. (Huxley, 1960.)

tion when the electrode was over the Z-line. This suggests that when the muscle membrane is occupied by an action potential, the depolarization of the membrane is transmitted into the interior of the muscle along the Z-line (or a structure associated with the Z-line, *vide infra*) and then spread longitudinally in the sarcomere to excite a sliding movement of the myofilaments past one another. This occurs at each sarcomere as the membrane becomes successively excited by the propagating action potential.

Apparently it is not the currents flowing inside the muscle as a result of an action potential which engages the contractile machinery (Sten-Knudsen and Buchtal, 1959). Currents led longitudinally in the cell below the membrane do not excite contraction (Sten-Knudsen, 1960). The recent studies of Axelsson and Thesleff (1958) indicate that it is not the depolarization *per se*, but the movement of some ion or ions resulting from depolarization of the membrane which excites the contractile mechanism. There are a

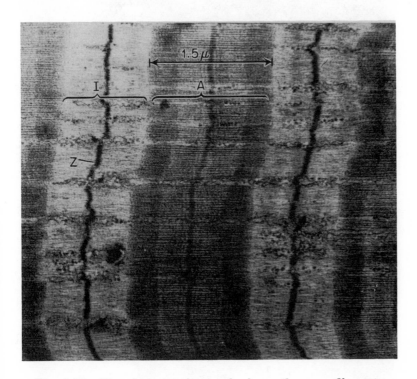

Fig. 9.15. The electron micrograph shows the neurofilaments composing the myofibrils. Within the A-band the thick myofilaments are found. The thin myofilaments extend from the Z-lines in the light-staining I-band into part of the A-band. (Courtesy, S. G. Page.)

number of older observations which indicate that Ca^{2+} is the ionic link between the excited muscle membrane and the contractile machinery (Shanes, 1958). Calcium ion has little effect on the outside surface of the fiber but, when injected via a micropipette into the fiber, very small concentrations are required to excite a contraction. Niedergerke (1956) found that Ca^{2+} was required in the medium for mechanical responsitivity of the heart muscle, indicating that this ion could be the link.   The action potential in some way increases Ca^{2+} influx thereby initiating contraction (Niedergerke, 1963).   Frank's (1960) studies of frog muscle also supported this hypothesis (cf. Lüttgau, 1963).   Quite possibly the Ca^{2+} enters

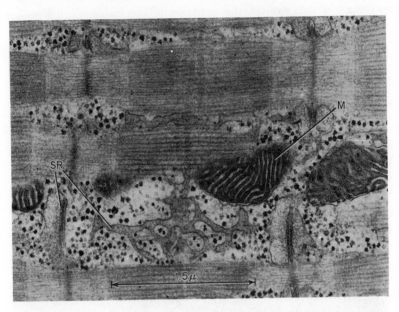

Fig. 9.16. The sarcoplasmic reticulum (SR) of frog skeletal muscle. Not shown are fibers where the central tubules of the sarcoplasmic reticulum found along the Z-line approaches close to the membrane.   Dense dots are glycogen granules; (M) mitochondria.   (Courtesy, S. G. Page.)

the interior via the central tubules of the *sarcoplasmic reticulum* which are seen to be closely related to the Z-line (Peachey and Porter, 1959) (Fig. 9.16).   Some such special mechanism is required to explain the speed with which the contractile elements deep below the surface are excited, a speed faster than that of simple diffusion of ions.

The phenomenon known as *contracture* is the engagement of the contractile machinery without the usual action potential.   It is a reversible contraction of relatively long duration which is seen when various pharmacological agents are applied to muscle (Gasser, 1930). These appear to have their effect by depolarizing the membrane.   The local contraction seen when a small region of the membrane is depolarized by use of a pore electrode is similarly a contracture. The pore electrode must be small and in contact with the membrane or else a sufficiently large area will be involved and an action potential excited (Gelfan and Gerard, 1930).

Denervation and trophic control of muscle excitability

When motor nerve fibers are interrupted, a series of characteristic changes take place in the denervated muscle (Gutmann, 1962). In a few days indirect excitation through the nerve is no longer possible as the amputated portion of the nerve fibers innervating the muscle undergo Wallerian degeneration. The muscle shows the longer chronaxie typical of muscle fibers rather than the short one of indirect excitation through its nerve (Chapter 2). The excitability of the muscle then increases in the next weeks. This is shown for example by the decrease of its rheobase to one-fifth the normal value.

Visible changes occur in the muscle after denervation also indicating increased excitability. As early as five days after interruption of the sciatic nerve of cats, the calf muscles may show scattered momentary contractions over the surface. A few days later more fibers enter on this fibrillatory activity until finally all the surface shows an uncoordinated surface agitation. This observable *fibrillatory activity* is correlated with the *fibrillatory potentials* which can be recorded from these muscles (Denny-Brown and Pennybacher, 1938). These fibrillatory potentials are a diagnostic sign of denervation (Hnik and Skorpil, 1962). Another is the *simple atrophy* of the fibers. The shrinkage in diameter starts at different times in different species. In the rabbit, the tibial muscle shows a one-third reduction within a month; its size gradually decreases over the next eight months (Gutmann and Zelená, 1962). This stage of *simple atrophy* is followed by *degeneration* where muscle material is removed and replaced by connective or fatty tissue. Fibrillation potentials are gone when the stage of degeneration is reached or if *reinnervation* has ensued. In that case, the excitability gradually returns to normalcy and the shorter chronaxie characteristic of an indirect excitation through the nerve reappears (Chapter 2).

Fibrillation is to be contrasted with the large coarse twitches seen in some muscle diseases known as *fasciculations*. Here motor units discharge one at a time, or several motor units may discharge together, in the latter case giving rise to visible limb movements.

Fasciculations usually have their origin in an abnormally increased excitability of the motoneurons.

Using microelectrodes for recording intracellularly from denervated muscles, spikes similar in appearance to those of normal muscle were recorded, except for a slower descending portion and a longer duration (Li *et al.*, 1957). The membrane potential showed slow oscillations which appear to represent the appearance of an augmented intrinsic rhythmic mechanism. These oscillations can fire the fibrillation spikes if they attain critical level.

The denervated muscle has long been known to be abnormally sensitive to ACh. This was shown by the contractions produced by injection of ACh into the blood stream in a vessel close to the muscle in amounts smaller than usually effective to excite normal muscle. This phenomenon is called *denervation supersensitivity* (Cannon and Rosenblueth, 1949). Recently this supersensitivity has been shown to be due to an increase in the region of the membrane sensitive to acetylcholine, a region normally confined to the immediate vicinity of the end-plate (Axelson and Thesleff, 1959; Miledi, 1960a). After denervation the ACh-sensitive region gradually spreads out from the end-plate region to include the whole length of the membrane of the muscle fiber. After regeneration of the nerve and reinnervation of the muscle, the susceptible region gradually shrinks back to the original highly localized end-plate region.

Along with the increase in the area of membrane sensitive to topical application of ACh, a further membrane change is shown by an increase in resistance and length-constant (λ) of the membrane (Nicholls, 1953; Jenkinson and Nicholls, 1961). The resting membrane potential is unaltered but the threshold for excitation is reduced. The flux of Ca^{2+}, Na^+ and K^+ is increased. The K^+ concentration inside the muscle fiber decreases while Na^+ increases in concentration. A decrease in ATP and phosphocreatine content is also found. Muscle glycogen shows a decrease as early as 48–72 hours after denervation.

The changes which occur in muscle after denervation are believed to be due to the loss of a *trophic* substance which passes from the nerve ending into the muscle fiber at the end-plate, the trophic substance acting to reduce the excitability of the membrane to ACh outside the end-plate region. As an alternative hypothesis it might be considered that there is no trophic substance and that nerve activity acts to keep muscle excitability normal. However, denervation hypersensitivity and atrophy do not occur if action potential discharges passing from nerve to muscle are blocked. Nerves may

)e partially constricted so as to prevent passage of nerve impulses vithout interrupting the axoplasmic continuity of the nerve fibers Denny-Brown and Brenner, 1944). In this case muscle does not how denervation changes.

While it is considered that the nerve action potentials themselves are not required to keep the muscle normal, the continuous discharge of MEPPs could act trophically by the continuous transfer of ACh Thesleff, 1960). In support of this possibility botulinum toxin was used to block MEPP release. This toxin is selectively taken up by he nerve endings from the circulation and acts to prevent the release of ACh from the nerve terminations. The MEPPs are blocked for a prolonged period of time by the toxin and the muscles show ypical signs of denervation changes after 1 to 2 weeks. While this vidence is an accord with the hypothesis that the ACh released by MEPPs could be the trophic substance, the possibility exists that he release of other substances including the trophic substance could also be blocked by the toxin. This was indicated by a study of egeneration of neuromuscular junctions by Miledi (1960b). As already noted, after denervation of the frog sartorius, MEPP activity disappears and then a few days later a low-frequency MEPP dis-harge is found. Miledi used the characteristic differences of the MEPP discharge of innervated and denervated muscle to study he effects of reinnervation. Upon reinnervation the area of the muscle membrane sensitive to ACh shrank back down to the small egion around the end-plate as is typical of normally innervated muscle. During this time MEPPs still showed the low rate of dis-harge typical of the denervated pattern and stimulation of the nerve was ineffective to excite the junction. Therefore, while the s yet unknown trophic substance enters the muscle and decreases he area of the muscle membrane sensitive to ACh, the MEPPs have till not returned to their normal pattern. This order of events indicates that the MEPPs are not the causal factor in the membrane changes. A further point of interest in Miledi's experi-ments was that the old end-plate gutters became reinnervated by the egenerating fibers, rather than new innervation sites being formed lsewhere on the muscle membrane. A neurotropic influence from he end-plate on the nerve terminal is thereby indicated (Chapter 8).

There may actually be several trophic substances supplied by the nerve. Using the early changes in glycogen metabolism as an index of denervation atrophy, Gutmann and his associates compared the onset of these metabolic changes when the nerve supplying the muscles were either cut close to or further away from the muscle.

The metabolic changes of denervation had a shorter latency with nerves cut closer. This would be expected if the nerve continued to supply trophic material for a short while before Wallerian degeneration occurred (Gutmann and Hnik, 1962).

Evidence for yet another very special kind of material supplied by nerve to control muscle characteristics was indicated by Buller *et al.* (1960a, b). In the first few weeks of the life of the kitten, the *fast* and *slow* skeletal muscles become differentiated. The response of muscles to a single excitation of motor nerve in the slow muscles, *soleus* and *crureus*, takes 70–75 msec to reach maximum twitch height. This contraction time is to be contrasted with the fast muscles, *flexor digitorum longus* or *medial gastrocnemius*, which require approximately 30 msec to reach maximum twitch height. In the newborn cat the fast muscles have a long contraction time and then during the first 2–4 weeks of life the contraction time gradually shortens to the fast twitch characteristic of the adult. The slow muscles start out with similarly prolonged contraction times. They gradually increase in speed until about 4 weeks; then unlike the fast muscles they show a return to the slow contractions characteristic of the adult slow muscle. The nerves to the slow and fast muscles of kittens were cut and cross-sutured so that these muscles would then reinnervate the opposite types of muscle. The contraction times of the muscles of these animals were studied after reinnervation. The result was that the slow soleus muscle inner vated by the fast muscle nerve now produced fast contractions, and the fast muscle was slowed down. The inference is that some substance transmitted by the nerve causes these changes in the muscles.

Slow muscle fibers

The terms 'fast muscle' and 'slow muscle' used in reference to those muscles showing faster and slower twitch contraction times in the preceding section should not be confused with the similarly designated *slow fibers* found more or less scattered throughout the skeletal muscles of frogs. These slow fibers may be few or absent in a muscle such as the sartorius, or present in large number in other muscles such as the rectus abduminus. The slow fibers do not give rise to the usual fast twitch contraction. They have a much slower mechanical response and require repetitive stimulation of their motor nerve fibers to give a good mechanical response (Kuffler and Gerard, 1947; Kuffler and Vaughn-Williams, 1953). Because the slow muscles are innervated by fibers of smaller diameter than the fast twitch fibers, responses from them were originally referred to as *small nerve junctional potentials* (s.j.p.). The s.j.p., unlike EEPs, do not excite a propagated action potential response in the slow fibers. Presumably it is the presence of s.j.p. at numerous intervals along the membrane which is sufficient to engage the contractile mechanism of the muscle.

The lack of a propagated action potential in slow muscle fibers was shown also by the failure to excite them with cathodal currents passed through the membrane. For this purpose one microelectrode was inserted into a fiber for recording purposes and another into the same fiber for passing current through the membrane (Burke and Ginsborg, 1956). The slow muscle fiber is therefore said to be *electrically inexcitable*.

The study of the effects of current passed through the membrane showed that it had a delayed rectification similar to that seen in the giant axon. The electrical resistance was found to increase with an inward (anodic) current and decrease with an outward (cathodic) current. The membrane behaves electrically as a rectifier, its resistance falling with a delay after the onset of an outward current (Burke and Ginsborg, 1956). Spontaneous small discharges analogous to the MEPPs are found in the slow muscles (Burke, 1957). The release of quanta of transmitter substance most likely occurs at the multiple sites of innervation along these slow fibers. The effect of higher concentrations of Mg^{2+} and low Ca^{2+} on the MEPPs is similar to that on fast twitch fibers, i.e. the release of the transmitter is blocked.

Invertebrate muscle

The emphasis usually placed on the twitch muscle of vertebrates has tended to obscure the wide variety of neuromuscular systems found in nature (Hoyle, 1957; Furshpan, 1959). Crustacean muscle shows a number of interesting and important neuromuscular properties (Wiersma, 1941). A few giant nerve fibers innervate these muscles, the fibers branching to innervate the individual muscle cells. At a muscle fiber a large number of collaterals terminate at sites along the fiber (van Harreveld, 1939). The actual terminals are not seen by the use of light microscopy because they are too small in size to be resolved.

The nerve fibers innervating crustacean muscle have been divided into the *slow axons*, those nerves innervating muscles which give a slower rising contraction and require repetitive stimulation for contraction, and *fast axons*, those nerves innervating muscles giving rise to faster and often stronger contractions (Wiersma and van Harreveld, 1938). There may be from one to four excitatory motor nerve fibers causing contractions of different velocities and, in addition, an inhibitory fiber (*vide infra*).

Microelectrode recordings from crustacean muscles reveal potentials which resemble EPPs of skeletal muscle (Fatt and Katz, 1953a)
These arise from the multiple innervation sites present along the
fiber. When a fast axon is excited, a spike-like response may be
seen in addition to the graded EPP-like responses (Hoyle and Wiers
ma, 1958). These spike-like responses are not propagated from the
end-plates throughout the rest of the membrane as is the case for
the action potential in the vertebrate muscle. They may have some
function to increase the degree of depolarization and, therefore, the
speed of contraction. Dudel and Orkand (1960) have shown the
presence of miniature potentials in these muscles similar in their
nature to the miniature potentials found in the slow muscles and
the MEPPs of skeletal muscle (cf. Dudel and Kuffler, 1961a).

The transmitter substance acting at the crustacean neuromuscular
junctions may resemble glutamic acid (van Harreveld, 1959). Low
concentrations of glutamic acid were found effective in depolarizing
the muscle and excite contraction. Electrophoretic release of
glutamic acid from a micropipette excited potentials at highly
localized spots along the crustacean muscle fiber membrane (Takeu
chi and Takeuchi, 1963), to be expected if there are a number of in
nervation sites (*vide supra* and Fatt and Katz, 1953c). Glutamic acid
has become of great interest in view of its potent excitatory effect
on neurons of the mammalian CNS (Chapter 19).

A feature of crustacean muscle not found in the vertebrate is the
presence of *inhibitory nerves*. Upon stimulation of the inhibitory
nerves, a contracted muscle relaxes. The mechanism of this
inhibitory action was shown by microelectrode studies to be due
to an increased permeability of the muscle membrane to Cl⁻
(Fatt and Katz, 1953b). The increased permeability to Cl⁻
brings the membrane potential toward the equilibrium potential for
this ion which is close to that of the resting membrane potential
(Boistel and Fatt, 1958). If the membrane is hyperpolarized
stimulation of the inhibitory nerve gives rise to a depolarization; if
the membrane has been depolarized, inhibitory nerve action gives
rise to a hyperpolarizing wave. The effect of the inhibitory trans
mitter therefore is to *clamp* the membrane at its equilibrium potential
level. It is this clamping action which prevents the depolarization
in response to excitatory nerve discharges and inhibits a contraction
of the muscle.

The inhibitory transmitter substance produces its action by
increasing Cl⁻ permeability and a similar Cl⁻ permeability increase
is also brought about by the amino acid, gamma-aminobutyric acid

GABA). The similarity of its action and the low concentration required suggests the possibility that GABA is the natural inhibitory transmitter agent in this nerve (Kuffler and Edwards, 1958). In line with this possibility is the rather high concentration of GABA, up to 0.5% of wet weight, found in the inhibitory fibers while none is found in motor fibers (Kravitz, Kuffler and Potter, 1963). Picrotoxin appears to block the action of GABA in crustacean muscle much as curare does ACh in vertebrate muscle (van der Kloot and Robbins, 1959). GABA also is a neurophysiologically important substance having an inhibitory action on neurons of the vertebrate CNS which is the reverse of glutamic acid's action and will be discussed further in Chapter 19.

Presynaptic inhibition has been described for neuromuscular transmission of the crustacean (Dudel and Kuffler, 1961b). This phenomenon is seen when stimulation of the inhibitory nerve reduces the junction potential produced by excitatory nerve stimulation. It is to be distinguished from failure of the nerve terminals to discharge, for example due to hypoxia in rat diaphragm muscle (Krnjevic and Miledi, 1959).

Presynaptic inhibition is brought about by synapses of the inhibitory terminals present on the terminations of excitatory nerve endings acting to prevent a release of transmitter substance. GABA also has this action on the release of excitatory transmitter. Presynaptic inhibition within the CNS has recently been intensively studied by Eccles and his colleagues and will be discussed in Chapters 17 and 21.

Electric organs

Certain electric fish have organs which can give rise to considerable electrical currents in the surrounding water, sufficient to stun prey or to protect themselves from predators. The effects produced by these fish were known to the ancient Greeks, and Galvani commented on the electrical nature of the mechanism. The cells producing the electrical currents in some forms such as *Torpedo* and *Raia* appear to be modified muscle cells. High voltages are brought about by the arrangement of these cells in series, with the usual membrane voltage of each individual cell adding to that of the next, etc. These cells or *electroplaques* are excited by the nerves innervating them in a repetitive series of high voltage discharges. Synaptic elements found in the electroplaques are similar to those of the neuromuscular junction. An account of the various properties of the electric organs, especially the synaptic properties of the electroplaques, may be found in Grundfest's (1957) comprehensive review.

REFERENCES

Adrian, E. D. and Bronk, D. W. (1929).   The discharge of impulses in motor nerve fibres.   Part II.   The frequency of discharge in reflex and voluntary contractions.   J. Physiol. **67**: 119–151.

Axelsson, J. and Thesleff, S. (1958).   Activation of the contractile mechanism in striated muscle.   Acta Physiol. Scand. **44**: 55–66.

Axelsson, J. and Thesleff, S. (1959).   A study of supersensitivity in denervated mammalian skeletal muscle.   J. Physiol. **147**: 178–193.

Birks, R., Huxley, H. E. and Katz, B. (1960).   The fine structure of the neuromuscular junction of the frog.   J. Physiol. **150**: 134–144.

Birks, R., Katz, B. and Miledi, R. (1960).   Physiological and structural changes at the amphibian myoneural junction, in the course of nerve degeneration.   J. Physiol. **150**: 145–168.

Boistel, J. and Fatt, P. (1958).   Membrane permeability change during inhibitory transmitter action in crustacean muscle.   J. Physiol. **144** 176–191.

Brown, M. C. and Mathews, P. B. C. (1960).   An investigation into the possible existence of polyneuronal innervation of individual skeletal muscle fibres in certain hind-limb muscles of the cat.   J. Physiol. **151**: 436–457.

Buller, A. J., Eccles, J. C. and Eccles, R. M. (1960a).   Differentiation of fast and slow muscles in the cat hind limb.   J. Physiol. **150**: 399–416.

Buller, J., Eccles, J. C. and Eccles, R. M. (1960b).   Interactions between motoneurons and muscles in respect of the characteristic speed of their responses.   J. Physiol. **150**: 417–439.

Burke, W. (1957).   Spontaneous potentials in slow muscle fibers of the frog J. Physiol. **135**: 511–521.

Burke, W. and Ginsborg, B. L. (1956).   The electrical properties of the slow muscle fibre membrane.   J. Physiol. **132**: 586–598.

Burns, B. D. and Paton, W. D. B. (1951).   Depolarization of the motor end plate by decamethonium and acetylcholine, J. Physiol. **115**: 41–73.

Cannon, W. B. and Rosenblueth, A. (1949).   The Supersensitivity of Denervated Structures.   Macmillan Co., New York.

Couteaux, R. (1958).   Morphological and cytochemical observations on the post-synaptic membrane at motor end-plates and ganglionic synapses Exptl. Cell. Res. Suppl. **5**: 294–322.

Dale, H. H., Feldberg, W. and Vogt, M. (1936).   Release of acetylcholine at voluntary motor nerve endings.   J. Physiol. **86**: 353–380.

del Castillo, J. and Katz, B. (1956).   Biophysical aspects of neuromuscular transmission.   Progr. Biophys. **6**: 121–170.

Denny-Brown, D. and Brenner, C. (1944).   Paralysis of nerve induced by direct pressure and by tourniquet.   Arch. Neurol. Psychiat. **51**: 1–26 Lesion in peripheral nerve resulting from compression by spring clip Ibid. **52**: 1–19.

Denny-Brown, D. and Pennybacher, J. B. (1938).   Fibrillation and fasciculation in voluntary muscle.   Brain **61**: 311–334.

Dudel, J. and Kuffler, S. W. (1961a).   The quantal nature of transmission and spontaneous miniature potentials at the crayfish neuromuscular junction.   J. Physiol. **155**: 514–529.

Dudel, J. and Kuffler, S. W. (1961b).   Presynaptic inhibition at the crayfish neuromuscular junction.   J. Physiol. **155**: 543–562.

Dudel, J. and Orkand, R. K. (1960). Spontaneous potential changes at crayfish neuromuscular junctions. *Nature* 186: 476–477.

Eccles, J. C. (1964). *The Physiology of Synapses*. Academic Press, New York.

Eccles, J. C., Katz, B. and Kuffler, S. W. (1941). Nature of the 'end-plate potential' in curarized muscle. *J. Neurophysiol.* 4: 362–387.

Elliot, T. R. (1904). On the action of adrenalin. *J. Physiol.* 31: xx–xxi.

Fatt, P. and Katz, B. (1951). An analysis of the end-plate potential recorded with an intra-cellular electrode. *J. Physiol.* 115: 320–370.

Fatt, P. and Katz, B. (1953a). The electrical properties of crustacean muscle. *J. Physiol.* 121: 374–389.

Fatt, P. and Katz, B. (1953b). The effect of inhibitory nerve impulses on a crustacean muscle fibre. *J. Physiol.* 121: 374–389.

Fatt, P. and Katz, B (1953c). Distributed 'end-plate potentials' of crustacean muscle fibers. *J. Exptl. Biol.* 30: 433–439

Frank, G. B. (1960). Effects of changes in extracellular calcium concentration on the potassium induced contracture of frog's skeletal muscle. *J. Physiol.* 151: 518–538.

Furshpan, E. J. (1959). Neuromuscular transmission in invertebrates. *Handbook of Physiology—Neurophysiology.* Vol. 1, pp. 239–254. American Physiological Society, Washington, D.C.

Gasser, H. S. (1930). Contractures of skeletal muscle. *Physiol. Rev.* 10: 35–109.

Gelfan, S. and Gerard, R. W. (1930). Studies of single muscle fibres. II. A further analysis of the grading mechanism. *Am. J. Physiol.* 95: 412–416.

Gopfert, H. and Schaefer, H. (1938). Über den direkt und indirekt erregten Aktionsström und das Funktion der motorischen Endplatte. *Pflügers Arch. Ges. Physiol.* 239: 597–619.

Grundfest, H. (1957). The mechanism of discharge of the electric organs in relation to general and comparative electrophysiology. *Progr. Biophys.* 7: 1–85.

Gutmann, E. and Hnik, P. (1962). Denervation studies in research of neurotropic relationships. *The Denervated Muscle.* Edited by E. Gutmann. Chapter 1. Publishing House Czechoslovak Acad. Sci., Prague.

Gutmann, E. and Zelená, J. (1962). Morphological changes in the denervated muscle. *The Denervated Muscle.* Edited by E. Gutmann. Chapter 2. Publishing House Czechoslovak Acad. Sci., Prague.

Hnik, P. and Skorpil, V. (1962). Fibrillation activity in denervated muscle. *The Denervated Muscle.* Edited by E. Gutmann. Chapter 5. Publishing House Czechoslovak Acad. Sci., Prague.

Hodgkin, A. L. and Horowicz, P. (1959). Movements of Na^+ and K^+ in single muscle fibres. *J. Physiol.* 145: 405–432.

Hodgkin, A. L. and Nastuck, W. L. (1950). The electrical activity of single muscle fibers. *J. Cell. Comp. Physiol.* 35: 39–74.

Hoyle, G. (1957). *Comparative Physiology of the Nervous Control of Muscular Contraction.* Cambridge University Press, Cambridge.

Hoyle, G. and Wiersma, C. A. G. (1958). Excitation at neuromuscular junctions in crustacea. *J. Physiol.* 143: 403–425.

Huxley, A. F. and Taylor, R. E. (1958). Local activation of striated muscle fibres. *J. Physiol.* 144: 426–441.

Huxley, H. E. (1960). *The Cell; Biochemistry, Physiology, Morphology* Edited by J. Brachet and A. E. Mirskey. Vol. 4. Academic Press, New York.

Jenkinson, D. H. (1960). The antagonism between tubocurarine and sub stances which depolarize the motor end-plate. *J. Physiol.* **152**: 309–324

Jenkinson, D. H. and Nicholls, J. G. (1961). Contracture and permeability changes produced by acetylcholine in depolarized denervated muscle *J. Physiol.* **159**: 111–127.

Kravitz, E. A., Kuffler, S. W. and Potter, A. D. (1963). Gamma-amino butyric acid and other blocking compounds in crustacea, III. Their relative concentrations in separated motor and inhibitory axons. *J Neurophysiol.* **26**: 739–751.

Katz, B. (1958). Microphysiology of the neuromuscular junction. A physiolog ical quantum of action at the myoneural junction, I. *Bull. Johns Hopkin. Hosp.* **102**: 275–295; and Microphysiology of the neuromuscular junction The chemoreceptor junction of the motor end-plate, II. *Ibid.*, 296–312

Katz, B. (1962). The transmission of impulses from nerve to muscle anc the subcellular unit of synaptic action. *Proc. Roy. Soc. B.* **155**: 455–477

Katz, B. and Kuffler, S. W. (1941). Multiple innervation of the frog'i sartorius muscle. *J. Neurophysiol.* **4**: 207–223.

Krnjevic, K. and Miledi, R. (1959). Presynaptic failure of neuromuscula propagation in rats. *J. Physiol.* **149**: 1–22.

Krnjevic, K. and Mitchell, J. F. (1961). The release of acetylcholine in the isolated rat diaphragm. *J. Physiol.* **155**: 246–262.

Kuffler, S. W. (1943). Specific excitability of the end-plate region in norma and denervated muscle. *J. Neurophysiol.* **6**: 99–110.

Kuffler, S. W. and Edwards, C. (1958). Mechanisms of gamma-aminobutyri acid (GABA) action and its relation to synaptic inhibition. *J. Neuro physiol.* **21**: 589–610.

Kuffler, S. W. and Gerard, R. W. (1947). The small-nerve motor system t skeletal system. *J. Neurophysiol.* **10**: 383–394.

Kuffler, S. W. and Vaughn-Williams, E. M. (1953). Small-nerve junctiona potentials. The distribution of small motor nerves to frog skeleta muscle, and the membrane characteristics of the fibers they innervate *J. Physiol.* **119**: 95–109.

Langley, J. N. (1909). On the contraction of muscle, chiefly in relation to th presence of 'receptive' substance. Part IV. The effect of curare and of some other substances on the nicotine response of the sartorius and gastrocnemius muscles of the frog. *J. Physiol.* **39**: 235–295.

Li, C. L., Shy, G. M. and Wells, J. (1957). Some properties of mammaliai skeletal muscle fibres with particular reference to fibrillation potentials *J. Physiol.* **135**: 522–535.

Lüttgau, H. C. (1963). The action of calcium ions on potassium contracture of single muscle fibres. *J. Physiol.* **168**: 679–697.

Miledi, R. (1960a). The acetylcholine sensitivity of frog muscle fibres afte complete or partial denervation. *J. Physiol.* **151**: 1–23.

Miledi, R. (1960b). Properties of regenerating neuromuscular synapses i the frog. *J. Physiol.* **154**: 190–295.

Nastuk, W. L. and Hodgkin, A. L. (1950). The electrical activity of singl muscle fibers. *J. Cell. Comp. Physiol.* **35**: 39–74.

Nicholls, J. G. (1956). The electrical properties of denervated skeletal muscle. J. Physiol. **131**: 1–12.

Niedergerke, R. (1956). The potassium chloride contracture of the heart and its modification by calcium. J. Physiol. **134**: 584–599.

Niedergerke, R. (1963). Movements of Ca in beating ventricles of the frog heart. J. Physiol. **167**: 551–580.

Peachey, L. D. and Porter, K. R. (1959). Intracellular impulse conduction in muscle cells. Science **129**: 721–722.

Robertson, J. D. (1956). The ultrastructure of a reptilian myoneural junction. J. Biophys. Biochem. Cytol. **2**: 369–379.

Shanes, A. M. (1958). Electrochemical aspects of physiological and pharmacological action in excitable cells. Part I. The resting cell and its alternation by extrinsic factors. Pharm. Rev., **10**: 59–164. Part II. The action potential and excitation. Ibid., 165–273.

Sten-Knudsen, O. (1960). Is muscle contraction initiated by internal flow? J. Physiol. **151**: 363–384.

Sten-Knudsen, O. and Buchthal, F. (1959). Impulse propagation in striated muscle fibers and the role of the internal currents in activation. Ann. N.Y. Acad. Sci. **81**: 422–445.

Takeuchi, A. and Takeuchi, N. (1959). On the permeability of end-plate membrane during the action of transmitter. J. Physiol. **154**: 52–67.

Takeuchi, A. and Takeuchi, N. (1960). Further analysis of relationship between end-plate potential and end-plate current. J. Neurophysiol. **23**: 397–402.

Takeuchi, A. and Takeuchi, N. (1963). Glutamate-induced depolarization in crustacean muscle. Nature **198**: 490–491.

Thesleff, S. (1955a). The mode of neuromuscular block caused by acetylcholine, nicotine, decamethonium and succinylcholine. Acta Physiol. Scand. **34**: 218–231.

Thesleff, S. (1955b). The effects of acetylcholine, decamethonium and succinylcholine on neuromuscular transmission in the rat. Acta Physiol. Scand. **34**: 386–392.

Thesleff, S. (1960). Effects of motor innervation on the chemical sensitivity of skeletal muscle. Physiol. Rev. **40**: 734–752.

van Der Kloot, W. G. and Robbins, J. (1959). The effects of γ-aminobutyric acid and picrotoxin on the junctional potential and the contraction of crayfish muscle. Experientia **15**: 35–36.

van Harreveld, A. (1939). The nerve supply of doubly- and triply-innervated crayfish muscles related to their function. J. Comp. Neurol. **70**: 267–284.

van Harreveld, A. (1959). Compounds in brain extracts causing spreading depression of cerebral cortical activity and contraction of crustacean muscle. J. Neurochem. **3**: 300–315.

van Harreveld, A. and Tachibana, S. (1961). Innervation and reinnervation of cricothyroid muscle in the rabbit. Am. J. Physiol. **201**: 1199–1202.

Viersma, C. A. B. (1941). Neuromuscular activation in crustacea. Biol. Symp. **5**: 259–289.

Viersma, C. A. G. and van Harreveld, A. (1938). The influence of the frequency of stimulation on the slow and the fast contraction in crustacean muscle. Physiol. Zool. **11**: 75–81.

10

Peripheral Autonomic Nervous System

The earlier distinction between voluntary and involuntary (reflex actions (Gaskell, 1916) seemed to find expression when an anatomically separate peripheral nervous system was found. This was the *involuntary* or *sympathetic* nervous system which supplies the heart and blood vessels and other visceral organs. These nerves originate from *ganglia* located along the vertebral column. The cells of the ganglia are supplied from cell bodies in the spinal cord. Later a second similar system was found arising from the brain stem and sacral regions of the cord and called the *parasympathetic* nervous system to distinguish it from the sympathetic nervous system. The two together are referred to as the *autonomic* or *visceral* nervous system (Fig. 10.1(a) and (b)).

The course of the sympathetic fibers from their cell bodies in the cord to the ganglia where synapse is made is shown in Fig. 10.2. These nerve fibers fall into the *B* and *C* groups. The pattern of parasympathetic nerve outflow is different. Fibers leave the brain stem or cord and then pass to the organ they innervate before synapsing in ganglia located near or within the organs. Therefore the postganglionic fibers of parasympathetically innervated organs are generally shorter than those of the sympathetic division (Kuntz, 1945).

A strict identification of voluntary control with the somatic and involuntary control with the autonomic nervous system was modified with the recognition that control of skeletal muscle has involuntary aspects, and that sensory inputs influencing voluntary actions occur via autonomic nerves. The autonomic nervous system is recognized as an important system which helps regulate the internal functions of the organism and by its control of visceral organs keeps constant the *internal milieu*. This involves a number of homeostatic mechanisms of the body. The autonomic nervous system is involved in those rapid changes in body function required in a state of emergency. The two parts of the autonomic nervous system may play different roles (Kuntz, 1945). Sympathetic effects are predominant when an animal is in a threatening situation, one leading to *fight* or *flight*

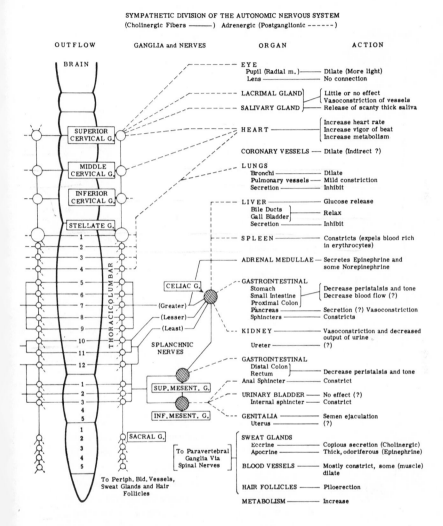

Fig. 10.1(a). Sympathetic division of the autonomic nervous system showing outflow of fibers from the cord, connection to ganglia and the innervation of the body organs with their indicated actions. (C. F. Rothe in Selkurt, *Physiology*, Little Brown and Co., 1962.)

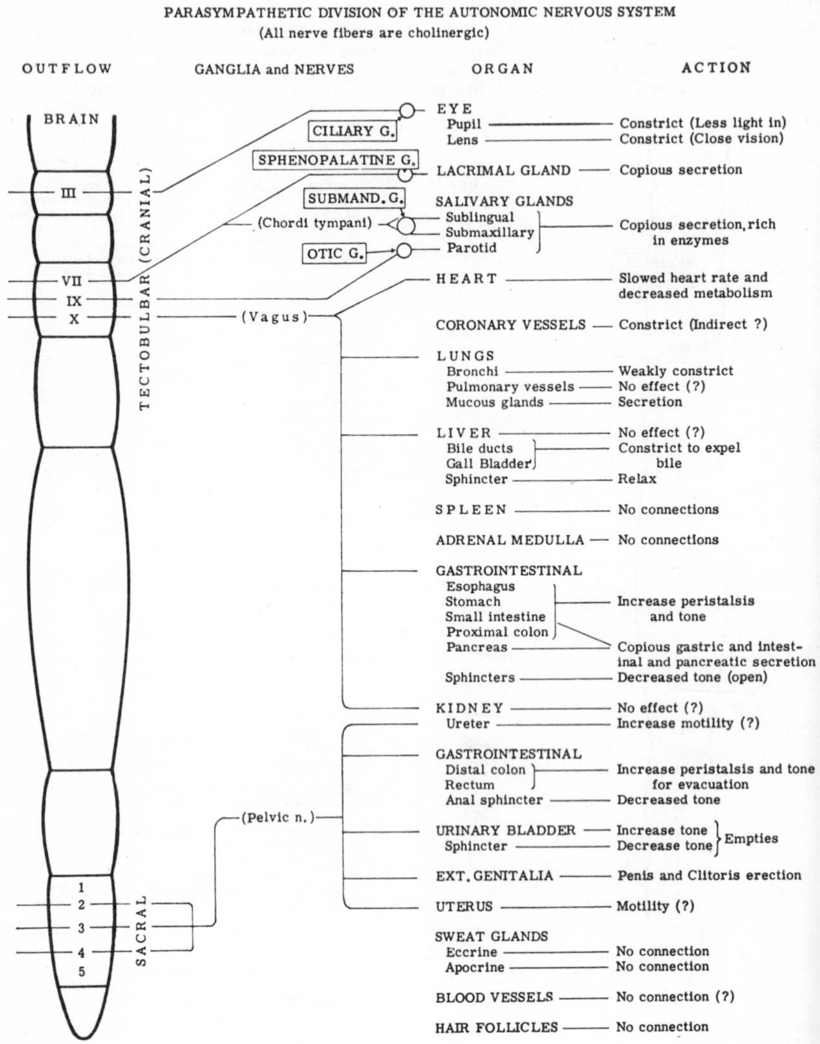

PARASYMPATHETIC DIVISION OF THE AUTONOMIC NERVOUS SYSTEM
(All nerve fibers are cholinergic)

OUTFLOW	GANGLIA and NERVES	ORGAN	ACTION

BRAIN

CILIARY G.

SPHENOPALATINE G.

III

SUBMAND. G.

(Chordi tympani)

OTIC G.

VII
IX
X

(Vagus)

TECTOBULBAR (CRANIAL)

EYE
Pupil —————— Constrict (Less light in)
Lens —————— Constrict (Close vision)

LACRIMAL GLAND —— Copious secretion

SALIVARY GLANDS
Sublingual
Submaxillary } Copious secretion, rich in enzymes
Parotid

HEART —————— Slowed heart rate and decreased metabolism

CORONARY VESSELS — Constrict (Indirect ?)

LUNGS
Bronchi —————— Weakly constrict
Pulmonary vessels —— No effect (?)
Mucous glands —————— Secretion

LIVER — No effect (?)
Bile ducts }
Gall Bladder } Constrict to expel bile
Sphincter —————— Relax

SPLEEN —————— No connections

ADRENAL MEDULLA — No connections

GASTROINTESTINAL
Esophagus
Stomach
Small intestine } Increase peristalsis and tone
Proximal colon
Pancreas —————— Copious gastric and intestinal and pancreatic secretion
Sphincters —————— Decreased tone (open)

KIDNEY —————— No effect (?)
Ureter —————— Increase motility (?)

GASTROINTESTINAL
Distal colon }
Rectum } Increase peristalsis and tone for evacuation
Anal sphincter —————— Decreased tone

URINARY BLADDER —— Increase tone }
Sphincter —————— Decrease tone } Empties

EXT. GENITALIA —————— Penis and Clitoris erection

UTERUS —————— Motility (?)

SWEAT GLANDS
Eccrine —————— No connection
Apocrine —————— No connection

BLOOD VESSELS —————— No connection (?)

HAIR FOLLICLES —————— No connection

(Pelvic n.)

1
2
3
4
5

SACRAL

Fig. 10.1(b). Parasympathetic division of the autonomic nervous system showing outflow of fibers from cranial and sacral parts of the CNS passing to ganglia and body organs with their indicated actions. (C. F. Rothe in Selkurt, *Physiology*, Little Brown and Co., 1962.)

(Cannon, 1929). In such *stress* situations the pupils dilate, hair rises, paws sweat, claws unsheath, blood pressure increases, muscle blood flow increases, bronchials dilate and respiration deepens and increases in rate. While these activities are augmented, other activities are temporarily held in abeyance, e.g., digestion, micturition, defecation (cf. Fig. 10.1(a) and (b)).

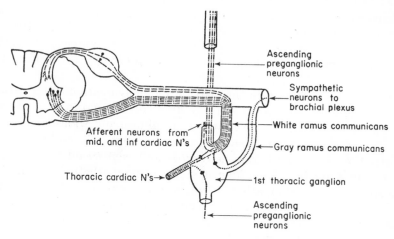

Fig. 10.2. Efferent fibers of the sympathetic motoneurons are shown passing out through the ventral root to synapse in cells of the autonomic ganglia or to pass through the ganglia and ascend or descend in the nerves connecting the ganglia. Nerve (N) fibers from the ganglia innervate the viscera. (From White and Smith-wick, *The Autonomic Nervous System*, Kimpton, 1942.)

If an animal is deprived of the sympathetic system by surgery (a complex procedure), peripheral manifestations of the sympathetic innervation are eliminated. For example, heat regulation is impaired and environmental temperatures must be elevated sufficiently to maintain body temperature. Animals which survive this operation perform at a decreased level of somatic activity and are characterized as weak and apathetic. Vascular adjustments may be insufficient to sustain the increased demands placed on them by prolonged or severe exertion. They have a diminished resistance to anoxia and other conditions which may lead to death in states of stress (Cannon *et al.*, 1929).

Parasympathetic actions are generally considered to be those maintaining the internal milieu over longer periods of time. In general, though there are exceptions, the parasympathetic system is antagonistic in its action to that of the sympathetic system (Kuntz, 1945). For example, stimulation of sympathetic nerves may cause vasoconstriction, while excitation of the parasympathetic system causes vasodilation. However, not all the effectors receive innervation from both sympathetic and parasympathetic divisions. For example, blood vessels may only have a sympathetic innervation, dilation being due to cessation of sympathetic activity. Effector organs with dual innervation also may not give reciprocal responses in response to excitation of each type of nerve (Rosenblueth, 1950). For instance, salivary glands secrete on both sympathetic and parasympathetic activation; the salivas produced are different, however.

In part the difference in the distribution of sympathetic and parasympathetic nerves conforms to the differences found in their mode of action. Sympathetic excitations are diffuse and widespread due to the large amount of branching of these fibers. In addition, the adrenal medulla discharges *adrenalin* and *noradrenalin* into the blood and these have been identified as the sympathetic transmitter substances. Parasympathetic innervation, on the other hand, is more selective. The motor fibers have a smaller amount of collateral branching and terminate in a more localized fashion.

Autonomic effector organs

The autonomic nerves act via an innervation of smooth muscles which in turn control the activity of organs such as the blood vessels, gastrointestinal tract and genitourinary tract, or they terminate onto gland cells to modulate the production and output of their secretions. For the most part, the actions of the visceral organs properly belong to other branches of physiology and will only be discussed here in a general way. Our attention will be directed to what is known about the mechanisms of the neural control exerted by the autonomic nervous system.

Much less is known about the innervation pattern of the smooth muscles which characterize the autonomic nervous system than the skeletal muscles. Some muscles appear to have a *motor-unit innervation* similar to skeletal muscles, with the branches of a nerve fiber innervating a number of muscle fibers. The motor-unit type of innervation is found in the iris muscles of the eye, pre-capillary sphincters of blood vessels, piloerector muscles, etc. However, other smooth muscles such as those of the intestine, ureter, urinary bladder, uterus, etc., cannot be described in this manner. It has long been known that a rich neural plexus of autonomic nerves is associated with these smooth muscles, but their final termination on the cells is below the resolution possible with the light microscope (Fulton *et al.*, 1960).

Sperlakis and Prosser (1959) considered some of the possible alternative means by which smooth muscles could be excited other than by a direct innervation. After some smooth muscle fibers are excited, others could be indirectly activated by one or more of the following ways: (a) protoplasmic continuity by small bridges between muscle fibers, (b) electrical transmission via spread of currents of activity from fiber to fiber (*ephaptic spread*), (c) mechanical excitation afforded by the contraction of one fiber on its neighbor, or (d) a diffusive spread of a chemical transmitter substance from fiber to fiber. Their studies supported the possibility of a spread by electrical currents from fiber to fiber. Some support for this is seen in electron micrographs where cells appear to be closely apposed at peculiar contact sites or *nexi*.

The electron microscope studies of Caesar *et al.* (1957) of such smooth muscles as urinary bladder, uterus, and gall bladder has shown the individuality of the muscle fibers composing the tissue, i.e., its nonsyncytial nature. Their studies also revealed the presence of autonomic nerve axons running between the cells, the nerve axons ranging in size from 200 to 1700 mμ and averaging 400 mμ. The nerve fiber terminals end at a number of points along the muscle in depressions or pockets within the muscle membrane. The *vas deferens* is a richly innervated smooth muscle structure and Richardson (1962) was able to more readily show the form of the termination of nerve fibers on smooth muscle cells in electron micrographs (Fig. 10.3). The terminal of the fiber ends in a groove on the surface of the smooth muscle fiber in an elongated fashion with a cleft 180 A to 250 A wide between nerve and muscle membranes. Within the nerve terminals both thick and thin neurofilaments are found, though these are missing from some fiber endings. Masses of vesicles are present in the nerve terminals. The vesicles are either granular with an average diameter of 520 A, or agranular and 450–600 A in diameter. Mitochondria are also present. Therefore, the nerve endings innervating smooth muscles are similar to those described for striated muscle, and this may also be the case in other smooth muscles less densely innervated.

Electron microscope studies have also shown filaments inside the smooth muscle cell. Unlike the regular array of filaments found in striated muscle (Chapter 9), smooth muscle fibers contain longitudinally oriented filaments in a much less regularly ordered array.

Cell extracts of smooth muscle showed actomyosin present, and it is likely that the filaments found in the smooth muscle constitute the contractile machinery.

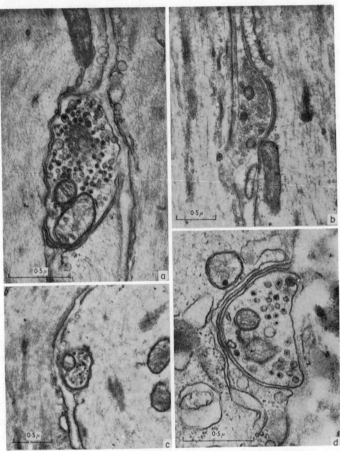

Fig. 10.3. Electron micrographs of neuromuscular junctions (a–d) of smooth muscle (vas deferens) shows vesicles, filled granules and mitochondria within the nerve terminal. The post-junctional membranes do not have the folds characteristically present in striated muscle. (Richardson, 1962.)

Possibly the differences in the myofilaments may explain a characteristic feature of smooth muscle—their prolonged contraction durations. The problem is whether some special 'catch' mechanism is triggered by nerve transmission to maintain contraction as is found in molluscan muscle (Johnson, 1962), or whether a

epetitive discharge of the muscle membrane is required for con-
inued contraction. Microelectrode studies of individual muscle
ibers made by Bülbring (1955) have shown that smooth muscle
ibers have resting membrane potentials similar to those found in
keletal muscle and that the degree of tension in the muscle is
elated to the rate of repetitive action potentials recorded from these
ells (Fig. 10.4). Smooth muscle differs from skeletal muscle in

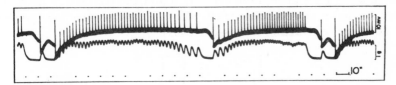

Fig. 10.4.   Upper trace shows resting potential and action potential
discharges of smooth muscle (taenia coli).   Tension is recorded
on the bottom trace.   An increased rate of spike discharge is
found associated with increased tension.   (Courtesy, E. Bülbring;
Bülbring, 1962.)

giving rise to locally initiated slow waves or 'graded' potentials as
well as all-or-none propagated action potentials.   Each of the cells
has the capability of acting as a *pacemaker*; an intrinsic rhythmic
series of slow potentials or all-or-none action potentials initiated by
the pacemaker spread to other cells to excite discharges in them.
Transmission is variable with the pacemaker function shifting from
cell to cell making the pattern of excitability in the tissue complex.
The stretch of a smooth muscle causes a depolarization of the muscle
membranes and it is the level of depolarization which determines
the rate of firing of action potentials and the resulting tension
(Bülbring, 1962). A strikingly slow K^+ influx was found.   The
resting membrane potential is in part controlled by Na^+, at least
the fluctuations of the membrane potential under various conditions
of stretch which is characteristic of smooth muscle.   Furthermore,
for the action potential, both Na^+ and Ca^{2+} are important.   Removal
of Ca^{2+} ion from the medium causes membrane instability and
oscillations of potential.   Excess Ca^{2+} acts as a stabilizing agent.

    In respect to neural control some smooth muscles were found
to be similar to skeletal muscle.   Burnstock and Holman (1961),
recording with microelectrodes from single smooth muscle of the
vas deferens, found resting membrane potentials ranging from
50–80 mv and varying slowly by 10 mv over periods of several
minutes.   In response to a single volley to its nerve supply, depolarizations similar to EPPs were found.   These *junction potentials*

ranged in amplitude from 1–20 mv and showed summation.   Usually
a number of repetitive stimulations of the nerve were required before
a large action potential with overshoot was excited by the junction
potentials (Fig. 10.5).   A spontaneous discharge of *miniature junction
potentials* similar to the MEPPs of skeletal muscle was also seen.
These had amplitudes as high as 15 mv and appeared on the average
once or twice every 2 sec.   The possibility that Ca^{2+} participates in
the link between membrane activation and the contractile mechanism of smooth muscle (Chapter 9) was indicated by the requirement
of Ca^{2+} for contraction (Axelsson, 1961).

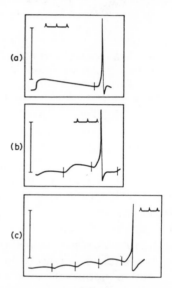

Fig. 10.5.   Junctional (synaptic) and spike potentials of smooth
muscle seen with different rates of stimulation (and numbers of
nerve fibers stimulated) in a, b and c.   Synaptic potentials are
seen similar to EPPs.   When depolarization reaches sufficient
amplitude action potentials are elicited which have a large
positive   after-hyperpolarization.   Calibration,   100   msec   and
50 mv.   (From Burnstock and Holman, 1961.)

Autonomic transmitter substances

A release of transmitter substances from autonomic nerves was first
shown in the classic experiment of Loewi (1921) using isolated frog
hearts arranged so that the Ringer solution flowing through one heart
could in turn bathe a second (Fig. 10.6).   Stimulation of the vagus
nerve of the first heart either slowed or stopped the beat of the
second heart.   It was shown that after such vagus nerve stimulation,

the Ringer solution collected from the first heart contained an inhibitory substance which Loewi called the *vagus-stoffe* (vagal material). The vagus-stoffe has since been identified as acetylcholine. If blood was the bathing medium used, the experiment would fail because the acetylcholinesterase present in blood would hydrolyse the ACh. If a cholinesterase inhibitor such as *eserine* is added to the blood, the released ACh can then be demonstrated.

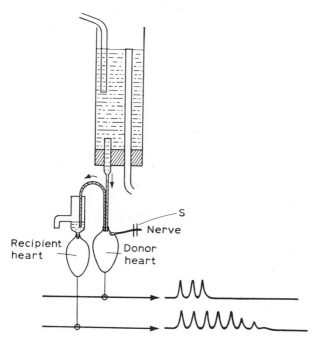

Fig. 10.6. In the Loewi experiment a frog heart muscle is perfused from one vessel and the perfusate used to perfuse a second heart. Stimulation (S) of the vagus nerve innervating the donor heart causes it to slow and soon afterwards the recipient heart also slows owing to the vagal material (acetylcholine) entering its perfusate from the stimulated heart. (From Bain, *Quart. J. Exptl. Physiol.*. **22**: 269, 1932.)

Esterases in the blood serve to restrict the action of ACh to the autonomic effectors innervated by parasympathetic nerves. However, in certain experimental situations a limited spread of ACh may be shown. Although these are rather special experiments, a description will indicate some principles of autonomic transmission. When the motor innervation of the skeletal muscle of the tongue was interrupted, then some days or weeks later it showed denervation

hypersensitivity to ACh (Chapter 9).   Upon stimulation of the parasympathetic nerve to the tongue (chorda tympani) a slow contraction
of the tongue muscle was found (the Phillipeaux–Vulpian reaction).
This and similar reactions were found to be due to the diffusion of
ACh from the terminals of the parasympathetic nerves to excite the
hypersensitive denervated skeletal muscles (Cannon and Rosenblueth, 1949).   However, in similar experiments using other types of
effector cells previously sensitized by denervation there was no discharge by nerve stimulation which should have released sufficient
transmitter agent to diffuse to those cells.   On this and other
grounds, Hillarp (1960) believes that normally only the individual
muscle fibers which receive an innervation are activated (*vide
supra*).

The ACh receptor substance of smooth muscle differs from that of
skeletal muscle.   This is shown by the relative ineffectiveness in the
blocking action of D-tubocurarine on smooth muscle.   Atropine is
an effective blocking agent for smooth muscle and not nearly as
effective for skeletal muscle.

Historically, the concept of a neurotransmitter arose from a
comparison of the pharmacological action of adrenalin extracted
from the adrenal glands with the effects of stimulation of sympathetic nerves on sympathetically innervated organs.   Adrenalin
is one of a number of *catecholamines* produced by the adrenal
medulla and released from this organ into the blood stream during
stress.   The two chief catecholamines released are adrenalin and
noradrenalin.   These circulate in the blood to act on sympathetic
effector organs and augment those autonomic effectors active in
the emergency state of fight or flight which has been previously
described.   Some of these reactions seen in the human include
sweating, vasodilation and a feeling of apprehension as part of the
stress reaction.   A number of these reactions, including the feeling
of apprehension, are mimicked by injections of adrenalin.

The release of catecholamines during stress can be demonstrated
in the cat following denervation of the eye.   Removal of the
cervical ganglia and the sympathetic nerve to the radial (dilator
muscles of the iris) causes it to become supersensitive to circulating
adrenalin.   Such procedures as pinching the skin or occluding the
trachea for a brief period of time are effective in releasing catecholamines as shown by dilation of the denervated eye (Gellhorn, 1943).

Whether supersensitivity involves an increase of the area of the
autonomic muscle fibers sensitive to the autonomic transmitter, as
is the case for striated muscle (Chapter 9), remains to be determined.

Because of the smaller size of the smooth muscle fibers it is difficult to establish this point. Unlike striated muscle which atrophies upon denervation, the smooth muscle fibers do not atrophy and may show little evidence of any histological change, though histological changes have been seen in some denervated glands which have become supersensitive (Emmelin, 1952).

The effect of adrenalin and acetylcholine on a single smooth muscle fiber (taenia coli) is shown in Fig. 10.7. Acetylcholine

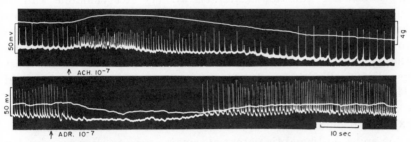

Fig. 10.7. In the upper part of the figure addition of acetylcholine to the taenia muscle causes an increase in the rate of intercellularly recorded action potential discharge (lower trace) and an associated increase in tension of the muscle (upper trace). Conversely, in the muscle shown in the lower part, after addition of adrenalin there is a decrease in rate of discharge and a corresponding decrease in tension. (Courtesy, E. Bülbring; Bülbring, 1962.)

stimulates this cell, depolarizes it, and increases the rate of action potential discharge and the tension. Conversely, adrenalin decreases firing and tension (Bülbring, 1962). The hyperpolarization induced by adrenalin is greater if the membrane potential is low to start with, and the depolarization induced by acetylcholine is greater if the membrane potential is high. Adrenergic substances appear to have their action by changing the membrane permeability to Na^+ through a mechanism in which Ca^{2+} is also involved. In actuality the neurotransmitter substance present in adrenergic nerves is noradrenalin (Euler, 1961). Evidence for this is the extraction of noradrenalin from nerves. Vesicular-like particles 0.03–0.2 μ in diameter are seen in electron micrographs of ultracentrifuged extracts which are high in noradrenalin content.

Ganglionic transmission

Autonomic ganglia affords another type of tissue wherein synaptic transmission properties may be studied (Eccles, 1953). However, it does not have the simplicity once ascribed to it and should, perhaps, be considered a specialized type of transmission center. Presynaptic nerve fibers in the B and C diameter range are found synapsing on cell bodies, and fibers are also found passing through ganglia without synapsing. The stellate ganglion of the cat is simpler and has a single type of synaptic junction between preganglionic and postganglionic fibers. The transmitter substance appears to be ACh. The evidence is similar to that given for the transmitter at the skeletal neuromuscular junction (Chapter 9): (1) Acetylcholine can be collected from the ganglion perfused with saline or eserinized blood upon stimulation of presynaptic fibers with one stimulus calculated to release 10^{-15} grams per ganglion cell. (2) Acetylcholine added to the perfusate of the ganglion caused a discharge of the postganglionic cell with 5×10^{-7} grams/cell required to reach threshold. The frequency of discharge recorded from single postganglionic axons is increased upon addition of a greater concentration of ACh. (3) D-Tubocurarine can block the excitation of the postganglionic axon and a postsynaptic potential remains present after curarization. This potential is similar to the EPP recorded in the muscle near the neuromuscular junction in curarized preparations. (4) D-Tubocurarine blocks excitation by occupying sites on the postsynaptic neuronal membrane on which the transmitter acts. This is shown in the curarized ganglia by the efflux of ACh upon presynaptic stimulation.

The single cell microelectrode studies of Rosamond Eccles (1955) show the properties of transmission in the ganglion cell. A synaptic potential like an EPP (Chapter 9) may be recorded from inside the postganglionic cell body, and with increased stimulation strengths an action potential is excited (Fig. 10.8).

In a more recent study of intracellular recordings from single ganglion cells (superior cervical ganglia), R. M. Eccles (1963) used the curare-like substance *dihydro-β-erythroidine* (*DHE*) to produce a block of the postsynaptic action potential without a membrane depolarization. The action then is homologous with that of curare at the end-plate of skeletal muscle (Chapter 9).

A variety of blocking agents is known for the ganglion synapse. These have been classified by Paton and Perry (1953) as depolarizing or competitive blocking agents. Among the depolarizing agents are ACh, nicotine and tetramethylammonium (TMA). Competitive blocking agents other than DHE include D-tubocurarine, decamethonium, eserine and tetraethylammonium (TEA). Decamethonium at the ganglion is competitive in its action, unlike its action at the neuromuscular junction where it is a depolarizer. Nicotine is considered to have a dual action, a depolarization followed by competitive block, but this may be characteristic for the depolarizing group as a whole.   A further similarity of ganglionic transmission to other synaptic junctions is shown by the spontaneous occurrence of miniature synaptic potentials recorded from the sympathetic ganglion cell of the frog (Blackman, Ginsborg and Ray, 1963). Synaptic transmission is depressed by curarization and by an increase

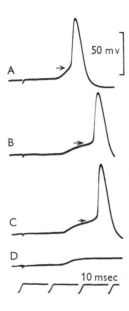

Fig. 10.8.   Action potential recorded from inside a single ganglion cell in response to a single preganglionic volley (A).   Responses seen at reduced stimulus strengths (B–D).   Arrow shows where spike originates from synaptic potential.   (R. M. Eccles, 1955.)

in the Mg^{2+}/Ca^{2+} ratio.   The evidence presented by these workers is consistent with the concept that the synaptic potential is a summed release of transmitter quanta (Eccles, 1964).

Upon interruption of its preganglionic innervation the ganglion shows denervation hypersensitivity.   In addition, a' *retrograde degeneration* of the cells was found after cutting the postganglionic nerve.   An impaired transmission occurs several weeks after cutting the postganglionic nerve.   This is followed by a recovery (Acheson and Remolina, 1955).

A number of studies of transmission through different types of

ganglia indicate a complex organization or at least that a simple
one-to-one transmission is not the rule. Instead, some control
appears to be exerted within the ganglia modulating transmission
through it. This was shown when two preganglionic branches
were stimulated separately and then together; the response in
the postganglionic nerves in the latter case was found to be more than
the sum of each separately, an example of *spatial summation* or
facilitation (Bronk, 1939). This is explained by the presynaptic
fibers branching and each synapsing on the postsynaptic neurons.
The opposite effect, of occlusion or of inhibition, has been observed
(Lorente de Nó and Laporte, 1950; cf. Chapter 14).

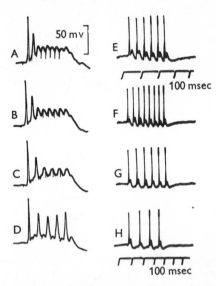

Fig. 10.9. A series of intracellularly recorded action potentials
from a ganglion cell in response to a train of preganglionic stimuli at
the following frequencies: 160 (A), 125 (B), 100 (C), 80 (D), 35 (E),
20 (F), 15 (G) and 10 (H) per sec. Calibration, 100 msec.
(R. M. Eccles, 1955.)

A patterning effect is also likely to be brought about by the
manner in which the ganglia transmit repetitive discharges. A
failure to keep pace with the rate of preganglionic discharge, caused
perhaps by refractoriness or rapid decline of the transmitter substance ACh, appears to limit high frequency rates of transmission.
A decline of synaptic potentials was observed by R. M. Eccles (1955)
after the first 2 or 3 responses to a rapid tetanic stimulation (Fig.
10.9). It is of interest in this regard that, normally, discharges

recorded from the ganglia have low firing rates. For example, in the musculature of blood vessels, which are innervated by post-ganglionic nerve fibers, the constrictor tone is maintained by an impulse rate of 1–2/sec in their fibers. Intense constrictor activity is attained with nerve discharge rates of 5–6/sec, and 6–18/sec is probably the upper limit (Folkow, 1952). These low frequencies match the long durations of the mechanical responses of smooth muscles.

REFERENCES

Acheson, G. H. and Remolina, J. (1955).   The temporal course of the effects of post-ganglionic axotomy on the inferior mesenteric ganglion of the cat. *J. Physiol.* **127**: 603–616.

Axelsson, J. (1961).   Dissociation of electrical and mechanical activity in smooth muscle. *J. Physiol.* **158**: 381–398.

Blackman, J. G., Ginsborg, B. L. and Ray, C. (1963).   Spontaneous synaptic activity in sympathetic ganglion cells of the frog. *J. Physiol.* **167**: 389–401; and On the quantal release of the transmitter at a sympathetic synapse. *Ibid.* 402–415.

Bronk, D. W. (1939).   Synaptic mechanisms in sympathetic ganglia. *J. Neurophysiol.* **2**: 380–401.

Bülbring, E. (1955).   Correlation between membrane potential, spike discharge and tension in smooth muscle. *J. Physiol.* **128**: 200–221.

Bülbring, E. (1962).   Electrical activity in intestinal smooth muscle. *Physiol. Rev.* **42**: *Suppl.* **5**, 160–186.

Burnstock, G. and Holman, M. E. (1961).   Transmission of excitation from autonomic nerve to smooth muscle. *J. Physiol.* **155**: 115–133.

Caesar, R., Edwards, G. A. and Ruska, H. (1957).   Architecture and nerve supply of mammalian smooth muscle tissue. *J. Biophys. Biochem. Cytol.* **3**: 867–878.

Cannon, W. B. (1929).   *Bodily Changes in Pain, Hunger, Fear and Rage.* 2nd Ed.   Appleton, New York.

Cannon, W. B. and Rosenblueth, A. (1949).   *The Supersensitivity of Denervated Structures.* MacMillan, New York.

Cannon, W. B., Newton, H. F., Bright, E. M., Menkin, V. and Moore, R. M. (1929).   Some aspects of the physiology of animals surviving complete exclusion of sympathetic nerve impulses. *Am. J. Physiol.* **89**, 84–107.

Eccles, J. C. (1953).   *The Neurophysiological Basis of Mind.* Oxford University Press, Oxford.

Eccles, J. C. (1964).   *The Physiology of Synapses.* Academic Press, New York.

Eccles, R. M. (1955).   Intracellular potentials recorded from a mammalian sympathetic ganglion. *J. Physiol.* **130**: 572–584.

Eccles, R. M. (1963).   Orthodromic activation of single ganglion cells. *J. Physiol.* **165**: 387–391.

Emmelin, N. (1952).   'Paralytic secretion' of saliva. An example of supersensitivity after denervation. *Physiol. Rev.* **32**: 21–46.

Euler, U. S. von (1961).   Neurotransmission in the adrenergic nervous system. *Harvey Lectures* **55**: 43–65.

Folkow, B. (1952).   Impulse frequency in sympathetic vasomotor fibres correlated to the release and elimination of the transmitter. *Acta Physiol. Scand.* **25**: 49–76.

Fulton, G. P., Lutz, B. R. and Callahan, A. B. (1960).   Innervation as a factor in control of microcirculation. *Physiol. Rev.* **40**: *Suppl.* **4**, 57–64.

Gaskell, W. H. (1916).   *The Involuntary Nervous System.*   Longmans, Green and Co., London.

Gellhorn, E. (1943).   *Autonomic Regulations, Their Significance for Physiology, Psychology and Neuropsychiatry.*   Interscience, New York.

Hillarp, N-A. (1960).   Peripheral autonomic mechanism. *Handbook of Physiology—Neurophysiology.*   Vol. 2, pp. 979–1006.   American Physiological Society, Washington, D.C.

Johnson, W. H. (1962).   Tonic mechanisms in smooth muscle. *Physiol. Rev.* **42**: Suppl. 5, 113–143.

Kuntz, A. (1945).   *The Autonomic Nervous System.*   Lea and Febiger, Philadelphia.

Loewi, O. (1921).   Über humorale Übertragbarkeit der Herznervenwirkung. *Pflügers Arch. Ges. Physiol.* **189**: 239–242.

Lorente de Nó, R. and Laporte, Y. (1950).   Refractoriness, facilitation and inhibition in a sympathetic ganglion. *J. Cell. Comp. Physiol.* **35**: *Suppl.* **2**: 155–192.

Paton, W. D. M. and Perry, W. L. M. (1953).   The relationship between depolarization and block in the cat's superior cervical ganglion. *J. Physiol.* **119**: 43–57.

Richardson, K. C. (1962).   The fine structure of autonomic nerve endings in smooth muscle of the rat vas deferens. *J. Anat.* **96**: 427–442.

Rosenblueth, A. (1950).   *The Transmission of Nerve Impulses at Neuroeffector Junctions and Peripheral Synapses.*   John Wiley and Sons, New York.

Sperlakis, N. and Prosser, C. L. (1959).   Mechanical and electrical activity in intestinal smooth muscle. *Am. J. Physiol.* **196**: 850–856.

11

Sensory Reception—Peripheral Aspects

Sensory categories and transduction

It is commonly accepted that objects in the external world act upon sensory receptors to give rise to a variety of simple *sensations* recognized as patches of light, sounds, smells, etc. From these various primary sensations it is further supposed that the higher parts of the nervous system organize sensations into *perceptions* of recognizable objects which are more complex integrations. However, even the presumed simple sensation does not appear to be a conscious appreciation of a single sensory excitation. As we shall see, the afferent mechanisms report complex aspects of a stimulus and even the primary receptor afferents themselves are subject to CNS mechanisms of control which will modify the sensory input, such control of the sensory input depending on the state of consciousness or attention to one thing or another in the environment. We shall refer to central mechanisms controlling sensory reception in Chapter 21. In this chapter the initial transformation of the stimulus into an activation of sensory neurons will be discussed.

Sensory endings of afferent nerves may terminate as *free nerve endings* or may be found associated with specialized secondary structures to form *receptor organs*. In the course of evolution, the receptor organs or free sensory nerve endings came to have a lower threshold to one chemical or physical change than to others. For example, a receptor organ such as the eye may respond to only a few quanta of light. Vibrational displacements of the order of an Ångstrom unit are appreciated in sound reception. Sexual attraction of moths by smell has been reported to occur over distances of more than a mile (Fabre, 1943); the odor at such distances is excited by only a few score of molecules.

The sensory nerve endings perform the function of *transduction*, changing the various forms of physical energy acting on them into trains of action potentials in the nerve axons. These rhythmic discharges constitute the *sensory code* transmitted by the sensory nerve into the CNS whereby the pattern of discharge represents the original physical or chemical agent (*vide infra*).

Classically we are considered to have five senses—sight, hearing, touch, taste and smell. However, there are a variety of sensory inputs of which we are unaware. We have *chemoreceptors* which respond to changes in the level of various substances in the blood, such as glucose and various ions. There are the *pressoreceptors* which respond to the internal changes of blood pressure within the vessels and the *stretch receptors* in the muscle (*vide infra*). In lower organisms there are, in addition, senses which do not appear to have counterparts in vertebrates. The eye of *Limulus* and of the bee can detect the polarization of light by which these species orient themselves. The *lateral-line organs* of fish are sensitive to vibrations and water movement. There is also the example of the electric fish, *Gymnarchus*, which surrounds itself with an electrical field which is altered by approaching objects signaling their presence (Lissmann, 1963).

We can categorize sensation by the type of physical stimulation required to evoke it: mechanical, radiant or chemical. In the category of mechanical stimuli are those senses of touch, pressure, stretch (length and tension changes), the special vibratory sense of sound and of the vestibular apparatus relating to equilibrium and motion which will be discussed in Chapter 12. Under radiant energy are sensations of warmth and cold which will be considered in the section on cutaneous receptors, although such receptors are present elsewhere, e.g. in the tongue. The reception of light by the eye will be discussed in Chapter 12. Taste and smell, the chemoreceptor senses of which we are conscious, will be discussed briefly in a later section of this chapter.

Rather than group sensory receptors by the type of stimulus used to excite the receptors, receptors may be grouped according to the relation of the stimulus to the organism as was done by Sherrington (1906). *Exteroceptors* are those sensory receptors responding to light, heat and sound stimuli impinging on the animal from external sources. *Proprioceptors* are sensory receptors within the body responding to its own operations as, for example, impulses from receptors in muscles, joints and tendons which signify the position of parts of the body in relation to the whole. Those include the vestibular receptors responding either to static gravitational influences or to acceleratory movements of the head (Chapter 12). The *interoceptors* were originally considered to be receptors within the intestinal tract which is not properly part of the body. The modern use of the term interoceptors includes receptors of all the viscera including the blood vessels.

Another type of categorization is *epicritic* and *protopathic* sensations (Head, 1920). The epicritic sensations are those which can be sharply localized in the skin surface. Touch is an epicritic sensation which is measured by means of the *two-point discrimination* test. Using a pair of pointed dividers, a subject is asked to determine if one point or two points on the surface of the skin have been simultaneously excited. A discrimination of points very close together is possible over the fingertips, nose and, in general, the exposed and protruding regions of the body which have a more extensive innervation. Protopathic sensations are those very poorly localized within the skin surface and, in general, are experienced as disagreeable or painful. Head's categorization is too general but it does appear to be of use with respect to pain, as will be discussed in a later section.

The sensory code

Adrian (1928) and his collaborators pioneered in studies of sensation using single sensory fibers isolated from the rest of the nerves while the sensory receptor organ, or sensory field it innervates, could be excited and action potentials recorded from the fiber. We shall discuss the nature of sensory organs found in muscle in more detail in Chapter 12. The stretch receptor was historically the first receptor studied showing the relation of its repetitive discharge of action potentials in response to stimulation. Different stretching loads were applied to the muscle and the frequency of the resulting discharge in single fibers of these stretch receptors was found to be related to the degree of applied stretch (Fig. 11.1).

Upon application of the stretch, the frequency of the afferent sensory nerve discharge was fast and then soon afterwards the rate decreased. This reduction of discharge in the face of a maintained stimulus, as shown for a photoreceptor in Fig. 11.2, is called *adaptation*. Other receptors similarly investigated were found to have differing degrees of adaptation (Fig. 11.3). Those of the touch receptors adapted rapidly while others were found to adapt little, if at all. Some receptors such as the carotid pressure receptor would not be expected to show much adaptation as it signals the steady state level of pressure in the blood vessel so that reflex CNS changes can be made to maintain the homeostatic level. Adaptation may in part underlie awareness, or lack of awareness, to stimuli from the environment. Many long-maintained stimulations are not attended to, such as, for example, our lack of attention to the contact of clothes on our body. The problem of *discrimination*, the attention to some stimuli

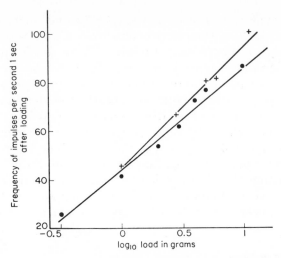

Fig. 11.1.   Intensity of stimulus and associated rate of neural discharge of stretch receptor of frog muscle from two experiments (+, •).   Frequency determined 1 sec after the onset of the stretching load.   (From Mathews, *J. Physiol.*, **71**, 64, 1931.)

and not to others, is not simply due to differences in adaptation of the sensory receptors.   Discrimination involves a variety of complex CNS mechanisms some of which will be discussed in Chapter 20.

Taking a convenient fixed interval of time after the onset of a maintained stimulus, the rate of nerve impulses excited in the sensory fibers is related to the intensity of the applied stimulus in a regular and consistent way as indicated in Fig. 11.1.   Examples are shown in Fig. 11.4 (taken from an optic fiber responding to different

Fig. 11.2.   Light stimulus maintained at a constant strength and repetitive discharge of photoreceptor shows a faster rate at onset gradually diminishing (adapting) to a constant level.   Filled bar indicates duration of light stimulus.   Time intervals 0.2 sec. (After Hartline; from Bronk, *Res. Publ. Assoc. Nervous Mental Disease*, **15**: 60, 1934.)

intensities of light, and from a carotid receptor fiber).   A logarithmic
relationship was found between the intensity of the stimulus applied
to the receptor and the resulting frequency of discharges in the afferent
fibers over most of the range of stimulus intensities.   The logarithmic
relation fits with the *Weber–Fechner law* (Granit, 1955).   This is a
psychophysical relationship between neural events and the conscious

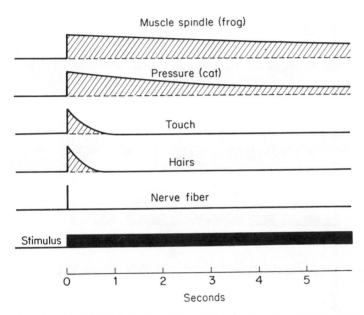

Fig. 11.3.   Adaptation of various sense organs in response to a
constant stimulation shown in diagrammatic fashion.   Height
of the curve indicates rate of discharge.   (Adrian, 1928.)

discrimination of incremental changes in the strength of the stimulus.
For example, small weights are put into the palm of the hand of a
blindfolded subject in standardized fashion.   The size of the just-
noticeable increment of weight depends on the weight already
present.   The relation of stimulus (weight) to sensation is indicated
by the following equation:

$$\Delta R/R = k\,\Delta S \tag{11.1}$$

where ΔS is the increment of weight, k is a constant, R the amount of
weight already present, and ΔR is the amount added to give the just-
noticeable difference in sensation.

A logarithmic relationship between R and S was derived by making the hypothesis that this would hold for ΔR and ΔS in the limit as $\Delta R \to dR$ and $\Delta S \to dS$. Integration gives the Weber–Fechner law in the following form:

$$S = a \log R + b \tag{11.2}$$

where S is the sensation of weight which increases logarithmically with the added stimulus and a and b are constants.

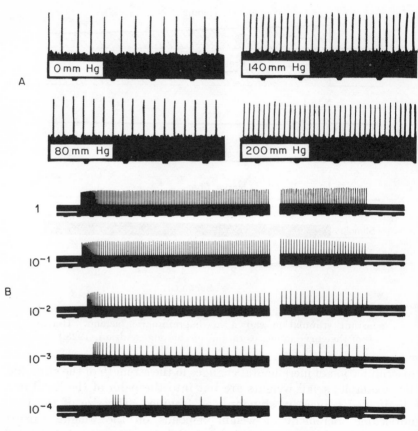

Fig. 11.4. The rate of discharge of a nerve fiber from a carotid sinus pressure receptor (A) is shown at different levels of inter-carotid pressure. (After Bronk, and Stella, *Am. J. Physiol.*, **110**: 708, 1935.) The discharge from a single optic receptor nerve fiber of the *Limulus* eye (B) is shown at different intensities of illumination. The filled bar underneath signifies the duration of stimulation. (After McNichol, in Grenell and Mullins (Eds.), *Molecular Structure and Functional Activity of Nerve Cells*, American Institute of Biological Science, 1956.)

While the rate of discharge in single afferent fibers of a number of different sensory receptors in general corresponds to the logarithm of the applied stimulus (Granit, 1955), deviations from the logarithmic relation occur at the extremes of the stimulus range. Stevens (1961) studied a number of different sensory qualities in human subjects comparing stimulus intensities in a number of ways and concluded that a power law and not a logarithmic law best represents the psychophysical relationship. Considering the evidence obtained from *Limulus* eye receptors showing an excellent fit to a logarithmic relationship, Rushton (1961) points out that the logarithmic relation has the property of maintaining a constant signal-to-noise discrimination ratio. Subjective factors present in the type of comparisons made with human subjects may be responsible for a deviation from a logarithmic relationship.

Nerve specificity

Muller's *law of specific energies* states that when specific nerves are excited, only a certain sensation will be experienced. As an example, stimulation of the retina either by pressure applied to the side of the eyeball or by an electrical current will be experienced as an optical sensation. Similarly, stimulation of auditory nerves by any means is experienced as a sensation of sound. We can infer that the sensory fibers terminate in specific regions of the CNS to give rise to the appropriate sensation. In addition, we can suppose that the receptor terminals have become specifically sensitive to the appropriate stimulus in the course of evolution.

The concept of nerve specificity gained considerable force from the demonstration that upon appropriate stimulation of the skin sensations were distributed in separate spots. This was seen when upon searching over the surface of the skin with a pointed cold metal bar as a stimulus, a sensation of cold was only found in certain spots, presumably where an underlying cold receptor was present to give rise to the sensation of cold. Further, punctate receptors for heat, touch or pressure, and pain could be similarly mapped out on the surface of the skin. For each of the sensory categories the points were presumably due to the activation of one of the receptors located at that site while reception did not occur elsewhere unless by spread of the stimulus to a receptor. In the skin and various other tissues, including mucosa and peritoneum, a number of receptor organs were identified and to them a sensory receptor function assigned. These as usually listed are: Meissner's corpuscle (touch), Merkel's disc (touch), Golgi–Massoni corpuscle (touch-pressure),

Pacinian corpuscle (touch-pressure), Ruffini endings (warmth), Krause's end-bulbs (cold), with the free nerve terminations reserved for pain reception.

However, careful examination of the skin failed to show the expected correlation of anatomic receptor organs with sensory spots (Weddell, 1961). The hairy skin of the human body (which represents 90% of the surface) shows only two types of sensory nerve terminations. These are the free nerve endings with many branches overlapping in a plexiform meshwork and sensory fibers innervating the hair follicles. The follicles are innervated by 2–30 separate axons. A large number of follicles may be served by one axon, making the pattern of nerve innervation of hairs complex. It is only in specialized regions such as in the palmar and plantar skin that the specialized Meissner's corpuscles and Merkel's discs are found. Krause's end-bulbs are found in exposed mucous membranes such as lips, nipples, etc. Therefore, little anatomical basis is seen for a correlation of sensory qualities with definite end-organ structure over most of the skin surface. One of the classical supports for an identification of pain sensation with free nerve endings was that stimulation of the cornea by any means was supposed to give rise to the sensation of pain and corneal nerve terminations are predominantly free nerve endings. Upon more careful examination it was shown that sensations of touch and temperature could also be elicited from corneal stimulation (Lele and Weddell, 1956). Therefore, a sensory modality is not to be identified with an end-organ structure although some end-organs such as the Pacinian corpuscle (Chapter 12) are associated with one type of sensation, namely touch-pressure.

For the law of the specific nerve energies to be valid requires only that the sensory nerve endings subserving a particular sensation have a molecular organization which makes it more sensitive to one type of stimulation. Said in another way, the validity of the law of specific nerve energies rests on whether an afferent fiber can be readily excited by more than one mode of stimulation. A partial answer to this question was supplied by Douglas and Ritchie (1959) who assessed the activity in single C group afferent fibers when the sensory skin field was excited by cold, heat, mechanical or pain-arousing stimulation. All these categories of stimulation excited C fiber discharges. They found evidence that both cold and touch are represented in the same fiber, a finding which is not in accord with the law of specific nerve energies. The specific receptors subserved by C fibers were grouped by Iggo (1959) into those of (a) hair receptors, (b) touch or pressure receptors and (c) thermoreceptors.   The thermoreceptors included fibers responding to large temperature increases or decreases of 15–20°C; these are the cold or hot receptors. Those fibers responding to temperature changes of only a few degrees are the cool or warm receptors.   Fibers identified as mechanoreceptors were also stimulated by temperature decreases of 4–10°C. However, temperature stimulation of mechanoreceptor afferents gave rise to a much lower rate of firing (5/sec) than did mild mechanical stimulation of the skin which gave discharge rates of 50/sec in those same fibers.

Chemoreception—taste and smell

Chemoreception is perhaps the most fundamental sense.   It is found in motile unicellular organisms where it is shown by *chemotaxis* —the movement of the organism in response to chemical agents, for example toward sources of food.   The chemoreception of unicellular organisms perhaps has some similarity to the specialized cells of the multicellular organisms, which in the course of evolution have become chemoreceptor cells.   Both for smell and taste the appropriate chemical substances must come in contact with the receptor cell.   For the sense of taste, substances dissolved in the saliva excite *taste buds* in the papillae of the tongue.   Taste in humans is considered as a combination of one or more of four categories—sour, sweet, bitter or salty.   Using different dilutions of HCl, sucrose, quinine and NaCl to give rise to each of these taste sensations respectively, it would appear that the thresholds to these various test substances are approximately similar in a variety of species (Beidler, 1961).

These categories may not be fundamental in that a specific receptor exists for each of these tastes.   Pfaffman (1941) found that acid could excite discharges in single fibers also responding to salt; other fibers were found reacting only to acid.   Zotterman (1958), recording from single taste fibers, found a number of fibers responding to water without added solute present.   These 'water' fibers were found in the cat, dog, pig and rabbit but not in the rat, calf and lamb.   The cat lacks receptors responding to sweet substances. The variations among animal species in regard to their feeding behavior no doubt have their basis in the particular types of taste receptors they have.

For man, smell appears to be of secondary importance except where we enjoy the smells of food.   It is much more important for other animals for feeding, sex and alertness to predators.   Little

is known of the neural mechanisms of smell.   In the vertebrate,
odiferous substances in the nose come in contact with, dissolve
in and act on the *olfactory mucosa*.   The mucosa contains rod-
shaped detectors with hair-like fibrils at the surface which are
probably the true receptive elements.   The other end of the receptor

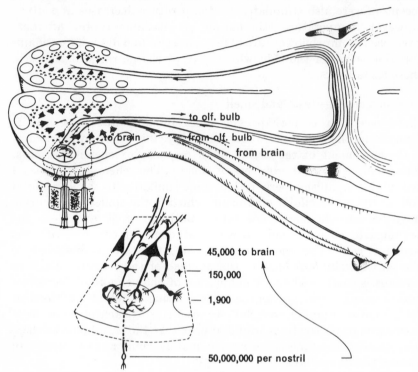

to olf. bulb

to brain

from olf. bulb

from brain

45,000 to brain

150,000

1,900

50,000,000 per nostril

Fig. 11.5.   The rabbit's olfactory bulb shown in diagrammatic
fashion with olfactory receptor neurons synapsing on mitral cells
in the glomeruli (circled).   Mitral cell axons connect to the brain.
Axons of tufted cells in the glomeruli also pass to the opposite
bulb.   (Green, *Endeavor*, **22**: 80, 1963.)

passes into the *olfactory bulb* (an extension of the brain) to make
contact with the tufted end of the secondary olfactory neuron,
the *mitral cell* (Fig. 11.5).   From the mitral cell, axons pass into
other parts of the brain and eventually to regions of the cerebral
cortex in which olfactory stimuli are perceived.   From the axons of
the mitral cell Adrian (1950) was able to record unit discharges to
olfactory stimulation.   These electrical changes are, however, at
least one step removed from the primary receptor.   A slow potential change has been found in the olfactory mucosa when it is ex-

cited by odiferous substances. This *olfactory receptor potential* is negative in polarity and lasts several seconds in response to a puff of air containing an odoriferous substance (Ottoson, 1958). The potential is similar to the receptor potentials of other sensory organs to be discussed in Chapter 12. However, there is evidence against the causal relation of the olfactory receptor potential to olfactory nerve discharges (Shibuya, 1964).

The chief as yet unresolved problem with respect to olfaction is the relation of chemical structure of the odiferous substance to the excitation of the receptors. Many theories have been proposed but hold true only to a limited extent (Moncrieff, 1951). Amoore (1963) classifies odiferous substances into a number of primary odors, each having a characteristic molecular shape. A specific odor sensation is excited when the properly shaped substance fits into a surface receptor region or 'socket'. The seven primary odors are given as: camphoraceous, pungent, ethereal, floral, pepperminty, musky and putrid. Such odors as almond, aromatic and aniseed, lemon, cedar, garlic and rancid are complex, being composed of two or more primary odors (cf. Amoore, 1964).

Using an early theory of Dyson that there is a relation between a vibrational movement in an odiferous molecule to that of the receptor, Wright (1963) drew attention to the distinctive yellow or brown pigment present in the olfactory membrane. Odiferous substances by their vibratory movement are considered to change the energy level of the pigment.

In any theory thus far presented what is left unexplained is the exact mechanism of olfactory transduction in the membrane of the sensory nerve terminals.

Pain and related sensations

Pain is a protean sense, which we infer to be present to some degree in all organisms by their reaction to noxious stimulation. Sherrington (1906) drew attention to the fact that pain is excited by influences which damage the tissues or are potentially damaging stimuli. Pain, therefore, is a signal of potential damage from noxious stimulation—a *nociceptive* sensory system. Two theories of pain have been considered. One is that excessive stimulation of any of the sensory nerves will give rise to pain. It is common experience that intense noises, very bright lights, pressures on the body and very hot or cold stimuli are painful. The other theory which has now gained general acceptance is that there are special nerve fibers which can be characterized as pain receptor fibers. Recording from sensory nerve fibers innervating an area of a cat's skin subjected to noxious stimuli able to excite pain (light burning), Zotterman (1933, 1939) found that impulses associated with those stimuli excited a slow conducting, small diameter group of fibers, those falling into the small δ group of A and into the C fiber range. In the human, pressure cuffs were applied to the arm to shut off blood supply. After 15–20 minutes, touch and other epicritic sensations were lost and pain sensations arose and became severe. Touch then produced pain. Studies on asphyxiation of nerves indicated that the smaller fibers are more resistant to lack of oxygen than the larger ones; the small ones continue to conduct such pain sensations for a relatively long time.

If the hot ember of a match is touched to the skin of the toe, a bright prick-like sensation of pain is experienced, the *first pain*, followed after a brief delay by a more diffuse (protopathic) burning *second pain*. The *double-pain* sensation may be related to the delta group of A and the C class of nerve fibers carrying pain (Zotterman, 1959). The protopathic second pain, compared to the epicritic first pain, appears to be more resistant to asphyxiation. It is the second type of pain which persists in the pressure cuff experiments cited above. A study of the time delay between the double pains when the place stimulated on the skin is moved successively closer to the CNS shows a decrease in latencies expected of velocities of a δ group of A fibers and of C fibers subserving these two pains. However, the study of double pain is difficult because of the subjective nature of the experiments and there is no agreement among observers on this phenomenon (Gasser, 1943).

While pain appears to be carried in the smaller fibers, other sensations such as mechanical stimulation of hair and skin, temperature and pressure are also carried in C fibers as was noted in the preceding section. This reopens the possibility that C fibers subserve more than one sensory modality. Iggo (1959) suggested that the least sensitive pressure receptors and thermoreceptors of the C group could mediate pain. Tickle and itch are sensations often related to pain and believed by some to be an excitation of pain fibers at a level below that exciting a sensation of pain. However, itch (*pruritus*) appears to be a separable sense quality; in some cases it can be present in intense degree without pain (Arthur and Shelley, 1959).

Some of the relations between itch and pain and damage are shown by the *triple response* elicited by a skin scratch which has itching as an associated sensation. The triple response is seen as a *red* line along the scratch, a *flare* spreading around the scratch and a *weal* which occurs later along the line of the scratch.   The flare is due to a vaso-dilation which may extend several centimeters or even scores of centi-meters from the scratch.   Diffusion of released substances cannot account for spreads over such distances and an *axon reflex* has been invoked.   An axon reflex is an excitation of one branch of an axon with propagation up to and then down the other terminal branches of that axon (Fig. 11.6).   In this case the axon reflex causes a vaso-dilation.   The axon reflex is shown not to require the CNS by the following experiment.   The nerve supplying an area of skin is cut

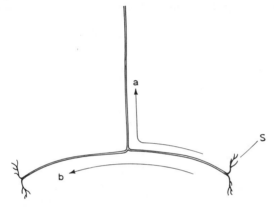

Fig. 11.6.   Stimulation (S) of one branch of an afferent sensory nerve causes an orthodromic volley to pass centrally (a) and also antidromically (b) along other nerve branches to give an axon reflex.

and the flare response of the triple reaction can still be elicited until, after several days, the nerve degenerates and then the axon reflex can no longer be elicited.

Many forms of injury are found to have redness (vasodilation) and pain associated together—*erythralgia*.   The surrounding area becomes *hyperalgesic*, is painful on mechanical stimulation (pin prick) which does not evoke pain in normal skin.   The develop-ment of a hyperalgesic region around a point of damage induced by strong faradic stimulation is shown in Fig. 11.7.

The observations of Lewis (1942) led him to consider that a number of small-diameter fibers present in the sensory nerves constitute a *nocifensor* system of fibers.   The fibers which are afferent in their function also have *antidromic* effects at their distal terminals. Excitation of one branch gives rise by an axon reflex to release of some chemical substances at the other afferent terminals (Fig. 11.6).

Bayliss (1901, 1902) reported that stimulation of sensory fibers in the dorsal roots could by antidromic action give rise to a vaso-dilation in peripheral structures.   Sonnenschein and Bernstein (1957) found that dorsal root section and subsequent degeneration of the fibers did not prevent the triple response.   The triple response is therefore most likely due to the action of efferent fibers.   However, there is other evidence that antidromic activity in sensory fibers can have effects on sensory discharges.   When a region of skin is trau-matized it gives rise to a discharge of slow potentials which appear to arise from small fibers.   Such *sensitized* skin can show an increase in its discharge to a light mechanical stimulus if the nerve supply to the

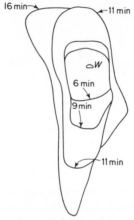

Fig. 11.7.   In an area of injury a weal (*W*) is found with a larger area of hyperalgesia around it.   The area of hyperalgesia spreads as indicated by the times shown.   Approximately ¼ actual size.   (From Lewis, *Clin. Sci.*, **2**: 373, 1936.)

skin is antidromically stimulated (Habgood, 1950).   The overlapping of the peripheral fields of sensory terminations permits a substance released from the terminals of one set of nerves to augment discharges or even to give rise to spontaneous discharges in the other nerve. Habgood also showed that if the inner surfaces of two pieces of frog skin were apposed, each with their nerve innervation intact, anti-dromic stimulation of one nerve could augment sensitized discharges of the other.   The released substance appears to be *histamine* as shown by the marked effectiveness of an antihistamine to block the action of the released substance.   Histamine or histiminic substances are released from traumatized cells and these can activate the small pain fibers.   Rosenthal and Sonnenschein (1948) found that histamine when intradermally injected was effective in exciting pain described as 'pricking,' 'tingling' or 'stinging' at threshold.   Concentrations as low as 10^{-18} M were effective and itch appeared when higher concentrations of histamine were used.   This observation is of interest because of the concept that itch is due to a lower level excitation of pain fibers.   A separate set of pain and itch fibers appears likely but there is a close association of these senses and also the sense of tickle.

Experiments made with blister bases have been used in a study of substances exciting pain and itch.   A blister is produced by applying an irritant such as *cantharidin* to the skin (Arthur and Shelley, 1959). The epithelial surface is raised by the blister exudate leaving the basal skin layers with its innervation exposed.   Various substances may then be injected into the blister or applied to it after removing the epithelium.   Histamine was found effective to excite itch and pain in low concentration.   Histamine combined with acetylcholine was even more effective, and the proteolytic enzyme, papain, was also effective.   Apparently itch is produced at lower concentrations in these preparations where the epithelium is removed and a better diffusion into the basal cell layers where nerve terminals are present is assured (Arthur and Shelley, 1959).

Rather than specific terminals for pain sensation, Weddell (1961) has suggested that the sensation is determined by the pattern of innervation in the periphery.   In the skin the peripheral nerve terminals branch profusely as previously noted so that at any one region branches from two or more nerves are present.   If one nerve branch is cut, stroking or touching the skin gives rise, via the remaining terminations, to sensation which is 'disagreeable,' a protopathic sensation.   When the nerves regenerate and the usual pattern of overlapping is resumed, the protopathic response to touch disappears.

There is evidence that the pattern of sensory input will determine the quality of other sensations.   In the arm-cuff experiments (Zotterman, 1933) after a period of asphyxiation, touch is experienced as pain.   In the normally innervated skin stimulation by pressure will partially suppress pain (Lewis, 1942).   These observations suggest that the impulses in fibers responding to touch and pressure will in the CNS act to inhibit the sensations of pain.   A discussion of CNS properties involved in sensation will be deferred until Chapter 21. However, it is important to appreciate that the CNS affects what appears to be a simple determination, a threshold for pain sensation. Techniques of assessing pain threshold which have been used include electrical stimulation of tooth nerves by currents led in via dental fillings, heated wires applied to the skin, substances injected into the skin or applied to wounds or a blister as already noted. In the technique used by Hardy *et al.* (1943) a radiant heat source (a high wattage lamp) was focused on the skin of the forehead blackened with carbon pigment. Depending on the strength of the heat applied, a quick, sharp stinging sensation of pain is experienced after a fairly definite interval. The strength of the heat required to reach this point just at the end of a 3-second exposure was the end-point used to determine the pain threshold. An increase of the threshold appeared when a clinically effective pain relieving (*analgesic*) drug such as morphine was administered. However, too many subjective aspects are involved in this type of measurement. As pointed out in Beecher's (1959) critique of the use of such pain threshold determinations in the human, the apparent threshold for pain is readily increased or decreased by suggestion. Unexpected wounds may even be sustained without pain if attention is directed elsewhere. For example, one-third of the victims of severe war injuries did not experience pain at the time of injury (Beecher, 1959).

REFERENCES

Adrian, E. D. (1928). *The Basis of Sensation. The Action of the Sense Organs.* Christophers, London.

Adrian, E. D. (1950). The electrical activity of the mammalian olfactory bulb. *Electroenceph. Clin. Neurophysiol.* **2**: 377–388.

Amoore, J. E. (1963). Stereochemical theory of olfaction. *Nature* **198**: 271–272.

Amoore, J. E., Johnston, J. W. Jr. and Rubin, M. (1964). The stereochemical theory of odor. *Scient. Am.* **210**: 42–49.

Arthur, R. P. and Shelley, W. B. (1959). The peripheral mechanism of itch in man. *Pain and Itch Nervous Mechanisms.* Ciba Symposium No. 1, pp. 84–97. Churchill, London.

Bayliss, W. M. (1901). On the origin from the spinal cord of the vaso-dilator fibres of the hind limb, and on the nature of these fibres. *J. Physiol.* **26**: 173–209.

Bayliss, W. M. (1902). Further researches on antidromic nerve impulses. *J. Physiol.* **28**: 276–299.

Beecher, H. K. (1959). Measurement of subjective responses. *Quantitative Effects of Drugs.* Oxford University Press, New York.

Beidler, L. M. (1961). Mechanisms of gustatory and olfactory receptor stimulation. *Sensory Communication.* Edited by W. A. Rosenblith. Pp. 143–157. John Wiley and Sons, New York.

Douglas, W. W. and Ritchie, J. M. (1959). The sensory functions of the non-myelinated nerve fibres from the skin. *Pain and Itch Nervous Mechanisms.* Ciba Symposium No. 1, pp. 26–39. Churchill, London.

Fabre, J. H. (1943). *Social Life in the Insect World.* Translated by B. Miall. Pelican, London.

Gasser, H. S. (1943). Pain-producing impulses in peripheral nerves. *Assoc. Res. Nervous Mental Disease* **23**: 44–62.

Granit, R. (1955).   *Receptors and Sensory Perception.*   Yale University Press, New Haven.

Habgood, J. S. (1950).   Sensitization of sensory receptors in the frog's skin. *J. Physiol.* **111**: 195–213.

Hardy, J. D., Wolff, H. G. and Goodell, H. (1943).   The pain threshold in man.   *Assoc. Res. Nervous Mental Disease* **23**: 1–15.

Head, H. (1920).   *Studies in Neurology.*   Oxford University Press, London.

Iggo, A. (1959).   A single unit analysis of cutaneous receptors with C afferent fibres.   *Pain and Itch Nervous Mechanisms.*   Ciba Symposium No. 1, pp. 41–56.   Churchill, London.

Lele, P. P. and Weddell, G. (1956).   The relation between neurohistology and corneal sensibility.   *Brain* **79**: 119–154.

Lewis, T. (1942).   *Pain.*   Macmillan Co., New York.

Lissmann, H. W. (1963).   Electric location by fishes.   *Scient. Am.* **208**: 50–59.

Moncrieff, R. W. (1951).   *The Chemical Senses.*   2nd Ed.   John Wiley and Sons, New York.

Ottoson, D. (1958).   The slow electrical response of the olfactory end organs. *Exptl. Cell. Res. Suppl.* **5**: 451–469.

Pfaffman, C. (1941).   Gustatory afferent impulses.   *J. Cell. Comp. Physiol.* **17**: 243–258.

Rosenthal, S. R. and Sonnenschein, R. R. (1948).   Histamine as the possible chemical mediator for cutaneous pain.   *Am. J. Physiol.* **155**: 186–190.

Rushton, W. A. H. (1961).   Peripheral coding in the nervous system. *Sensory Communication.*   Edited by W. A. Rosenblith.   Pp. 169–181. John Wiley and Sons, New York.

Sherrington, C. (1906).   *The Integrative Action of the Nervous System.*   Yale University Press, New Haven.   Rev. Ed. 1947.   Cambridge University Press, Cambridge.

Shibuya, T. (1964).   Dissociation of olfactory response and mucosal potential. *Science* **143**: 1338–1340.

Sonnenschein, R. R. and Bernstein, M. (1957).   Relation to the central nervous system of neural pathways mediating histamine flare and nicotine sweating.   *J. Appl. Physiol.* **11**: 481–485.

Stevens, S. S. (1961).   The psychophysics of sensory function.   *Sensory Communication.*   Edited by W. A. Rosenblith.   Pp. 1–33.   John Wiley and Sons, New York.

Weddell, G. (1961).   Receptors for somatic sensation.   *Brain and Behavior.* Edited by M. A. B. Brazier.   Pp. 13–48.   Vol. 1.   American Institute of Biological Sciences, Washington, D.C.

Wright, R. H. (1964).   *The Science of Smell.*   George Allen and Unwin, London.

Zotterman, Y. (1933).   Studies in the peripheral nervous mechanism of pain. *Acta Med. Scand.* **80**: 185–242.

Zotterman, Y. (1939).   Touch, pain and tickling: An electrophysiological investigation on cutaneous sensory nerves.   *J. Physiol.* **95**: 1–28.

Zotterman, Y. (1958).   Studies in the nervous mechanism of taste.   *Exptl. Cell Res. Suppl.* **5**: 520–526.

Zotterman, Y. (1959).   The peripheral nervous mechanism of pain: A brief review.   *Pain and Itch Nervous Mechanisms.*   Ciba Symposium No. 1, pp. 13–25.   Churchill, London.

12

Mechanical, Auditory and Visual
Receptor Properties

Generator potentials

Just as in neuromuscular transmission a special type of mediating potential is found (the EPP, Chapter 9), so also in sensory organs slow potentials are found which appear to mediate between an adequate stimulus to a receptor and the resulting afferent nerve discharge. This concept was developed by Granit (1947) in studies of the retinal potentials which have a relationship to the rate of discharge of action potentials in the optic fibers passing to the brain. Following Davis' (1961) example it will be convenient to reserve the term *generator potential* for those cases where a slow potential change occurs in one part of the sensory nerve termination itself, with another portion elsewhere giving rise to the repetitive discharge. As will be seen, this is the case in the stretch receptors found in muscle and in the Pacinian corpuscles subserving touch. *Receptor potentials* are found in the more complex receptor organs of the labyrinth, ear, and eye to be described in this chapter. Receptor potentials arise from specialized cells to in turn act on the nearby sensory fiber terminals to depolarize them and initiate repetitive action potentials.

Muscle stretch receptor

The peculiar muscle-like structures found in skeletal muscles described as *muscle spindles* because of their shape, were shown by Sherrington (1894) to be sensory receptors. In the cat the ventral motor roots were cut and after the motor fibers degenerated the fibers of large diameter originating from the spindles remained intact showing that they arose from the dorsal (sensory) root. These are the receptors responsible for afferent discharge on stretch of a muscle (Chapter 11). In the frog, the sensory nerves are wrapped around the central portion of the receptor spindles and then terminate in thin nonmyelinated fibers consisting of a series of bead-like expansions (Fig. 12.1). These *flower-spray* endings were found in electron microscope studies to have small filaments which attach to the muscle at their beaded expansion where the mechanical excitation of the terminals take place (Katz, 1961).   The central region of the spindle does not have the filamentous structure of striated muscle which is seen in the rest of the spindle.   The central region appears to consist of a visco-elastic material.   In the mammalian spindle

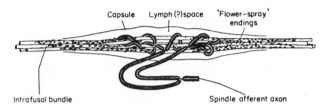

Fig. 12.1.   The middle portion of the frog spindle has afferent myelinated axons wrapped around it, the fibers terminating in beaded 'flower-spray' endings.   This region is enclosed by a capsule which presumably contains lymph.   (Gray, *Proc. Roy. Soc.*, **146**: 416, 1957.)

receptor the main sensory fiber terminates by wrapping around the central portion as the *annulospiral* ending.   Several types of sensory terminations are present on spindle receptor organs differing in sensory properties.   In addition the vertebrate spindle has a motor innervation found on the muscular part of the spindle receptors on either side of the central portion.   These features will be discussed in Chapter 17; the emphasis here is placed on the receptor properties of the primary afferent fiber of the spindle and the nature of the transduction process.

The properties of a receptor may be shown by placing one recording electrode on the nerve close to the muscle spindle and the second recording electrode on an electrically indifferent site, the muscle tendon (Katz, 1950).   Upon stretch of the receptor, a repetitive series of propagated action potentials was found superimposed on a slow potential change (Fig. 12.2).   This slow potential is the generator potential originating from the sensory endings on the spindle.   Upon stretch of the receptor organ the sensory nerve terminals are deformed and depolarized, the resulting electrotonus spreading out in the membrane of the sensory nerve fibers as expected from the cable properties of nerve (Chapter 6).   The difference in mechanism of the generator potential and the resulting action potentials was shown by applying the local anesthetic *procaine* to the muscle.   With this substance it was possible to block action potential discharges leaving intact the generator potential as shown in Fig. 12.3. Action potential discharges could also be blocked without decreasing the generator potentials by soaking the preparation in a low-Na$^+$ Ringer solution.

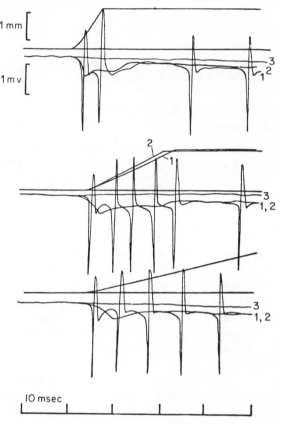

Fig. 12.2. Three different examples of application of stretch to the spindle receptor are shown. Upper line shows rate of stretch which results in a number of action potential responses, (1). The slow depolarization or generator potential remains present after procaine application, (2). Without stretch there is no potential, (3). Negative change is downward in the records. (Katz, 1950.)

The relationships of the depolarization to the rate of action potential discharge was further investigated. The rate of discharge was greatest during stretch, i.e. during *dynamic* stretching. With a constant or *static* level of stretch imposed, a steady depolarization level was maintained. At the end of a stretch, the generator potential either ceases abruptly or is followed by a brief period of hyperpolarization (Fig. 12.3).

The stretch receptor shows adaptation by the decreased discharge rate soon after the onset of a maintained stretch. Is adaptation due to the elastic properties of the mid-portion of the receptor or does the

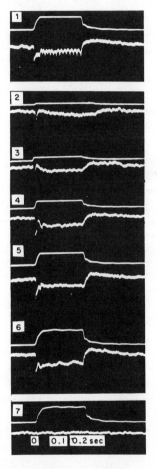

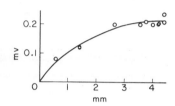

Fig. 12.3. Action potentials from a stretch receptor (lower trace of 1), in response to stretch (upper trace) becomes blocked by procaine leaving the slow generator potentials. These are recorded at different strengths of stretch (2–6). After the nerve was crushed, the slow potential was not observed on stretching (7). The amplitude of the generator potential is shown in the graph as a function of applied stretch. (Katz, 1950.)

nerve fiber itself accommodate to a constant depolarization of its terminals? This question was studied in the isolated cat muscle spindle receptor by Lippold *et al.* (1960). In this preparation, response to stretch is shown in the upper line of Fig. 12.4. An early fast rate of discharge is followed by a gradually slower rate. The generator potential during such applied stretches shows a corresponding larger phase of depolarization just after stretch followed by a

slower declining phase.   Depolarizing currents were then applied
to the receptor terminus as shown in the lower traces of Fig. 12.4
and a steady discharge of action potentials was recorded for as long
as the depolarization was maintained.   It appears that the discharge
rate is directly proportional to the level of depolarization present in
the nerve terminals.   The variations in the level of depolarization

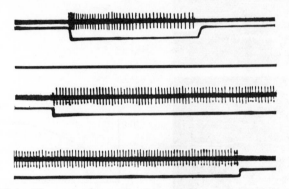

Fig. 12.4.   Top set of records shows action potential discharges
recorded from a cat spindle receptor in response to stretch on the
trace just below it.   In the next set of records below the plain
ruled line, the action potential responses to the onset of a long-
lasting depolarization of the receptor are shown, and in the last
set which is continuous with it, the termination of polarization.
(Lippold *et al.*, 1960.)

of the generator potential most likely reflects the variations in the
visco-elastic properties of the central portion of the spindle receptor.

The analysis of the generator potential and its relation to sensory
discharge was advanced by the use of the stretch receptors of the
lobster and crayfish present in tail sections of the exoskeleton of
these crustacea (Fig. 12.5).   The receptors were first described
anatomically by Alexandrowicz (1951).   Wiersma *et al.* (1953)
proved that these structures are stretch receptors.   Two types of
stretch receptors were found: a slowly adapting (tonic) stretch
receptor (RM1) and a more rapidly adapting (phasic) receptor
(RM2) (Fig. 12.6).

In these receptors the cell bodies of the afferent fibers are found
close to their terminal arborizations upon the muscular portion of the
receptor.   It is, therefore, possible to enter the soma of the sensory
cell with microelectrodes to record a sizeable generator potential
spreading electrotonically from the nearby dendritic terminals
(Eyzaguirre and Kuffler, 1955a).   The term dendrite is used in

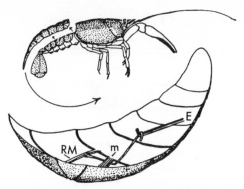

Fig. 12.5. Stretch receptor (RM) showing bridging a segment
of the exoskeleton of the crayfish.   Electrode (E) placed on nerve
records afferent discharges on stretch; m, a muscle.

reference to these branching terminals found wrapped around the
muscular portion of the receptor, similar in appearance to the
dendrites of other neurons.   The generator potentials and spike
discharges recorded from the soma with the stretch receptor subjected to stretch are shown in Fig. 12.7.   The generator potential
is larger with increased stretch and the rate of discharge corresponds directly to the size of the generator potential.   As in the vertebrate stretch receptor, repetitive action potential discharges were

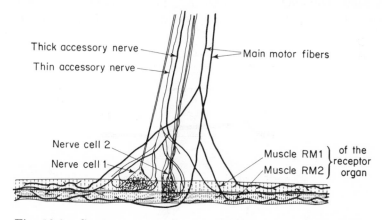

Fig. 12.6. Crustacean stretch receptor shown in diagrammatic
fashion. The sensory fibers of the receptor have cell bodies
(nerve cells 1, 2) close to the modified muscular parts of the
receptor with dendritic portions wrapped around them. RM1
and RM2 receptors have different rates of adaptation and are
referred to as slow and fast adapting receptors. (Alexandrowicz,
1951.)

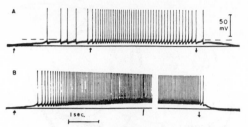

Fig. 12.7.   Stretch of slow adapting crustacean receptor (A) applied at the time of the first arrow recording with a microelectrode: depolarization and five irregularly spaced action potentials.   At the next arrow the stretch is increased and the discharge rate rises.   At the downward arrow stretch is removed and the slow potential diminishes and discharge stops.   In the next example (B) stretch was gradually increased over four seconds between the first arrow and the vertical line.   There is a rise in the slow potential level and action potential discharges increase to a high and regular rate.   At the second arrow relaxation is followed by a small transient phase of hyperpolarization.   (Eyzaguirre and Kuffler, 1955a.)

selectively blocked by application of procaine to the tissue while the generator potential was unaffected (Fig. 12.8).

These studies of the crustacean stretch receptor have clearly shown the electrotonic spread of depolarization from the deformed dendritic terminals reaching into the soma.   The problem is: where in the neuron do the rhythmic action potentials arise in response to this

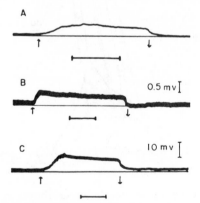

Fig. 12.8.   In response to a stretch of a crustacean receptor (A) where the spike discharges have been blocked by procaine, the externally recorded generator potential (B) and the intercellular recorded generator potential (C) are greater at the onset than at some time later, a change related to the adaptation of the discharge.   (Eyzaguirre and Kuffler, 1955a.)

generator potential.   Eyzaguirre and Kuffler (1955b) studied this problem using *antidromic* invasion of the soma.   The axon was excited so that action potentials were propagated toward the soma in a direction opposite to that of the normal or *orthodromic* propagation of impulses.   If the stretch receptor is relaxed the resting potential of the soma is higher and an antidromic impulse often fails to invade the soma to give rise to an action potential.   In that case, a small potential is recorded in the soma.   This small spike-like

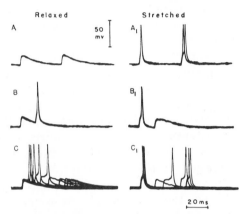

Fig. 12.9.   In the left-hand column a slow stretch receptor is relaxed and a resting membrane potential of -70 mv recorded with a microelectrode.   In the right-hand column with a light stretch the resting potential is -60 mv.   Two antidromic volleys are fired into the relaxed cell where each impulse was insufficient to invade the cell with a full action potential (A).   When the second antidromic volley is brought closer in time to a first, an action potential is generated (B).   Different intervals between the two impulses (C).   In the stretched cell the additional depolarization allows invasion of the cell body with a full action potential (A_1).   Refractoriness is seen after the first response $(B_1$ and $C_1)$.
(Eyzaguirre and Kuffler, 1955b.)

potential is the electrotonic spread of the action potential in the axon just central to the soma which has failed to invade the soma (Fig. 12.9).   The action potential in the axon fails to invade the soma because it cannot depolarize the soma membrane sufficiently to reach critical level for excitation of a spike.   If stretch is applied to the receptor, then the generator potential from the dendrites spreads into the soma and lowers its membrane potential and the depolarization level required to excite the soma membrane.   Antidromic invasion of the soma and a full action potential occurs when threshold is reached.

It would appear that antidromic action potentials which do invade the soma either do not propagate further into the dendrites or they do not affect the mechanisms giving rise to the generator potential in the dendrites. The generator potential and the rhythm of the repetitive discharge remains unchanged following an antidromic invasion (Kuffler and Eyzaguirre, 1955). On this basis we may conclude that the dendrites give rise to the generator potential but all-or-none action potentials do not propagate into that part of the cell. Evidence has been obtained that the generator potentials excite repetitive action potentials from the axon just proximal to the soma. Such a proximal axon site of impulse initiation was supported by the work of Edwards and Ottoson (1958). They recorded external action potential responses from various points along the surface of stretch receptor neurons excited by stretch and found that the latency was least at the axon just central to the soma and then after a delay the soma was fired. The firing level for initiation of action potentials is lower at the initial part of the axon than it is in the soma. This was found by comparing orthodromic and antidromic invasion of the slow adapting receptor. When a depolarization of 20–25 mv was attained by an antidromic volley the soma was excited. On the other hand, the soma was fired in response to orthodromic excitation when a depolarization level of 8–12 mv was reached. This is explained if the firing level of the initial axonal segment of the cell has a lower firing level than that of the soma. The generator voltage spreads electrotonically past the soma to excite action potentials at the initial segment (Kuffler, 1958).

The crustacean stretch receptor also has an inhibitory innervation. The inhibitory nerve branches to supply the slow and fast adapting receptors as shown in Fig. 12.10. Advantage was taken of this branching so that stimulation of the nerve at one termination excited a discharge passing up the branch and then down the other branch of inhibitory fibers terminating on the other receptor. When the inhibitory nerve is stimulated, repetitive discharges in the receptor afferent fiber are blocked (Fig. 12.10). The effect of the inhibitory action is to bring the membrane potential of the receptor fibers back toward the original level of polarization (Kuffler and Eyzaguirre, 1955). When the membrane is depolarized by a certain degree of maintained stretch, stimulation of the inhibitory nerve will hyperpolarize it. On the other hand, if the cell is hyperpolarized by means of current applied to the cell through a microelectrode, the cell becomes depolarized upon stimulation of the inhibitory nerve; again the membrane is brought back to its original level of potential. This 'clamping' action produced by inhibitory nerve activity is due to an increase in ionic permeability similar to that found in crustacean muscle (Chapter 9). GABA mimics the action of inhibitory fibers on the stretch receptor as it does the action of inhibitory fibers on that muscle, and therefore it was suggested to be the

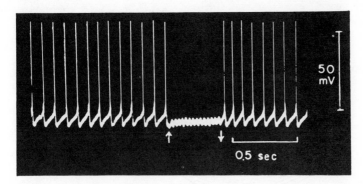

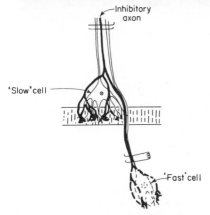

Fig. 12.10. In the diagram stimulating electrodes are placed at the nerve to the lower fast cell to excite the inhibitory branch terminating on the slow cell dendrites (cf. Fig. 11.6). The inhibitory effect on the slow cell (arrow up) shown in the record is to block afferent responses to stretch. After cessation of the inhibitory effect (arrow down), there is a quick return of afferent discharge. (From Eyzaguirre and Kuffler, 1955b; after Kuffler, 1958.)

transmitter substance of the inhibitory fibers of the stretch receptor (Kuffler, 1958; cf. Chapter 19).

Touch-pressure receptor

Deformation of membranes to give rise to a generator potential has been further investigated by study of the Pacinian corpuscle. The nonmyelinated terminal portion of this pressure-sensitive nerve fiber is surrounded by an onion-like series of lamellae (Fig. 12.11). The corpuscle is relatively large and can be removed from the body for

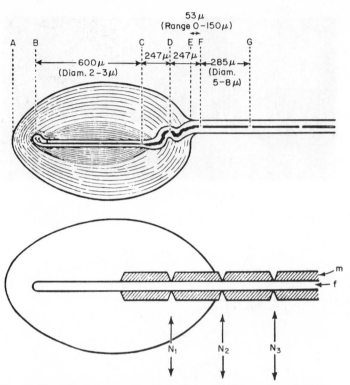

Fig. 12.11.   Pacinian corpuscle is shown in diagrammatic fashion. The nonmyelinated nerve terminal is enclosed in onion-like lamellae of the corpuscle with the first node of Ranvier (N_1) located inside the corpuscle; m, myelin, f, fiber.   (From Gray, 1959.)

study of its receptor properties.   A Rochelle salt crystal has been used to mechanically stimulate the corpuscle.   An electric pulse to the crystal causes a movement which can be applied to the Pacinian corpuscle via a fine stylus.   With a sustained depression of the surface only a brief discharge of impulses is seen in the axon.

By applying procaine, the propagated action potentials are blocked and a brief generator potential is seen to persist (Fig. 12.12). The amplitude of the generator potential increases with increasing strengths of pressure and it has a short duration accounting for the fast adaptation of the action potential discharge upon maintained stimulation (Gray, 1959).   The correspondence of generator potentials with the degree of pressure is expected from the graded nature of a generator potential as compared to the all-or-none action potential.

If two generator potentials are excited at short times after one another they show summation (Fig. 12.13).   If the second generator pulse falls at a somewhat later time, though within 10 msec, a decrease

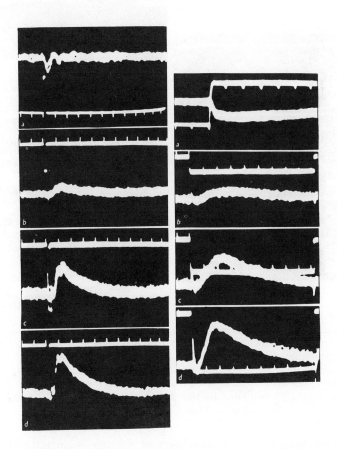

Fig. 12.12.   In column on left, brief pressure pulses of increasing strength (a-d) applied to a Pacinian corpuscle produce brief generator potentials.   In the column on right, longer-maintained pressures of increasing strengths (a-d) give rise to similarly fast-adapting generator potentials.   (Gray and Sato, *J. Physiol.* **122**: 610, 1953.)

of the later generator potential is found (Lowenstein and Alta
mirano-Orrego, 1958).   At still later time intervals an increase
excitability of the second generator potential is seen (Lowenstein
1958).

The properties of the receptor do not reside in the lamellae whic
surrounds the terminal nonmyelinated part of the axon.   This wa

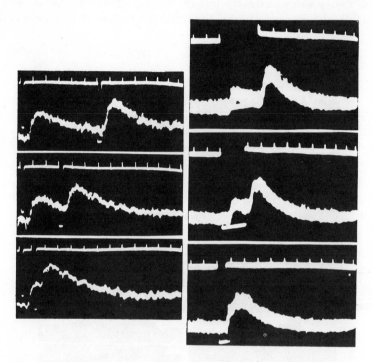

Fig. 12.13.   In column at left the effect of two brief pressure
impulses presented at different time intervals is shown to result
in summation of their generator potentials.   A similar effect is
seen in right-hand column with longer-lasting pulses of pressures,
the summation taking place at the make ('on' response) and
break ('off') response to the pressure pulse.   (From Gray and
Sato, *J. Physiol.*, **122**: 610, 1953.)

shown by removing the lamellae and finding essentially the same
receptor properties (Lowenstein and Rathkamp, 1958).   Such de
lamellated Pacinian fibers permit a more detailed study of the
properties of the receptor terminal.   Damage by compression of the
nonmyelinated portion of the terminal afferent abolishes the generato
potential in the part distal to the damaged site.   The remaining

ortion proximal to the crush can still give rise to a generator
potential. The generator potential arises upon mechanical defor-
nation when a general increase in ion permeability takes place.
The chief ion involved is Na^+ although not in the selectively per-
neable fashion of the all-or-none action potential. The lamellae
of the Pacinian corpuscle greatly hinder ion movement and, therefore,
perfusion of the corpuscles is required to show the effects of altered
ion composition, e.g. the conduction block found with low Na^+
(Gray, 1959).

It has been thought that a distinctive feature of the nonmyelinated terminal is that it can only give rise to a generator
potential and not to an all-or-none action potential. The depolarizing current acts to excite propagated action potentials at the first
node of the afferent fiber. However, the experiments of Hunt and
Takeuchi (1962) using delamellated afferents showed that the nonmyelinated terminal can also support a propagated action potential.
The axon was antidromically excited and recordings made at various
distances along the nonmyelinated terminal of the axon. A progressive increase in the latency of spike responses was recorded at
successively increased distances along the nonmyelinated terminal
showing a propagation into the terminal. It appears that normally
the generator potential initiates action potentials in the nonmyelinated terminal (Ozeki and Sato, 1964).

An interesting but also as yet little understood phenomenon is the
excitation of the crustacean stretch receptor by ACh (Wiersma et al.,
1953) and the terminals of mechanoreceptors which also appear to
be sensitive to ACh (Gray, 1959). Is there a chemical mediation
involved in reception? We have discussed the indirect evidence
that pain and related sensations appear to be excited by some tissue
component, possibly histamine. More well-defined recent studies
of the visual receptor of the *Limulus* eye suggests a chemical mediation in this receptor (*vide infra*). However, the evidence, at least
for the Pacinian corpuscle, appears to be against a chemical mediation
(Gray, 1959).

Vestibular labyrinth receptors

A series of hair-like receptors, the *lateral line receptors*, are found along
the sides of fish (Fig. 12.14). From these primitive receptors the
organs sensitive to gravity and acceleration in the higher forms have
evolved (de Vries, 1956).

Around the individual *hair cells* of the lateral line receptor (Fig.
12.15a) a paddle-shaped structure is found, the *cupula*. The currents

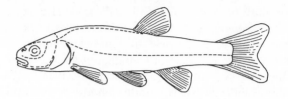

Fig. 12.14.   Lateral line system of fish shown by dotted lines.
(de Vries, 1956.)

of water move the cupola and deform the hair cells, thereby exciting
neural discharges.   In higher forms secondary cells have formed
around the hair cells to comprise the *otolith* organs (Fig. 12.15b
found in the vestibule of the ear.   In another development hair
cells are found in the *semicircular canals* (Fig. 12.15c).

The fine structure of (vestibular) hair cells of the vertebrate has
been studied by electron microscopy (Engström and Wersäll, 1958)
As shown in diagrammatic fashion in Fig. 12.16 hair cells of globular
and cylindrical shape are seen with fine cilia-like hairs extending from
their outer surface.   The termination of the sensory neuron is in
contact with the base of the hair cells.   Deformations of the hairs
excites discharges in the neuron ending applied to the base.   Hair
cells of the otolith organs have a small concretion of calcium
resting on their surface giving rise to a constant deformation of
the hair cells.   The two otolith organs in the labyrinth on either
side of the head therefore are constantly exposed to the tonic effects
of gravity.   Changes in the position of the head causes a movement

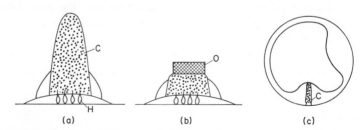

Fig. 12.15.   Lateral line sensory organ (a) with paddle-like
structure (cupula, c) extending into the water and hair cells (H)
at base.   Otolith organ (b) with small calcium otoliths (O) on
top of the hair cells shifted by gravity.   Hair cell of semicircular
canals of the ear (c) where fluid movements inside enclosed canal
system acts on the crista (C) of the hair cell.   (de Vries, 1956.)

of the otolith and in this way stimulates the hair cells of the otolith organs present in the *utricles* and *saccules* (Fig. 12.17).

Rotation or a change of velocity of the head is signalled by the hair cells in the semicircular canals, three duct-like tubes with each canal arranged in three intersecting planes of space (Fig. 12.17). Within the semicircular canals the liquid present, the *endolymph*, can flow and by its movement deform the cupula of hair cells in the ampullar part of the canals. A rapid rotation of the head sets up

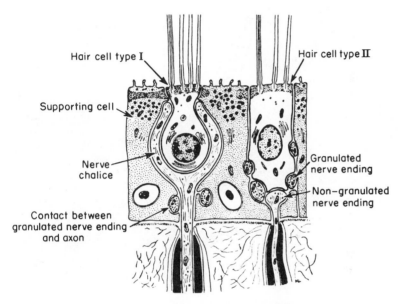

Fig. 12.16. The structure of two hair cell types (I, II) revealed by electron microscopy shown in diagrammatic fashion. From the top of the cell hair-like extensions are seen, and at the base the nonmyelinated terminal of the sensory axon is closely apposed. (Wërsall, in *Neural Mechanisms of the Auditory and Vestibular Systems*, Rasmussen and Windle (Eds.), Charles E. Thomas, 1960.)

a rotatory movement of fluid which displaces the cupula of the hair cells, and this activates a discharge in the sensory nerves of the hair cells giving information on the movement of the head in space.

Because there are three sets of canals, each approximately located in one of three intersecting planes, a rotation in any direction can be adequately accounted for by the resultant neural discharges from the three receptors. The relationship of discharges from the semicircular

canal receptors and the extraocular muscles controlling the
position of the eyes is shown by rotating subjects in a revolving
chair (Barany chair). Early during rotation, with the head placed
so that the rotation is in the plane of the horizontal canals, the eye
balls move slowly in a direction opposite to that of the rotation
movement serving this reflex is to maintain the eyes fixed on the

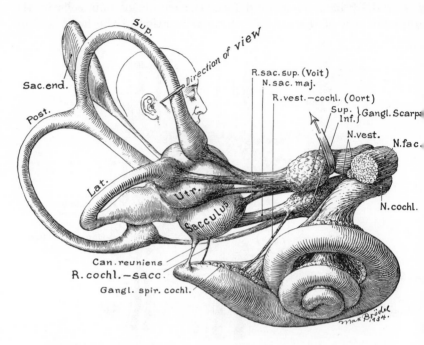

Fig. 12.17. Superior, posterior and lateral semicircular canals
shown in relation to their orientation in the human head. The
otolith organs, utricule and saccule, and the auditory organ, the
cochlea, are closely related structures. (Hardy, *Anat. Rec.*, **59**;
403, 1934.)

visual field. There is a quick movement of the eyes toward the direc
tion of rotation followed by their slow movement opposite to the
rotation. This zig-zag oscillation is called *nystagmus* and the direction
of nystagmus is by convention identified by that of the quick phase of
movement. Upon continued rotation the nystagmus abates. When
the rotation is abruptly stopped and the eyes observed, a nystagmus
begins again but in the reverse direction, with the quick phase opposite
to the direction in which the subject had been turning. This *post
rotatory nystagmus* slowly decreases over a period of 20 seconds

hese rotatory and post-rotatory effects at the onset and cessation
f rotation are explained by the inertia of the fluid contained in the
emicircular canal. At the onset of rotation the endolymph lags
ehind the movement of the canals and the cupulas of the hair cells
1 the ampullae bend one way to excite nystagmus. Upon cessation
f rotation, the continued movement of endolymph acts to bend the
upulae the other way. Direct observation of the cupula in animals
hows it filling the lumen of the ampulla with a swing-door action
pon displacement by endolymph (Hallpike and Hood, 1953).

he ear—cochlear apparatus

he hair cells evolved to become the complex receptor organ of the
ar, shown in diagrammatic fashion in Fig. 12.18 with the helical coch-

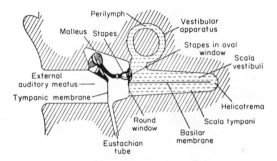

Fig. 12.18. Diagram of the ear with the cochlea straightened out.
Sound waves enter the external ear, vibrate the tympanic membrane
and in turn the three small ossicles of the middle ear—malleus,
stapes and incus. The incus is inserted into the oval window of
the cochlea transmitting vibrations to the scala vestibuli to
deform the ductus cochlearis (not shown) and in turn the basilar
membrane (cf. Fig. 12.19) where the vibrations excite impulses
in the auditory nerve filters passing to the brain. The sound
vibrations of the scala vestibuli pass via the helicotrema at the tip
of the cochlea, thence to the scala tympani and the round window.
(von Bekesy and Rosenblith, 1951.)

ea straightened out. Sound waves are funneled by the external ear
anal to act on the *tympanic membrane*, the movement of which, in
urn, acts on a series of small bones or *ossicles*: the *incus, malleus*
nd *stapes*. The stapes is fastened to a membrane covering the *oval*
window of the *cochlea* of the *inner ear* where sound vibrations are
ransduced within the cochlea. This is a helical structure containing
wo membranes wound lengthwise along its turns dividing the cochlea

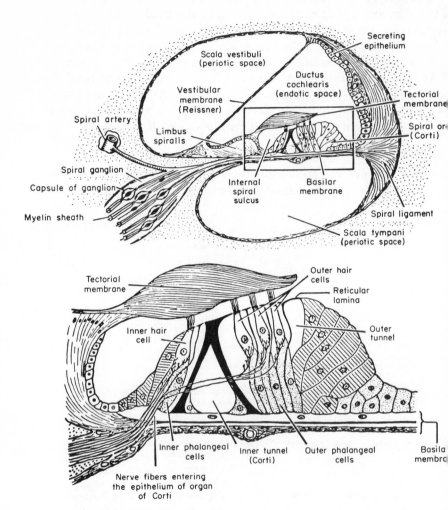

Fig. 12.19.   In the upper diagram the organ of Corti found along the basilar membrane in the ductus cochlearis is shown.   Vibrations transmitted to the ductus cochlearis and the basilar membrane cause deformation of the hair cells.   The tectorial membrane appears to serve an important function in causing a shearing action to be exerted on the hairs.   Organ of Corti shown in enlarged view in bottom diagram with auditory nerve endings apposed to the bases of the hair cells.   (Rasmussen, *Outlines of Neuroanatomy* (3rd. Ed.) William C. Brown, 1943.)

into three fluid-filled chambers. Vibrations are transmitted to the cochlea from the *oval window* by the stapes. A sound vibration will displace the fluid along the chamber called the *scala vestibuli* out to the tip of the cochlea, the *helicotrema* where an opening exists, back down the chamber called the *scala tympani*, and finally the fluid displacement acts to push out the membrane over the *round window*. In between these two chambers is the *ductus cochlearis*, or *scala media*, containing hair cells and the terminals of the auditory nerves

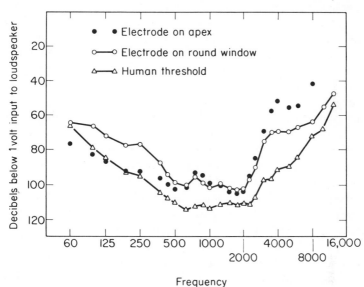

Fig. 12.20. Threshold for sounds of different frequencies shown for the human (△). For the guinea pig the threshold was determined by the just-detectable electric responses (the cochlear microphonic potential) recorded from the apex (●) and the round window (○). (From Stevens, Davis and Lurie, *J. Gen. Psychol.* **13**: 297, 1935.)

close to them in the *organ of Corti* (Fig. 12.19). Fluid displacements of the scalae and the basilar membrane caused by sound vibrations excite the hair cells and auditory receptor nerve terminals of the organ of Corti. The arrangement of the hair cells and their associated auditory nerve terminals along the basilar membrane of the organ of Corti suggests a relationship to the frequency of sound received. The frequency of the sound waves sensed by man ranges from a low of approximately 20 cycles per second (cps) to a high of 20,000 cps, the greatest sensitivity found at approximately 1,000 cps (Fig. 12.20). According to the *place theory*, high frequencies are appreciated at the basal end of the cochlea where the basilar membrane is narrowest (0.15 mm) and progressively lower frequencies along the turns of the cochlea to the tip where the basilar membrane is widest (0.4 mm). The basilar membrane was considered to be mechanically selective to different vibration frequencies because of presumed differences in tension at various places along its length much as piano wires of different lengths and thickness will resonate to different frequencies. Direct studies of the mechanical properties of the basilar membrane showed that a very sharp selective mechanical responsivity of the basilar membrane did not occur. Excitation with sound waves of different frequencies gives rise to rather large movements along considerable lengths of the membrane. A *traveling wave* is set up along the basilar membrane by given frequencies transmitted to it by the oval window as shown by direct observations and recordings made from the basilar membrane (von Bekesy and Rosenblith, 1951). The traveling wave has a crest which gives rise to a greater displacement at one place along the membrane, depending upon the frequency of the sound (Fig. 12.21). Therefore, unlike the original concept of the basilar membrane as being composed of tuned vibrating structures resonating at different frequencies, there is a gradation of stiffness with a degree of localization along the membrane at the crest of the traveling wave. Model experiments by von Bekesy (1960) using vibration sensation in the skin with membranes imitating such crests shows that localization of the crest can be sensed within a rather narrow range.

The basilar membrane is displaced at the crest of the traveling wave and swinging up gives rise to a shearing deformation of the hair cells above the membrane, the tips of the hair cells apparently in contact with the tectorial membrane extending over the protruding hairs. How does this deformation of the hair cells come to be transmitted to the auditory nerve endings in contact at their base. It would appear that the phenomenon of the *cochlear microphonic* potential is connected with this transduction. The cochlear microphonic potential is an electrical duplication of sound waves presented to the ear and produced by the piezoelectrical properties of the inner ear. It can be picked up with fairly large amplitude from the round window and after amplification listened to in a loudspeaker. The transformation of sound to a cochlear microphonic potential is not unduly irregular, as indicated by the intelligibility of the amplified potentials (Wever and Bray, 1930). The cochlear microphonic potential is brought about by the steady potential of $+ 8$ mv found inside the scala media (Davis, 1961). This potential

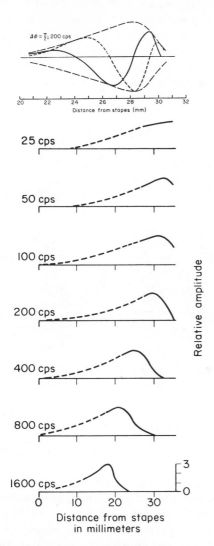

Fig. 12.21. Top, a 200 cps wave is shown to have a crest of greatest displacement along the cochlea 28–29 mm from the stapes. Two waves are shown by the continuous line and short dashed lines. Long dashed line gives the results of a series of such determinations. Below, the maximum amplitude displacement along the cochlear partition is shown for a number of different frequencies. These take place closer to the stapes with the higher frequency sound waves. (von Bekesy and Rosenblith, 1951.)

produced by the *stria vascularis* in the wall of the scala media (Fig 12.22). This is the *endocochlear voltage* which adds its voltage to that of the membrane potential of the hair cells to give a total of 140 mv acting across the membranes of the hair cells. Deformation of the hair cells by vibration causes the relatively large voltage changes of the cochlear microphonic potentials. Another potential

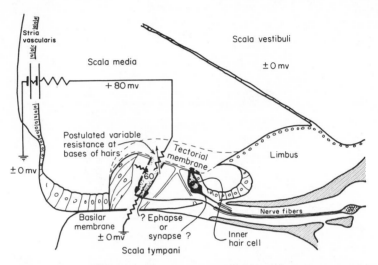

Fig. 12.22.   A potential of + 80 mv is found within the scala media (ductus cochlearis) believed to originate from the stria vascularis. This potential source is indicated by the battery.   This voltage is imposed across the hair cells.   When sound waves excite the hair cells, there is a decrease in their electrical resistance and the resulting current passes through the hair cell to excite responses in the auditory nerve endings.   (Davis, 1961.)

is found when recording from within the organ of Corti.   This is the *summating potential* which is more closely related to discharge activity in the auditory nerve fibers and in this respect appears more like receptor potentials found elsewhere (Davis, 1960. Cochlear microphonic and summating potential changes of the hair cells are classed as receptor potentials because these potentials arise from changes in the hair cells which in turn depolarize the closely applied receptor (auditory) nerve terminals.   Davis considers the cochlear microphonic potentials to be generated by deformation of the external hair cells and the summating potential to be produced by the internal hair cells.   At the basal turn both lower and higher frequencies of the microphonic potentials are found.   At the apical turn only the low frequencies are found (Fig. 12.23). This would follow from the different mechanical properties of the basilar membrane in these places.

In an analysis of auditory nerve activity and the place of auditory nerve origin along the basilar membrane the intensity as well as the frequency of the sound must be considered. The threshold curve

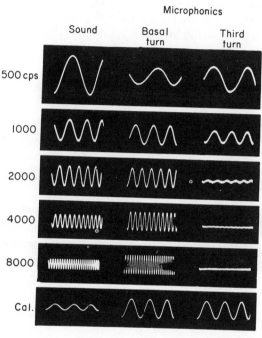

Fig. 12.23. The cochlear microphonic potentials recorded at the basal and apical (third turn) of the cochlea in response to sound frequencies from 500 to 8000 cps. There is a diminished response to the higher frequencies in the third turn. (Tasaki, 1954.)

of the normal range of sound frequencies was given in Fig. 12.20. A similar curve may be constructed for animals which have been psychologically conditioned to respond to sounds of different frequencies (Chapter 25). Subsequent damage at various places along the organ of Corti results in a selective deafness in these animals correlated to the place of damage. Damage at the helicotremal end results in a loss of responsiveness to low frequencies; loss to higher frequencies is caused by damage nearer the basilar turn. By drilling into the guinea pig cochlea at different places, Tasaki

(1954) was able to record discharges from single auditory nerv
fibers in response to various frequencies. Those at the apical tur:
responded to low frequencies. Fibers from the basal turn responde
to both low and high frequencies. The discharge of the auditor;
nerve is repetitive and the rate was increased when an increase
intensity of sound stimulation was presented. The responses of
single fiber are not highly selective to the sound frequencies. Ther
is a minimal sound intensity at some narrow range but response
occur over a wide range of frequencies depending on the intensit
(Fig. 12.24). The relation of sound threshold required to excite

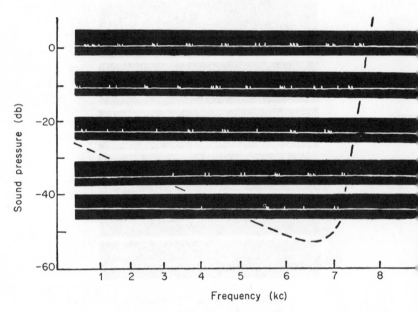

Fig. 12.24.   Microelectrode recordings from a single auditory fiber.
Sound pips of different frequencies and strengths were introduced
into the ear and the fiber's response shows a peak between 6 and
7 kcps which is relatively broad.   The peak is sharper at lower
intensities of sound.   (Tasaki, 1954.)

shown by the dashed line of Fig. 12.24, has a rapid rise in threshol
at the high frequency side with a less rapid rise on the low frequenc
side. After synapse of the primary auditory fibers, the next orde
of auditory fibers have an even sharper dip in threshold at th
frequency specific for the particular auditory fiber from which it w:
recorded (Fig. 12.25) (Katsuki et al., 1958). The overall sensitivit
of the ear is remarkable; vibrations of the order of a few Ångstro:

nits can be detected.   This is close to the ultimate limit, the noise
iven by the molecular instability of the membrane of the auditory
erve terminals.

he eye

mages of the external *visual field* are focused by the lens of the eye
nto the back of the eyeball where the primary receptor elements,
ie *photoreceptors*, are found in the retina (Fig. 12.26).   The photo-
·ceptor elements are the *rods* and *cones* which are found at the most

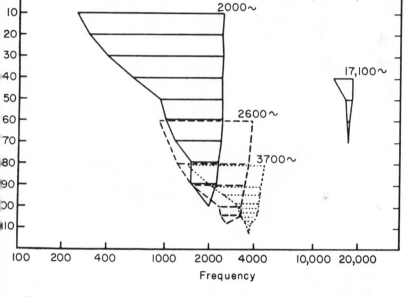

Fig. 12.25.   Single fiber analysis of auditory neurons (only later
recognized as second order fibers) shows a sharp sensitivity at a
particular frequency (cf. Fig. 12.24).   The response 'areas' of
four different fibers are shown.   (Galambos and Davis, *J. Neurophysiol.*, **6**: 39, 1943.)

·sterior portion of the retina.   The rods are seen as thin columnar
·ructures, and the cones are tipped or flask-shaped.   The other layers
 retina are complex and contain a number of different types of
·urons as shown in Fig. 12.27 and in simpler fashion in Fig. 12.28.
ie *bipolar cells* synapse onto the rods and cones with one of their
·ocesses, the other terminal of the bipolar cells synapsing on *ganglion*
·*ls.*   A number of other cells with numerous connections are found,

these synapsing on the ganglion cells and on bipolar cells.   The axons
of the ganglion cells leave the retina and constitute the optic nerve
passing centrally to the optic centers of the brain (Chapter 21).

   Along with their different structures there is a difference in visual
function of the rods and cones.   The rods are more sensitive than

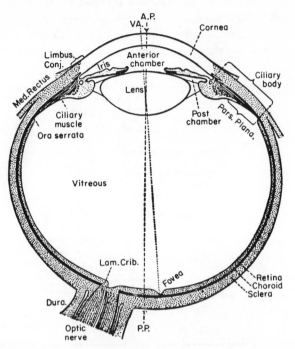

Fig. 12.26.   The course of light rays entering the anterior pole (A.P.)
of the eye at the top is shown passing through the cornea, lens and
thence to the retina in the posterior pole (P.P.) of the eye.   The
most sensitive area of detailed and color vision is present in the
fovea along the visual axis (VA).   (Davson, *Physiology of the Eye*,
Churchill, 1950.)

the cones.   However, the detail of visual reception possible with
rod vision is less than with cones and rods are not sensitive to color
as are the cones.   The cones are found present in greatest number
in the *fovea*, the center of the retina, on which the lens focuses.   This
is the portion of the retina with which we as humans do most of our
seeing.   More laterally placed in the retina are the rods which give
us our 'peripheral' vision.   In a species such as the hunting birds
the cones predominate, and night vision animals have a rod-type
retina (Detwiler, 1943; Tansley, 1950).

In an eye such as man's containing both rods and cones, the differences between rod and cone vision is shown by their different thresholds to light of different wavelengths. The rods respond better to the shorter wavelengths, the cones to the longer wavelengths. This is shown by the *scotopic* (rod-vision) and *photopic*

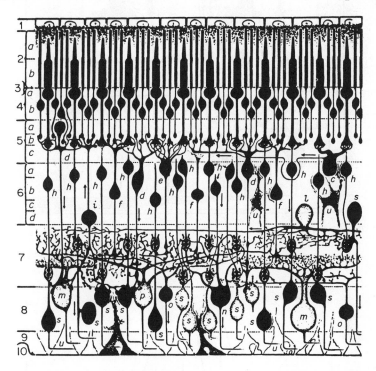

Fig. 12.27. The photoreceptor elements are the rod and cones present in layer 2 at the rear of the retina. In synaptic contact with the base of the rods and cones are axons of bipolar cells (h) having their cell bodies in layer 6. The other axon of the bipolar cell is in synaptic contact with the ganglion cells (m, p, s) having profuse dendritic extensions in layer 7; their cell bodies in layer 8. The axons of the ganglion cells leave the retina in the optic nerve. (Polyak, 1941.)

cone-vision) curves of Fig. 12.29. To obtain the scotopic curve the subject remains in a dark room and becomes *dark-adapted*. During dark-adaptation, the sensitivity of rod-vision gradually increases over several scores of minutes. The threshold to light of different wavelengths is then tested and plotted and the scotopic curve is obtained. The subject is required to compare the relative intensity

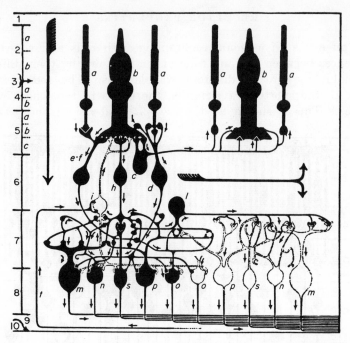

Fig. 12.28.   A simplified version of retina cells of the primate eye and their connections (cf. Fig. 12.27).   (Polyak, 1941.)

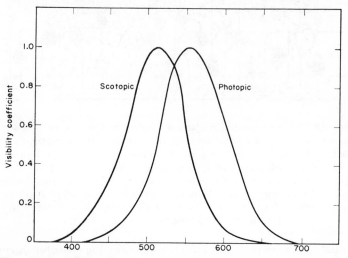

Fig. 12.29.   The relative sensitivities at different wavelengths for dark-adapted (scotopic) and light-adapted (photopic) states of vision are shown.   The wavelengths of light are on abscissa, relative light intensity on ordinate.   Two different sensitivity curves are found.   (From Hecht and Williams, *J. Gen. Physiol.*, **5; 1, 1922.**)

f different wavelengths of light to a standard luminous spot.   If the ubject does this in ordinary light at a relatively high intensity, rod ision is swamped and the photopic curve is then obtained.   The urves show the relative changes in comparison thresholds made at ue different wavelengths.   The subject does not see the different olors in the determination of the scotopic curve; a barely visible ade of white is reported.

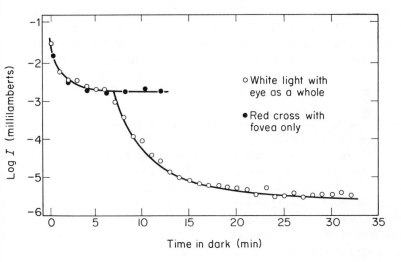

Fig. 12.30.   The threshold for white light (○) and for red light (●) during dark adaptation.   Intensity of light I on ordinate. The threshold falls at first similarly for both types of stimuli, but with white light and rod vision there is after 7–8 minutes a further decrease in threshold.   (From Hecht in Murchison (Ed.), *A Handbook of General Experimental Psychology*, Clark University Press, 1934.)

As can be seen in Fig. 12.29 in the red range (650 mμ) the rods cotopic vision) are insensitive.   Practical use is made of this by ue roentgenologists who must have sensitive rod vision to see fficient contrast in the roentgen screen.   By wearing red goggles, hereby rods are not affected, before entering their examination ooms they need not spend time in a dark room to become suffi- ently dark-adapted.

Measurement of the threshold to light during the course of dark laptation shows the two different processes of adaptation of rods nd cones (Fig. 12.30).   The threshold to light falls gradually and uen a break occurs before a still greater fall in threshold.   If the

light used for the test is a red light to which only the cones respond
the curve does not break but levels off.   The explanation is that th
break and greater fall in threshold is due to the response of the rod
to the weaker light intensities.

A *photochemical* process is involved in the transduction of ligh
into neural discharges.   A purple pigment called *rhodopsin* or *visua*
purple can be extracted from the retina.   This pigment has th
interesting property of being bleached by light to the related yello
colored pigment *retinene*.   In the dark, retinene is transforme
back to the purple color of rhodopsin with the slow time-cours
characteristic of dark adaptation.   A study of the power of ligh
of different wavelengths to bleach rhodopsin shows a close matc
with the scotopic curve of rod vision.   Such evidence indicates tha
the pigment rhodopsin is the photoreceptor substance of the rod
The essential steps in photochemical transduction is the reversibl
change in the configuration of the retinene molecule from a *trans* t
cis form (Wald, 1959).

With excessive exposure to light, retinene may be further broke
down to a protein and vitamin A which has a structure close to tha
of rhodopsin.   It is known that vitamin A is required in the diet o
man to prevent *night-blindness*, a condition in which vision unde
conditions of low illumination is impaired.   Further evidence fo
the connection of vitamin A with the rods is the rod damage see
after deprivation of vitamin A (Detwiler, 1943).

A variety of different theories to explain color vision have bee
proposed, but the foundation on which all subsequent work wa
built was the one proposed by Young and later modified by Helm
holtz, the Young–Helmholtz Theory (Brindley, 1960).   This *thre*
color or *trichromacy* theory proposes that there are three primar
color receptors in the retina—blue, green and red.   Any individua
color in the continuous spectrum of colors is perceived upon stimu
lation of these three hypothetical receptors in different proportion
This was based on Newton's work showing that any color includin
white light can be decomposed into a few simple primary colo
and these mixed back again to give rise to the original color.   Diffe
ent proportions of the three primary colors; blue (440 mμ), gree
(540 mμ) and red (575 mμ) can match any given color.

Three separate primary color receptors are suggested from th
observations made of those individuals who are *color-blind*.   Som
of these individuals apparently are unable to distinguish colo
and they are classed as the *monochromats*.   Others appear to hav
only two color receptors, these are the *dichromats*.   The dichromat

ense colors by means of different proportions of excitation of their
wo color receptors. The most common dichromats are those who
ppear to lack the receptor for red. They cannot, for example, tell
he difference between red and a dark shade of gray or black. These
re the *protanopes*, lacking the first (red) type of color receptor. The
euteranopes lack the second (green) color receptor and cannot sense
he color of the middle of the spectrum, the blue–green range is
onfused. Finally, the *tritanope*, rarest of all the dichromats, lacks
he third color receptor and they are insensitive to blue.

Recently it has been found possible to measure the absorption
pectra of single cones near the macula lutea, in the parafoveal
egion, of isolated human and primate retinal preparations. The
ods and cones can be identified by their characteristic shapes
fter stripping the rear covering of the retina. A microspectropho-
ometer positioned over an individual cone allows light of different
vavelengths to pass through it to measure the absorption for each
vavelength. Cones were found with a peak absorption in the blue
445 mμ), others with a peak absorption in the green (535 mμ) and
et others with peak absorption in the red (570 mμ) range (Marks,
Dobelle and MacNichol, 1964). Similarly, Brown and Wald (1964)
eported absorption curves for single cones of human retinae with
heir individual absorption peaks at 450, 525 and 555 mμ. These
wo studies thus convincingly demonstrate that there are, indeed,
hree different primary color cone receptors present in the retina.

Earlier support for the trichromacy theory came from micro-
lectrode studies of neuron activity of the retina exposed to the
pectrum of light frequencies. By this means Granit (1945) found
hat the neural discharges from these units were grouped around
hree wavelengths, each unit responding either to the blue, green or
ed part of the spectrum (Fig. 12.31). The recordings made by
Granit were most likely from ganglion cells or at least from elements
everal steps removed from the photoreceptors themselves. There
s room for complex interactions in the retina and Granit (1955)
onsiders the various primary color receptors, the *narrow band*
eceptors, to be neuronally connected with those sensitive to a
vider frequency range, the *dominators*, as shown in Fig. 12.32.
There is not a private line between a single photoreceptor and a
nerve fiber representing that one point leading to the brain (Polyak,
.941, 1957). Multiple intersynaptic connections are found between
photoreceptors and bipolar cells and between these and ganglion
ells acting to give rise to divergent spreads and convergence of
neuronal activity in the retina, not only for those mechanisms

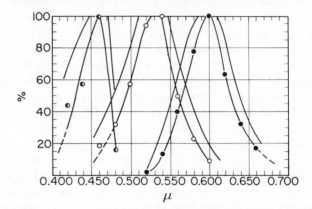

Fig. 12.31. Single unit recordings from ganglion cells of the retina show, after selective adaptation to their complementary colors, the presence of red (●), green (○) and blue (◑) color receptors. (Granit, 1945.)

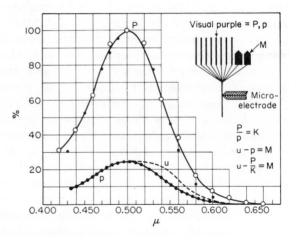

Fig. 12.32. The dark-adapted eye of the cat shows an average sensitivity (P) given by open large circles of the scotopic (dominator) receptor. The small dots on the scotopic curve shows absorption due to rhodopsin at those frequencies. The scheme in the insert shows how the rods are connected to give rise to the scotopic dominator curve recorded by the microelectrode. The curve u shows the overall averaging from which p is subtracted to give the effect of the modulator (M). (Granit, 1945.)

underlying color reception but as well for *visual acuity*, the separation of two close-by points of excitation (Chapter 21). A detailed microelectrode study of the neuronal elements within the retina shows some of these complex interactions in terms of the characteristic repetitive responses to a brief period of light stimulation (Kuffler, 1952). In one type of neuron the response to a light is a series of spikes at the onset of the light with the rate decreasing during its continuance (Fig. 12.33). This is an *'on'* element. Neuronal

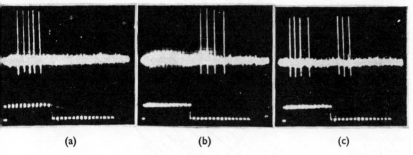

(a)   (b)   (c)

Fig. 12.33.   A flash of a point source of light 0.2 mm in diameter is moved to three different positions within the retinal receptor field of a ganglion cell and responses recorded with a microelectrode.   In one region, a repetitive discharge occurs during the onset of the light; this 'on' response is shown in (a) in the upper trace with the light flash shown on the lower trace.   With the light stimulus placed 0.5 mm laterally from that position (b), a response is seen at the termination of the light flash, the 'off' response.   At an intermediate position (c), a repetitive response occurs at the onset and at the termination of the light flash, the 'on-off' response.   Interruptions of the lower trace at 20 msec intervals as time calibration.   (Kuffler, 1952.)

elements designated as *'off'* units respond only upon the cessation of a period of light.   Those giving a repetitive discharge at the beginning and also upon cessation of a light stimulation are the on–off' elements.   A complex interaction of retina elements was shown further by Kuffler when single units were recorded from cells in and around a small illuminated area of the retina.   Within the illuminated area the cells were found to give 'on' type responses. Around this area light gave rise to 'on-off' responses and around that region 'off'-type responses were found (Fig. 12.34).   Therefore, we can see that upon excitation of a small area, interretinal connections will give rise to patterns of activity spread over a relatively wide area.   The relation of 'on' and 'off' types of patterns

of cell discharge is one of a reciprocal pattern of excitation an⟨
inhibition. An 'on'-type of activity acts to suppress or inhibi⟨
other cells giving rise to the 'off' responses. A reciprocal interactio⟨
for color receptors was seen by Wagner *et al.* (1960) in the cone-typ⟨
retina of the fish. A color from one end of the spectrum gave ris⟨

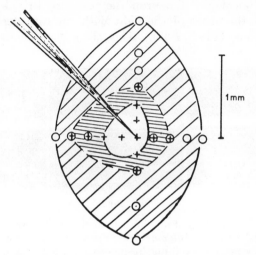

Fig. 12.34. The distribution of 'on', 'off' and 'on-off' responses
in the receptor field of a ganglion cell located in the retina by a
microelectrode (cf. Fig. 12.33). The area giving 'on' responses
(+) to a small probe of light is surrounded by an area of 'on-off'
responses (horizontally hatched) and around it is a zone giving 'off'
responses (diagonal hatching) on illumination. (Kuffler, 1952.)

in one type of unit to an 'on' response while color from the othe⟨
end of the spectrum gave rise to an 'off' response in that same uni⟨
(Motokowa, 1963).

The retina is developmentally a part of the brain. It has ⟨
complex structure and we should expect that neuronal interaction⟨
are also complex. This is particularly the case with respect to th⟨
slow potential changes developed by the retina and considered to b⟨
a generator potential (Granit, 1947, 1955). With an electrod⟨
placed on the eye (Fig. 12.35) or more directly by means of electrode⟨
on or in the retina, a *retinogram* is seen following light stimulatio⟨
with components labelled A, B, C and D. Some evidence suggest⟨
that the B wave arises from the photoreceptors or bipolar cell⟨
(Brindley, 1960).

The difficulties inherent to the study of the mechanism of trans⟨
duction in such a complex structure as the vertebrate retina led t⟨

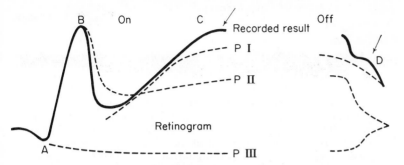

Fig. 12.35. The retinogram obtained from the retina in response to a flash of light is a slow potential change with phases A, B, C, and at its terminus, D. (An upward deflection is positive.) In the analysis of Granit (1955) the retinogram is considered to be composed of phases labeled P I, P II and P III as shown by the dashed lines. (After Ruch and Fulton, *Medical Physiology and Biophysics*, 18th Ed., Saunders, 1960.)

n analysis of the much simpler visual receptor of the crab (*Limulus*). *Limulus* has a compound eye composed of a large number of imple *ommatidia*, each ommatidium composed of a ring of 12 light eceptors with a single neuron, the *eccentric cell*, alongside the group Fig. 12.36). Light shined on the ommatidium excites a repetitive lischarge in the neuron and in addition a slow negative potential Fig. 12.37). The slow potentials resemble the generator potentials of stretch receptors (Hartline *et al.*, 1952). Cathodal currents increase ind anodal currents decrease the firing rate (MacNichol, 1958). This vould follow if the generator potential is acting on or arising from

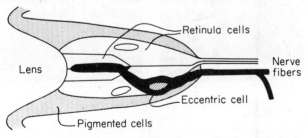

Fig. 12.36. The simple eye of *Limulus* (crab) is composed of a number of ommatidia. Each ommatidium is composed of a number of pigmented rhabdomere cells clustered under a simple lens. Nearby is the terminal of the neural element, the eccentric cell, with its efferent axon leading to the brain. (After Lipetz; from Davis, 1961.)

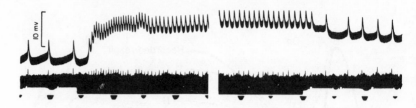

Fig. 12.37. Action potentials and slow generator potential shown in the upper trace recorded with a microelectrode from an ommatidium in response to a prolonged illumination whose duration is indicated by the black band under the lower trace. Lower trace shows during illumination an increased discharge recorded from the optic nerve bundle. Time intervals, 200 msec.
(Hartline *et al.*, 1952.)

the eccentric cell in which the repetitive discharge takes place Fuortes (1959) proved this by inserting a microelectrode directly into the eccentric cell. Light excitation caused depolarization of the eccentric cell and an associated repetitive firing related to the

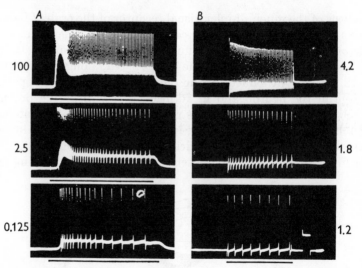

Fig. 12.38. Responses to illumination recorded intracellularly from the eccentric cell of an ommatidium (column A), the numbers giving the relative intensities of the light used. The duration of light stimulation is indicated by the black bar under the response. Adaptation of the rate of discharge is seen. Responses recorded from the eccentric cell to applied depolarizing currents (column B). The numbers indicate the relative strength of depolarizing currents in milliamps. Little adaptation seen. Square wave pulse for calibration in last trace, 20 mv. Time line, 1 sec. (Fuortes, 1959.)

epolarization.   Cathodal depolarization introduced into the eccen-
ric cell caused a similar repetitive firing (Fig. 12.38).   Rushton
1959) pointed out that Fuortes' studies showed that the membrane
esistance of the eccentric cell was decreased upon illumination.
'he decrease in resistance in turn causes the depolarization of the
ccentric cell and this in turn causes repetitive firing.   Such de-
reases in resistance are found present when a transmitter substance
hanges membrane permeability as in the case of neuromuscular

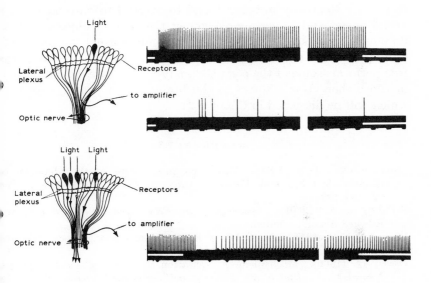

Fig. 12.39.   Light is shown exciting an ommatidium (a) with
repetitive responses recorded from a fiber separated from the
optic nerves passing to the brain.   In (b) light on the ommatidia
to the side causes an inhibition via the lateral plexus of the response
to light.   (Ratliff, 1960.)

ransmission.   On that ground a transmitter substance, released by
he ommatidium when it is exposed to light, has been suggested.
\ chemical transmission between the vertebrate rod photoreceptor
ind the bipolar cell is inferred from the structures seen in the rods and
ipolar cells of vertebrates in electron micrographs (de Robertis,
1958).   The bipolar cells in the retinal of vertebrates have processes
nserted into the base of the rod and vesicular structures present in

the rod which are similar in form to those found at other synapti
junctions.

Perhaps some of the comments made imply that complexity (
function is a province of the retina of higher forms.   However, eve
in the simpler eye of *Limulus*, complex interactions betwee
ommatidia are seen.   Illumination and excitation of one ommat
dium causes an inhibition of activity of the surrounding ommatidiur
(Ratliff, 1960) as shown in Fig. 12.39.   A similar *lateral inhibitio*
is seen in other sensory systems of vertebrates (Chapter 21).   Also
in the frog retina, complex aspects of the visual field appear to b
received.   Neuronal units are found to respond to movements of
visual object and to certain aspects of the form of objects such a
its boundary or shape, in addition to the more usual 'on' and 'off
units (Lettvin *et al.*, 1960).   It would appear that the retina of th
frog performs some of the complex analytical features found presen
in the higher visual centers in the brain of vertebrates, a subjec
which will be discussed in Chapter 21.

REFERENCES

Alexandrowicz, J. S. (1951).   Muscle receptor organs in the abdomen o
   Homarus vulgaris and *Palmurus vulgaris*. *Quart. J. Microscop. Sc*
   92: 163–199.
Brindley, G. S. (1960).   *Physiology of the Retina and the Visual Pathwa*
   Edward Arnold, London.
Brown, P. K. and Wald, G. (1964).   Visual pigments in single rods and cone
   of the human retina.   *Science* **144**: 45–52.
Davis, H. (1960).   Mechanism of excitation of auditory nerve impulse
   Neural Mechanisms of the Auditory and Vestibular Systems.   Edited b
   G. L. Rasmussen and W. F. Windle.   Chapter 2.   Charles C. Thoma
   Springfield.
Davis, H. (1961).   Some principles of sensory receptor action.   *Physio*
   Rev. **41**: 391–416.
de Robertis, E. (1958).   Submicroscopic morphology and function of th
   synapse.   *Exptl. Cell Res. Suppl.* **5**: 347–369.
Detwiler, S. R. (1943).   *Vertebrate Photoreceptors*.   Macmillan Co., New Yorl
de Vries, H. (1956).   Physical aspects of the sense organs.   *Progr. Biophy*
   6: 207–264.
Edwards, C. and Ottoson, D. (1958).   The site of impulse initiation in a nerv
   cell of a crustacean stretch receptor.   *J. Physiol.* **143**: 138–148.
Engström, H. and Wersäll, J. (1958).   The ultrastructural organization o
   the organ of Corti and of the vestibular epithelia.   *Exptl. Cell Res. Supp*
   5: 460–492.
Eyzaguirre, C. and Kuffler, S. W. (1955a).   Processes of excitation in th
   dendrites and in the soma of single isolated sensory nerve cells of th
   lobster and crayfish.   *J. Gen. Physiol.* **39**: 87–119.

Jyzaguirre, C. and Kuffler, S. W. (1955b). Further study of soma, dendrite and axon excitation in single neurons. *J. Gen. Physiol.* **39**: 121–153.

uortes, M. G. F. (1959). Initiation of impulses in visual cells of *Limulus*. *J. Physiol.* **148**: 14–28.

ranit, R. (1945). The color receptors of the mammalian retina. *J. Neurophysiol.* **8**: 195–210.

ranit, R. (1947). *Sensory Mechanisms of the Retina.* Oxford University Press, London.

ranit, R. (1955). *Receptors and Sensory Perception.* Yale University Press, New York.

ray, J. A. B. (1959). Mechanical into electrical energy in certain mechanoreceptors. *Progr. Biophys.* **9**: 286–324.

Iallpike, C. S. and Hood, J. D. (1953). The speed of the slow component of ocular nystagmus induced by angular acceleration of the head: its experimental determination and application to the physical theory of the cupular mechanism. *Proc. Roy. Soc. B.* **141**: 216–230.

Iartline, H. K., Wagner, H. C. and MacNichol, E. F. Jr. (1952). The peripheral origin of nervous activity in the visual system. *Cold Spring Harbor Symp. Quant. Biol.* **17**: 125–141.

Iunt, C. C. and Takeuchi, A. (1962). Responses of the nerve terminal of the Pacinian corpuscle. *J. Physiol.* **160**: 1–21.

Katsuki, Y., Sunie, T., Uchiyama, H. and Watanabe, T. (1958). Electric responses of auditory neurons in cat to sound stimulation. *J. Neurophysiol.* **21**: 569–588.

Katz, B. (1950). Depolarization of sensory terminals and the initiation of impulses in the muscle spindle. *J. Physiol.* **111**: 261–282.

Katz, B. (1961). The terminations of the afferent nerve fibre in the muscle spindle of the frog. *Proc. Roy. Soc. B* **243**: 221–240.

Kuffler, S. W. (1952). Neurons in the retina: Organization, inhibition and excitation problems. *Cold Spring Harbor Symp. Quant. Biol.* **17**: 281–292.

Kuffler, S. W. (1958). Synaptic inhibitory mechanisms. Properties of dendrites and problems of excitation in isolated sensory nerve cells. *Exptl. Cell Res., Suppl.* **5**: 493–519.

Kuffler, S. W. and Eyzaguirre, C. (1955). Synaptic inhibition in an isolated nerve cell. *J. Gen. Physiol.* **39**: 155–184.

Lettvin, J. Y., Maturana, H. R., Pitts, W. H. and McCulloch, W. S. (1960). Two remarks on the visual system of the frog. *Sensory Communication.* Edited by W. A. Rosenblith. Pp. 757–776. John Wiley and Sons, New York.

Lippold, O. C. J., Nicholls, J. G. and Redfearn, J. W. T. (1960). Electrical and mechanical factors in the adaptation of a mammalian muscle spindle. *J. Physiol.* **153**: 209–217.

Lowenstein, W. R. (1958). Facilitation by previous activity in a Pacinian corpuscle. *J. Gen. Physiol.* **41**: 847–856.

Lowenstein, W. R. and Altamirano-Orrego, R. (1958). The refractory state of the generator and propagated potentials in a Pacinian corpuscle. *J. Gen. Physiol.* **41**: 805–824.

Lowenstein, W. R. and Rathkamp, R. (1958). The sites for mechanicoelectric conversion in a Pacinian corpuscle. *J. Gen. Physiol.* **41**: 1245–1265.

MacNichol, E. F. (1958). Subthreshold excitatory processes in the eye (
Limulus. Exptl. Cell Res. Suppl. 5: 411–425.

Marks, W. B., Dobelle, W. H. and MacNichol, E. F. Jr. (1964). Visua
pigments of single primate cones. Science 143: 1181–1183

Motokawa, K. (1963). Mechanisms for the transfer of information along th
visual pathways. Intern. Rev. Neurobiol. 5: 121–181.

Ozeki, M. and Sato, M. (1964). Initiation of impulses at the non-myelinate
nerve terminals in Pacinian corpuscles. J. Physiol. 170: 167–185.

Polyak, S. L. (1941). The Retina. University of Chicago Press, Chicago.

Polyak, S. L. (1957). The Vertebrate Visual System. University of Chicag
Press, Chicago.

Ratliff, F. (1960). Inhibitory interaction and the detection and enhancemen
of contours. Sensory Communication. Edited by W. A. Rosenblitl
Pp. 183–203. John Wiley and Sons, New York.

Rushton, W. A. H. (1959). A theoretical treatment of Fuortes' observation
upon eccentric cell activity in Limulus. J. Physiol. 148: 29–38.

Rushton, W. A. H. (1961). Peripheral coding in the nervous system. Sensor
Communication. Edited by W. A. Rosenblith. Pp. 168–181. Joh:
Wiley and Sons, New York.

Sherrington, C. S. (1906). The Integrative Action of the Nervous System
Yale University Press, New Haven. Rev. Ed. (1947). Cambridg
University Press, Cambridge.

Tansley, K. (1950). Vision. Soc. Exptl. Biol. Proc. 4: 19–33.

Tasaki, I. (1954). Nerve impulses in individual auditory nerve fibers o
guinea pig. J. Neurophysiol. 17: 97–122.

von Bekesy, G. (1960). Experimental models of the cochlea with and with
out nerve supply. Neural Mechanisms of the Auditory and Vestibula
Systems. Edited by G. L. Rasmussen and W. F. Windle. Pp. 3–2(
Charles C. Thomas, Springfield.

von Bekesy, G. and Rosenblith, W. A. (1951). The mechanical properties o
the ear. Handbook of Experimental Psychology. Edited by S. S. Stevens
Pp. 1075–1115. John Wiley and Sons, New York.

Wagner, H. G., MacNichol, E. F. Jr. and Wolbarsht, M. L. (1960). The respons
properties of single ganglion cells in the goldfish retina. J. Gen. Physiol
43: 45–62.

Wald, G. (1959). The photoreceptor process in vision. Handbook of Physi
ology—Neurophysiology. Vol. 1, pp. 671–692. American Physiologica
Society, Washington, D.C.

Wever, E. G. and Bray, C. W. (1930). Action currents in the auditory
nerve in response to acoustical stimulation. Proc. Natl. Acad. Sci
U.S. 16: 344–350.

Wiersma, C. A. G., Furshpan, E. and Florey, E. (1953). Physiological and
pharmacological observations on muscle receptor organs of the crayfish
Cambarus clarkii. Quart. J. Exptl. Biol. 30: 136–150.

13

Reflex Behavior and the Nervous System

The reflex as a segment of behavior

The motor behavior of living organisms is complex and varied. One moment a cat may be running, then suddenly it may turn to avoid an unfriendly dog or leap at a bird anticipating the position of the prey in flight. Yet, although diverse, there are certain behavioral characteristics which are unmistakenly associated with a given animal species. From observation certain kinds of behavior typical of frogs, chickens, cats, monkeys, man, etc. are expected, and even relatively small deviations from the normal can be detected. There are also similarities of behavior of a simpler sort which are seen in all the species. These are the stereotyped simple acts or aspects of behavior known as *reflexes* which were first clearly described by Descartes in the 17th century. An example he gave is of a foot burned by contact with fire and rapidly withdrawn (Fearing, 1930). The fire stimulates nerve fiber paths, pictured by Descartes as passing to the brain where central connections are made. From these connections in the brain nerve fibers pass down to the appropriate limb muscles to initiate a quick movement of the foot away from the fire. For this particular reflex, as well as many others, we now know that the central connections underlying this type of reflex are contained within the spinal cord. This is shown by the elicitation of the reflex in the decapitated animal (*vide infra*). However, the essentials of the reflex were rightly discerned by Descartes as composed of a specific stimulus activating sensory peripheral neural pathways to the CNS where the reflex is initiated via a neural path back to the appropriate muscles to give rise to a characteristic motor response to that particular stimulus. The appropriateness of the response with respect to the stimulus is shown by the nature of the stimulus. Fire is a painful and potentially damaging stimulus and the movement of the limb is 'protective,' i.e. the limb is moved away from this source of danger. Very bright light is inefficient for vision or even potentially damaging, and in response to a sudden increase of light, the pupil constricts. Aspirated objects or fluid evoke coughing or sneezing, resulting in the ejection of the material from the respiratory tract. Tickling of the hairs on the inside of the ear of a dog or cat causes a characteristic reflex flicking of the ear which may be followed by vigorous shaking of the head, the *pinna reflex*. Such reflex behavior helps prevent insects and foreign bodies from entering the external ear. We are not aware of other reflexes, e.g. the adjustment of blood pressure or of the glucose level in the blood, but these are nonetheless appropriate adjustments of the internal milieu to keep it constant (Chapters 11, 23)

In the next several chapters an analysis of reflex actions of the simplest type will be presented with respect to the neuronal actions involved and the mechanisms underlying them. The purpose of this chapter is to discuss the reflex with relation to the operation of the entire nervous system and how reflexes operate together or how one set follows another to give rise to observed behaviors of the intact organism.

Neuroidal and elementary nervous systems

In the course of evolution organisms have developed progressively more complicated nervous systems along with more complex behavioral patterns. By examining the nervous systems found in the lower organism, we might perhaps more easily discover the essential machinery necessary for reflex and other behavior (Pantin 1950).

However, observation of even the single cell organisms shows that its behavior is complicated. In the *Amoeba*, local alterations at a site anywhere over its apparently homogeneous surface membrane may excite a retraction of the cell or initiate the development and extension of a *pseudopodium* toward the stimulus (Jennings, 1906).

The movement of the organism follows upon the pseudopodia extension toward various substances in the medium (Bell and Jeon 1963). These *chemotactic* influences may cause pseudopodia extension by means of a depolarizing action on the cell membrane. Ciliated and flagellated unicellular organisms move by means of a rhythmic ciliary beat. They may move forward, stop or reverse the direction of ciliary beating, depending upon environmental circumstances. For example, a mild noxious stimulus, such as a needle probe, can cause them to move toward the stimulus; if stronger, the organism moves away from the source of excitation (Jennings, 1906). The controlled pattern of ciliary movement in these organisms is brought about by small *organelles* within the cell which have been described as *neuroidal*, i.e. they appear to perform excitatory and regulative functions usually associated with the neurons of higher multicellular forms of life. Thin fibrils are found coursing between and connecting small organelles at the base of each cilium. These fibrils appear to coordinate the beating of the individual cilia so that they can effect movement. It was shown that when the inter-connections were cut microsurgically ciliary function and movements were lost (Rees, 1922). Similarly, in the flagellated organism, *Euplotes*, intracellular fibrils were shown necessary for coordination of the flagella. When the fibrils were cut (Fig. 13.1) this resulted

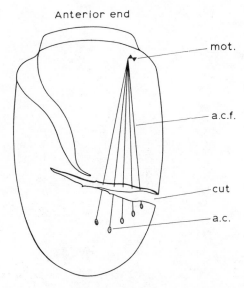

Fig. 13.1.   Cut made in the cell body of ciliated organism (*Euplotes*) transects neuroidal fibers (a.c.f.) passing from a coordinating center (mot., motorium) to granules (a.c.) controlling the ciliary beat. (From Taylor, 1920.)

in uncoordinated ciliary beating and inability of the organism to perform some of its movements (Taylor, 1920).

Electron microscopy (Roth, 1958; Roth and Shigenaka, 1964) has shown that the coordinating fibrils are in turn composed of bands of thinner *filaments* which connect at the *rod* organelle present at the base of the cilium (Fig. 13.2). As shown in this figure, the cilia cut in cross-section are composed of filaments arranged in a ring around a central pair. These filaments are contractile and bring about the beating movement of the cilia.

The mechanism of excitation and conduction in these subcellular organelles is at present unknown. Calcium and potassium ions are involved in control of cilia as demonstrated by Jahn (1962). There

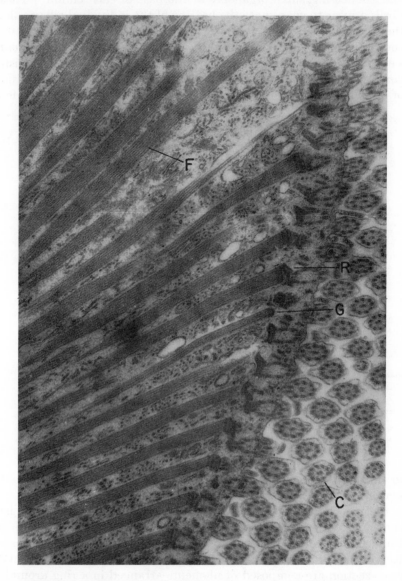

Fig. 13.2.   Electron microscope section at base of ciliary projections show filaments (F) in tight bundles attaching at dense rods (R) and granules (G) at base of cilia.   At the right, cross-sections of the cilia are seen with the typical array of peripheral and central filaments surrounded by an outside membrane. *Ophryoscolex* (× 47,000).   (Courtesy L. E. Roth; Roth and Shigenaka, 1964.)

may be a similarity of this subcellular conduction system to that of the cannular system of the sarcoplasmic reticulum of muscle, where (as was indicated in Chapter 9) excitation of the membrane is followed by a spread of excitation inward in the tubules of the reticulum to activate the myofilaments and the mechanical response of the muscle.

Of interest is another similarity of the ciliary system to the neuronal and muscular cells of higher organisms. Acetylcholine and its related esterase have been found present in these lower organisms and the anticholinesterase eserine can stop ciliary beating (Seaman and Houlihan, 1951). Bülbring et al. (1953) in their study of the ciliary movements on the gill plates of the clam, Mytilis, also found ACh present. Furthermore, ACh when applied in low concentrations increased the rate of ciliary beating while larger concentrations decreased it. A blocking action of D-tubocurarine on the beat was shown, and also atropine blocked ciliary action when larger amounts were used. These results were considered as evidence for an ACh system present in these organisms, in which ACh acts not as a transmitter, for there are no true nerve fibers, but as a rate-modulating substance. A difference in the action of the subcellular fibrils from that of nerve was shown by the ineffectiveness of 2% cocaine on ciliary action. Adrenalin appears also to be a rate-modulator, causing an increase in the rate of ciliary movement.

The multicellular organisms, the metazoa, soon show a specialization of cellular function. Some cells become specialized for stimulus reception, others for neuronal conduction and interconnection, others for contraction. In the lowly sponge the cells around the various pores contract in response to flow of water currents and probably to chemical (food) stimulation (Parker, 1919). The cells contracting around the pore are apparently localized effector structures. There is little evidence of the development of a neuronal system organizing the behavior of all the pores in the sponge as a whole (Jones, 1962).

Complex behavior arises when neural elements arise to integrate the various effector activities. Neurons interposed between sensory receptor and motor elements are first seen in the wall of the coelenterata (e.g. sea anemone, hydra and jellyfish) constituting the nerve net (Fig. 13.3). The nervous system of the mammal takes origin from this humble beginning. In some tissues of the higher mammal, namely, in the gastrointestinal and genitourinary systems, this type of primitive nerve net system is retained. Within the nerve net, neural fibers cross and recross to form the net and at their synaptic junctions excitation is transmitted from one neuronal element to the other. Because of the multiplicity of these synaptic connections, spread is diffuse throughout the nerve net. Pantin (1950) summarized the properties of the nerve net from his studies of *actinozoa* as follows: (a) excitation will be conducted diffusely in all directions from the site of stimulation, (b) the response varies in character according to the strength of the stimulus, and (c) the stronger the stimulus, the further will its effects be propagated by the addition of more elements.

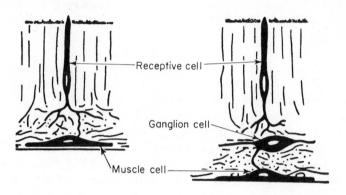

Receptive cell

Ganglion cell

Muscle cell

Fig. 13.3.   Simple neuromuscular system of coelenterata shown at left with sensory receptor cell synapsing on an effector muscle cell. In other parts of the organism (right) an interposed neural cell has evolved. (From Parker; after Bard, *Modern Physiology*, 10th Ed., Mosby, 1956.)

The jellyfish is an example of an animal with *radial body symmetry*, these coelenterata having the shape of a dome or umbrella. Long and short periods of rhythmic activity of the body wall may appear in a small portion or over larger parts of this organism. Stimulation, e.g. by electrical shock, may induce changes in the pattern of its rhythmicity sometimes lasting for hours. The means of locomotion in these organisms is by jet propulsion, produced by a contraction of the dome with the forced expulsion of water. Contraction of dome muscles is controlled by nerve elements present at the margin of its bell. Eight sense organs known as *marginal bodies* are located at the edge of the bell rim in *Aurelia*. From the marginal bodies activity passes via its neuronal connections to spread centrally and reach the large circular sheet of muscle that forms a sphincter midway between central mouth and bell edge. Contraction of the muscles and propulsion of water follows upon nervous discharge. Afterwards the

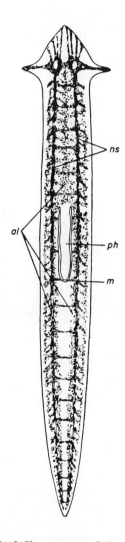

Fig. 13.4.   Longitudinal fiber tracts of the nervous system (ns) passing from the headward ganglia to the individual body segments of the worm, *Planaria*.   Lateral branches to muscle and skin of the segments.   The pharynx (ph) with mouth (m) and alimentary (al) canal is also shown. (After Child; from Kuntz, 1946.)

muscles passively relax.   The spread of excitation via these neural elements was shown by cutting the bell in various ways.   The spread of excitation was not blocked as long as a bridge of tissue containing neural fibers remained and conduction via muscle was excluded (Parker, 1919).   Excision of all the marginal bodies blocks locomotion.   If only one marginal body remains, it can act as a *pacemaker* with a continuation of rhythmic discharges causing pulsations of the bell muscle.

The lowest of the species with linearly organized bodies are the worms.   Their bodies are composed of a series of similarly constructed segments.   Nerve tracts pass from the head end to the back end of

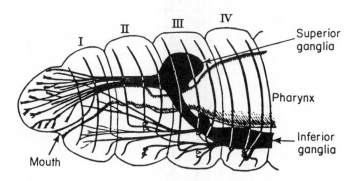

Fig. 13.5.   The superior and inferior ganglia constituting the 'brain' of the earthworm is shown in diagrammatic form with the sensory nerves leading to the mouth and to the forward tactile regions.   (After Shipley and McBride; from Kuntz, 1946.)

the organism with branches to the muscles of the individual segments (Fig. 13.4).   Via these tracts the segments are brought into harmonious conjoint action.   In worms with appendages (bristles or protrusions), these are moved by the segmental muscles one after another in proper sequence to carry the body of the animal forward. As the organism moves forward into the environment it first encounters varied stimulation at the head end.   The primitive chemical and mechanical sensory apparatus present there and the *circumesophageal ganglia* and nerves (Fig. 13.5), controlling feeding and burrowing, became developed in the higher phylogenetic forms into the distance sense receptors for sight, hearing and smell.   The greater and greater accumulation of neurons dealing with these exteroceptor functions constitutes a large part of the brain of the higher organisms.

Encephalization and purposiveness (goal-direction)

With the increased phylogenetic development of the anterior portion of the linearly organized nervous system, until it becomes the brain of the higher form, the lower segmental neural mechanisms of the primitive forms have also undergone modifications.   The relatively greater autonomy and generality of function of the individual body segments was lost as the controlling mechanisms of the upper centers took over more and more of their function in the interest of greater coordination.   The gathering of more functions into the brain of the higher forms and modification of the lower segmental nervous system is known as *encephalization*.   Comparing the morphology of the brains of a few representative species (Fig. 13.6) (Kuntz, 1946), the evolution of the forward part of the brain, the *telencephalon*, and in turn its youngest part, the *cerebral cortex*, can be inferred.   So great is the relative expansion of the cortical surface area that to accommodate it in the limited volume of the brain case the cortex becomes folded and shows fissures or *sulci*.   The relative changes in size of the brain of higher forms is shown in sections of the brain cut in the antero-posterior direction in the midline, the *sagittal view* (Fig. 13.7).   However, with these great differences in brain development, behavior does not appear to have radically changed with evolutionary advance. The differences in behavior between, say, a rat and a cat, or a cat and a monkey, are quantitative rather than qualitative (Chapter 25).

Because of the linear organization of the vertebrate CNS, it is relatively easy to sever the connections between the spinal cord and the brain.   Whytt (1751) showed that when the brain of an amphibian was pithed, after a few minutes of flaccidity the animal assumed a nearly normal posture.   It did irrevocably lose its spontaneity of action and many of its responses to the environment.   However, when the leg of such a spinal preparation was pinched, the leg was quickly drawn back in an apparently normal manner.   Whytt called these responses the 'vital faculties' (known to us as reflexes) and contrasted their invariant and automatic nature to the more varied voluntary actions possible in an animal with its brain intact. Animals higher in the scale of life than the amphibia show a more severe and prolonged depression of activity before the return of reflex activity.   The phase of depressed reflex responses which may last for hours, days or months was called *spinal shock*, a subject to be discussed in Chapter 22.

Very clearly it would appear from the studies of Whytt and others that after entering the spinal cord afferent impulses need not be transmitted by fibers to the brain and then downward to the nerve leading to the muscles as Descartes had supposed.   However, there were certain philosophical difficulties concerning the nature of the reflexes of the spinal cord which hindered acceptance of these facts. There was an implication that somehow the soul was present in the spinal cord because of the purposive nature of the reflexes which we have already noted.   The question asked was whether there could

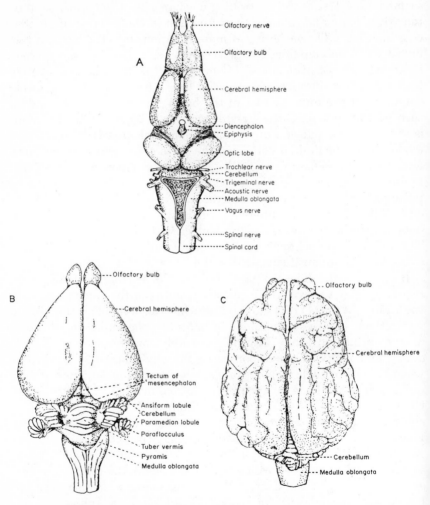

Fig. 13.6.   Dorsal view of the frog brain with its relatively small cerebral hemispheres (A) compared to that of the rabbit (B). In the dog (C) fissures of the cerebral hemisphere develop with the still greater relative enlargement in surface area of the cerebral cortex.   (Kuntz, 1946.)

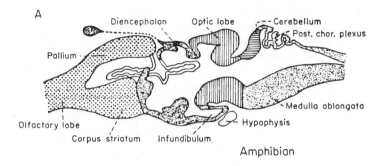

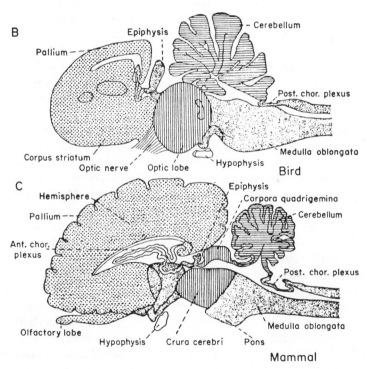

Fig. 13.7.   The relatively great growth of the forward end of the brain, in higher forms seen by comparing sagittal sections of the brain of amphibian (A), bird (B) and mammal (C).   (After Edinger; from Kuntz, 1946.)

be, corresponding to the reflexes remaining, a rudimentary 'mindness' existing in the spinal cord. This problem was clearly expressed by Aristotle when he observed that:

> '. . . certain insects go on living when divided into segments; this means that each of the segments has a soul (mindness) . . . for both of the segments for a time possess the power of sensation and local movement' (McKeon, 1941).

Marshall Hall (1833) clearly distinguished the reflexes as mechanisms locally controlled in the spinal cord with additional fibers leading to the brain for conscious awareness, and fibers from the brain leading to lower motor centers for voluntary motor control (Liddell, 1960). In part, the difficulty was due to the lack of anatomical information at that time. The separation of sensory functions to dorsal roots and motor function to ventral roots was known through the work of Bell and Magendie (Fearing, 1930). However, the course and the connections of fibers within the cord and to the brain were unknown. Although Hall's view of a machine-like reflex behavior present in the isolated spinal cord preparation with higher functions reserved to the brain was generally accepted, the question arose again later in the 19th century in the form of the *Pflüger–Lotze controversy* (Fearing, 1930). Pflüger, drawing upon clinical experience, formulated a series of so-called laws of the nervous system. These are mainly of historical interest and after a too-long vogue were shown by Sherrington to be misconceptions (Liddell, 1960). However, on the basis of his laws Pflüger supported the notion that some primitive form of consciousness resided in the spinal cord of the spinal animal, citing as evidence the protective action of reflexes. It is, indeed, impressive to see how a decapitated frog suspended vertically will, if a piece of paper dipped in an irritant such as acetic acid is placed on its skin, bring its leg up and in a series of wiping movements attempt to brush it away. And, if the leg on that side is held, the other leg is brought up to wipe away at the irritation site on the other side. Lotze noted that there were other reflexes which lead by their mechanical performance not to a protection but to an increased damage of the organism. Sherrington (1906) helped resolve the question. He took an evolutionary viewpoint, and theorized that reflex performances which in the past may have involved consciousness were through time no longer necessarily connected with mindness after they had become genetically fixed. This is similar to what we experience in forming a habit, where at first the performance is attended by conscious effort or concern and then later done subconsciously. It is interesting that with the development of modern electronic technology and the development of feed-back instruments and control systems the notion of purposiveness no longer need imply consciousness or a soul. We have purposive (goal-directed) mechanisms which can imitate the behavior of living organisms (Wiener, 1961). An example of an inanimate goal-directed device is radar. A beam of radio waves is transmitted through the air and reflected back from objects, the difference in time between transmitted and received waves giving a measure of the distance of the object. Bats make use of this same principle using high frequency sound waves to detect flying food objects or obstacles in their path of flight (Griffin, 1958).

Reflex action is not to be considered as the province of the spinal cord only. Behavior controlled by the brain appears to have various orders of complexity ranging from the more stereotyped to the more complex and variable. Jackson (1887) using his clinical experience and influenced by the philosophy of Spencer, assigned three types of levels of function to the human nervous system. First, at the lowest level are the completely stereotyped motor actions exemplified by reflex action. To this level on the sensory side are assigned sensations. Second, at the intermediate level are those combinations of reflexes which occur in a rhythmic movement of a limb where a number of reflexes are combined into a pattern of action. On the sensory side perceptions are a property of this intermediate level. And third, at the highest level are the complex motor patterns under the control of volition (the will) exemplified by those interactions of muscular activities required for speaking. Corresponding to this highest level on the sensory side is mentation, including ideation, judgment and consciousness (Chapter 25).

These categories were meant to draw attention to the different aspects of behavior and as such are generally useful. However, there has been a tendency to identify these functional levels with anatomic regions of the CNS—the lowest level with the spinal cord, intermediate level with the brain stem and highest level with the cerebral cortex. The shortcomings of such an approach will become apparent in our discussions in later chapters, particularly in Chapter 25.

Instinctive behavior and its genetic basis

The problem raised by the purposiveness of reflexes arises also with respect to the behavior of the lower organisms. The spinning of webs by spiders, nest building of birds, etc., have long interested biologists as examples of *instinct*, a complex form of reflex activity. Instinctive behavior has been considered as similar to Jackson's intermediate level functions of the higher nervous system—of combinations of reflexes and of perceptions without the higher functions of ideation and consciousness present. However this may be, a study of the behavioral patterns of animals such as birds and fish in nature suggests a set of reflex-like sequences (Lorentz, 1950; Tinbergen, 1951). Ethologists have observed that when specific and appropriate stimulation was presented, such as food to a hungry animal, a series of stereotyped responses—grasping, swallowing, etc., are elicited, each typical of the species. In response to sexual stimulation of receptive animals, changes in coloration and a stereotyped mating behavior ensues, e.g. the peculiar 'dance' courtship of birds. Such specific instinctive patterns of behavior are said to be *released* by the appropriate stimulus. This term implies that the behavior although complex is like a simple reflex, a self-contained functional unit with its neural apparatus so constituted that upon presentation of the appropriate stimulation it becomes discharged into the observed motor performance. Careful observation is required to separate those responses which are inborn or *innate* from those which are learned. For example, birds raised in isolation have songs typical of their species (Lade and Thorpe, 1964). However, in some birds both innate and learned songs can be distinguished.

To account for the complex innate behavior typical of an intact animal, it is considered that each released pattern of behavior will bring the animal into position for another type of reflex-like release of responses to yet another releasing stimulus. This, in turn, leads to a new position and the possibility for a further release, etc. An example of this given by Tinbergen (1951) is of the peregrine falcon which when hungry begins a hunting drive. It flies on a characteristic search path over a hunting territory. The sight of prey releases diving and harrying maneuvers. Proximity to the prey releases catching, then killing, then eating behavior. In all of this one response leads to the next possibility for a releasing stimulus and in this way a complex sequence of responses is elicited.

Most important in the above example is the hunger *drive* which leads to increased activity. If sufficiently intense, behavior may be released without a food object actually present. In starlings which have been starved, the whole sequence of watching, killing and swallowing may occur without any source of food present. Such inappropriate behaviors have been called *vacuum activities*. Even in organisms as low as the coelenterata behavior which may be classed as vacuum activity has been seen. *Metridium* uses its tentacles to wave food in the water into its mouth. If sufficiently starved, such tentacle responses occur spontaneously.   Such inappropriate behavior can be stopped by feeding or simply by injecting mussel juice into the animal (Parker, 1919).

Complex behavior explained as a series of chained reflexes has been considered by the *reflexologic school* to arise as the result of a form of learning which takes place during development.   It is known for example that *Amblystoma* embryos go through a series of characteristic reactions in their early development.   They first show simple bending of one side of their bodies forming a C.   Later on, a reverse bending occurs and their bodies assume the form of an S. Still later this S shape is repeated in rapid sequence as part of their swimming movements.   The reflexologic view is that the simpler reflex must be performed before the next stage is 'learned.'   In opposition to this, Coghill (1929) considered that the 'total pattern' of activity is laid down developmentally, the local reflexes shown by C or S responses representing 'partial patterns' abstracted from it. In this view of development, the sensory and motor systems may have different rates of growth, but when all systems are present the first motor responses are orderly.   The studies of Weiss (1939) support this 'whole pattern' view.   *Amblystoma* embryos were anesthetized continuously for days during the time when normal embryos of the same age began to swim.   When the narcosis was removed from the anesthetized animals, they at once performed all the complex motor behaviors shown by normal animals at that stage of development.   Even though they skipped the more primitive motor reactions there was no loss of later behavioral abilities.   This result supports the concept of an innate, whole-pattern organization of behavior.   Further evidence in support of the innate concept was an example given by Weiss of some species of salamander so tightly enclosed in their egg that a learning process or evocation of primitive behavior was not possible before their free-living life commenced. Upon hatching, complex behavior was immediately performed.   A similar example cited is the butterfly enclosed in its pupal case with no possibility of movement of its wings.   After emergence it unfolds its wings and flies with well-coordinated movements.   Similar studies in the human (Hooker, 1944) also appear to support this concept.

Complicated patterns of behavior as an expression of an inborn pattern of neuronal connectivity genetically determined for each species is shown with respect to the sensory aspect of behavior by the *imprinting* observed in the duckling soon after hatching.   Upon perceiving the mother duck, it normally walks after her.   However, in the absence of the mother, the duckling will follow a model resembling the mother duck. Its readiness to do so is increased the closer the model approaches to the characteristics of a live duck in its shape, size, color etc. This propensity to follow a model of a mother duck is very strong for only a few days after hatching, during the *critical period*, and then is reduced (Lorentz, 1950). A similar readiness to react to particular sensory inputs without previous experience is the fear reaction of young birds to a model of a falcon passed over it. The model need only have the general shape of their natural predator (Hartley, 1950). These studies indicate that sensory and motor patterns required of such behavior are genetically determined. Those specific stimulatory aspects of the environment on which biological value has been phylogenetically placed are responded to with release of appropriate behavior. It is on the basis of this inborn propensity for behavior that learning occurs and memories are acquired (Chapter 25). This concept differs from the *tabula rasa* of Locke (1690), the 'blank sheet' which is the nervous system at birth on which experiences will be written.

REFERENCES

Bell, L. G. E. and Jeon, K. W. (1963). Locomotion of *Amoeba proteus*, *Nature* **198**: 675–676.

Bülbring, E., Burn, J. H. and Shelley, H. J. (1953). Acetylcholine and ciliary movement in the gill plates of *Mytilus edulis*. *Proc. Roy. Soc. B.* **141**: 445–466.

Coghill, G. E. (1929). *Anatomy and the Problem of Behavior*. Cambridge University Press, Cambridge.

Fearing, F. (1930). *Reflex Action*. Williams and Wilkins Co., Baltimore.

Griffin, D. R. (1958). *Listening in the Dark*. Yale University Press, New Haven.

Hall, M. (1833). On the reflex function of the medulla oblongata and medulla spinalis. *Phil. Trans. Roy Soc.* **123**: 635–665.

Hartley, P. H. T. (1950). An experimental analysis of interspecific recognition. *Soc. Exptl. Biol. Symp.* **4**: 313–336.

Herrick, C. J. (1924). *Neurological Foundations of Animal Behavior*. Henry Holt and Co., New York.

Hooker, D. (1944). *The Origin of Overt Behavior*. University of Michigan Press, Ann Arbor.

Jackson, J. H. (1887). Remarks on evolution and dissolution of the nervous system. *J. Mental Sci.* **33**: 25–48; other papers in *Selected Writings of John Hughling Jackson*, Two vols. 1931 and 1932. Edited by J. Taylor. Hodder and Stoughton, London.

Jahn, T. L. (1962). The mechanism of ciliary movement II. Ion antagonism and ciliary reversal. *J. Cell. Comp. Physiol.* **60**: 217–228.

Jennings, H. S. (1906). *Behavior of the Lower Organisms*. Reprinted 1962 with an introduction by D. D. Jensen. Indiana University Press, Bloomington.

Jones, W. C. (1962).   Is there a nervous system in sponges?   *Biol. Rev.* **37**: 1–50.

Kuntz, A. (1946).   *A Textbook of Neuroanatomy.*   4th Ed.   Baillière, Tindall and Cox, London.

Lade, B. I. and Thorpe, D. H. (1964).   Dove songs as innately coded patterns of specific behavior.   *Nature* **202**: 366–368.

Liddell, E. G. T. (1960).   *The Discovery of Reflexes.*   Clarendon Press, Oxford.

Locke, J. (1690).   *Essay Concerning Human Understanding.*   1894 Edition. Fraser, London.

Lorentz, K. Z. (1950).   The comparative method in studying innate behavior patterns.   *Soc. Exptl. Biol. Symp.* **4**: 221–268.

McKeon (1941).   Translation of Aristotle's *De Anima.*   *The Basic Works of Aristotle.*   Random House, New York.

Pantin, C. F. A. (1950).   Behavior patterns in lower invertebrates.   *Soc. Exptl. Biol. Symp.* **4**: 175–195.

Parker, G. H. (1919).   *The Elementary Nervous System.*   J. B. Lippincott Co., Philadelphia.

Rees, C. W. (1922).   The neuromotor apparatus of *Paramecium.*   *Science* **55**: 184–185.

Roth, L. E. (1948).   Ciliary coordination in the protozoa.   *Exptl. Cell Res. Suppl.* **5**: 573–585.

Roth, L. E. and Shigenaka, Y. (1964).   The structure and formation of cilia and filaments in rumen protozoa. *J. Cell. Biol.* **20**: 249–270.

Seaman, G. R. and Houlihan, R. K. (1951).   Enzyme systems in *Tetrahymena geleii* S.   *J. Cell. Comp. Physiol.* **37**: 309–321.

Sherrington, C. S. (1906).   *The Integrative Action of the Nervous System.* Yale University Press, New Haven.   Rev. Ed. (1947).   Cambridge University Press, Cambridge.

Taylor, C. V. (1920).   Demonstration of the function of the neuromotor apparatus in Euplotes by the method of microdissection.   *Univ. Calif. Publ. Zool.* **19**: 403–470.

Tinbergen, N. (1951).   *The Study of Instinct.*   Oxford University Press, London.

Weiss, P. (1939).   *Principles of Development.*   Henry Holt and Co., New York.

Wells, M. J. (1962).   *Brain and Behavior in Cephalopods.*   Stanford University Press, Stanford.

Whytt, R. (1751).   *An Essay on the Vital and Other Involuntary Motions of Animals.*   Hamilton, Balfom and Neill, Edinburgh.

Wiener, N. (1961).   *Cybernetics, or, Control and Communication in the Animal and the Machine.*   2nd Ed.   Massachusetts Institute of Technology Press, New York.

14

General Properties of Reflexes

We shall follow the historical development of reflex mechanisms in this and in the next three chapters.   The basic studies of Sherrington (1906) were made using specified sensory afferent stimuli, and from the resulting reflex behavior, the general nature of the connectivity of the CNS was inferred.   In later advances, nerve stimulation was used to study reflex properties (Creed *et al.*, 1932).   The general principles arrived at form the subject matter of this chapter.   Electrical recording of reflex responses was then used to reveal more clearly the nature of cellular activities involved, and the results of those studies will be presented in Chapter 15.   Within recent years microelectrode studies of the cell have been used to investigate the nature of the synaptic processes involved, and these will be described in Chapter 16.   In Chapter 17 the integration of reflexes on that basis will be discussed.

With the complications of upper brain center control removed, the *spinal preparation* has a greatly simplified range of response. Shown in Fig. 14.1 are a number of different transections of the brain producing various types of preparations used in reflex studies.   A cut just below the medulla of the brain stem produces a *high spinal preparation*.   Spinal preparations made by transection of the spinal cord below the cervical 4th level where the phrenic nerve controlling the muscle of respiration exits will not interfere with respiratory control.   Such *low spinal preparations* are favored because in the cat and dog, while some reflex excitability returns from spinal shock within a few hours, it becomes greater after several weeks.   The reflexes of the lumbar segment of the cord controlling the hind muscles have been intensively investigated by Sherrington and his colleagues using this *chronic spinal preparation*.

The anatomical studies of the spinal cord by Ramón y Cajal (1909) revealed that there were two types of distribution of the sensory fibers entering the cord via the dorsal roots (Fig. 14.2).   One type of afferent fiber distribution is circumscribed.   The nerve fibers pass directly down through the gray matter of the segment of the cord into which the roots enter to synapse on the large motoneurons in the ventral horn of the gray matter.   These fibers are the *reflexo-motor collaterals*

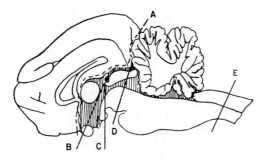

Fig. 14.1. Midsagittal diagram of cat's brain showing transections producing various types of preparations. The dotted line (A) shows the removal of the forebrain to produce a decorticate preparation; removal of the forebrain and thalamus (B). Section behind the hypothalamus produces a midbrain preparation (C). Section between the colliculi of the midbrain (D) produces a decerebrate preparation. Section behind the medulla (E) produces a high spinal preparation. (Modified from Wang *et al., J. Neurophysiol.*, **19**:340, 1956.)

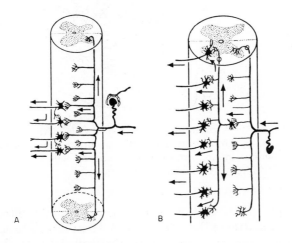

Fig. 14.2. Circumscribed type of cord connectivity (A), the reflexo-motor collaterals of Cajal of dorsal root afferents synapsing on the motoneurons of that segment. Widespread type of connectivity (B) with afferents synapsing on interneurons which in turn send axons to synapse on motoneurons in a number of cord segments.
(From Ramón y Cajal, 1909.)

of Cajal and generally are distributed with greatest density to the motoneurons in the segment in which the dorsal roots enter (Fig. 14.3) though some fibers pass to nearby segments. The other type of distribution of entering afferent fibers shown in Fig. 14.2 is of a more widespread pattern of connectivity in the cord. These fibers

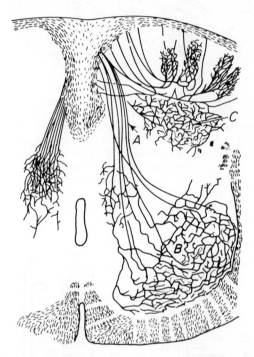

Fig. 14.3. The reflexo-motor collaterals of Cajal (A) ending on motoneurons in the ventral horn (B). Another group of fibers are seen ending in an intermediate group of cells (C). (From Ramón y Cajal, 1909.)

have a widespread termination on interneurons in the intermediate part of the gray matter of the spinal cord. These interneurons in turn make synaptic connections on many other cells within neighboring segments thereby spreading neuronal activity over a wide territory. The interneurons have their effect by their termination onto ventral horn motoneurons of the various segments. The motoneurons in the ventral horn of the spinal cord on which the synaptic influences of direct and indirect connections terminate are known as the *final common paths.* Their discharge activates the muscle units they innervate (Chapter 9). The motoneurons are commonly referred to by the name of the muscle they supply, i.e. gastrocnemius, semi-tendinous, quadriceps motoneurons, etc. All the regular patterns of motor activity come about by their discharge.

Flexion reflexes

Many of the fundamental spinal reflexes may be readily demonstrated in the chronic spinal animal with the body of the animal suspended

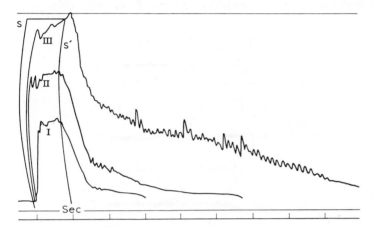

Fig. 14.4.   The graph shows in its upward direction (I) the movement of the limb of a spinal animal upon noxious stimulation of the skin of its paw. With a stronger stimulus (II) and more so with a still stronger stimulus (III) a prolonged and irregular declining descent of the limb is seen. S and S′ the onset and cessation of the stimulus. Time in seconds. (Sherrington, 1906.)

in a harness and its legs pendant. When a foot is pinched to a degree which would cause pain (nociceptive stimulus), by the application of a spring clip to the paw, the leg responds with flexion upward and away from the stimulus source. By affixing a recording system to the leg, this *flexor reflex* has been recorded (Fig. 14.4). An increase in intensity of the nociceptive stimulation gives rise to larger and more prolonged flexions. Observation of the leg shows that with a weaker nociceptive stimulus only the foot or lower leg may be flexed. When a stronger stimulation is used, the hip musculature is also activated to give rise to a further increase in the degree of flexion. The entry of the hip muscles into the recorded pattern of flexion is indicated by a break in the response curve. The term *irradiation* has been used to signify an entry of additional groups of motoneurons into a given response; in this case, the flexors of the hip muscles in the flexor reflex withdrawal. When the stimulus is removed, the leg does not abruptly re-extend. The leg only gradually returns to its normal extension with irregularities in the course of relaxation. This slow return from the height of reflex flexion may be due either to a continued discharge, an *after-discharge* of those motoneurons controlling the muscle, or to a prolonged discharge of the sensory receptors in the skin keeping up a continued reflex activity of those motoneurons. To test the latter possibility, nerves from the skin or muscle

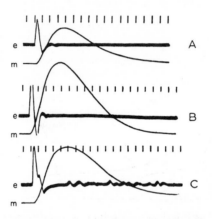

Fig. 14.5. Mechanical record of reflex response (m) and the electromyographic record of response (e) of tibialis anticus elicited by a brief single shock to the popliteal nerve (A). Response elicited by stimulation of the peroneal nerve (B). Response with stronger stimulus (C). Note prolonged after-discharge in the electromyographic record of C. Time intervals 10 msec.
(Creed *et al.*, 1932.)

were isolated and stimulated electrically to elicit flexor reflexes. In response to brief stimulations of nerve trunks, a quick twitch-like reflex contraction of the muscle is seen (Fig. 14.5) rather than the long-lasting contraction found when stimulating the nociceptive receptors of the skin. In this example, the peroneal nerve was cut and the central portion of the nerve was stimulated. The tendon of the tibialis anticus muscle was attached to a myograph to record the reflex tension produced. An electromyographic recording was also taken from the tibialis muscle during its reflex contraction. A reflex muscle action potential is found present after a short delay and is then followed by a brief period of smaller-sized after-discharges. These after-discharges last for scores of milliseconds, and not for the several seconds or so when nociceptive stimulation of the skin has been used as shown in Fig. 14.4.   Therefore, the prolonged reflex flexion seen upon skin pinch is due to a continued sensory discharge from the skin.   The flexion reflex by brief electrical stimulation of various peripheral nerves is subserved by the more diffuse type of central connection (Fig. 14.2) and shows the phenomenon of *fractionation*.   To show fractionation, the reflex tension produced in a flexor muscle (the anterior tibialis) is measured by a torsion

TABLE 1

M. TIBIALIS ANTERIOR	MAXIMUM MOTOR TENSION 2160 GRAMS	
AFFERENT NERVE STIMULATED	TENSION OF MAXIMAL REFLEX TETANUS IN GRAMS	REFLEX TENSION EXPRESSED AS PERCENTAGE OF MAXIMAL MOTOR TETANUS
Internal saphenous	800	32
Superficial obturator	165	6.7
Deep obturator	400	16
Nerve to quadriceps and sartorius	1190	44
Branch of peroneal	1700	69
External plantar	1240	50
Internal plantar	1330	54
Small sciatic	680	28
Hamstring	565	23
Nerve to sural triceps	300	12
Total	8370	

myograph.   Various muscle nerves are then selected, cut and their central ends maximally stimulated electrically.   The afferent nerves of these stimulated muscle nerves will eventually, after passing through various interneurons, excite a reflex response in the motoneurons supplying the muscles of the anterior tibialis.   In other words, the motoneurons of the anterior tibialis constitute the final common path of these various intermediating neurons.   The tension produced upon stimulation of each of these nerves is shown in Table 1. If each of the reflex tensions produced in the anterior tibialis by stimulation of the various muscle nerves are added together, the sum of these reflex tensions is greater than the maximum tension which can be produced by the muscle itself when its motor nerve is maximally stimulated. Therefore, the afferent nerves eventually will terminate on a fraction of most, if not all, of the various motoneuron groups of the muscles of the hind limb. Conversely, each of the motoneurons has many afferent sources acting on it.

We may refer to this inferred connectivity as *divergence* and *convergence*. The effect of divergence and convergence is further shown by the reflex interactions found when stimulating two afferent nerves concurrently and comparing the reflex tension with the reflex excited by each stimulus input separately. When two such afferent nerve sources are maximally stimulated concurrently, the resulting reflex

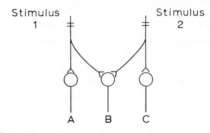

Fig. 14.6. Stimulus of afferent nerve input 1 results in reflex activation of motoneuron groups represented by C and B. Stimulation of input 2 activates groups B and C. Stimulation of 1 and 2 at the same time gives a total reflex effect which is less than the sum of reflex responses to each separately—occlusion.

contraction may be less than the sum of each afferent excited separately and then added together algebraically. This phenomenon of a deficit in reflex tension found when both sources are excited concurrently is called *occlusion* and has a similarity to the occlusion discussed in relation to the possibility of multiple innervation of muscle (Chapter 9). The basis for an occlusion effect in the CNS is shown diagrammatically in Fig. 14.6 where the final common path motoneurons of A and B are each eventually excited by stimulation of nerve S_1 and the final common path motoneurons B and C by stimulation of nerve S_2. Stimulation of both S_1 and S_2 at the same time gives a response due to A, B, and C. With S_1 and S_2 excited separately, the response is A, B, and B, C, respectively. Combined stimulation of the two nerves would, therefore, result in a lesser reflex tension, the occlusion due to the sharing of final common path motoneurons, B. Continuing in this phenomenological vein, the term *facilitation* was first used when a weaker stimulation of each of the nerves S_1 and S_2 are combined and, as shown in Fig. 14.7, only a subliminal excitation of the group labeled B takes place by each such stimulation. This B group of motoneurons constitutes a *fringe group* of cells which are subliminally excited with respect to the actively responding motoneuron pool. In the diagram of Fig. 14.7, stimulation of nerve S_1 will discharge final common path motoneurons represented by A, and the dotted lines carry a subliminal excitation to the fringe group of motoneurons represented by B. In the same way, excitation of S_2 will fire a group of motoneurons represented by C and subliminally excite the fringe group of B motoneurons. When both the afferent nerves S_1 and S_2 are excited together, the subliminal excitations of B motoneurons will add to reach threshold for the B

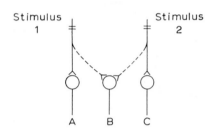

Fig. 14.7. Stimulation of afferent nerve input 1 gives rise to a response of motoneuron group represented by cell A and subliminal excitation of the motoneuron group represented by B. Stimulation of input 2 excites C and, subliminally, B. Stimulation of 1 and 2 at the same time brings motoneuron group B to threshold in addition to those of groups A and C. The total response, therefore, is greater than the sum of separate stimulation of 1 and 2— facilitation.

group, and the combined reflex is a response of motoneuron groups A, B, and C. The reflex response to stimulation of each nerve separately was a response of A and of C motoneurons with a sum of tensions less than that found with a combined stimulation of nerves S_1 and S_2. The type of facilitation exemplified is *spatial facilitation* brought about by addition of effects from two spatially different afferent sources with synaptic endings on a common group of fringe cells. *Temporal facilitation* is seen when two shocks are presented in succession via one afferent source. The second shock gives rise to a larger response than a single shock by itself. Facilitation is now known to be brought about by synaptic processes which are similar to the EPPs described in neuromuscular transmission. We shall discuss these synaptic processes and the inverse inhibitory synaptic processes acting to decrease excitability of the neurons in the following chapters.

Stretch and tendon reflexes

The flexor reflexes discussed in the preceding section are brought about by the widespread type of neuronal connectivity involving discharges in the motoneurons of many muscle groups. The more restricted type of connectivity (Fig. 14.2) underlies the reflex response found following a stretch of muscle. The resulting reflex contraction of the muscle occurs only in that muscle, or even of the part of the muscle which is stretched. The manner of stretching the muscle is used to distinguish two types of similar stretch reflex responses. A maintained stretch lasting for scores of

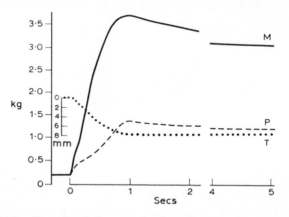

Fig. 14.8. Stretch of the muscle gives rise to reflex contraction recorded myographically as shown by the solid line (M). Part of the tension is non-reflex and this component (P) is shown by cutting the nerve and again stretching the muscle. The applied tension is given by dotted line T. (Liddell and Sherrington, 1925.)

seconds, or longer, gives rise to a *stretch reflex*. The *tendon reflex* is a form of stretch reflex excited by a brief or momentary stretch as when a muscle tendon such as the patellar tendon is tapped with a hammer. This reflex is also termed the *myotatic, knee-jerk* or *patellar reflex*. In these studies, to avoid interaction of the reflex activity of one muscle with that of another when the limb moves, the limb muscles are freed from their insertions and the tendons connected to isometric levers and torsion levers or strain gauges to record separately the increase in muscle reflex tension (Creed *et al.*, 1932). The reflex is elicited by a solenoid or similar device arranged to produce a brief quick pull on the tendon or to give a maintained stretch.

The stretch reflex excited by a maintained stretch of the muscle is shown in the myographic record of Fig. 14.8 where the solid line, M,

ndicates the increase in reflex tension in response to the imposed
stretch shown by the dotted line, T. Some of the tension increase is
due to the elastic properties of the non-muscular tissues. This
passive tension is shown after denervation by the dashed line in the
figure. The true reflex tension of the muscle is determined by the
subtraction of this passive elasticity from the total reflex response.
The receptor for the stretch reflex is the spindle receptor found in the
muscle (Liddell and Sherrington, 1924). Its properties in relation to
reflex control will be discussed in a later chapter. The stretch reflex

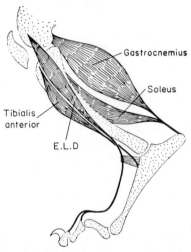

Fig. 14.9. Some extensor and flexor muscles of the cat hind limb
used in reflex studies. The gastrocnemius is a fast type of extensor
muscle, soleus a slow extensor muscle. The tibialis anterior and
extensor longis digitorum (E.L.D.) are flexors of the foot. (From
Lloyd in Fulton, *A Textbook of Physiology*, 7th Ed., Saunders,
1955.)

usually occurs only in the muscle reflexly stimulated and not in
other muscles of the limb; however, other muscles may show a
brief period of subliminal facilitation. This facilitation takes place
in the muscles *synergistic* to the reflexly activated muscle. Synergists
are those muscles which have the same action in the movement of the
limb. In addition, there are also fibers which pass to other motoneurons within the CNS and act to decrease their excitability. This
inhibitory action occurs in motoneurons controlling the *antagonistic
muscles*, those which act in an opposite direction with respect to the
rotation of a limb about a joint. Some of the hind limb muscles of
the cat commonly used in reflex studies are shown in Fig. 14.9. As

may be seen from this diagram, the anterior tibialis by its contraction will flex the foot upward, the antagonistic gastrocnemius and soleus muscles act to extend the foot.   In another set of antagonistic muscles acting on the upper hind limb, the quadriceps muscle on contraction extends the lower leg, the hamstring muscles flex the leg at the knee.   The inhibitory effect of activation of one of the antagonistic pairs of muscles is shown in Fig. 14.10.   The quadriceps (M) is stretched and an increase of tension ensues, the stretch reflex. Then at the time indicated by the arrow, the antagonistic hamstring muscle (biceps) is stretched causing a rapid decrease of reflex tension

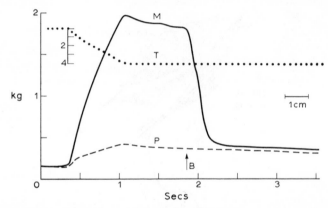

Fig. 14.10.   Stretch reflex contraction of the quadriceps muscle shown by solid line (M).   At the arrow stimulation of an antagonist flexor nerve, biceps (B), causes a reflex inhibition as shown by the drop of tension to that of the non-reflex elastic tension curve (P).   Applied   tension   (T).   Time   in   seconds.   (Liddell and Sherrington, 1925.)

in the quadriceps, i.e., its motoneurons have become inhibited. Depending on which of the muscle pairs is selected, the opposite muscle is considered the antagonist; inhibition occurs in either direction.   Therefore, the muscles are said to be *reciprocally inner-vated.*   In general, antagonistic pairs of reciprocally innervated muscles are found at all the limb joints.   The cellular aspects of the inhibitory action which is initiated in the motoneurons will be discussed in Chapters 15 and 16.

A tap on the tendon of the quadriceps muscle, for example, causes a minute extension of the muscle and of the spindle stretch receptors contained within that muscle.   Extension of the spindle stretch receptors excites a discharge of action potentials in those sensory afferents. In turn the volley in these fibers enters the cord and passes by Cajal's reflexo-motor collaterals directly down within that segment of the spinal cord to synapse on the quadriceps motoneurons and give rise to a motor discharge in those axons. The result is the quick reflex contraction of the quadriceps muscle and an upward movement of the lower leg. Tendon reflexes can similarly be shown in other extensor muscles and as well in flexor muscles where a similar brief extension of the muscle is elicited by plucking on the tendon. It is in that case therefore referred to as the *pluck reflex*.

A very small latency was found between the brief stretch stimulation and the onset of the myotatic reflex muscle response (Fig. 14.11).

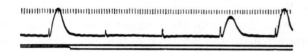

Fig. 14.11. Solid line shows the myographic records of tendon reflexes elicited at 3/sec. Stimulation of an antagonistic ipsilateral sensory nerve beginning at the time shown in lower signal line causes for the next two tendon taps an inhibition of the reflex. Reflex response to the third tendon tap is smaller than normal height with normal reflex response present at the next stimulus. (Creed *et al.*, 1932.)

The very small latency and the apparent peculiarity of the restriction of the reflex contraction to the muscle stretched prevented its acceptance as a true reflex for many years. Its reflex nature was indicated by the prolonged inhibition shown following a sensory nerve stimulus and by the measurable delay found for transmission through the spinal cord after subtracting the time required for conduction in the nerves to and from the cord (Jolly, 1911). With the use of electrical stimulation and recording, accurate measurements of central delay times showed that the central time delay for the reflex was 0.5 to 1.0 msec, a time delay which allows one synapse, as expected if the reflexo-motor collaterals of Cajal synapse directly on the motoneurons. Central synaptic transmission will be discussed more fully in Chapters 15 and 16.

Posture and movements

The stretch reflex and tendon reflex correspond to the normal activation of *tonic* (*postural*) and *phasic* (*movement*) reflexes (Sherrington, 1910).

The term *tone* is used to describe the firmness of muscles, actually due to some maintained degree of continued contraction. An increased tone is felt in the muscles of the wakeful animal, as opposed to the lax muscles observed in sleep or death. A cat crouched and ready to spring shows a highly tonic state of its musculature. Depending on the stimulus and resulting response of the animal, some muscles which are tonically active become phasically active and other muscles have their tone inhibited.

In some of the lower organisms such as the shellfish, a remarkably strong maintained tonus is present keeping the shell closed, with little expenditure of the energy of metabolism. No similar special tonic mechanisms are found within the muscle of vertebrates. Electro myographic recording of muscles has shown that the degree of tonus in mammalian muscle is directly related to the rate of spike discharge of motoneurons leading to their muscles and the number of such motoneurons which are active (Chapter 9). During maintained tonus, such as may occur in the leg and trunk muscles in standing upright, motoneurons can continue to discharge at a given rate for a long period of time (Denny-Brown, 1929).

Phasic reflex movements are produced by a rapid afferent volley exciting a short-lasting and rapid discharge of motoneurons. For example, this might occur when the feet strike the ground following a leap, the sudden excitation of spindle receptors causing a large number of motoneurons to become synchronously active to extend the legs. Electromyographically, this type of phasic reflex response is similar to the tendon reflex evoked by a tendon tap or a similar reflex evoked by stimulation of the muscle nerve afferents with a single electrical shock.

The stretch reflexes and tendon reflexes appear to be similar systems subserved by the restricted type of central connectivity (Fig. 14.2). However, the skeletal muscles appear to be differen tiated into tonic or slow and phasic or fast muscles, and the moto neurons controlling them have different properties (*vide infra*). In our discussion of muscle (Chapter 9), reference was made to the slow muscles, those having a longer twitch contraction duration Generally in the vertebrate the slow muscles are more red in color This is due to the greater content of myoglobin in slow muscles than in the pale fast muscles. However, this difference in myoglobin is not always associated with different contraction speeds. Some limb muscles are composed almost entirely of slow fibers and others of fast muscle fibers, but mixed muscles containing both fast and slow fibers are most common. Slow muscles are mainly found distributed in the limb extensors where in the maintained tonic state of standing, the stretch of gravity is mainly placed on the extensor muscles. In the sloth where the flexors maintain the tonic resting state, the slow tonic muscles are found in the flexor muscle group.

Corresponding to the different twitch times of the slow and fast muscles, their motoneurons have different reflex response properties. In response to a maintained stretch of a slow tonic muscle such as the soleus muscle, a much greater degree of reflex tension will be found than with a similarly maintained stretch of a fast phasic muscle such as the gastrocnemius. The soleus can develop over 90% of its maximum possible tension, the gastrocnemius developing only 10% of its maximal in response to a maintained stretch (Denny-Brown, 1929). During this time, the maximum rate of discharge in the tonic muscle may be 15/sec; but this is sufficient in these slower contracting muscles to give rise to tetanic fusion. In the fast muscles with a faster twitch duration of the muscle, such a low rate would be insufficient. In these muscles a reflex produces a greater rate of discharge, up to 40/sec or more. There is therefore a matching of the rate of discharge of the two types of motoneurons with respect to the contraction times of their muscles. The mechanisms controlling the rate of discharge in slow and fast motoneurons will be discussed in Chapter 16.

Decerebrate rigidity

Closely allied to the mechanisms of tonic discharge is the decerebrate preparation in which tonic reflex mechanisms are much exaggerated. As described by Liddell and Sherrington (1924), *decerebrate rigidity* results from a transection of the brain stem between the colliculi at an angle directed forward and downward (Fig. 14.1). Soon after the cut is made, if the animal is not too deeply anesthetized, a state of rigid extension occurs in the limbs and tail (Fig. 14.12). When placed on its legs, the decerebrate animal may be propped into a standing position. This phenomenon has been aptly described as a caricature of standing. It is an exaggeration of the tonic stretch reflexes controlling standing in those muscles which are normally acted on by gravity (Liddell and Sherrington, 1924). We have noted with respect to the postural state that it is brought about by activity of the motoneurons controlling tonic muscles. In the case of the decerebrate rigid animal the tonus is surprisingly high, but no new principles are involved; a large number of motoneurons are firing. The reflex nature of the rigidity is shown by the fact that an afferent discharge from the muscle stretch receptors is required to maintain the reflex activity of the tonic motoneurons. Flaccidity appears

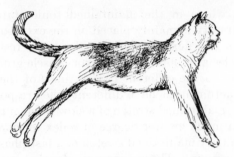

Fig. 14.12. Decerebrate rigidity after a transection of the brain stem at the intercollicular level (cf. section D, Fig. 14.1). Legs hyperextended and resist attempts at flexion. The head and tail are elevated. (Pollock and Davis, *J. Comp. Neurol.*, **50**:377, 1930.)

immediately upon section of the dorsal roots.   How the reflex rigidity is dependent on local sensory influx from the spindle stretch receptors in the muscles will appear in our later discussions of the integrated reflex loop in Chapter 17.   Along with the increase of tonus, phasic stretch reflexes are also enhanced to some degree in decerebrate rigidity, as shown by a deeper and stronger tendon reflex. *Clonus* may also appear, a long repeated series of contractions and relaxations of a foot or limb (Fig. 14.13).   To produce clonus, the quadriceps-soleus is stretched by flexion of the foot and a stretch reflex elicited. This is followed after relaxation by another discharge, and so on.

If an attempt is made to flex the decerebrate rigid leg, a great resistance to flexion is felt and force must be exerted to bend the limb.   Then, at a certain stage of bending, the resistance to flexion suddenly melts.   This sudden reduction in resistance is called the *lengthening* or *jack-knife* reaction.   Inhibitory mechanisms are involved, which will be discussed in Chapter 17.   If after the lengthening reaction has occurred, and the flexed leg is re-extended a little,

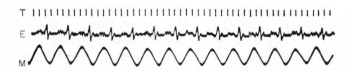

Fig. 14.13.   A sustained clonic discharge elicited in the decerebrate preparation by a brief extension of the muscle.   The myograph (M), electrical discharge (E).   Time marks (T), 20 msec.   (Creed *et al.*, 1932.)

the slack is taken up and the muscle again resists flexion.   Extending
the limb a little further again results in the muscle taking up the
slack with an increased extensor reflex activity at that shortened
length.   The return of reflex rigidity characteristic of the decerebrate
state at these different lengths of shortening is therefore called the
shortening reaction.   The shortening reaction enables muscles to
reflexly maintain a given degree of reflex tension at varied muscle
lengths.   In this way tonus is reflexly adjusted to the same degree
instead of to the different tensions a muscle might have at different
lengths.

Reflex interaction

As previously noted, interneurons play an important role in the diffuse
type of connectivity underlying flexion reflexes.   The interneurons
control the pattern and extent of the reflex response which is elicited,
i.e. its irradiation within the CNS.   Some of the 'laws' given to
'explain' irradiation were that reflex activity increases with the
strength of the stimulus; that the reflex is more easily elicited locally
than distally (*short reflexes* across the cord compared with *long
reflexes* between hind and forelimbs); that irradiation in the cord
spreads more easily downward than upward.   These 'laws' are formal
descriptions of rather complex interactions of interneurons within
the CNS.   The real problem is how the various reflex patterns are
brought about by interneurons; how switching occurs from one set to
another.   Sherrington (1906) analysed reflexes from this point of
view.   As an example he showed how the *scratch reflex* evoked in
chronic spinal dogs and cats competes with other reflexes for the
final common path motoneurons.   The scratch reflex is produced by
moving a pointed cog wheel over the skin of the flank to imitate the
tickling stimulation of a flea, or a weak tetanic electrical stimulation
may be applied to the skin for this purpose.   The reflex response
appears as a series of scratching movements of the hind limb directed
toward the stimulated spot, the scratching rhythm having an average
rate of 4 to 5 per sec (Fig. 14.14).   The orientation of the scratching
movements of the hind leg toward the stimulated site is an example
of *local sign*, i.e. localization of sensory inputs sufficient to direct a
response toward that specific part of the body surface.   However, in
the spinal animal localization is deficient, the limb makes rhythmic
motions only in the general direction of stimulation.   Local sign is
shown by the fact that stimulation of the skin on the left side induces
reflex scratching movements by the left hind leg and stimulation of

the skin on the right side causes a response to be made by the right hind foot (Sherrington, 1906).

The rhythms of the scratch reflex are not always exactly the same on each side. If two stimuli are presented together on the one side, will there be an averaging of the two frequencies? The result of this

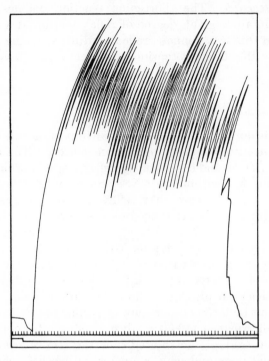

Fig. 14.14.   Scratching movements of a hind limb in response to a stimulation of the skin giving rise to the reflex with rhythmic extension and flexion at a rate similar to a normal scratch-ing rhythm.   Time marks at .20 sec intervals.   Lower signal shows time of onset and termination of the skin stimulation.
(Sherrington, 1906.)

experiment made by Sherrington is that the rhythm excited by one or the other stimulus will control the rate; in other words one input will *dominate* the final common path motoneurons.

Another type of reflex interaction is shown when two incompatible reflex inputs compete for the same motoneurons, for example a scratch reflex and a flexor reflex.   The flexor reflex is more powerful in commanding control of the motor output; it is *prepotent* over the scratch reflex.   This prepotency is shown in Fig. 14.15 where a rhythmic scratch reflex was first initiated and then supplanted by a flexor reflex response to a nociceptive stimulation delivered to the skin of that same side.

The final common path motoneurons are few with respect to the interneuron patterns flowing through these final common path motoneurons. The reflex patterns which do appear are brought about by unknown switching mechanisms within the various groups of interneurons.

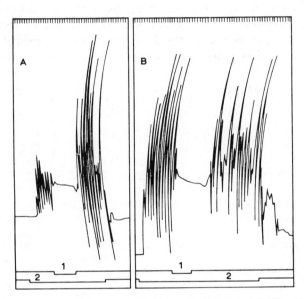

Fig. 14.15. (A) shows the rhythmic scratch reflex (cf. Fig. 14.14), produced by stimulation of the skin beginning at the time shown by signal line 2. Noxious stimulation given at the time shown by signal 1 causes prompt cessation of the reflex. In (B) during a stronger scratch reflex, interruption by noxious stimulation has a later onset with a less vigorous return. Upper line shows time signals at .20 sec intervals. (Sherrington, 1906.)

Reflex interaction in locomotion

The interplay of one reflex with another is also shown in the co-ordinated patterns of reflexes involved in running or walking. A number of phasic reflexes may be excited in the chronic animal which appear to be fragments of the coordinated interaction of reflexes in locomotion. If the paws of the pendant limbs of a chronic spinal dog are gently pressed upward, a quick downward thrust of the leg takes place, the *extensor thrust* reflex (Sherrington, 1906). This reflex would come into play in locomotion when the leg is extended forward to take a step. As the paw meets the ground the extensor thrust reflex is excited, the leg stiffening into a rigid pillar-like support to produce a pole-vaulting effect for the body.

Reflexes which occur concomittantly in the motoneurons on the other side of the cord controlling the muscles of the opposite leg, the *crossed reflexes*, are important in locomotion. When the limb of a decerebrate animal is forcibly flexed and the extensors of that limb are inhibited during the lengthening reaction, the extensors of the leg on the opposite (*contralateral*) side are excited to contract and that leg becomes extended, the *Philippson reflex* (Creed *et al.*, 1932). This crossed reflex most likely occurs in the rhythmic alternation of

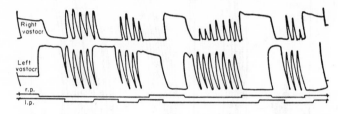

Fig. 14.16. Myographic records of right and left vastocrurei (extensor) muscles of the two hind limbs showing alternating reflex contraction. Stimulation of right peroneal nerve (r.p.), and of left peroneal nerve (l.p.) causes corresponding muscles to contract (downward for right vastocrurius, upward for left). On concurrent stimulation alternate contraction and relaxation occurs—the stepping reflex. (Myographic records are not in vertical register.) (Creed *et al.*, 1932.)

flexion and extension of the legs in locomotion. Sometimes a crossed reflex does not terminate simply as an extension of the contralateral limb, but following a brief flexion of one limb a repeated series of flexions and extensions alternates in the two limbs. Thus a walking or *stepping reflex* is excited. Reflex stepping may be maintained for considerable periods of time with a regular rate of 2 to 3 per sec (Fig. 14.16). Interestingly, when flexing the hind limb of a rabbit, a crossed flexion reflex occurs in the leg on the opposite side. In other words, both legs will rhythmically flex and extend together as in the thrust of a hop which is the more common type of locomotion in the rabbit (Sherrington, 1910).

In the decerebrate preparation not only may reflexes of the contralateral hind limbs be seen, but also reflex effects in the forelimbs are observed which resemble the positions taken by the four limbs of a our-legged animal in walking or running (Fig. 14.17). These *reflex figures* are examples of *long reflexes*. Functional connections are present in the cord between the motoneurons of fore and hind limbs which determine the coordination required of the four limbs in locomotion. In the human, there are similar long reflexes present. The

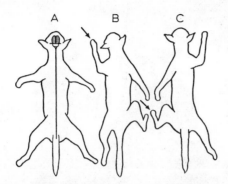

Fig. 14.17. Hyper-extension of the limbs after decerebration (A). Flexion of the foreleg (B) produced by noxious stimulation (arrow) with extension of contralateral forelimb and flexion of the contralateral hind limb and rotation of the head toward the stimulus source. Noxious stimulation of the hind leg (arrow) causes flexion of that limb with a flexion of the contralateral foreleg (C). (Sherrington, 1906.)

arms swing along with the normal leg movements and help act as a counterbalance to keep the body from twisting at each step. In decerebrate rigidity in the human an extension of hind limbs and a flexion of the arms is seen.

Reflexes of the brain

Reflexes have been studied in their most elementary fashion in the spinal cord of the spinal animal or of the decerebrate preparation. Yet, reflexes are found at all levels of the CNS. The cranial nerves subserve brain stem reflexes such as the *corneal reflex*—a lid closure on touching the cornea, reflex swallowing movements with reciprocal inhibition of respiration, the *masseter* reflex—a myotatic reflex which is a rapid closure of the lower jaw in biting, etc. Somatic postural reflexes, the *placing* and *hopping* reflexes, have a central component within the cerebral cortex (Bard, 1933). An animal suspended so that the dorsum of its paw is made to touch the edge of a table reflexly raises the paw and moves it forward to place it on top of the table. This placing reflex enables the animal to position itself on

various surfaces.   If an animal is made to bear its weight on only one
leg and its body is moved sideways or forward, at a certain angle the
leg will be reflexly raised and then lowered in a short hopping movement.   This hopping reflex enables the animal to reflexly maintain

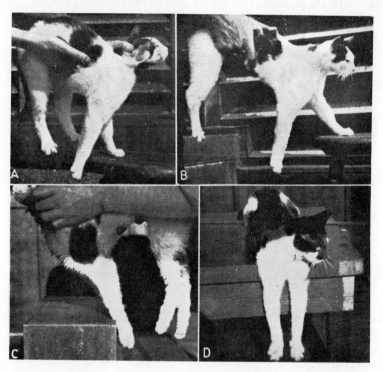

Fig. 14.18.   A cat with sensorimotor cortex ablated on the left
side shows defect of placing reactions in right leg (A and B) as the
dorsum of the forelegs was brought in contact with the edge of a
table.   The normal animal will on contact raise the limb and place
it on the surface as shown by the left foreleg.   Sensorimotor
areas on both sides destroyed (C) and placing reaction lost in both
legs.   The bilaterally decorticated preparation placed with the
legs over the edge of a surface (D) remains so.   The normal animal
would raise its legs to recover its position on the surface of the
table.   (From Bard, 1933.)

a steady standing position.   These reflexes require that the sensorimotor portion of the cerebral cortex be intact.   When the sensorimotor cortex is destroyed, placing is lost as shown in Fig. 14.18.
Conversely, the reflexes are retained if all the rest of the cerebral
cortex is destroyed while this region remains intact.

Autonomic reflexes

Autonomic functions are also controlled by reflex mechanisms similar to those of somatic reflexes. Like the somatic nervous system, the central connections of the reflex are found in the spinal cord though their cell bodies are in the intermediary part of the gray matter (Chapter 10). Vasomotion, sweat gland activity, gastrointestinal, and genito-urinary functions are reflexly controlled. In some cases the somatic and autonomic nervous systems appear to act conjointly. For example, along with reflex muscle activity, blood flow to that limb is increased, a mechanism apparently helping to support the increased metabolic requirements associated with the increased activity of the skeletal muscles. This is in addition to vascular changes brought about by metabolic events following muscle activity. Some of these reflex control mechanisms will be discussed in Chapter 23.

REFERENCES

Bard, P. (1933). Studies on the cerebral cortex. 1. Localized control of placing and hopping reactions in the cat and their normal management by small cortical remnants. *Arch. Neurol. Psychiat.* **30**: 40–74.

Creed, R. S., Denny-Brown, D., Eccles, J. C., Liddell, E. G. T. and Sherrington, C. S. (1932). *Reflex Activity of the Spinal Cord.* Oxford University Press, London.

Denny-Brown, D. (1929). On the nature of postural reflexes. *Proc. Roy. Soc. B.* **104**: 252–301; and The histological features of striped muscle in relation to its functional activity. *Ibid.*, 371–411.

Jolly, W. A. (1911). On the time relations of the knee-jerk and simple reflexes. *Quart. J. Exptl. Physiol.* **4**: 68–87.

Liddell, E. G. T. and Sherrington, C. S. (1924). Reflexes in response to stretch (myotatic reflexes). *Proc. Roy. Soc. B.* **96**: 212–242; and (1925), Further observations on myotatic reflexes. *Ibid.*, **97**: 267–283.

Ramón y Cajal, S. R. (1909). *Histologie du Système Nerveux de l'Homme et des Vertébrés*, Vol. I. Maloine, Paris, Republished 1952. Instituto Ramón y Cajal, Madrid.

Sherrington, C. S. (1906). *Integrative Action of the Nervous System.* Yale University Press, New Haven. Rev. Ed. (1947), Cambridge University Press, Cambridge.

Sherrington, C. S. (1910). Flexion-reflex of the limb, crossed extension-reflex and reflex stepping and standing. *J. Physiol.* **40**: 28–121.

15

Reflex Transmission

In this chapter we shall continue the analysis of observed reflex responses in terms of the cellular mechanisms which underlie more complex behavior. A great advance was made when instead of mechanically recording reflex responses in the muscles, electrical recordings were taken from the efferent fibers in muscle nerves and from the ventral roots. The dorsal roots can be readily stimulated with a brief electrical shock and an electrical recording of the resulting reflex taken from the ventral motor roots to study the properties of reflex transmission through the cord. It will be useful to describe in some detail the 'Lloyd preparation' used for such studies. The

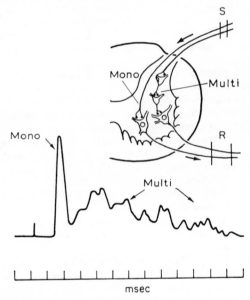

Fig. 15.1. Cross section of the spinal cord shown diagrammatically with dorsal root afferent fibers synapsing directly on motoneurons (Mono), others on interneurons in turn synapsing on motoneurons (Multi). Upon stimulation (S) of the dorsal root a monosynaptic potential followed by a multisynaptic discharge is recorded (R) in the ventral root.

ower part of the cord is exposed by laminectomy and the long roots
rising from the lower lumbar and upper sacral segments of the cat
pinal cord are cut 2–4 cm from the cord and the central ends of the
oots placed on electrodes.   The cord and roots are then covered with
nineral oil maintained at body temperature to prevent drying and
lso to serve as an electrical insulation.   The lower spinal cord is also
ften isolated from the rest of the CNS by transection or deep levels
f anesthesia (barbiturates) administered so that excitatory effects
rom the upper centers do not obscure the local reflex patterns of
he cord (Chapter 22).

When the central end of the cut dorsal spinal root is stimulated
vith a brief electrical shock, a typical electrical reflex discharge
attern is recorded in the ventral root of that segment (Fig. 15.1).
The first reflex discharge appears after a latency of approximately
.5 msec and is a smooth monophasic wave, the *monosynaptic response*,
asting several milliseconds.   This response is then followed by a
onger-lasting discharge of irregular waves, the *multisynaptic response*,
asting 10–15 msec.

ynaptic delay

The monosynaptic response has the short latency expected of only a
ingle synapse in the reflex arc composed of fibers passing directly from
he dorsal root down in the central gray to synapse on the ventral horn
notoneurons (Fig. 14.3).   The terminations of these afferent fibers on
he cell bodies and dendrites of the large motoneurons found in the
entral horn of the spinal cord are shown by histological investigations
f the cell body to be numerous.   The enlarged axon terminals syn-
psing on the motoneurons are the *boutons*, which are visible with
pecial staining techniques (Fig. 15.2).   Not all the synaptic endings
n the cell membranes are stained with the silver stains commonly
sed, particularly those synaptic endings present on the further reaches
f the dendrites of the motoneurons.   Electron microscopic studies
f the CNS have shown that a very large number of axon endings
re present on the surface of the cell body and dendrites.   The bou-
ons contain mitochondria and vesicles 300–500 A in diameter
ypical of synapses operated by transmitter substances (Fig. 15.3).
These vesicles are most likely related to the mechanism of synap-
ic transmission as will be discussed in Chapter 16.

The latency of the monosynaptic response includes both synaptic
elay and the conduction time for the volley passing in the dorsal
oot fibers down to the motoneurons and in the motoneuron axons
o the recording site on the ventral root.   The true delay of synaptic

transfer between boutons and motoneurons is estimated by subtracting these conduction times. In the diagram of Fig. 15.1 the total latency of the monosynaptic response amounted to 1.5 msec. The distance between the stimulating electrodes on the dorsal root and the cord was 2.7 cm, and the distance between the cord and the recording electrodes on the ventral root also 2.7 cm. Therefore, the total conduction path was 6 cm when the fiber path length of the collaterals within the cord was also added to this length. Using an approximate value of 60 m/sec for the conduction velocity of the large fibers involved in the monosynaptic response, the conduction

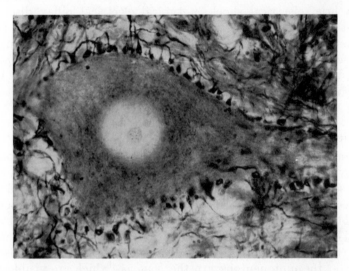

Fig. 15.2. A spinal cord motoneuron is shown with darkly stained synaptic endings present on its surface. There are a large number of synaptic terminations present over the surface of the cell membrane. (Courtesy J. Z. Young.)

time would be 1 msec. Subtracting this time from the total central latency, a time of 0.5 msec remains as the calculated synaptic time for the monosynaptic reflex response. However, it must be shown whether the 0.5 msec remaining is the synaptic delay time occupied by a single synapse or whether a series of synapses is involved.

In order to more closely determine the synaptic delay, fine electrodes electrically insulated but for their tips were inserted into the ventral horn in the vicinity of the terminations of fibers synapsing on motoneurons in order to electrically stimulate these elements in localized fashion. When inserted into the ventral horn of the spinal cord a brief depolarizing pulse of current was passed through the tip causing a localized stimulation of elements in the nearby region. The stimulation gives rise to two spike-like responses which were recorded in the ventral root. The example shown in Fig. 15.4 is taken from the classical studies of Lorente de Nó (1939) made on oculomotor neurons. A weak shock may excite only a late appearing response (s) after a latency of 0.5–1 msec. With an increased strength of

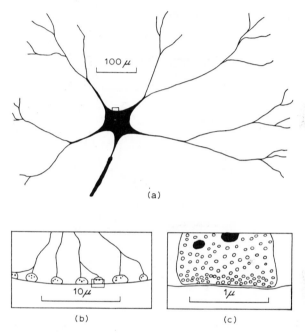

Fig. 15.3. Diagrammatic representation of a motoneuron (a). The small rectangle on the soma is shown enlarged in (b) where boutons on the surface are indicated. The rectangle over a bouton in (b) is further enlarged in (c) to show the vesicles and the larger dark mitochondria present in the presynaptic bouton terminal. (Eccles, 1957.)

stimulation an early response (m) occurs with a shorter latency 0.1–0.2 msec. This m response has the time relations expected of a direct excitation of motoneurons with a latency corresponding to the expected conduction time from the motoneurons down their axons to the recording electrodes placed on the ventral roots. When the latency for the m response was subtracted from the latency of the s response, the difference is the synapse time of the monosynaptic response—0.5–1.0 msec. Two groups of neurons are excited to give rise to the m and s responses. The m response is due to a directly excited group; the s response follows stimulation of presynaptic fibers which terminate on another group of motoneurons and excite discharges after a synaptic delay. The s response latency varies over a range of time from 0.5–1.0 msec, but it is never less than 0.5

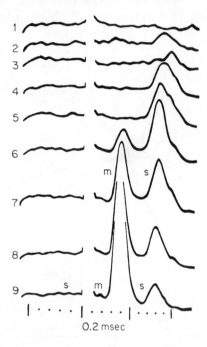

0.2 msec

Fig. 15.4. Responses recorded in ventral root fibers in response to needle stimulation of motoneurons at successively increasing strengths of stimulation (1–9). Stimulus artifact indicated by gap in the baseline. At the lower strengths (1–5) the latency of the response (5) is greater than 1 msec. An earlier response (m) occurs at greater strengths (6–9) having a much shorter latency. (Modified from Lorente de Nó, 1939.)

msec. An irreducible synaptic delay was also found in more direct single cell studies of synaptic transmission (Chapter 16). As the strength of needle stimulation is increased, the m response increases in amplitude while the s response decreases. This is interpreted as due to a decrease in the number of motoneurons left available for synaptic excitation as the pool of directly excited motoneurons is made larger.

If an animal is asphyxiated while being excited with needle

electrodes, the s response is lost within 3–4 minutes. This is also the time taken for the monosynaptic reflex to disappear after asphyxiation. The m response survives asphyxiation longer (for 20 minutes or more), a result compatible with the interpretation that the m response is a direct excitation of the motoneuron and that it is more resistant to the effect of asphyxia. Although the m response was considered an excitation of the cell body membrane it may possibly be the result of a direct excitation of dendrites as indicated by the needle stimulation experiments of Åström (1948); or more likely as indicated by recent studies on the site of impulse origin (Chapter 16), direct excitation occurs at the initial segment of nonmyelinated axon near the soma. These possibilities would introduce relatively minor revisions in the interpretation of the m and s responses given above.

The functional significance of monosynaptic and multisynaptic discharges

The motor fibers of a nerve can be eliminated after cutting the ventral roots so that all the motor fibers degenerate. The remaining fibers found in the nerves of hind limb muscles are sensory and they have been grouped by size as: Group I, 20–12 μ; Group II, 12–6 μ; and Group III, 5–1 μ (Lloyd and Chang, 1948). These groups may be compared to the distribution of sizes found for the sensory nerve fibers arising from skin nerves (Fig. 15.5). The largest of the Group I fibers of muscle nerves are the Group *IA fibers* representing afferent fibers from the annulospiral endings of the spindle stretch receptors of the muscles (Bradley and Eccles, 1953). These fibers branch on entering the spinal cord to give rise to the collaterals which directly terminate monosynaptically on the motoneurons of that segment. This was shown by Lloyd (1943b) on comparing the monosynaptic discharges excited by stimulation of the dorsal root with the responses to natural excitation of muscle spindles produced by sudden pull on a muscle (Fig. 15.6). The discharge volley excited by the sudden stretch of the muscle receptors is carried by the large fast conduction IA fibers to the afferent dorsal roots. The time between the appearance of this volley in the dorsal root afferents and the resulting monosynaptic reflex recorded in the ventral root was .5 msec, and due to a single synaptic delay. Another correspondence of the monosynaptic discharge response to the excitation of afferents subserving the stretch reflex is the similar localized distribution of the monosynaptic discharge within a segment and back to the muscle of origin (Lloyd, 1943a). To show this, nerves innervating a muscle were cut close to the muscle and stimulated. A reflex monosynaptic discharge was transmitted back to that same nerve on which recording electrodes were placed. Reflex discharges into other muscle nerves were in general not found.   The threshold of the motor nerves to electrical stimulation is close to that of the large afferents of the spindle-receptor fibers.   However, this experiment is complicated by an antidromic discharge back into the motoneurons of those motor fibers.

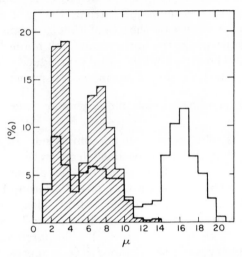

Fig. 15.5.   Diameters of afferent fibers in a muscle nerve show a bimodal distribution of the large, medium and small fibers. Cutaneous nerve fibers shown by the shaded graph have a different distribution of medium and small sizes.   (From Fulton, *A Textbook of Physiology*, 17th Ed., Saunders, 1955.)

To obviate an antidromic effect when stimulating a muscle nerve, the ventral roots are cut and recording electrodes placed on the central part of a ventral root known to supply that muscle.   Stimulation of a muscle nerve will then give rise to a monosynaptic response in that root with a latency duration determined by the additional conduction distance involved.   The use of muscle nerve stimulation rather than dorsal root stimulation is useful in studies of the interaction of synergistic and antagonistic nerves in reflex transmission which we shall presently discuss.   Both extensor and flexor muscle nerves give rise to monosynaptic responses.   These correspond to myotatic reflexes.   Flexor muscles, as was previously noted, also show the myotatic reflexes.

The smaller fibers of Groups II and III associated with nociceptive

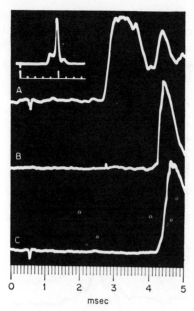

Fig. 15.6. Response recorded in ventral root to a sudden stretch of muscle activating spindle receptors (A). Brief electrical stimulus applied to the dorsal root at the time the afferent volley reaches the dorsal root route (as shown in the upper insert) gives rise to the monosynaptic response (B). Monosynaptic response (C) found when electrically stimulating the motor nerve near the muscle. (From Lloyd, 1943b.)

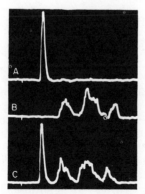

Fig. 15.7. Stimulation of muscle nerve at strengths just above threshold to excite the monosynaptic response (A). Stimulation of sural nerve, a sensory nerve of the skin, excites a multisynaptic response (B). A strong stimulation of a muscle nerve excites both a monosynaptic and multisynaptic discharge (C). (Lloyd, 1943a.)

stimulation and flexor reflexes give rise on excitation to the multi-synaptic discharges. When a skin nerve such as the *sural* is excited, the resulting electrical reflex discharge in the ventral root consists of a multisynaptic discharge without a preceding mono-

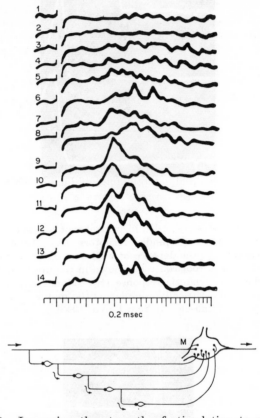

0.2 msec

Fig. 15.8. Increasing the strength of stimulation to a pool of responding motoneurons gives rise to larger sized multisynaptic responses (traces 1–14). Beneath is a diagram showing hypothetically how the neural circuits are arranged in various orders of synaptic linkage to explain the prolonged duration of the discharge. (Lorente de Nó, 1938.)

synaptic response (Fig. 15.7). It is similar in form to the irregular multisynaptic discharge which follows the monosynaptic response when a muscle nerve is excited with moderate to strong stimulations sufficient to excite both large and small diameter groups of fibers (Lloyd, 1943a).

The multisynaptic response discharge is recorded from the roots
f a number of neighboring spinal cord segments, a pattern which
ollows from the widespread type of interneuronal distribution within
he cord.   This distribution also corresponds with the widespread
attern of flexion reflex responses elicited by nociceptive stimulation
Chapter 14).   It suggests the identification of the multisynaptic
attern of discharge, at least in part, with the flexor reflex to noci-
eptive stimulation.   The temporal spread of the multisynaptic
ischarge over a period of 10–15 msec was considered by Lorente de
Jó (1938) to be due to a series of neuronal groups connected together
s shown diagrammatically in Fig. 15.8.   Re-excitation could occur
hrough neurons connected in series of parallel loops as shown in the
ower part of this figure.   Alternatively, a long-maintained repetitive
fter-discharge may be brought about in neurons by long persisting
xcitatory states in the cell membrane (Creed et al., 1932).   Single cell
tudies of neurons of the CNS (Chapter 16) have shown that inter-
eurons often give rise to a maintained repetitive discharge rather than
single response to an afferent volley as is typical of motoneurons.

xcitability of a pool of motoneurons

'he excitability of a reflex pool is measured by the number of moto-
eurons activated by an afferent volley.   The monosynaptic dis-
harge affords a simple system whereby inferences concerning the
ffect of synaptic activity on the excitability of neurons can be made.
he amplitude of the monosynaptic discharge is measured while
radually increasing the strength of the afferent volley used to excite
.   The height of the monosynaptic response increases with increased
imulus strength in an S-shaped curve.   This input-output relation-
ip indicates that some of these cells are excited more readily than
thers, i.e. the number of active synapses on some cells may be
reater than on other cells.   The size of the monosynaptic response
erefore is statistically related to the number of cells which have
een brought to threshold and have fired a discharge into their axons.
his input-output relationship is similar to the relation of the size of
ction potential responses of nerve to the number of active fibers
red at different strengths of stimulation (Chapter 3).   And in
milar fashion, changes in the amplitude of the monosynaptic
sponse are used to measure excitability changes.   Motoneurons
ibliminally excited by a weak stimulus constitute a fringe group of
iotoneurons and as more motoneurons of a responding pool are
red, the fringe group becomes smaller.   However, even with the
rongest shocks a substantial fringe group of undischarged cells still

remains as can be shown by the phenomenon of *post-tetanic potentiation (PTP)* (Lloyd, 1949).   Dorsal roots or afferent nerves are excited
at a high rate of stimulation, for example, at 555/sec for 12 sec.   Then
returning to the usual slow rate of stimulation used for testing
once every 2.4 sec, a striking augmentation of the monosynaptic
test response was observed (Fig. 15.9).   The increase in amplitude

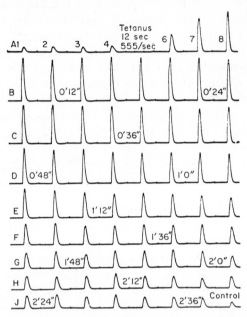

Fig. 15.9.   The effect of a period of tetanic stimulation (555/sec
for 12 sec) is seen to be followed by an augmentation of the monosynaptic discharge post-tetanic potentiation, with its slow sub-
sidence over a period of minutes.   Tests at intervals of 2.4 sec.
(From Lloyd, 1949.)

gradually subsides over a period of several minutes, depending on the
duration of tetanization.   By comparing reflex responses with
directly excited ventral root responses it was shown that a sufficiently
strong PTP can cause the whole of the motoneuron pool to be engaged
by a single afferent stimulus (Jefferson and Benson, 1953).

   The effect of post-tetanic potentiation appears to be restricted t
those synaptic terminals which have been subjected to repetitiv
activation (Lloyd, 1949) similar to the post-tetanic potentiatio
(post-activation potentiation) found in some neuromuscular junc
tions.   This would suggest that the phenomenon is caused b

ιe mobilization of transmitter substance at the excitatory syn-
ϱses. The topic of transmitter substances will be reserved for
ιscussion in Chapter 16. The point to be made here is that ordi-
ιrily there is a proportion of motoneurons in the pool which poten-
ιally can discharge, but which are not brought to firing levels until
ιdditional excitatory mechanisms are brought into play (*vide infra*).

ιcilitation and inhibition of motoneurons

ιn increase in subliminal synaptic excitability which will bring more
ιotoneurons to discharge in response to a test afferent volley is
ιlled facilitation. This term was described in general terms in
ιhapter 14. Our present concern is to investigate the connections
ι neurons subserving facilitation and inhibition making use of the
ιonosynaptic reflex response. We would expect from the observa-
ιons on reciprocal innervation (Chapter 14) that there will be
ιcilitatory effects found acting on synergistic motoneurons and
ιhibitory effects acting on antagonist motoneurons. Weak electrical
ιocks are used to stimulate the lowest threshold Group IA fibers
ιising from the muscle spindles. The ventral roots are cut and the
ιsulting monosynaptic test response is recorded in the central end of
ιe ventral root. Synergistic pairs of muscle nerves are selected, e.g.
ιe lateral and medial gastrocnemius nerves. A conditioning shock
ι delivered to one of these synergists at such a reduced strength
ιat by itself it will produce no response in the ventral root. The
ιst response to stimulation is elicited as is usual in two-shock
ιxperiments (Chapter 3). When the stimuli to test and conditioning
ιerves are given concurrently, the test monosynaptic response
ιmplitude is augmented in size (Fig. 15.10). Then as the test
ιimulus follows the conditioning stimulus at increasingly greater
ιtervals, the facilitation is gradually reduced until no facilitation
ιffect appears at time separations greater than 12–15 msec.

Because the facilitation effect occurs when the two shocks are pre-
ιnted to the two nerves concurrently, there cannot be an interven-
ιg neuron between the conditioning afferents and the motoneurons
ι which the collaterals end to give rise to facilitation; an extra 0.5
ιsec would have to be allowed for a synaptic delay if this were the
ιse. This type of facilitation was therefore termed *direct facilitation*
ιΛloyd, 1946). The facilitating collateral fibers split off from
ιorsal root fibers passing to motoneurons to end directly on syner-
ιistic motoneurons without an intervening neuron.

An inhibitory effect is found when an antagonistic muscle nerve is
ιsed to condition a test monosynaptic response excited from its

antagonistically related muscle nerve (Lloyd, 1946).   As an example
a volley to the anterior tibialis nerve may be used to inhibit the
response to a gastrocnemius nerve stimulus and vice-versa.   In this
case, unlike facilitation, the test monosynaptic response is not
maximally decreased until it is given 0.5 msec after the inhibiting
conditioning volley (Fig. 15.11).   Further temporal separation
between conditioning and test volleys results in a gradual decrease of
the inhibitory effect, the curve of decreasing inhibitory effect having

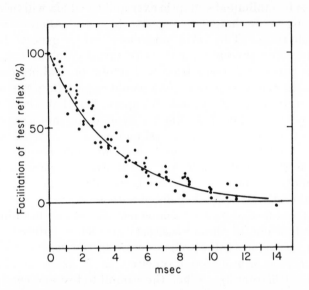

Fig. 15.10.   The facilitation curve shown in the upper figure was
determined by the increase in the amplitude of a monosynaptic
test response following at the different intervals shown after a
conditioning shock to a synergistic nerve.   At coincidence of the
two shocks there is 100% increase of the test response above control
(0) levels.   (From Lloyd, 1946.)

a time course similar in form to that of the decline of the facilitation
effect.   This inhibition effect has in the past (cf. Eccles, 1953) been
referred to as 'direct' inhibition, believed to be caused by inhibitory
fibers passing directly from afferent fibers to motoneurons because
its earliest appearance occurs before the minimal time of 0.5 msec
required for an intervening synaptic delay.   However, evidence for
an interposed inhibitory neuron has since been obtained (Eccles,
1957) and the short latency of inhibition shown to be due to the range
of latencies encountered when a population of neurons rather than

ıdividual cells is investigated. We shall discuss this subject
ırther in Chapter 16.

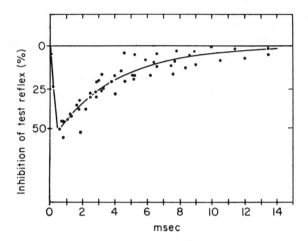

Fig. 15.11. A double shock technique similar to that of Fig. 15.10
was used to derive the inhibitory curve where the conditioning
shock was delivered to an antagonistic nerve of the nerve used to
elicit the test response. At coincidence the inhibition is small
and greatest at a temporal separation of 0.5 msec between conditioning and test shocks. Thereafter the inhibition decreases with
further temporal separations back to control (0) level. (From
Lloyd, 1946.)

REFERENCES

ström, K. E. (1948). On the functional organization of the motoneurons in
the spinal cord. *Acta Physiol. Scand.* **16**: *Suppl.* **55**. 67 pp.

Bradley, K. and Eccles, J. C. (1953). Analysis of the fast afferent impulses
from thigh muscles. *J. Physiol.* **122**: 462–473.

Creed, R. S., Denny-Brown, D., Eccles, J. C., Liddell, E. G. T. and Sherrington,
C. S. (1932). *Reflex Activity of the Spinal Cord.* Oxford University Press,
London.

Eccles, J. C. (1953). *The Neurophysiological Basis of Mind.* Clarendon
Press, Oxford.

Eccles, J. C. (1957). *The Physiology of Nerve Cells.* Johns Hopkins Press,
Baltimore.

Jefferson, A. and Benson, A. (1953). Some effects of post-tetanic potentiation
of monosynaptic response of spinal cord of cat. *J. Neurophysiol.* **16**:
381–396.

Lloyd, D. P. C. (1943a). Neuron patterns controlling transmission of ipsilateral hind limb reflexes in cat. *J. Neurophysiol.* **6**: 293–315.

Lloyd, D. P. C. (1943b).   Conduction and synaptic transmission of the reflex response to stretch in spinal cats.   *J. Neurophysiol.* **6**: 317–326.

Lloyd, D. P. C. (1946).   Facilitation and inhibition of spinal motoneurons. *J. Neurophysiol.* **9**: 421–444.

Lloyd, D. P. C. (1949).   Post-tetanic potentiation of response in monosynaptic reflex pathways of the spinal cord.   *J. Gen. Physiol.* **33**: 147–170.

Lloyd, D. P. C. and Chang, H.-T. (1948).   Afferent fibers in muscle nerves *J. Neurophysiol.* **11**: 199–207.

Lorente de Nó, R. (1938).   Analysis of the activity of the chains of internuncial neurons.   *J. Neurophysiol.* **1**: 207–244.

Lorente de Nó, R. (1939).   Transmission of impulses through cranial motor nuclei.   *J. Neurophysiol.* **2**: 402–464.

16

Excitability of Motoneurons, Synaptic Transmission

Until recently the excitability changes in motoneurons brought about by synaptic activity had to be inferred from the behavior of the response of a population of neurons giving rise to the monosynaptic discharge as described in the preceding chapter. To study the behavior of motoneurons, Eccles (1953, 1957, 1961a, 1964) and his colleagues successfully applied the microelectrode technique of Ling and Gerard (Chapter 4). These microelectrodes are slowly driven into the ventral horn of the spinal cord until the sudden appearance of a steady negative potential, approximately 70 mv, indicating entry of the electrode tip into a cell. The relatively large size of the cell bodies of the motoneurons (50–70 μ in diameter) increases the probability that the tip of a microelectrode will enter this part of the cell rather than a dendrite, axon or another smaller cell. The location of the tip of the electrode within the cell must be inferred from functional evidence, as its actual location cannot be directly observed (Brock *et al.*, 1952).

Action potential from single motoneurons

When recording from a motoneuron with a microelectrode inserted into it, the cell may be activated in either the normal (orthodromic) direction by stimulating the dorsal root, or in the reverse (antidromic) direction by stimulating the ventral root. A comparison of orthodromic and antidromic responses of the motoneuron is shown in Fig. 16.1. In both cases the action potential has an overshoot similar to that obtained from axons and muscle fibers (Chapter 5). The response seen on antidromic stimulation has a small latency, nearly all of which can be accounted for by conduction of the action potential in the ventral root axon of the soma from which it is recorded. On this basis the cell is identified as a motoneuron. If the cell penetrated by the microelectrode were an interneuron, then antidromic stimulation of motoneuron axons would not give rise to a discharge with such short latencies, for at least one synapse and synaptic delay

would be involved.   Furthermore, a motoneuron discharge is charac‑
teristically followed by a small but long-lasting hyperpolarization
(positive after-potential).   An interneuron does not have this
property and its spike duration is generally shorter (Frank, 1959).

The brief latency of the antidromic spike is to be contrasted with
the orthodromic response recorded from the same cell upon stimula‑
tion of its afferent nerve fibers.   The orthodromic discharge has an
irreducible latency which cannot be accounted for by conduction

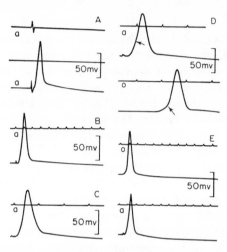

Fig. 16.1.   Intracellular microelectrode in a spinal cord moto‑
neuron records a resting membrane potential of approximately
− 70 mv.   Action potential responses to antidromic (a) and
orthodromic (o) activation.   Different sweep speeds in A–E.
Arrow at inflection on leading edge.   (From Brock *et al.*, 1952.)

time.   This latency is the true synaptic delay similar to that seen in
the case of neuromuscular transmission.   In the case of orthodromic
synaptic transmission in the motoneuron, as in neuromuscular trans‑
mission, this latency is an argument against the theory of electrical
transmission at this synapse, i.e. where electrical currents from the
presynaptic fiber would excite the membrane of the postsynaptic cell.
Such electrical transmission is seen in some synapses of certain lower
species (*vide infra*).   In the case of the motoneuron, the delay between
the electrical activity present in the presynaptic terminals and the
appearance of the response is sufficient evidence to eliminate the
possibility of electrical transmission.   A further similarity of synaptic
transmission at this cell to other chemically mediated synapses is a
synaptic potential excited in the membrane of the motoneuron with

roperties similar to the EPP, to be described in the following
ection. Also, the bouton terminals ending on the surface membrane
f the motoneurons have vesicles present in them (Fig. 15.3), a
tructure typically found at synaptic junctions and thought to con-
ain the transmitter substance released to excite the postsynaptic
nembrane.

xcitatory postsynaptic potential (EPSP)

f the strength of a stimulus used to produce an orthodromic spike is
educed, a point is reached where the orthodromic spike is replaced
y a smaller amplitude longer-lasting potential, a response similar to
he EPP. This response arises from the membrane of the motoneuron following synaptic excitation and is therefore referred to as the
xcitatory postsynaptic potential (*EPSP*). While the EPSP has the
ame functional significance as an EPP obtained from the end-plate
f a muscle cell, the motoneuron is an integrating cell having many
undreds or thousands of synaptic terminations on the membrane
urface of its soma and dendrites (Chapter 15). As a result there are
ariations in the EPSPs elicited by successive stimulations, the
ariations indicating momentary changes in the number of such
ynaptic bombardments occurring at any one time. To overcome this
ariability an *averaging technique* is used whereby a number of low
ntensity oscilloscope traces of the response are overlayed (usually
0–40 such traces) to produce an average response (Fig. 16.2).
ariability of synaptic activity is more apparent at the lower strengths
f stimulation as indicated by a thicker EPSP record of the averaged
esponse. A subliminal bombardment of synaptic activity of the
notoneuron occurs continuously, such activity coming from the
lischarge of interneurons in the spinal cord. The level of this back-
round synaptic activity determines the excitability. An increase in
ackground synaptic activity requires a smaller afferent volley to fire
propagated discharge of the motoneuron. Variations in back-
round excitability will cause an action potential to be excited earlier
r later with respect to a volley exciting an EPSP. This is shown in
ig. 16.3 by an EPSP set near the critical level for firing an action
otential. Only the leading edge of the action potentials arising
rom the EPSPs are shown in this figure. Of interest is the latency
vith which the spike takes origin from the EPSP. As can be seen in
his figure the latency varies between 0.5–1 msec, a range similar to
hat found for the latency variation of monosynaptic response
licited with different strengths of afferent stimulation (Coombs *et al.*,
955b; cf. Chapter 15).

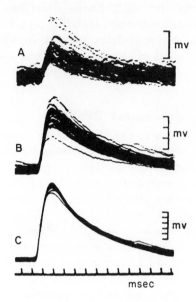

Fig. 16.2.   EPSPs recorded from a biceps-semitendinosus motoneuron (A–C) with afferent volleys of increasing strengths.   A
number of responses are recorded which by their overlap give the
average response.   The EPSP becomes larger with increased
stimulus strength and the variability decreases.   (Coombs *et al.*,
1955b.)

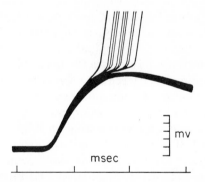

Fig. 16.3.   EPSPs excited in a motoneuron at a stimulus strength
close to threshold.   Action potentials arise from EPSPs with a
variation in time of approximately 1 msec.   Only the leading edges
of the action potentials are shown.   (Coombs *et al.*, 1955b.)

If the EPSP is similar to the EPP of the neuromuscular junction, does an increase of permeability occur in the motoneuron similar to that found for the neuromuscular junction? We might expect a brief increase in permeability to a number of ion species followed by a passive electrotonic change in the membrane for the remainder of the EPSP. In order to investigate this, the effect of changes of the resting membrane potential on the EPSP was studied using a double-barreled microelectrode. These are made from two glass capillary tubes with tips drawn-out and lying side by side. These double-barreled microelectrodes, though larger than the single ones, can still be inserted into the relatively large soma of the motoneuron without too much damage. Current is passed through the membrane of the motoneuron soma via one of the barrels while the other barrel is used to record the EPSP. The effect of the changed resting membrane potential on the EPSP amplitude is shown in Fig. 16.4. As the resting membrane potential is increased by hyperpolarization, the amplitude of the EPSP increases. As the resting membrane potential is decreased, the EPSP amplitude is reduced until the inside of the cell is made sufficiently positive and the EPSP has a reversed sign. The *equilibrium potential for the EPSP*, where the orthodromic volley neither produces a negative nor positive EPSP, is found to be close to zero. The relationship found between the various levels of the resting potential and the amplitude of the EPSP was linear for only part of the range. As can be seen in Fig. 16.4, in the higher ranges of hyperpolarization there is no further increase of EPSP amplitude. At these higher levels of hyperpolarization the amplitude of the EPSP may be reduced by an electrical effect of the applied voltages acting on the electrical charge of the transmitter substance (*vide infra*).

A double-barreled microelectrode or a single microelectrode with a special Wheatstone bridge device to balance it (Frank, 1959) may be used to determine the passive electrical properties of the membrane by introducing a step of depolarizing or hyperpolarizing current into the cell and measuring the time constant of the resulting potential change (Chapter 6). For the cell bodies, the time constant of the membrane is the time required for the potential to fall to $1/e$ of the original level following introduction of a depolarizing current or to rise to $1 - (1/e)$ with an inward hyperpolarizing step of current. The time constant of the motoneuron of the spinal cord determined in this way was about 2.5 msec. This time is shorter than the falling phase of the EPSP which has a time constant of approximately 4.7 msec. Therefore, the longer time course of the

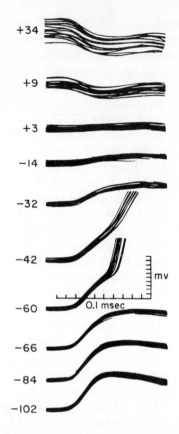

Fig. 16.4. The membrane potential is altered from an original value of − 66 mv by current from one barrel of a multiple barrel microelectrode and the effect on the size of the EPSP and spike determined by another barrel.   Potential levels are given at the left of the traces.   With moderate depolarization to − 60 to − 42 mv, spikes are generated.   With further depolarization the spikes fail and the EPSP becomes smaller and reversed in sign when the membrane level goes beyond the equilibrium potential for the EPSP.   (Coombs *et al.*, 1955b.)

EPSP in the motoneuron cannot all be simply a passive discharge Rall (1960) calculates that a spread of electrotonic current into the dendrites could contribute to the prolonged time course of the EPSP Eccles (1961b), however, considers that the discrepancy in the time courses is due to a residual longer-lasting action of a synaptic trans mitter substance (Fig. 16.5).   In some other cells without dendrites e.g. those of ganglia, the much longer EPSPs found seem to require till more prolonged action of the synaptic transmitter substance Eccles, 1961a, 1964).

Small potentials have been observed in motoneurons which could be miniature excitatory postsynaptic potentials (Min EPSPs). However, it was not clear whether such 'synaptic noise' was indeed due to random quantal release of transmitter substance from the presynaptic terminals or to low level excitation of EPSPs. By use of

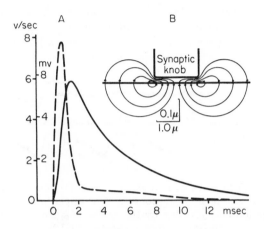

Fig. 16.5. The time course of the EPSP (A) is shown by the solid line with the dashed line indicating the brief period of increased permeability and current flow due to the transmitter substance. This is followed by a smaller prolonged effect. Resulting currents (B) flow under the activated synaptic knobs. (Eccles, 1957.)

the isolated frog spinal cord preparation, Katz and Miledi (1963) could block synaptic transmission with magnesium and conduction of impulses by excess potassium. They found Min EPSPs remaining under those conditions—consistent with their quantal origin from presynaptic terminals. There was a wide range of amplitudes and time courses of the individual Min EPSPs, most likely due to different electrical properties of the dendrites and soma over which the synaptic terminals are distributed (*vide infra*).

These investigations show that the EPSP has properties similar in some respects to the EPP of the neuromuscular junction, with differences brought about by the large number of synaptic boutons over the surface of the soma and dendrite membranes. The ionic changes and initiation of the propagated action potentials resulting from EPSP action will be discussed in later sections.

Inhibitory postsynaptic potential (IPSP) and the inhibitory line

A motoneuron supplying a given muscle is identified by delivering an orthodromic volley to that muscle nerve and recording an EPSP in that cell. After such identification, the effect of an afferent volley from antagonistic muscle nerve afferents on that cell can be assessed. As an example, the semitendinosus nerve was excited to give rise to an EPSP in a motoneuron, and this cell was therefore identified as a semitendinosus motoneuron. Upon stimulation of its antagonist muscle nerve, that of the quadriceps muscle, the response recorded from this semitendinosus motoneuron was a hyperpolarization with a time course similar to an EPSP but inverted in sign (Fig. 16.6). This hyperpolarization is postsynaptic, arising

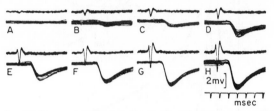

Fig. 16.6. Volleys of different strengths (A–H) in an antagonistic nerve giving rise to IPSP responses. The upper line indicates the size of the inhibitory volley by the triphasic spike recorded from the dorsal root. (Eccles, 1961.)

from the motoneuron membrane and because (as will be shown below) it is inhibitory in function it is referred to as an *inhibitory postsynaptic potential* (*IPSP*). The time course of the IPSP has a faster falling phase giving an estimated time constant of 3 msec, close to that of the passive electrical measurements of the membrane (*vide supra*). Therefore, a prolonged residual action of the inhibitory transmitter agent is not present (Fig. 16.7). A difference in the transmitter substances subserving the EPSP and IPSP is shown by the depolarization of the EPSP and the hyperpolarization of the IPSP. The different actions are due to the different effects of these two agents on the ionic permeabilities of the motoneuron membrane, a subject to be discussed in a later section.

We shall now discuss in more detail the evidence for the presence of an inhibitory cell interposed in the inhibitory path rather than a direct connection of collateral branches with the motoneuron (Chapter 15). The afferent fibers are shown in Fig. 16.8 to have collaterals which split off and synapse on these inhibitory cells in the intermediary part of the cord. The inhibitory neurons in turn send branches to the antagonistic motoneurons in the ventral horn. The

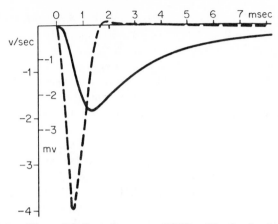

Fig. 16.7. The solid line shows an IPSP with the broken line indicating the brief period of large current flow brought about by the action of the inhibitory transmitter substance. (Eccles, 1957.)

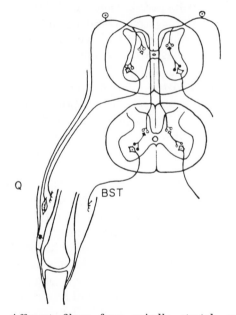

Fig. 16.8. Afferent fibers from spindle stretch receptors of the quadriceps (Q) are shown terminating on motoneurons, their efferent axons innervating that same muscle. Collateral branches from the afferent fibers are shown branching and in the next lower cord segment terminating on cells in an intermediate group of cord neurons. These are inhibitory cells terminating on biceps-semitendinosus (BST) motoneurons to inhibit their discharge. (Eccles, 1957.)

IPSP consistently shows a greater latency in response to an ortho dromic volley than does the EPSP, approximately 1.3 msec for the IPSP compared to 0.5 msec for the EPSP. This greater latency for the IPSP is consistent with an extra synaptic delay due to the inter calated inhibitory neuron. The presence of these inhibitory neurons in the intermediary part of the cord was shown by focal recording with microelectrodes having their tips ($1-5$ μ) placed along the fiber trajectories of the inhibitory paths within the cord. Volleys in the afferent fibers were recorded as small triphasic waves. These *field potential* responses were traced down into the spinal cord from the afferent fibers entering in the dorsal roots. In the case of the ex citatory path, these focally-recorded potentials were traced directly down to the motoneurons in the ventral horn of the cord. In the case of the inhibitory path, the potentials were traced from the collateral afferents to branches passing into the intermediary group of neurons in the spinal cord where a synapse is effected on inhibitory neurons. By stimulating in this region with focal needle electrodes, the axons of the inhibitory cells could be directly excited. Large EPSPs and IPSPs were recorded from the motoneurons with similar latencies: 0.50 msec for EPSP and 0.46 msec for the IPSP (Eide, Lundberg and Voorhoeve, 1961). Thus, the additional delay on the inhibitory line is due to the synaptic delay at the intermediating inhibitory neuron. Reciprocal innervation is brought about by afferents making excitatory connections with some motoneurons and collaterals from the same sensory fibers passing to inhibitory cells and these in turn to the antagonist motoneurons. For instance, when the quadriceps motoneurons are excited, collaterals excite the intermediating neurons which then produce inhibitory effects in the tendinosus muscles. When the tendinosus moto-neurons are excited, collaterals excite the intermediate neurons to produce inhibition of the quadriceps motoneurons.

The single-cell studies explain the maximum inhibitory effects at 0.5 msec when in population studies monosynaptic responses are examined (Chapter 15). The single cells show a range varying between 0.5–1.0 msec for the excitation of an action potential. The longer latency responses can be inhibited by a coincident volley in the antagonistic nerve despite the extra synaptic delay on the inhibitory line. As the time between the inhibitory conditioning volley and test responses is progressively increased the inhibitory effect increases as more and more of the IPSPs precede the EPSPs (Araki, Eccles and Ito, 1960). The maximum inhibitory effect occurs at 0.5 msec, the time required for an extra synapse in most intermediate inhibitory cells. Thereafter, the decline in inhibitory effect parallels the time course of the IPSP. The inhibition brought about by the IPSP appears to have two underlying mechanisms. This will be discussed in the next section in relation to the site of initiation of the action potential.

Origin of the motoneuron spike
Until recently it was thought that the spike originates from any part of the soma or dendrites when a number of synaptic boutons situated close together on the membrane of the cell become simultaneously active. The term *synaptic scale* was used by Lorente de Nó (1939) as a measure of the strategic spacing of a number of synaptic endings on a region of the membrane surface which are activated to excite a spike. When currents were passed into a motoneuron and then outward across the membrane by a microelectrode placed within a motoneuron, an action potential was excited at a level of depolarization of 10–12 mv (Araki and Otani, 1955). This voltage level is similar to the critical level for the excitation of a spike by an EPSP, i.e. a depolarization of 10 mv. However, there is a difference in the critical level required for direct depolarization with current or EPSP depolarization and that for an antidromic invasion which indicates that the soma is actually less excitable than the initial segment of the axon where spike discharge normally occurs. The action potential present in the soma occurs secondarily to this initial segment activation. This is shown by the block of invasion of an antidromic action potential into the soma. When an antidromic volley is initiated in a cell in which the soma potential is raised by hyperpolarizing the cell with inward current flow, a full-sized spike is not recorded. Instead, a smaller spike-like potential of 30–40 mv is observed (Fig. 16.9). This is termed the *initial segment (IS) spike* (previously called the NM spike) and it represents the electrotonic spread from a full-sized spike in the initial segment of the motoneuron axon into the soma. The IS spike in the axon cannot reach critical level to fire the hyperpolarized soma (Eccles, 1953). Excitability of the soma may also be reduced during the after-hyperpolarization following an orthodromic volley and only an IS spike is recorded in response to an antidromic volley. Fuortes, Frank and Becker (1957) in their study of this phenomenon use the term 'A' spike for the IS potential and 'B' spike for the action potential invading the soma and dendrites. The 'B' spike is equivalent to the *soma–dendrite* or *SD* spike in the terminology of Eccles (1957, 1961a). Even those successful antidromic invasions of the soma show on the leading edge of the SD

spike a change in the curvature at a potential level of 30–40 mv, indicative of a slight delay due to the local currents in the IS part of the axon to bring the soma membrane to firing. The safety factor is low and a brief utilization-time factor is involved (Chapter 3).

Closer examination of the rising phase of orthodromic spikes also revealed a small inflection at 30–40 mv. This was made more apparent by the use of an electrical differentiation technique, the

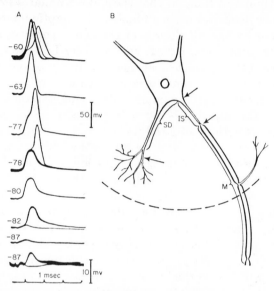

Fig. 16.9. (A) Invasion of the soma and dendrite of motoneuron by an action potential antidromically evoked in its axon gives the SD spike at a resting level of − 63 mv. When the membrane potential is increased to − 77 mv a break appears in the leading edge of the antidromic spike. Upon greater hyperpolarization, a smaller spike-like response of the initial segment, the IS spike, remains (at − 80 mv). A block at the axon gives rise to the smaller myelinated axon M response at − 87 mv. B shows the sites of these potentials (arrows) on the motoneuron. (Eccles, 1957.)

amplitude of the differentiation proportional to the rate of change of cell membrane voltage. This rate change is shown in Fig. 16.10 where a similar effect is seen on antidromic activation. This result indicates that the spike is excited first in the IS part of the axon and then moves back in the soma (Araki and Otani, 1955; Fuortes, Frank and Becker, 1957). This backward invasion of the soma by the action potential is similar to the sequence previously described for the crustacean stretch receptor cell (Chapter 12). To recapitulate,

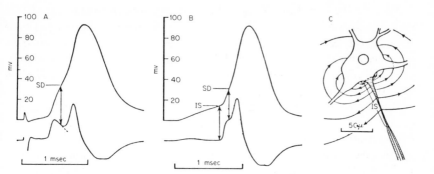

Fig. 16.10.   An antidromic SD response of motoneuron is shown
in the upper trace (A).   The change in curvature of the leading
edge corresponds to a slight delay in the invasion of the soma and
dendrites from the initial segment.   The lower trace shows by the
rate of change of the response the resulting current flow with two
peaks corresponding to IS and SD steps.   An orthodromically-
activated response shows similar peaks (B).   Current flows from the
initial segment to the soma and dendrites, (C).   (Eccles, 1961.)

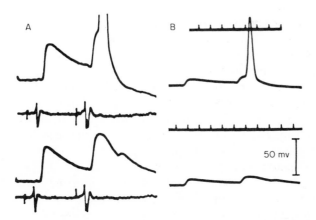

Fig. 16.11.   Summation of EPSPs shown using double shocks to
an afferent input at close intervals.   The second EPSP by adding
to the first can summate to excite an action potential as shown in
the upper part of A and with lower gain in B.   The lower traces in
A represent the dorsal root spikes.   Time in msec.   (Brock et al.,
1952.)

the sequence of events comes about in the following manner: (a) synaptic activity causes an EPSP; (b) local currents from these synaptic sites reach down to the initial segment and an IS spike is fired here when a critical level of 10 mv is reached; (c) the IS spike in turn initiates an action potential which is propagated down the axon and, also, an action potential is excited backwards in the soma and then into the dendrites for some undetermined distance.

Synaptic activity over all the soma and nearby dendritic membranes becomes integrated by EPSPs causing current outflow at the initial segment. If the motoneuron is synaptically excited by synergistic nerve volleys, the EPSPs from the two sets of synaptic terminals will add their depolarization effects (Fig. 16.11). Summation of EPSPs takes place for the time duration of an EPSP (a period of approximately 10–12 msec) and a spike is excited if the second EPSP brings the membrane to the critical level. This time course of facilitation of EPSPs is similar to that of the direct facilitation curve found for the monosynaptic responses (Chapter 15). Pure temporal facilitation is shown when two volleys are presented successively to the same afferent nerve (Curtis and Eccles, 1960). The resultant EPSPs add almost algebraically.

The hyperpolarization of an IPSP causes a flow of current in a direction opposite (Fig. 16.12) to that shown in C of Fig. 16.10. This current would increase the membrane potential at the IS membrane and by such hyperpolarization prevent the cell from attaining the critical level of depolarization. However, this is only part of the action of the inhibitory fibers giving rise to IPSP activity. The early phase of increased conductance brought about by the inhibitory transmitter substance has a marked effect in reducing EPSP activity. This is shown by a more careful study of the inhibitory curve of the monosynaptic potential (Araki, Eccles and Ito, 1960). A peak occurs during the early phase of IPSP conductance increase which is followed by a prolonged passive hyperpolarization action which declines exponentially (Fig. 16.12).

While the interaction of currents flowing from excitatory and inhibitory synaptic influences at the initial segment can explain the integrative action of the cell, a problem arises when we consider those synapses placed on dendrites far from the initial segment. EPSP currents from the far sites would be ineffective at the initial segment because of the decrease of electrotonic currents with distance as estimated from the space constant of the membrane (Eccles, 1957). Possibly some synaptic inputs may excite spikes in the dendrites. Such an origin has been shown in the chromatolysed cell (Chapter 8).

The motoneurons of chromatolysed cells have reduced EPSPs and superimposed on them are either dome-like depolarizations which behave as partial spikes or local discharges of the soma or spike-like potentials which appear to be full-sized all-or-none spikes originating in the dendrites which have not invaded the soma (Eccles, Libet and Young, 1958). The origin of the spike-like partial responses from remote dendrites was indicated by the failure to suppress these responses with a hyperpolarizing pulse introduced into the soma. If strong hyperpolarization did suppress the response, it did so in an all-or-none manner. The dome-like partial responses were more readily suppressed by hyperpolarization suggesting that these are

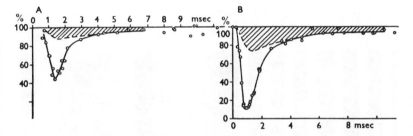

Fig. 16.12. The falling phase of the inhibitory curves (A, B) found with double-shock testing appears not to be exponential. Two phases are seen: a brief early phase due to the increased permeability caused by the inhibitory transmitter substance, and a smaller later phase shown by the shaded curve due to the hyperpolarization produced by the resulting current flow. (Eccles, 1957.)

local responses of the soma. Such responses suggest an increased excitability of the membrane of chromatolysed cells. This was also indicated by a lower threshold to direct excitation of the membrane using depolarizing currents introduced in the cell via a double-barreled microelectrode. It would appear that the partial responses start at patches of the membrane (possibly where the synaptic scale is high) though normally these patches are not large enough to fire a full-sized spike.

In the frog spinal cord, Brookhart and Fadiga (1960) have obtained evidence that the dorsal roots make monosynaptic connections on the remote parts of the dendrites while descending fibers in the lateral funiculus terminate on the proximal parts of the dendrites and on the soma. Some type of active response might explain the placement of remote dendritic synapses (cf. Chapter 18).

Ions and synaptic potentials

At least two different transmitter substances are involved in synaptic transmission at the motoneuron, as indicated by the depolarization produced by an EPSP and hyperpolarization by an IPSP. Some of the earlier difficulties found in recording the IPSP were traced to the leakage of Cl^- from the KCl filled microelectrodes usually used. Substitution of K_2SO_4 for the conducting fluid inside the microelectrode made the recording of the IPSP more reproducible. This suggested that the anion Cl^- had something to do with the action of the inhibitory transmitting substance. A special participation of Cl^- was found associated with the action of the inhibitory transmitter in

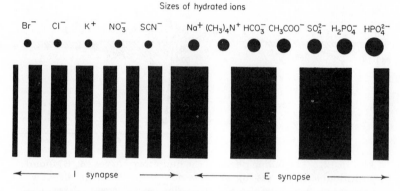

Sizes of hydrated ions

Br⁻ Cl⁻ K⁺ NO₃⁻ SCN⁻ Na⁺ (CH₃)₄N⁺ HCO₃⁻ CH₃COO⁻ SO₄²⁻ H₂PO₄⁻ HPO₄²⁻

I synapse   E synapse

Fig. 16.13. The results with ion substitutions using multiple barrel microelectrodes indicate that the smaller sized ions Br^- – SCN^- can pass through the inhibitory (I), activated synapses while after activation by the excitatory (E) transmitter substance, larger ions Na^+ – HPO^- can penetrate. The difference in the resulting equilibrium potentials will determine whether a depolarization or a hyperpolarization PSP will occur. (Eccles, 1957.)

the peripheral inhibitory nerve action on crustacean muscle (Chapter 9). The action of the crustacean inhibitory transmitter substance is to increase the permeability to Cl^- and bring the membrane to the equilibrium potential for Cl^-. To test this hypothesis in the motoneuron, the Cl^- concentration was electrophoretically increased inside the cell by means of one tip of a double-barreled microelectrode. In this technique a small electric current of the appropriate polarity was used to move Cl^- out of the barrel and into the cell. The IPSPs excited by a volley in an inhibitory nerve were recorded via the other microelectrode tip. The amplitude of the IPSP was reduced as internal Cl^- was increased, and the ratio of Cl^- across the membrane was reduced. The selective increase of Cl^- permeability could then lead to the usual inward movement of Cl^- and the hyper-polarization of the IPSP. The IPSP was not changed when $H_2PO_4^-$, HCO_3^-, CH_3COO^-, SO_4^{2-} or the glutamate ion was injected into the cell in the same manner as Cl^-. When the ions NO_3^-, Br^- and SCN^- were injected into the cell they acted like Cl^- to diminish the IPSPs. This latter group have in common with Cl^- and K^+ a smaller hydrated ionic diameter compared to the first group of ions as shown in Fig. 16.13. As indicated in this figure, the effect of the inhibitory transmitter substance is to open a pore of smaller size than is opened by the excitatory transmitter substance. The smaller pore opened by the inhibitory transmitter allows only the smaller ionic species to pass through the membrane while the larger ions are held back. The larger ions can, however, pass through the membrane when the excitatory transmitter substance acts. The direction of passage and the ions which pass are determined by the concentration gradients and electrical potential across the membrane (Chapter 4). For Cl^- and K^+ the electrochemical gradients will give rise during the permeability increase of the IPSP to an increase of membrane voltage from -70 to -80 mv (Coombs, Eccles and Fatt, 1955a; Eccles, 1961a, 1964). The excitatory transmitter, by allowing the movement of larger ions, in particular Na^+, causes a depolarization to an equilibrium potential below the critical level required for excitation (from -70 to -10 mv).

Renshaw system and the nature of transmitter substances

Following an antidromic volley in one group of motoneurons, other motoneurons in their vicinity which have not been invaded by a spike have a depressed excitability which lasts 50–100 msec (Renshaw, 1941). This excitability decrease was shown by use of orthodromic testing stimuli and monosynaptic recording of the responses. The test responses were also diminished when an anti-dromic volley was delivered to the neighboring cells. During the phase of depression, a group of interneurons within the ventral part of the cord were found to give rise to a repetitive discharge at a high rate and a causal relationship between the interneuron discharge and the long-lasting depression of excitability of motoneurons was sug-gested (Renshaw, 1946). Microelectrode investigation of these inter-neurons showed repetitive firing after an antidromic volley with rates as high as 1000/sec. These interneurons, designated as the *Renshaw cells*, are fired by collaterals branching from the axons of motoneurons (Ramón y Cajal, 1909) and in turn the Renshaw cells synapse on other motoneurons to produce in them a long-lasting hyperpolarization and inhibition (Fig. 16.14). The latency of the onset of hyperpolarization brought about in the motoneuron by Renshaw cell action is compatible with one synaptic delay occurring between the axon collateral of the motoneuron and the Renshaw cell. The hyperpolarization in the motoneuron is long lasting and shows brief ripples corresponding with a repetitive discharge of the Renshaw cell, the hyperpolarization of each inhibitory discharge summating in the membrane of the motoneuron.   The hyperpolarization brought about by Renshaw cell activity is produced by the same or a similar transmitter substance giving rise to an IPSP; both Renshaw cell hyperpolarization and IPSPs were altered in the same way by various

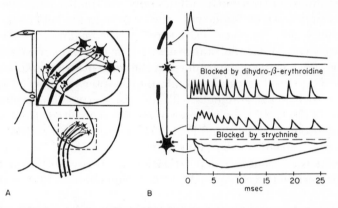

Fig. 16.14.   Axon collaterals from motoneurons synapse on Renshaw cells and give rise to a high frequency repetitive discharge in response to a single volley (A).   The Renshaw cell discharge is blocked by dihydro-β-erythroidine (B). The hyperpolarizing action of the Renshaw cell on the motoneuron (like IPSP transmitter action) is blocked by strychnine.   (Eccles, Fatt and Koketsu, 1954.)

procedures.   Strychnine, for example, can block both of these responses.   Strychnine is an agent long recognized as a spinal cord convulsant, and it was shown to block IPSP activity by Bradley, Easton and Eccles (1953).

It is a general rule that a neuron releases the same synaptic transmitter substance from any one of its axon terminations (Dale, 1935). At its muscular terminus the motoneuron releases ACh to effect transmission (Chapter 9) and this suggests that the collateral branches of the motoneuron synapsing on the Renshaw cells also release ACh at this particular synaptic site.   This hypothesis was tested by injecting various cholinergic-blocking and cholinesterase-inhibiting agents into the arterial supply of the spinal cord so that they could act centrally to augment or block ACh transmission (Eccles, Fatt and Koketsu, 1954). The agent dihydro-β-erythroidine is a curare-like blocking substance. However, unlike curare it is a tertiary ammonium compound and can, therefore, pass through the permeability barrier of the spinal cord (cf. blood-brain barrier, Chapter 19). When injected systemically into the blood supply, synaptic activation of the Renshaw cell was blocked as shown by a curtailment of the repetitive Renshaw discharge. Eserine also passes the barrier and enters the CNS. As expected from its anticholinesterase action on ACh transmission at the peripheral neuromuscular junction, it prolonged the Renshaw cell discharge.

The results were generally those expected of an ACh action at the Renshaw cell. This was better shown by use of a multibarreled microelectrode technique which allows the electrophoresis of compounds into the cord in the near vicinity of the motoneuron (Curtis and Eccles, 1958). By means of this technique, acetylcholine and nicotine have been shown to excite Renshaw cell discharges as would be expected of a cholinergic synapse. D-Tubocurarine blocked the excitatory action of these substances. However, there were some differences which could not be explained simply. Nicotine was more effective than acetylcholine, and dihydro-β-erythroidine more effective than D-tubocurarine. To explain these discrepancies a second barrier has been invoked—a *synaptic barrier* around the cells which acts to retain the normal transmitter substance and partially retard the action of substances injected directly into the CNS. This synaptic barrier is not related to the barrier between the CNS and the blood. Once inside the blood-brain barrier there is apparently a free communication of substances via the extracellular spaces. The pharmacological evidence, therefore, indicates that ACh is the transmitter substance at the synapse between motoneuron axon collaterals and the Renshaw cell. This is in marked contrast to the lack of effect of these same pharmacological agents on the synaptic transmitters giving rise to the EPSP and IPSP. The fact that these synapses are not at all effected is evidence that both the EPSP and the IPSP are brought about by synaptic transmitter substances other than ACh. As will be described later (Chapter 19), there are differences between motoneurons and neurons of the cerebral cortex with respect to the transmitters involved. The chemical nature of the transmitter substances are as yet unknown (McLennan, 1963).

Control of firing rate

For the most part, motoneurons do not normally discharge a single impulse as when a monosynaptic discharge is elicited by a brief volley.

Depending upon the degree of synaptic bombardment and the background excitatory state of the CNS, motoneurons discharge repetitively at rates of 10–20 per sec or up to 50 per sec, and in some cases faster. Our problem is to determine how the relatively rapid and irregular synaptic discharges brought to bear on the motoneuron membrane can give rise to the regular rhythm of impulses passing down the axon. One characteristic of the action potential of the motoneuron soma previously referred to is the prolonged *after-positivity* lasting 70–170 msec which follows an action potential. Such a positive after-potential must be distinguished from the hyperpolarization caused by Renshaw cell activity. According to a theory of Eccles (1953), the duration of the after-hyperpolarization determines the rate of discharge. If prolonged, the rate of discharge is reduced. If the excitatory level is increased, the background level of depolarization becomes higher and the rate of firing is increased. This theory was supported by the finding that different durations of the after-hyperpolarization could be correlated with the different firing rates of 'fast' (phasic) and 'slow' (tonic) motoneurons (Eccles, Eccles and Lundberg, 1958).

The different properties of these two kinds of motoneurons were shown by Granit, Henatsch and Steg (1956). A slip of ventral root was isolated so that the discharge rate of single motoneuron axons could be recorded. Following reflex excitation by a stretch of the muscle, only one or possibly two spikes were discharged. However, during post-tetanic potentiation of reflex transmission (Chapter 15) a marked difference was observed in the discharges of different motoneuron axons to such a test stretch. The tonic neurons had a long-lasting increase in their rate of discharge (Fig. 16.15). In contrast the phasic cells were not much influenced by stretch during the period of post-tetanic potentiation (Fig. 16.16). Of 100 cells, 53 were identified by this means as phasic, 16 highly tonic, 28 tonic but of lesser degree, and the remaining cells indeterminate.

Corresponding to these differences in their discharge rates on stretch, the amplitude of the spike in the tonic axons was generally smaller than that of the phasic axons. This corresponds anatomically with the smaller diameter of the axons of the tonic cells innervating the slow muscles. A microelectrode study of tonic and phasic motoneurons was made by Eccles, Eccles and Lundberg (1958). To excite these two types of response, nerves from slow (soleus) and fast (gastrocnemius) muscles were stimulated antidromically to give rise to responses recorded from the somas of those cells. Care was taken

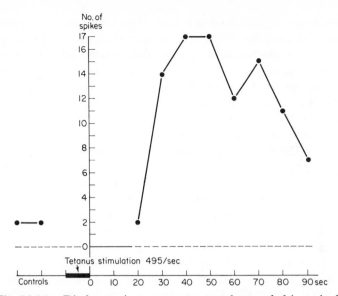

Fig. 16.15. Discharges in response to stretch recorded in a single ventral root fiber of a tonic neuron show only a few spikes in the control at the left. Following a period of tetanization of the afferent at 495/sec, there is a long period of increased rate of discharge to the stretch as shown in the record at the right. (From Granit, Henatsch and Steg, 1956.)

so that the after-potentials would not be confounded with the hyperpolarization of Renshaw cell activity. The Renshaw cells require a larger number of axons to be excited before they are activated. Therefore, in order to investigate the true antidromic response of the motoneuron a low intensity of stimulation is used to initiate an antidromic volley limited as much as possible to the cell

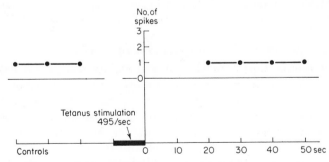

Fig. 16.16. Records of a phasic neuron (cf. Fig. 16.15) does not show a period of increased discharge after tetanization. (From Granit, Henatsch and Steg, 1956.)

under microelectrode observation so that true after-hyperpolarization could be recorded from the soma of that cell.   The slow tonic
motoneurons were found to have after-hyperpolarizations lasting
130 msec or longer; the fast motoneuron after-hyperpolarizations
were in the range of 50–110 msec.   This roughly corresponds with
different discharge rates found for the slow and fast motoneurons,
10–20/sec and 30–60/sec, respectively.   Therefore the rate of discharge of these two types of motoneurons did show a relation to the
durations of their after-hyperpolarization potentials.

However, not all the evidence suggests a simple control of firing by
the polarization level of the cell.   There is a reaction or 'rebound' of
the membrane following a period of altered membrane potential.
This was shown in the toad motoneuron by use of hyperpolarizing
currents with an abrupt onset declining to the original level (Fukami,
1962).   Near the end of the slow return of membrane potential to its
original level, a spike was excited.   The result suggests a decreased
accommodation of the membrane following a prolonged period of
hyperpolarization.   Similar rebounds in the hyperpolarizing direction have also been observed to follow generator potentials (Chapter
12).   We might suspect that the degree of hyperpolarization could
determine the time of onset of rebound and therefore the firing rate.

Alternatively, the repetitive discharge of the cell could be determined by some inherent rhythmic mechanism.   Kolmodin and
Skoglund (1958) have recorded intracellularly small depolarizing
fluctuations from repetitively discharging motoneurons, the sub-
threshold fluctuations occurring at a rate similar to that of the spike
discharge.   As previously noted, inherent rhythmicity is seen in
afferent receptor endings (Chapter 11), and under certain conditions
in peripheral axon (Chapter 5).   It would not be difficult to consider
that the motoneuron also has an intrinsically rhythmic mechanism
altered by the degree of synaptic activity prevailing.

Synaptic transmission in non-mammalian species

A troublesome aspect of the microelectrode studies we have been
describing is the inability to directly observe the site recorded from
within the cell.   The synaptic junction made between giant fibers
in squid can be observed and microelectrodes can be inserted into
a presynaptic fiber and into the postsynaptic element on the other
side of the synaptic junction (Bullock and Hagiwara, 1955; Hagiwara
and Tasaki, 1958).   The synapse of the stellate ganglion of the squid
has shown the salient features typical of chemical transmission at
this synaptic junction.   There is a small presynaptic spike, an

rreducible synaptic delay, and an EPSP out of which the propagated action potential arises. In the case of this simple one-to-one type of synapse, the EPSP is more regular than in the vertebrate motoneuron where many synapses are found terminating on a motoneuron and summation of the individual synaptic discharges takes place in the membrane.

Not all synaptic functions found in the lower species operate by means of a chemical mediator substance. Electrical transmission from the lateral fiber to the giant motor fiber of the crayfish has been shown by Furshpan and Potter (1959). When studied with microelectrodes, the synaptic delay across the synapse was found to be only 0.1 msec. Depolarizing current passed into the presynaptic element could cross the synapse and pass out through the postsynaptic membrane to excite it. However, depolarizing currents similarly introduced in the postsynaptic element could not cross the synapse in the antidromic direction to excite the presynaptic element. This result shows that the electrical transmission operating at this synapse has a *one-way rectifier* action allowing current and transmission in only one direction.

In the mollusc, *Aplysia*, the large cell bodies of its abdominal ganglia allow microelectrodes to be inserted for recording and micropipettes for giving electrophoretic injections. A number of interesting observations have been made. A rhythmic discharge in its cell body has been shown (Arvanitaki and Chalazonitis, 1957). As in the case of other cells the spike arises in the nonmyelinated initial segment of the axon (Tauc, 1960). Evidence that ACh is one of the transmitter substances has been obtained (Tauc and Gerschenfeld, 1962).

Evidence for both chemical and electrical mechanisms of synaptic transmission in different species has been accumulating (Eccles, 1964). The Mauthner cell of fish is a case where both electrical and chemical synapses are found in the same cell (Furakawa and Furshpan, 1963; Furshpan, 1964).

REFERENCES

Araki, T. and Otani, T. (1955). Response of single motoneurons to direct stimulation in toad's spinal cord. *J. Neurophysiol.* **18**: 472–485.

Araki, T., Eccles, J. C. and Ito, M. (1960). Correlation of the inhibitory postsynaptic potential of motoneurones with the latency and time course of inhibition of monosynaptic reflexes. *J. Physiol.* **154**: 354–377.

Arvanitaki, A. and Chalazonitis, N. (1957). Refractivités introduites par les potentials positifs du soma neuronique, enactivité autoentretenue. *Compt. Rend.* **245**: 445–447.

Bradley, K., Easton, D. M. and Eccles, J. C. (1953). An investigation of primary or direct inhibition. *J. Physiol.* **122**: 474–488.

Brock, L. G., Coombs, J. S. and Eccles, J. C. (1952). The recording of potentials with an intracellular electrode. *J. Physiol.* **117**: 431–460.

Brookhart, J. M. and Fadiga, E. (1960). Potential fields initiated during monosynaptic activation of frog motoneurones. *J. Physiol.* **150**: 633–655.

Bullock, T. H. and Hagiwara, S. (1955). Intracellular recording from the giant synapse of the squid. *J. Gen. Physiol.* **40**: 565–577.

Coombs, J. S., Eccles, J. C. and Fatt, P. (1955a). The specific ionic conductances and the ionic movements across the motoneuronal membrane that produce the inhibitory post-synaptic potential. *J. Physiol.* **130**: 326–373.

Coombs, J. S., Eccles, J. C. and Fatt, P. C. (1955b). Excitatory synaptic action in motoneurons. *J. Physiol.* **130**: 374–395.

Curtis, D. R. and Eccles, J. C. (1960). Synaptic action during and after repetitive stimulation. *J. Physiol.* **150**: 374–398.

Curtis, D. R. and Eccles, R. M. (1958). The excitation of Renshaw cells by pharmacological agents applied electrophoretically. *J. Physiol.* **141**: 435–445; and The effect of diffusional barriers upon the pharmacology of cells within the central nervous system. *Ibid.*, 446–463.

Dale, H. H. (1935). Pharmacology and nerve endings. *Proc. Roy. Soc. Med.* **28**: 319–332.

Eccles, J. C. (1953). *The Neurophysiological Basis of Mind.* Oxford University Press, Oxford.

Eccles, J. C. (1957). *The Physiology of Nerve Cells.* Johns Hopkins Press, Baltimore.

Eccles, J. C. (1961a). The mechanism of synaptic transmission. *Ergeb. Physiol.* **51**: 299–430.

Eccles, J. C. (1961b). Membrane time constants of cat motoneurons and time courses of synaptic action. *Exptl. Neurol.* **4**: 1–22.

Eccles, J. C. (1964). *The Physiology of Synapses.* Academic Press, New York.

Eccles, J. C., Eccles, R. M. and Lundberg, A. (1958). The action potentials of the alpha motoneurones supplying fast and slow muscles. *J. Physiol.* **142**: 275–291.

Eccles, J. C., Fatt, P. and Koketsu, K. (1954). Cholinergic and inhibitory synapses in a pathway from motor-axon collaterals to motoneurones. *J. Physiol.* **126**: 524–562.

Eccles, J. C., Libet, B. and Young, R. R. (1958). The behavior of chromatolyzed motoneurones studied by intracellular recording. *J. Physiol.* **143**: 11–40.

Eide, E., Lundberg, A. and Voorhoeve, P. (1961). Monosynaptically-evoked inhibitory post-synaptic potentials in motoneurones. *Acta Physiol. Scand.* **53**: 185–195.

Frank, K. (1959). Identification and analysis of single unit activity in the central nervous system. *Handbook of Physiology—Neurophysiology.* Vol. I, pp. 261–277. American Physiology Society, Washington, D.C.

Fukami, Y. (1962). Anodal break response of single motoneuron in toad's spinal cord. *Japan J. Physiol.* **12**: 279–292.

Fuortes, M. G. F., Frank, K. and Becker, M. C. (1957). Steps in the production of motoneuron spikes. *J. Gen. Physiol.* **40**: 735–752.

Furakawa, T. and Furshpan, E. J. (1963).   Two inhibitory mechanisms in the Mauthner neurons of goldfish.   J. Neurophysiol. 26: 759–774.

Furshpan, E. J. (1964).   "Electrical transmission" at an excitatory synapse in a vertebrate brain.   Science 144: 878–880.

Furshpan, E. J. and Potter, D. D. (1959).   Transmission at the giant motor synapses of the crayfish.   J. Physiol. 145: 289–325.

Granit, R., Henatsch, H. D. and Steg, G. (1956).   Tonic and phasic ventral horn cells differentiated by post-tetanic potentiation in cat extensors. Acta Physiol. Scand. 37: 114–126.

Hagiwara, S. and Tasaki, I. (1958).   A study of the mechanism of impulse transmission across the giant synapse of the squid.   J. Physiol. 143: 114–137.

Katz, B. and Miledi, R. (1963).   A study of spontaneous miniature potentials in spinal neurons.   J. Physiol. 168: 389–422.

Kolmodin, G. M. and Skoglund, C. R. (1958).   Slow membrane potential changes accompanying excitation and inhibition in spinal moto- and interneurons in the cat during natural activation.   Acta Physiol. Scand. 44: 11–54.

Lorente de Nó, R. (1939).   Transmission of impulses through cranial motor nuclei.   J. Neurophysiol. 2: 402–464.

McLennan, H. (1963).   Synaptic Transmission.   Saunders Co., Philadelphia.

Rall, W. (1960).   Membrane potential transients and membrane time constant of motoneurones.   Exptl. Neurol. 2: 503–532.

Ramón y Cajal, R. (1909).   Histologie du Système Nerveux de l'Homme et des Vertebrès.   Maloine, Paris. Repub. 1952. Instituto Ramón y Cajal, Madrid.

Renshaw, B. (1941).   Influence of discharge of motoneurons upon excitation of neighboring motoneurons.   J. Neurophysiol. 4: 167–183.

Renshaw, B. (1946).   Central effects of centripetal impulses in axons of spinal ventral roots.   J. Neurophysiol. 9: 191–204.

Tauc, L. (1960).   The site of origin of the efferent action potentials in the giant nerve cells of Aplysia.   J. Physiol. 152: 36–37P.

Tauc, L. and Gerschenfeld, H. M. (1962).   A cholinergic mechanism of inhibitory synaptic transmission in a molluscan nervous system.   J. Neurophysiol. 25: 236–262.

17

Integration of Reflexes

Muscle receptors

We have discussed the generator potential and repetitive discharge of frog muscle spindles excited by stretch (Chapter 12). In this chapter we shall enter into a more detailed discussion of the mammalian spindle receptor and the Golgi tendon organs from the point of view of their CNS effects. In the case of the spindles, we have to consider the effect of the CNS on the spindle as an example of a feedback loop. As described by Ruffini (1898) and Barker (1948), the mammalian spindle receptor is a complex receptor organ. We have already taken note of its chief feature, the thick *primary* afferent nerve terminating in the central region of the spindle receptor, in the annulospiral ending (Fig. 17.1). There is some variation in the spindles found in mammalian muscles. Some have a central grouping of nuclei—those with nuclear bags; others have nuclear chains in the equatorial region (Boyd, 1962). The spindle was shown to be sensory when it failed to degenerate after cutting the ventral motor roots (Sherrington, 1894). The smaller sensory fibers which terminate on either side of the central region in spray-like endings are the *secondary* afferent fibers of the spindle. The spindle on either side of the central visco-elastic portion shows typical muscle striations. On these muscular parts of the receptor small motor fibers terminate. That these fibers are motor in origin was shown by their degeneration after cutting the ventral roots. The important function of these small motor endings will be discussed in a later section.

The Golgi tendon organ is found on the tendinous ends of the muscles as a flower-spray termination of nerve terminals (Fig. 17.2). These were also shown to be sensory nerve endings by their remaining present after cutting the ventral motor roots.

The relative position of these two receptors shown in Fig. 17.3 with respect to the contracting muscle fibers is of the greatest importance to understanding their function, as was first pointed out by Fulton and Pi-Suñer (1927). The spindles are in parallel with the muscle fibers, while the Golgi tendon organs are in series with muscle fibers

342

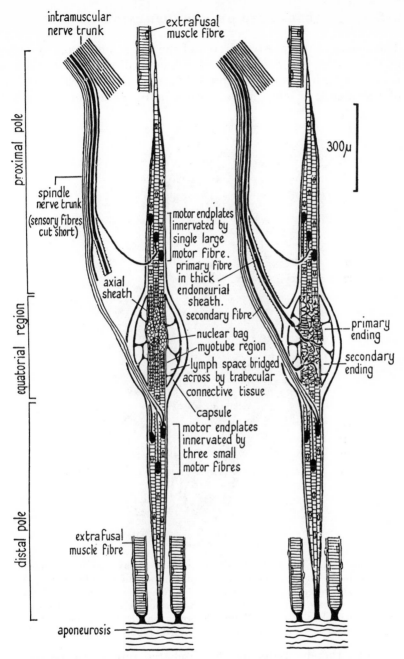

Fig. 17.1. The primary sensory nerve endings of the mammalian spindle terminate in an annulospiral configuration around the center in the nuclear 'bag region.' Other sensory fibers terminate at the sides. In addition, motor axons innervate the muscular portion of the receptor. (Barker, 1948.)

This means that a passive stretch of the whole muscle (as by pulling on the tendon) would be expected to excite a discharge in the sensory nerves of both types of receptors but an active twitch contraction of the muscle would 'unload' (cause a relaxation of) the spindle

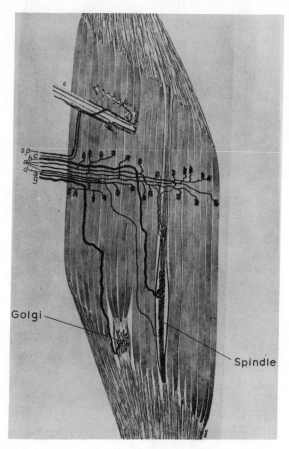

Fig. 17.2. The Golgi tendon organ has spray endings of nerve fibers on the tendinous ending of a group of muscle fibers. A spindle receptor is shown parallel to the muscle fibers. Motor nerves have end-plates present on muscle fibers. (Creed, Denny-Brown, Eccles, Liddell and Sherrington, *Reflex Activity of the Spinal Cord*, Oxford, 1932.)

receptor, thereby reducing the discharge rate in its nerve. The tendon organ, on the other hand, would be excited by an active contraction. The expected differing effects of an active muscle contraction on the rate of discharge of these two receptors was shown by

Mathews (1933).   By isolating single fibers from the muscle nerves, he found that some fibers had an increased rate of discharge during a twitch contraction (those from tendon organ) while other fibers showed a decrease in their rate (those from spindles).   This difference in response of the two types of muscle afferent fibers during an active muscle contraction has since been verified, e.g. by Kuffler, Hunt and Quilliam (1951), Eldred, Granit and Merton (1953), as shown diagrammatically in Fig. 17.3.

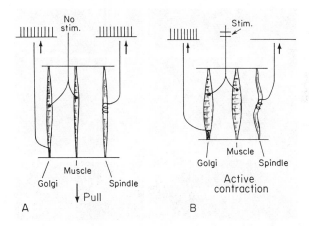

Fig. 17.3.   Golgi spindle receptors have a series relationship to the muscle fibers.   Spindles are in parallel.   Pull on the muscle increases the rate of firing of both receptors (A).   Active contraction of the muscles (B) will cause an increase in discharge of the Golgi tendon organ and a decrease in rate of discharge from the spindle.

In practice, single muscle receptor fibers may be more conveniently isolated by teasing apart dorsal rootlets of the spinal cord until recording is accomplished from a single dorsal root afferent fiber. A slow rate of discharge is recorded from such a fiber in response to a small degree of resting tension in the muscle.   When the muscle is caused to contract actively by stimulating the ventral root supplying that muscle or by electrodes applied to the muscle, the reduced tension on the spindle receptor causes the afferent discharge rate to fall during the twitch in the fiber shown in Fig. 17.4A.   This decrease in rate during the muscle contraction identifies that afferent nerve fiber as originating from a spindle receptor.   This decrease in the rate of a spindle afferent fiber is referred to as the *pause*.   Conversely, if a similarly isolated fiber of the dorsal root originates from a tendon organ, the series position of the receptor organ with respect to the muscle will result in a further increase in discharge rate during a twitch contraction (Fig. 17.4B).

A distinction between afferent fibers of the spindle and tendon organs has been based on the slight difference in size of the Group I fibers subserving these two receptors. Stimulation of muscle nerves near the muscle of origin showed a double spike volley recorded in the dorsal roots with an interval up to 0.2 msec between the two

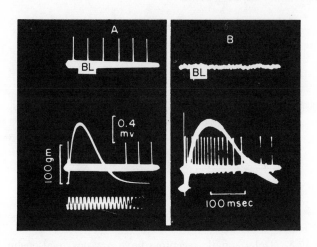

Fig. 17.4. The upper trace in A shows a resting level of discharge from a dorsal root fiber with a decrease in its rate during the muscle twitch shown by the curved line on the lower trace. This is the 'pause' and indicates that the muscle receptor fiber arises from a spindle. The upper traces in B show no activity at rest and an increase in discharge rate when the muscle contracts. This identifies the fiber as arising from a Golgi tendon organ. (Hunt, 1952.)

peaks (Bradley and Eccles, 1953). The first spike was ascribed to the larger diameter and faster conducting primary fibers of the spindle receptors, and the second spike to the slightly smaller and higher threshold fibers of the tendon organs. These fiber groups were designated as the *Ia and Ib Groups*, respectively. However, the identification of these recorded spikes with the fiber groups from primary spindle and tendon organ receptors is at present uncertain. Hunt (1954) tried to relate the calculated diameter of individual fibers from the dorsal root to their receptor properties. A considerable overlap was found rather than a clear separation into two groups by size. While there may not as yet be unanimity in the resolution of these two groups on the basis of size and excitability, we shall refer to primary spindle afferents as the Ia Group and afferents from the tendon organs as the Ib Group.

Two different systems of central terminations are subserved by the Ia and Ib Groups arising from these two receptors. The Ia Group gives rise to the monosynaptic reflexes and facilitatory action in synergist motoneurons, and inhibitory action in antagonist motoneurons. The tendon organs give rise to an 'inverse myotatic reflex' mechanism (Laporte and Lloyd, 1952). The action on motoneurons is inhibitory while the antagonist motoneurons are excited. At least one extra synapse is involved.

The inhibitory effect of the Ib Group was also shown by Eccles, Eccles and Lundberg (1957). They recorded IPSPs from the motoneurons with a latency of 0.5 msec above that of EPSPs as expected from an extra synaptic delay in another interneuron. The single-cell sampling studies of Eccles, Eccles and Lundberg (1957) revealed a more widespread inhibitory action present on both extensor and flexor muscles from this system rather than the inverse myotatic organization.

The secondary receptors of the spindle fall into the Group II fiber range. Their afferent fibers qualitatively show the same response as the primary receptor to muscle contractions, a pause on active contraction though with a higher threshold (Hunt and Perl, 1960). However, the central effects of the secondary afferents differ from those of the primary spindle afferents. The role of the secondary receptors is not yet fully understood (Barker, 1962; Boyd, 1962).

Gamma fiber (fusimotor) motor system

A cross section of a cat's ventral root and a histogram of the number of fibers of different sizes is shown in Fig. 17.5. By the older classification of fibers, those with larger diameters fall into the alpha group of A fibers, their axons innervating the skeletal muscles. In addition, there are a large number of smaller fibers falling into the gamma group of A fibers. The function of these smaller *gamma fibers* in the motor nerve supply of muscle was unknown for many years after Eccles and Sherrington (1930) directed attention to their presence. The gamma fibers to the muscles were thought to produce tonic contractions and, in the special case of frog's skeletal muscle, this was found to be the case, i.e. selective stimulation in the ventral roots of the small motor fibers increased muscle tension, up to 15% of a twitch tension (Kuffler and Gerard, 1947). A characteristic of the small-motor tonic increases was that repetitive stimulation was required.

The tonic type of small motor system found in the frog is not seen in mammal limb muscles. Leksell (1945) looked for a tonic action of the small motor fibers in the cat. By applying pressure to the

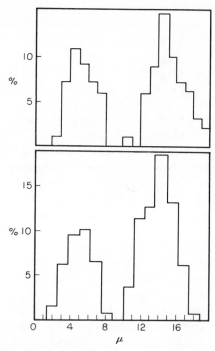

Fig. 17.5. The distribution of motor fiber sizes present in a ventral root shows in the upper graph peaks at approximately 4–6 μ and at 14–15 μ. In the lower graph the distribution of motor fibers in a deafferented nerve of the gastrocnemius muscle is shown. (After Eccles and Sherrington, from Ruch and Fulton, *Medical Physiology and Biophysics*, 18th Ed., Saunders, 1960.)

root or muscle nerve in a controlled fashion, conduction in the large alpha motor fibers can be blocked without blocking the smaller gamma fibers. Stimulation of the gamma fibers in the ventral roots after such alpha fiber blocks completely failed to produce tension changes in the cat muscles they supply, even when using a sensitive recording system. Leksell turned to an investigation of the effect of stimulation of the gamma motor fibers on the rate of discharge in afferent fibers recorded from the dorsal roots. The plan of the experiment is shown diagrammatically in Fig. 17.6. The discharge

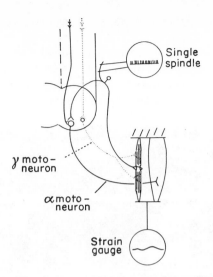

Single spindle

γ moto-neuron

α moto-neuron

Strain gauge

Fig. 17.6. Discharges recorded from a single spindle fiber in the dorsal root. The dotted line shows gamma motoneuron axons terminating on the spindle; the solid line alpha motoneurons terminating on muscle fibers. Upper CNS influences on these motoneurons are also indicated. (Granit, 1955.)

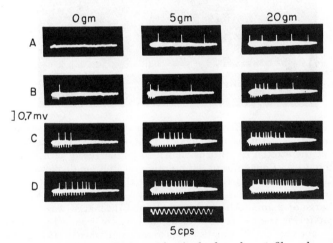

0 gm   5 gm   20 gm

A

B

] 0.7 mv

C

D

5 cps

Fig. 17.7. Afferent discharge in single dorsal root fiber shown in the three columns at muscle loads of 0, 5 and 20 gms. Without gamma stimulation (A), there is an increase in the rate of discharge with increased stretch; 4 to 6 stimulations of the gamma motoneurons leading to the spindles (B) increases the sensory discharge to stretch; 9 to 11 stimulations increased the rate or response to stretch still further (C). With 14 to 16 stimulations (D) the discharge rate was still further enhanced. (Kuffler, Hunt and Quilliam, 1951.)

rate of a single fiber isolated from the dorsal root and identified as coming from a primary spindle receptor was determined before and during gamma fiber stimulation.   Stimulation of the gamma motor fibers was found to increase the rate of discharge in the afferent fibers.

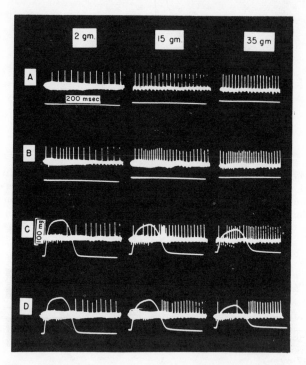

Fig. 17.8.   Three different levels of steady stretch were applied to muscle in the three columns; at 2, 15 and 35 gm.   The discharge rate of the stretch receptor is shown to be increased with greater stretch (A).   Concomitant stimulation of the small nerve fiber (9 stimuli at 100/sec) further increased the spindle rate (B).   A twitch in the early part of the record causes a decrease in sensory discharge at 2 gm.   Although a continued discharge was seen at 35 gm during the twitch (C).   The pause was overcome by gamma nerve activation.   Without concurrent small nerve stimulation a pause was seen at all three levels of stretch (D).   (Hunt and Kuffler, *J. Physiol.* **113**: 283, 1951.)

Therefore, gamma motor fibers which terminate on the spindle receptors act to increase the rate of firing of the spindle afferents (Hunt, 1952; Granit, 1955).   An increase in rate of spindle afferent discharge is seen to follow an increase in the frequency of gamma fiber stimulation (Fig. 17.7).

An increase in activity of the small motor system can compensate for a reduced muscle length (Hunt and Kuffler, 1951). Three levels of stretch (2, 15 and 35 grams) were placed on muscles to study the effect on spindle discharge rate of: (A) different levels of stretch alone, (B) added gamma activation produced by concurrent stimulation, (C) a twitch in the muscle during gamma activation and (D) a twitch produced without a concurrent gamma activation (Fig. 17.8) showing the compensating effect of gamma activity.

The small motor fibers influence only the spindle receptor discharge and not the Golgi tendon organ. This is shown by the lack of effect of gamma fiber stimulation on discharge rates of afferent fibers in the dorsal root which have been identified as originating from tendon organs.

Feedback control through the gamma loop

The primary spindle fibers, alpha motoneurons and the gamma fibers constitute a *feedback loop system* analogous to those used in engineering. Consider the operation of a voltage amplifier containing a feedback loop (Fig. 17.9). A portion of the output voltage is fed back to

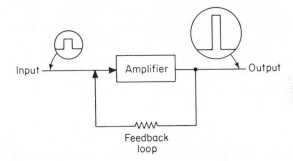

Fig. 17.9. A feedback system is diagrammed using as an example a voltage amplifier. A voltage pulse at the input is amplified and is larger at the output. A connection taken from the output, the feedback loop, is led back to the input either to augment (positive feedback) or to decrease the amplification (negative feedback).

the input to constitute the feedback loop. If the voltage in this feedback loop has the same polarity as the input voltage, we have a *positive feedback* loop. A small input voltage to the amplifier is augmented by the amplified voltage added to the input via the feedback loop, and this causes the voltage output to increase still further, up to a limit set by the capabilities of the system. If the voltage fed back to the input by the feedback loop is reversed in direction so that the input voltage to the amplifier is opposed by the feedback voltage, then the output voltage becomes reduced. This is a *negative feedback* loop. In engineering use, a negative feedback loop acts to increase stability at the expense of voltage amplification.

The analogy of the physical feedback system to the gamma loop is apparent. We can consider the spindle primary afferents as the input, the neural connections made in the CNS leading to the output responses of the muscle which is the amplifier. The gamma fibers in this analogy constitute the feedback loop acting at the input of the system.

Using this analogy as a guide, what can we expect during different reflex behaviors? Do the motor cells of the gamma fibers (also referred to as *fusimotor* neurons) receive excitatory synaptic impulses during reflex excitation so that by their discharge they can act on the spindle to compensate for the reduced muscle length? This would be an example of a positive feedback. The problem was studied in the tenuisimus muscle by comparing the discharge of alpha and gamma fibers passing down to the muscle under a variety of reflex conditions (Hunt, 1952). The tenuisimus muscle is a slender, band-like structure found among the hamstring muscles of the hind limb of the cat, and functionally it is a flexor muscle. The nerve innervating it contains few fibers, and these branch to supply two parts of the muscle (Fig. 17.10). One of the branches of the motor nerve innervating this muscle was cut and used to record the efferent discharge to the muscle. The other branch was left intact. Electrodes were also placed on the muscle so that muscle action potential discharges could be recorded at the same time, as shown in the bottom traces of this figure. No muscle action potentials were recorded while a gamma fiber motor discharge (the small amplitude potentials) was in progress (column A) with the muscles at rest. In response to a light touch of the foot (column B), the gamma discharge increased and along with it large alpha motor potentials appeared in the records. Corresponding in time to the appearance of alpha motor discharges in the nerve, muscle action potentials were recorded from the muscle as shown in the lower trace. The contralateral foot was touched, and both gamma and alpha fiber discharges were inhibited (column C). The experiment showed that the gamma and alpha motor discharges may, and in other cases may not, be activated together as would be expected from a positive feedback control.

The connections made in the spinal cord between sensory inputs and the fusimotor cells and alpha motoneurons will determine whether the feedback loop is positive or negative. A single-unit study of the discharge characteristics of the fusimotor cells was made by Hunt and Paintal (1958). The connections to the fusimotor cells appear to be made through interneurons, as shown by their long central delay. In response to excitation with a brief volley, they characteristically gave rise to a repetitive discharge of 3–4 spikes

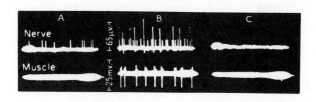

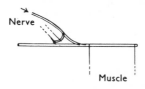

Fig. 17.10. Records taken from one peripheral branch of the nerve innervating the tenuisimus and from the muscle. Without any stimulation (A) there is a background discharge (upper trace) of the small nerve fibers, the small-sized action potentials, with an absence of muscle impulses. Upon reflex excitation of the moto-neurons and the gamma neurons there is an augmented small motor discharge and in addition larger amplitude alpha action potentials (B). These give rise to muscle action potentials as shown in the lower trace. Reflex stimulation of the contralateral foot (C) causes inhibition of background small nerve activity. (Hunt, 1952.)

at a rate of 300–500/sec. This behavior fits with the requirement of a repetitive stimulation of gamma fibers to activate spindles. Inso-far as they respond with a repetitive discharge to a single volley, the fusimotor cells behave like interneurons rather than motoneurons. A sampling of fusimotor cells showed that one-quarter to one-third generated a background discharge; the rest were silent until reflexly excited. Recordings were made from the fusimotor fibers supplying a number of hind limb muscle nerves while other hind limb muscle nerves and cutaneous nerves were stimu-lated to elicit reflex discharges. The results show that cutaneous nerves were more effective in exciting fusimotor discharge than were muscle nerves.   No identifiable pattern of distribution of fusimotor discharge on a reciprocal innervation basis was seen.   Both facilitatory and inhibitory effects were found distributed to the fusimotor fibers of the various muscles.

Returning to the feedback analogy, is a primary control of muscle contraction possible by means of an activation through the feedback loop?   In other words, can fusimotor cells be excited first and then followed by a discharge of the primary afferents of the spindles and in turn the motoneurons?   Evidence for this kind of

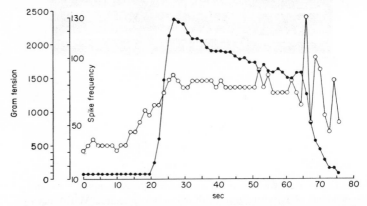

Fig. 17.11.   The tension in the muscle (•) indirectly measures the activity of alpha motoneurons.   The rate of afferent spindle discharge (○) indirectly gives a measure of gamma activity.   At zero on the abscissa the carotids were temporarily occluded to produce anemic decerebration.   An increase of spindle afferent discharge is seen to occur before an increase in muscle tension. With release of the occlusion there is a fall in tension and decrease in spindle activity.   (Granit, 1955.)

motor control initiated through the gamma system was given by Eldred, Granit and Merton (1953).   They recorded the discharge of gamma fibers in fibers isolated from peripheral nerve or ventral roots and also muscle tension.   Tonic activity was then increased by producing decerebrate rigidity.   The discharge rate of the gamma fibers increased before that of the alpha fiber discharge to increase tension (Fig. 17.11).   These findings are in accord with a primary control exerted on the fusimotor cells.   However, Hunt and Paintal (1958) have shown that there is a wide range of excitability in the individual fusimotor cells innervating a muscle.   Therefore, this type of control mechanism might only apply to a small group of low-threshold fusimotor cells. Other fusimotor cells would be excited secondarily as part of some reflex pattern or via upper brain centers of control (Chapter 22).

Autogenic effects and the Renshaw system

The interactions of central neurons in a reflex discharge were studied by Granit (1950), making use of a stretch reflex and testing the resulting excitability changes by means of monosynaptic responses

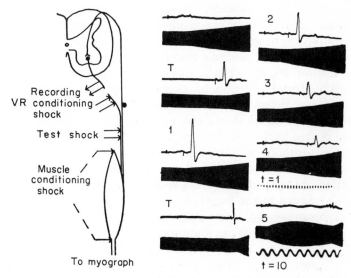

Fig. 17.12. A test shock is applied to the muscle nerve and the resulting monosynaptic response recorded in the cut ventral root. A conditioning shock is applied to the distal end of the cut ventral root and the muscle tension increase recorded with a myograph. The muscle can also be conditioned with a shock directly applied to the muscle. In each of the paired records the upper trace indicates changes in the size of the test monosynaptic discharge as a result of such autogenic conditioning, the thickness of the black band the degree of tension of the muscle. Top set, C, conditioning shock alone; T, test shock alone and the monosynaptic response. In 1–4 conditioning shocks and test shocks at different time intervals. T = 10 msec. (Granit, 1955.)

(Fig. 17.12). As shown in the diagram of the experimental plan (on the left in this figure), a weak shock was delivered to the muscle nerve giving rise to a monosynaptic response recorded in the cut ventral root. The amplitude of the monosynaptic response was used as a test for alpha motoneuron excitability. A contraction of that muscle was then produced by a conditioning volley delivered to the peripheral part of the cut ventral root. The time course of the resulting excitability changes produced by the reflexly contracting muscle is shown in the figure. An early increase in amplitude of the monosynaptic test response was found to last about 10 msec, followed by a long-lasting period of diminution of excitability. The term *autogenic inhibition* is used because the inhibition arises from a reflex excited in that same muscle. During contraction, the spindle receptors are unloaded while the Golgi tendon organs are excited; therefore, Granit (1950, 1955) considers that the prolonged inhibition occurs as a result of activity of the tendon organs. The concept of autogenic inhibition from the tendon organs was supported by the effect of local injections of procaine into the tendon regions containing the Golgi tendon organs. Such injections diminished autogenic inhibition on stretch (McCouch, Deering and Stewart, 1950; Libet, Feinstein and Wright, 1959). As described in Chapter 14, the leg of a decerebrate animal shows resistance to forcible flexion until at a certain degree of flexion the rigidity suddenly melts. Granit found that the threshold of autogenic inhibition is higher than that required to excite a stretch reflex. Therefore, we can equate the excitation of the tendon receptor with the autogenic inhibition of the muscle observed in the lengthening reaction.

If electromyograms are taken from subjects with a tonic background of reflex activity in a muscle and a myotatic reflex excited, a *silent period* lasting 50–100 msec (Fig. 17.13) follows the myotatic reflex (Granit, 1955). This silent period may be found in muscles other than those reflexly excited, for example, in the soleus after eliciting a knee-jerk in the gastrocnemius (Denny-Brown, 1928). The prolonged inhibitory states found in autogenic inhibition and during the silent period are most probably due to the action of Renshaw cells and inhibition in motoneurons. We have discussed Renshaw cells in Chapter 16 from the point of view of synaptic transmission. Our purpose now is to discuss some of the proposed functions of this apparently indiscriminate inhibition, one which appears in both extensor and flexor muscles. One view is that the function of general inhibitory action of Renshaw cells is to remove lingering states of subliminal fringe excitability and 'hold the reflex to its task' (Granit, 1961). A similar concept was presented earlier by Brooks and Wilson (1959), who considered that recurrent inhibition acts to 'sharpen' reflex effects by decreasing activity in the surrounding population of motoneurons.

Another possible function of the Renshaw system is based on the finding that Renshaw cell inhibition is distributed mainly to the tonic motoneurons (Granit, Pascoe and Steg, 1957; Kuno, 1959). The microelectrode studies of Eccles, Eccles, Iggo and Ito (1961), in which a large number of motoneurons were sampled, also showed a greater distribution to tonic motoneurons though tonic and phasic motoneurons are not two clearly separate groups, i.e. there are cells with

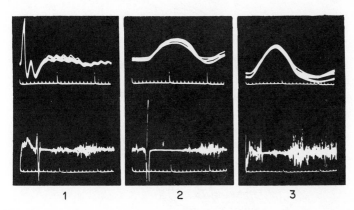

Fig. 17.13. Tension of the human soleus muscle recorded in the upper traces. In the lower trace the electromyogram of the muscle taken with needle electrodes is shown. Following a tendon jerk in the muscle (1) there is a decrease in the electromyographic activity—the silent period. A similar silent period is seen (2) following a shock to afferent fibers in the popliteal fossa. A silent period also follows a twitch excited in the gastrocnemius muscle which does not excite the soleus (3). (From Merton, in Granit, 1955.)

intermediate properties (Chapter 16). In any case, the tonic motoneurons do receive a more powerful Renshaw inhibition and it may be that the function of Renshaw inhibition is to suppress tonus and thereby remove resistance to phasic responses.

The nature of Renshaw cell activity is still an open question. There is also a recurrent facilitation instead of inhibition to consider (Wilson, Talbot and Diecke, 1960) though this facilitation is quantitatively much smaller than are the inhibitory effects (Eccles, Eccles, Iggo and Ito, 1961).

Presynaptic inhibition

In recent years a new type of neuronal control mechanism has been recognized, that of *presynaptic inhibition* (cf. Chapter 9). While recording from single motoneurons with microelectrodes, muscle

afferent volleys were found to produce inhibition by diminishing the
size of EPSPs without the intervention of IPSP activity (Frank and
Fuortes, 1957; Frank, 1959).   There was no change in ionic permeability, hyperpolarization or membrane excitability as tested
by current pulses, such as might be expected from IPSP activ-

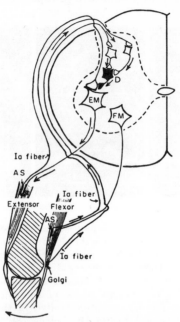

Fig. 17.14.   Diagrammatic representation of cells subserving presynaptic inhibition showing afferent annulospiral (AS) fibers of Ia
Group from an extensor and a flexor muscle terminating on dorsal
horn cells which in turn synapse on a *D* cell.   This cell synapses on
the terminals of the afferent fibers, in this case on the extensor
motoneuron (EM) to produce inhibition.   (FM is a flexor motoneuron.)   Golgi tendon organs can also terminate on and inhibit
afferents from the spindle receptor via the *D* cell.   (Eccles,
Kostyuk and Schmidt, 1962a.)

ity (Chapter 16).   Therefore, the inhibition was considered to be
'remote,' taking place either on dendrites far from the soma or on
the afferent terminals themselves in some manner which prevents the
normal discharge of transmitter substance.   The extensive investigations of Eccles and his colleagues (Eccles, Eccles and Magni, 1961;
Eccles, Kostyuk and Schmidt, 1962a,b; Eccles, Schmidt and Willis,
1962) showed that such a presynaptic inhibitory mechanism plays
an important role in the spinal cord (Eccles, 1964).   Investigations of

its neuronal mechanism showed that afferent fibers or collaterals from them terminate on certain interneurons in the dorsal horn. The interneuron axons in turn synapse on to the terminations of afferent fibers to inhibit their discharge (Fig. 17.14).

The axons ending on the afferent terminals act by depolarizing them, thereby reducing the amount of transmitter substances released from the terminals.

The depolarization of the sensory terminals by presynaptic depolarization explains the phenomena of *root* and *cord potentials* (Gasser and Graham, 1933; Lloyd, 1952; Bernhard, 1953). These long-lasting slow potentials are recorded with one electrode on the

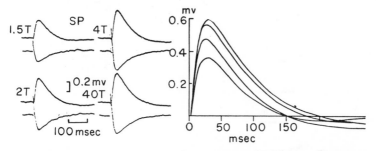

Fig. 17.15.   Dorsal root potentials shown at increasing strengths of stimulation from 1.5 to 40 times above threshold (T) to the left. The lower trace is a cord dorsum surface potential (SP) recorded slightly more caudal than the entry of the dorsal rootlet.   At the right, the dorsal root potentials are enlarged and superimposed to show their time course. The negative dorsal root potential is seen to be followed by a phase of positivity which can last 150–200 msec.   (Eccles, Kostyuk and Schmidt, 1962a.)

root close to the cord or on the dorsum of the cord with the other electrode placed further away on the root.   An amplifier with a long time constant or a d.c. amplifier is required.   As shown in Fig. 17.15, upon afferent stimulation in the same or a neighboring root, a prolonged *positive* (*P*) wave is found in the dorsum of the cord and a corresponding prolonged negative wave in the dorsal root, the *dorsal root potential* (*DRP*).   These cord and root potentials had generally been considered to arise in some fashion from interneurons and to reflect the reflex excitability of that group of cells.   This earlier interpretation was confirmed by Eccles, Kostyuk and Schmidt (1962a).   Microelectrodes were inserted into the dorsum of the spinal cord to record the field distribution of slow potentials at different depths in response to afferent stimulation.   The positive dorsal cord potential was inverted several millimeters below the surface to become a depolarization, in the region where the dorsal root fibers end in the dorsal horn of the cord (Fig. 17.16). These *field potentials* arising from groups of fibers agree with the micro-electrode studies of single sensory afferent fibers taken with a

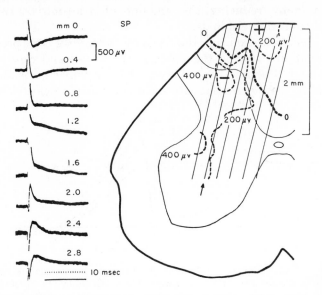

Fig. 17.16. At the left, records show slow field potentials elicited by single afferent volleys recorded at different depths within the dorsal region of the spinal cord. Depth below surface is given in mm. The relative distribution of these potentials are shown plotted on a cross-section of the spinal cord to the right along the paths of entry of the electrode at a fixed time of 40 msec after the volley. A negative focus present at this time is found within the dorsal horn, at the level of the cells subserving presynaptic inhibition. (Eccles, Kostyuk and Schmidt, 1962a.)

microelectrode by Koketsu (1956). Upon primary afferent ex-citation, a prolonged depolarization was found in those afferent fibers.

Microelectrode studies of the interneurons of the dorsal horn revealed some cells that were monosynaptically excited by afferent volleys. These interneurons synapse on the D cells, which terminate on presynaptic afferents to depolarize and inhibit them. The D cells have properties which fit with such an action. In response to a single volley, they give rise to a prolonged repetitive discharge. However, the whole of the long duration of inhibition (those lasting over several hundred msec) cannot as yet be explained. Possibly the mobilization of transmitter substances in the presynaptic terminals is blocked for very long times by presynaptic inhibition (Eccles, 1961).

A study of the effects of different types of sensory inputs giving rise to dorsal root and cord potentials showed that two presynaptic inhibitory systems are present. The cutaneous afferents and the high-threshold muscle afferents are part of one system with their afferent inputs ending on interneurons which then terminate via D cells on other afferents (Fig. 17.17). Excitation of the flexor reflex (Chapter 14) is one of its manifestations. The system is therefore referred to as the *FRA* (*flexor reflex afferent*) group (Eccles, Kostyuk and Schmidt, 1962a). Included in the system are receptors to hair movements, touch and pressure on skin and pressure on muscle (Eccles, Kostyuk and Schmidt, 1962b). Possibly also involved are nociceptive fibers exciting the flexor reflex (Chapter 14). The other presynaptic inhibitory system is comprised of Group I muscle afferents related to proprioceptive adjustments of muscle, predominately of the flexor muscles. These include both Ia and Ib afferents. A brief period of repetitive stimulation is most effective to excite the interneurons of this *Group I system* to give rise to presynaptic inhibition and a prolonged inhibition lasting over several hundred milliseconds.

The activations of these two types of interneuronal systems can be studied either by the dorsal root or cord potentials or by their effect on flexor reflexes. An interaction between the FRA and Group I systems is shown by the occlusive interaction of their dorsal root potentials. The relation between these systems is asymmetrical. The FRA system is activated by both the FRA inputs and Group I afferents. The Group I system does not activate the FRA system.

Presynaptic inhibition is a negative feedback system which discriminates against afferent impulses at their entry into the CNS. Such a mechanism appears to be of fundamental importance with respect to sensory excitation. By such means 'urgent' signals can be transmitted and 'trivial' signals suppressed. How far such a generalization holds can only be determined by future investigations.

A similar type of inhibitory termination on presynaptic afferent fibers has been found in other parts of the CNS. These will be discussed in Chapter 21.

REFERENCES

Barker, D. (1948). The innervation of the muscle spindles. *Quart. J. Microscop. Sci.* **89**: 143–186.

Barker, D. (1962). (Editor). *Symposium on Muscle Receptors.* Hong Kong University Press, Hong Kong.

Bernhard, C. G. (1953). Analysis of the spinal cord potentials in leads from the cord dorsum. *Ciba Foundation Symposium.* Churchill, London.

Boyd, I. A. (1962). The structure and innervation of the nuclear bag muscle fibre system and nuclear chain muscle fibre system in mammalian muscle spindles. *Phil. Trans. Roy. Soc. B* **245**: 81–136.

Bradley, K. and Eccles, J. C. (1953). Analysis of the fast afferent impulses from thigh muscles. *J. Physiol.* **122**: 462–473.

Brooks, V. B. and Wilson, V. J. (1959). Recurrent inhibition in the cat's spinal cord. *J. Physiol.* **146**: 380–391.

Denny-Brown, D. (1928). On inhibition as a reflex accompaniment of the tendon jerk and of other forms of active muscular response. *Proc. Roy Soc. B.* **103**: 321–336.

Eccles, J. C. (1964). *The Physiology of Synapses.* Academic Press, New York.

Eccles, J. C., Eccles, R. M., Iggo, A. and Ito, M. (1961). Distribution of recurrent inhibition among motoneurons. *J. Physiol.* **159**: 479–499.

Eccles, J. C., Eccles, R. M. and Lundberg (1957). Synaptic actions on motoneurons caused by impulses in Golgi tendon organ afferents. *J Physiol.* **138**: 227–252.

Eccles, J. C., Eccles, R. M. and Magni, F. (1961). Central inhibitory action attributable to presynaptic depolarization produced by muscle afferent volleys. *J. Physiol.* **159**: 147–166.

Eccles, J. C., Kostyuk, P. G. and Schmidt, R. F. (1962a). Central pathways responsible for depolarization of primary afferent fibers. *J. Physiol* **161**: 237–257.

Eccles, J. C., Kostyuk, P. G. and Schmidt, R. G. (1962b). Presynaptic inhibition of the central actions of flexor reflex afferents. *J. Physiol* **161**: 258–281.

Eccles, J. C., Schmidt, R. F. and Willis, W. D. (1962). Presynaptic inhibition of the spinal monosynaptic reflex pathway. *J. Physiol.* **161**: 282–297.

Eccles, J. C. and Sherrington, C. S. (1930). Numbers and contraction values of individual motor-units examined in some muscles of the limb. *Proc Roy. Soc. B.* **106**: 326–357.

Eldred, E., Granit, R. and Merton, P. A. (1953). Supraspinal control of the muscle spindles and its significance. *J. Physiol.* **122**: 498–523.

Frank, K. (1959). Basic mechanisms of synaptic transmission in the central nervous system. *IRE Trans. Med. Electron.* **ME-6**: 85–88.

Frank, K. and Fuortes, M. G. F. (1957). Presynaptic and postsynaptic inhibition of monosynaptic reflexes. *Federation Proc.* **16**: 39–40.

Fulton, J. F. and Pi-Súner, J. (1927). A note concerning the probable function of various afferent end-organs in skeletal muscle. *Am. J. Physiol.* **83** 554–562.

Gasser, H. S. and Graham, H. T. (1933). Potentials produced in the spinal cord by stimulation of the dorsal roots. *Am. J. Physiol.* **103**: 303–320.

Granit, R. (1950). Reflex self-regulation of the muscle contraction and autogenic inhibition. *J. Neurophysiol.* **13**: 351–372.

Granit, R. (1955). *Receptors and Sensory Reception.* Yale University Press New Haven.

Granit, R. (1961). Regulation of discharge rate by inhibition, especially by recurrent inhibition. *Nervous Inhibition.* Edited by E. Florey. Pp. 61–70. Pergamon Press, New York.

Granit, R., Pascoe, J. E. and Steg, G. (1957). The behavior of tonic and phasic motoneurons during stimulation of recurrent collaterals. *J. Physiol.* **138**: 381–400.

Hunt, C. C. (1952). Muscle stretch receptors; peripheral mechanisms and reflex function. *Cold Spring Harbor Symp. Quant. Biol.* **17**: 113–123.

Hunt, C. C. (1954). Relation of function to diameter in afferent fibers of muscle nerves. *J. Gen. Physiol.* **38**: 117–131.

Hunt, C. C. and Kuffler, S. W. (1951). Stretch receptor discharges during muscle contraction. *J. Physiol.* **113**: 298–315.

Hunt, C. C. and Paintal, A. S. (1958). Spinal reflex regulation of fusimotor neurons. *J. Physiol.* **143**: 195–212.

Hunt, C. C. and Perl, E. R. (1960). Spinal reflex mechanisms concerned with skeletal muscle. *Physiol. Rev.* **40**: 538–579.

Koketsu, K. (1956). Intracellular potential changes of primary afferent nerve fibers in spinal cords of cats. *J. Neurophysiol.* **19**: 375–392.

Kuffler, S. W. and Gerard, R. W. (1947). The small-nerve motor system to skeletal muscle. *J. Neurophysiol.* **10**: 383–394.

Kuffler, S. W., Hunt, C. C. and Quilliam, J. P. (1951). Function of medullated small-nerve fibres in mammalian ventral roots: efferent muscle spindle innervation. *J. Neurophysiol.* **14**: 29–54.

Kuno, M. (1959). Excitability following antidromic activation in spinal motoneurons supplying red muscles. *J. Physiol.* **149**: 374–393.

Laporte, Y. and Lloyd, D. P. C. (1952). Nature and significance of the reflex connections established by large afferent fibers of muscle origin. *Am. J. Physiol.* **169**: 609–621.

Leksell, L. (1945). The action potential and excitatory effects of the small ventral root fibres to skeletal muscle. *Acta Physiol. Scand.* **10**: *Suppl.* **31**: 1–88.

Libet, B., Feinstein, B. and Wright, E. W., Jr. (1959). Tendon afferents in autogenic inhibition in man. *Electroencephalog. Clin. Neurophysiol.* **11**: 129–139.

Lloyd, D. P. C. (1952). Electrotonus in dorsal nerve roots. *Cold Spring Harbor Symp. Quant. Biol.* **17**: 203–219.

Mathews, B. H. C. (1933). Nerve endings in mammalian muscle. *J. Physiol.* **78**: 1–53.

McCouch, G. P., Deering, J. D. and Stewart, W. B. (1950). Inhibition of knee jerk from tendon spindles of *crureus*. *J. Neurophysiol.* **13**: 343–350.

Ruffini, A. (1898). On the minute anatomy of the neuromuscular spindles of the cat, and on the physiological significance. *J. Physiol.* **23**: 190–208.

Sherrington, C. S. (1894). On the anatomical constitution of nerves of skeletal muscles; with remarks on recurrent fibres in the ventral spinal nerve-root. *J. Physiol.* **17**: 211–258.

Wilson, V. J., Talbot, W. H. and Diecke, F. P. J. (1960). Distribution of recurrent facilitation and inhibition in cat spinal cord. *J. Neurophysiol.* **23**: 144–153.

18

Electrical Properties of the Cortex

Neurons and cytoarchitecture of the cortex

The cerebral cortex is a relatively thin layer of gray matter covering the surface of the cerebrum. As the most recent phylogenetic acquisition of the brain, it has undergone relatively greater development than has other parts of the brain. The cortical surface has undergone a folding into *gyri* to accommodate its increased surface area in the limited brain case volume (Sholl, 1956). The correspondence of an increased cortical area with the higher position of a species in the phylogenetic scale early led to the inference that the cortex is related to higher functions. The greatest advance in relative growth has been in the *neocortex* present on the dorsal and lateral aspects of the brain. The different type of cortex present on the medial surface and base of the brain is known as the *paleocortex*, and it appears to be related to visceral functions (Chapter 23). We shall use the term *cortex* with reference to the neocortex unless otherwise specified.

A cross-section of the cortex and the underlying white matter is shown in Fig.18.1, with the cell bodies stained dark with a Nissl stain. The Nissl-stained cortex does not show the dendritic extensions of the cells and their axonic branches and collaterals. These are revealed by the use of a Golgi silver stain. Only a small proportion of the cells present are stained with the silver. In these cells the ramifications and the extent of the apical dendrites and axons of the cortical cells can be dramatically demonstrated (Fig. 18.2). The two main types of neurons found in the cortex are the *pyramidal* and *stellate* cells (Ramón y Cajal, 1911; Sholl, 1956). These are shown diagrammatically in Fig. 18.3 (e.g., cell 8 and cell 17). The pyramidal cells are identified by their pyramid-shaped cell body, at the top of which arises the apical dendrite extending upward toward the surface and branching like a tree. The apical dendrites are a prominent feature of the cell as found in a variety of species (A–D, Fig. 18.4).

The apical dendrites of the pyramidal cells reach the outermost or *molecular* layer of the cortex where they extend laterally for a fraction of a millimeter. In the molecular layer the branches of the

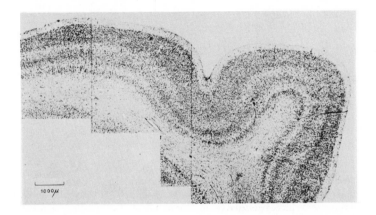

Fig. 18.1. Nissl stain of cerebral cortex from the cat. The layered appearance is produced by the different densities of cell bodies present in any given region. (Sholl, 1956.)

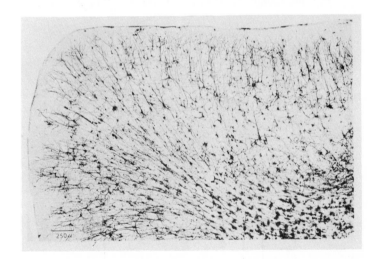

Fig. 18.2. Golgi stain of cat cerebral cortex showing the dendritic processes of pyramidal cells with shafts extending perpendicularly toward the surface of the cortex, branching at their upper ends. (Sholl, 1956.)

Fig. 18.3. The cell types present in layers I through VI of cerebral cortex (left) shown diagrammatically. Pyramidal cells (e.g. 7, 8, 9) have long apical shafts extending toward the surface. They also have dendrites at their base—the basilar dendrites. Stellate cells (e.g. 5) have dendrites extending in many directions around them. Specific afferent fibers are shown at right (a, b) ending in profuse branching terminating on neurons mainly in the 4th layer. Non-specific afferents (c, d) and association afferents (e, f) are found ending in many layers. (Fulton, 1949.)

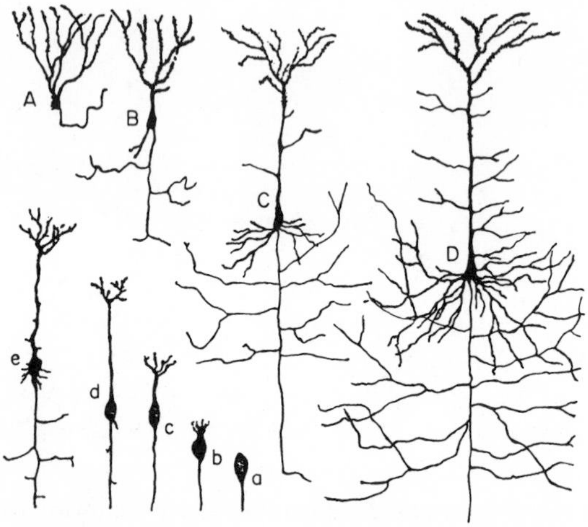

Fig. 18.4. Pyramidal cells of: A, frog; B, lizard; C, rat; D, man. In the lower series (a to e) the ontogenic development of a pyramidal cell is shown from the neuroblast stage (a) toward the mature state. (Ramón y Cajal, 1911.)

pical dendrites are packed close together, and because their terminal
ortions usually do not stain well, the molecular layer appears as a
hin light layer in the outermost part of the cortex.   Along the shaft
f the apical dendrites of pyramidal cells, minute bud-like extrusions
nown as *gemmules* or *spines* are found which are the sites of *axo-
endritic* synapses.   *Axosomatic* synapses are found on the membrane
f the soma.   Cortical cell synapses have recently been studied with
he electron microscope (Gray, 1959; Whittaker and Gray, 1962).   An
xample is shown in Fig. 18.5(a) with a number of different synaptic

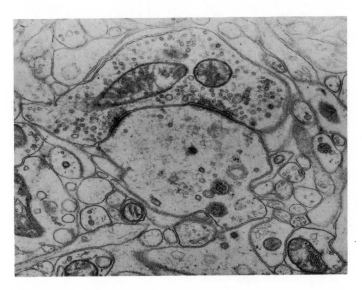

Fig. 18.5(a).   Electron micrograph of cortical synapse.   The
presynaptic terminal identified by vesicles and mitochondria
present in them.   Membrane thickening at synapse site on
dendrite.   (Courtesy, L. E. Westrum.)

ypes diagrammatically represented.   To be noted is the presence of
esicles and mitochondria in the presynaptic axon terminus, a
inding typical of synapses in general.   The *type 1* axodendritic
synapse has a thickened postsynaptic membrane opposite the 300A
left of the synapse.   The *type 2* axodendritic synapse has a 200A
left and no thickened postsynaptic membrane.   In the spines of
he apical dendrites on which a synapse is found a curious lamellated
structure of unknown function is seen under the postsynaptic
membrane, the *spine apparatus*.   Neurofilaments are present in
some axon endings, not in others (Boycott, Gray and Guillery,

1961; Gray and Guillery, 1961). Because many of the synaptic terminals in the cortex lack such neurofilaments, they do not stain well with Golgi-type silver stains. This explains the apparent lack of synaptic endings on the apical dendrites which was described in earlier studies.

The cerebral cortex is a vast interneuronal station with large numbers of afferent and efferent fibers entering and leaving any

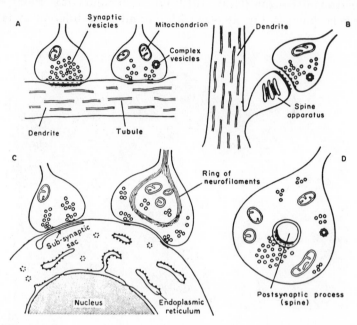

Fig. 18.5(b).   A, type 1 axodendritic synapse on a dendrite on the left, type 2 axodendritic synapse on the right; B, synapse present on a dendritic spine found on the apical shaft of pyramidal cells; C, axosomatic synapses; D, synapse with postsynaptic spine inside the presynaptic terminal.   (Whittaker and Gray, 1962.)

given region.   Efferent fibers pass to other cortical regions via the white matter under the cortex.   Other efferent fibers pass to various sub-cortical centers including the lower motor centers in the brain stem and spinal cord.   One class of cortical neurons has intracortical axons transmitting impulses only to neurons.   The stellate cell is such an intracortical element.   One type has an axon which ascends and synapses with apical dendrites.   Other stellate cells have axons synapsing on nearby somas.   Lorente de Nó (1944) showed a number of possible connections between the various neuron types

Fig. 18.6). A few of these pathways described anatomically have been confirmed by physiological means, as will be discussed in a later section.

Nissl-stained sections of the cortex show a layered appearance. Layering is brought about by the tendency of different types of cells to cluster at various levels in the cortex and by the density of afferent terminations in the cortex (Lorente de Nó, 1949). Pyramidal cells, particularly the large pyramidal cells which send their axons in

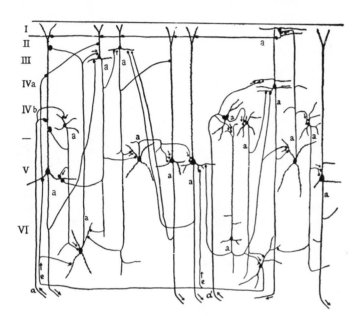

Fig. 18.6. Diagram of some intracortical connections suggested by anatomical studies. Axons (a); note synaptic junctions. Arrows show direction of impulses. (Fulton, 1949.)

the pyramidal tract to lower motor centers (Chapter 22) tend to have their cell bodies located in the lower layers. The molecular layer is composed mainly of apical dendrites arising from pyramidal cell bodies in the other layers. Six cortical layers are generally distinguished (Fig. 18.7).

The differences in the thickness and composition of the cell layers of various cortical areas have been used to characterize different regions of the cortex. Such a *cytoarchitectonic* mapping of the human cortex by Brodmann (1909) is shown in Fig. 18.8. Sholl (1956), among others, has pointed out that some of the variations

in cell shape on which such area designations are based are di⟨
tortions brought about by the folding of the cortical surface. A
present only major areas showing definite distinguishing features a⟨
usually considered to have a neurophysiological significance an
these will be discussed in later chapters. In this chapter the electric⟨
properties common to all cortical areas will be discussed.

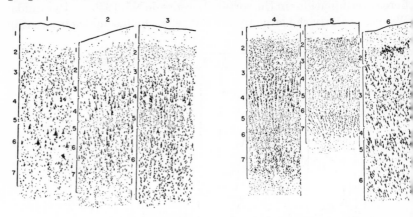

Fig. 18.7. The differences in the layered appearance of various
cortical regions of the human brain are shown where 7 layers are
considered instead of the usual 6. 1, motor cortex containing
the large pyramidal Betz cells in the 6th layer; 2, postcentral
(somesthetic cortex); 3, temporal (auditory cortex); 4, occipital;
5, striate (visual cortex); 6, pyriformis. (Fulton, 1949.)

Spontaneous electrical activity—the electroencephalogram

In 1875 Caton first obtained evidence of a spontaneous electric⟨
activity originating in the brain of animals (Brazier, 1961a). T⟨
relation of this electrical activity to cerebral function was shown ⟨
the observation that sensory stimulation could alter the ongoi⟨
electrical activity. We can sense the excitement of this discove⟨
by the early pioneers armed with the crude instruments of their da⟨
Here was a possible means to correlate electrical activity to sensatio⟨
and, as it seemed to some, to thought. Using the more sensiti⟨
string galvanometer, Berger (1929) was able to demonstrate ele⟨
trical activity recorded from the human brain through the inta⟨
skull. Such activity was termed the *electroencephalogram* (*EE(*
This advance (first suspect then confirmed) opened the way to t⟨
use of the EEG in clinical medicine, and it produced an increas⟨
interest in the neuronal mechanisms of the brain underlying t⟨
electrical activity. Since the early 1930's continual advances

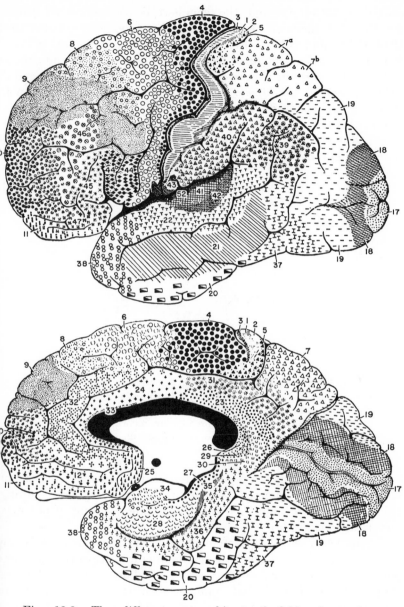

Fig. 18.8. The different cytoarchitectural fields shown by symbols and numbers. Upper drawing, lateral surface; lower drawing, medial surface; the black band seen in the medial surface is the corpus callosum—a thick tract of fibers connecting the two hemispheres. (Brodmann, 1909.)

electronic technique and the commercial production of reliabl
machines has made the EEG an everyday procedure (Jasper, 1941
1949; Gibbs and Gibbs, 1941; Cohn, 1949; Hill and Parr, 1963).

To record voltage changes from either the surface of the expose
cortex or through the skin over the head, electrodes are arranged fo
either *monopolar* or *bipolar* recording (Fig. 18.9). In monopola
recording one electrode (the *active lead*) is placed near the source o
electrical activity; the other lead (the indifferent one) is placed on th
ears, a site which is, electrically speaking, relatively distant from th
source of potential in the head. The active or *probe electrode* o

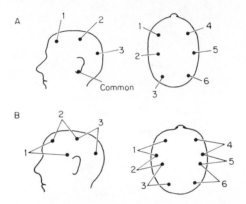

Fig. 18.9. A diagram of unipolar (A) electrode placements on the
human head is shown with each of the numbers connected to a
recording channel. The other lead is made to the ears as a
relatively indifferent site. For bipolar recording (B) the two
leads of each recording channel are placed on the surface of the
head.

the skull picks up the brain potential in its near vicinity. With bot
leads over active regions of the head (in the case of bipolar recording
the electrical record obtained is the algebraic resultant of potentia
under each electrode).

Figure 18.10 shows a sample of an EEG taken from a huma
subject. Irregular waves are predominant. However, at tim
portions of the record show a series of almost sinusoidal wave
Berger (1929) showed that humans with their eyes closed wei
most likely to give long trains of such regular waves at a frequenc
of 8–12 per second, and he referred to it as the *alpha rhythm*. Th
alpha rhythm is more prominent in the occipital region. Th
suggests that the alpha rhythm originates from the visual cortex. *
Berger first found, the alpha rhythm is rapidly interrupted (*alpl*

blocking) when the subject is asked to open his eyes (Fig. 18.11). However, the alpha rhythm is not necessarily related to the visual cortex. A less definite alpha rhythm is also found arising from other regions in the cortex. A difference in the degree of alpha rhythms in different individuals has been found. Besides visual stimulation, other stimuli can cause alpha blocking, and mental activity can give rise to alpha blocking as shown in Fig. 18.11 when the subject was

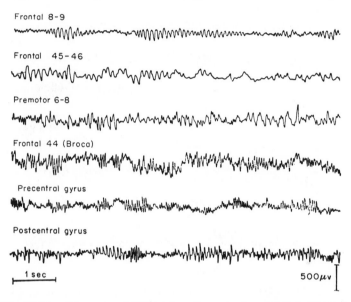

Frontal 8-9

Frontal 45-46

Premotor 6-8

Frontal 44 (Broca)

Precentral gyrus

Postcentral gyrus

1 sec   500μv

Fig. 18.10.   The normal EEG taken from various regions (frontal, premotor, precentral, postcentral) of the exposed human cortex. A pure beta rhythm is seen in the record from the precentral gyrus and a mixture of alpha and beta rhythms in the postcentral gyrus. (Jasper, 1949.)

asked to do an arithmetic problem. The relation of alpha blocking to consciousness and awareness of the environment will be further discussed in Chapters 20 and 25.

Waves of different frequencies ranging from 1–60 cps are present in the EEG (Gibbs, 1944). In addition to the fundamental alpha frequency of 8–12 cps, the frequencies are arbitrarily designated within certain ranges. The faster rhythms fall in the frequency range of 14–30 cps and are referred to as *beta* waves. The slow frequencies ranging from $\frac{1}{2}$–5 cps are referred to as *delta* waves. During sleep, shifts are seen in the frequency pattern of the EEG (Fig. 18.12). In the stage of 'early' or light sleep periods of the faster frequency components may be seen, these ranging around 20–24 cps ('asleep,' Fig. 18.12). Bursts of alpha waves at a frequency of 12 cps occur at random. In deeper sleep (bottom line, Fig. 18.12), large amplitude delta waves at a frequency of 3–4 cps are seen. They have a small amplitude, faster frequency wave superimposed on them. However, sleep is not a uniform state. At

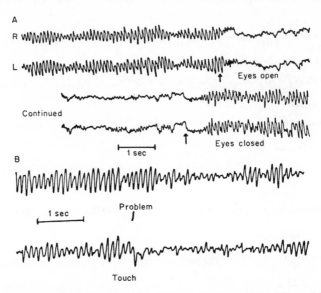

Fig. 18.11. EEG recorded simultaneously from right (R) and left (L) occipital poles of the human cerebrum. In A, on opening the eyes (arrow) the alpha rhythm is blocked and returns again soon after the eyes are closed again. In B a problem in mental arithmetic was given and a similar blocking of the EEG is seen to occur. In the lower trace a blocking occurs when the subject was touched. (From Jasper, in Penfield and Erickson, *Epilepsy and Cerebral Localization*, Thomas, 1941.)

intervals, a shift in the EEG pattern to a higher frequency and lowe amplitude occurs, which has been found to be associated wit dreaming. We shall discuss such periodic changes of the EEG durir sleep in Chapter 20.

Besides sleep, a number of physiological and biochemical alter tions are known to affect the EEG (Hill and Parr, 1963). Occl sion of the blood supply is followed by a rapid failure of the EE within approximately 15 seconds (Sugar and Gerard, 1938). Hype ventilation, which tends to reduce the partial pressure of CO_2, w cause a shift to lower frequencies and increase excitability. Th ocedure is used to bring out latent rhythmic disturbances (*vide fra*).

Barbiturates have an effect on the EEG pattern somewhat similar sleep.   After injection of a small dose of barbiturate, a higher equency, lower amplitude EEG was seen.   With higher doses lta waves of 3–4 cps were recorded (Brazier and Finesinger, 1945). utomatic frequency analysers have been used in an attempt

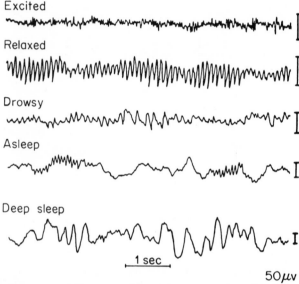

Excited

Relaxed

Drowsy

Asleep

Deep sleep

1 sec

50μv

Fig. 18.12.   In the alert subject the EEG as seen in the upper trace has a low amplitude, fast wave pattern.   In the relaxed state alpha waves appear.   During sleep runs of 14 per sec rhythms are found superimposed on the slow waves and termed 'sleep spindles.' (From Jasper, in Penfield and Erickson, *Epilepsy and Cerebral Localization*, Thomas, 1941.)

objectively examine the changes in the EEG under various rcumstances.   The principle of the frequency analyser is to rform a type of Fourier analysis by means of a series of filters hich respond to selected narrow portions of the frequency range of e EEG.   In recent years computer techniques have also been used an attempt to analyse the EEG (Brazier, 1961b).   An ultimate alysis of the EEG requires the knowledge of the neuronal mecha- sms of the cortex.

nchronization and pacemaker activity

ie apical dendrites passing up from cell bodies in the lower layers of e cortex branch profusely in the uppermost or molecular layer where they are found packed in greatest density (*vide supra*). It is this fact plus the vertical orientation of the pyramidal cells which is of special importance in understanding the electrical activity recorded from the cerebral cortex. The theory of electrical changes recorded from the surface is based on volume conductor principles applied to the vertical orientation of pyramidal cells (Fig. 18.13).

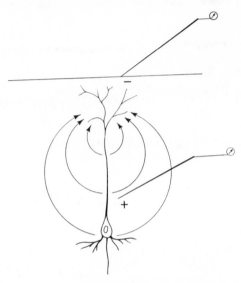

Fig. 18.13. In diagrammatic fashion a sink of activity is shown in the upper parts of the apical dendrites with current flowing from sources in the polarized parts of the rest of the pyramidal neuron. These currents in the volume conductor produce voltage differences between upper and lower parts of the cortex as shown by the probe electrodes present near the sink (−) and source (+).

As shown in this figure, a negative variation in the surface potential indicates a depolarization of the apical dendrites close to the surface According to volume conductor theory, current will flow from the polarized regions of the cells. In electrical terms these deeper parts act as current *sources* flowing into the depolarized *sink* region (cf Chapter 6). A depolarization present in the upper parts of the apical dendrites would result in a relatively large potential because of the great concentration of apical dendrites in the molecular layer so near the surface. A positive variation recorded by a surface electrode indicates a region of depolarization in deeper parts of the cortex with the apical dendrites near the surface acting as a source of current flowing to sinks in the cells deeper in the cortex.

A single cortical cell can give rise only to a small external current
nd a resulting small potential difference. Therefore, large numbers
f neurons must be synchronously active to give rise to the potentials
ecorded from the cerebral surface. The individual waves of the EEG
re of long durations (30–500 msec). How are these slow waves
roduced? They could be long-lasting depolarizations of the cell
nembranes, e.g. of the apical dendrites, or a summation of a number
f shorter duration responses which together appear as a longer wave
Bremer, 1958). In any event, a sufficiently large number of neurons
nust discharge together to give rise to cortical potentials. The
erm *synchronization* is used to describe the underlying process which
cts to bring a group of neurons into unified action. Synaptic
nterconnections between these cells are usually considered to
ring about synchronization (Burns, 1958) although electrical fields
ave been proposed as a possible mechanism (Gerard, 1941).

Besides the synchronization required for each wave of an EEG, the
eries of repeated waves suggests a rhythmic process and a *trigger* or
acemaker* mechanism which initiates such rhythmic action. By
neans of subpial knife cuts, 'chronic islands' of cortex may be
repared with all neuronal connections cut, but with the blood supply
om the surface pial vessels remaining intact (Kristiansen and
ourtois, 1949). Only a low level of EEG activity was found re-
naining in such islands. In the experience of Burns (1958), spon-
aneous EEG activity in an isolated island is rare and may be due to
mall unnoticed bridges of fiber connections bringing neuronal
ctivity into such an island. Though isolated islands of cortex may
ot show much spontaneous EEG activity, they have the ability to
espond rhythmically. This is shown by the rhythmic after-dis-
harges which can readily be elicited by means of single shocks. The
ference is that the various regions of the cortex although capable of
iving rise to rhythmic activity, require impulses transmitted to
hem from a pacemaker region to excite rhythmicity. Certain
egions in the thalamus appear to have this pacemaker function
Chapter 20.)

Direct cortical responses

The direct stimulation of the exposed cortex has been used to analyse
he nature of its electrical activity. Adrian (1936) first showed that
single brief electrical stimulation of the exposed cerebral cortex
ives rise to characteristic potential responses recorded via an
lectrode placed a few millimeters away. He called the surface
egative potential wave which was produced the *superficial response*.

A surface positive wave was seen when the cerebral cortex was stim
ulated below the surface, the *deep response*.   A variety of differen
types of cortical responses may be elicited by direct stimulation (*via
infra*).   All responses evoked by direct cortical stimulation will b
referred to as *direct cortical responses* (*DCRs*).   In this terminolog
the superficial response of Adrian is referred to as a *negative wav*
DCR.   This negative wave DCR is of especial interest; it i

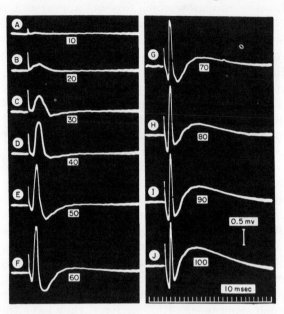

Fig. 18.14.   Negative wave direct cortical responses (dendritic
potentials) shown at successively increased stimulus strengths; the
duration is 20–30 msec.   The duration becomes shorter with
increased strengths of stimulation and a later second negative
wave of much longer duration appears as well.   (Chang, 1951.)

present in all regions of the cortex as a smooth slow wave lastin
10–20 msec (Fig. 18.14).   With increase in stimulus strength, i
increases to a maximum of several millivolts in amplitude.   Chan
(1951) called this negative wave DCR the *dendritic response*, consid
ering it to be a long-lasting action potential of the apical dendrite
Its lateral spread was considered to be due to a propagation in th
far-spreading branches of apical dendrites.   However, as pointed ou
by Burns (1951) and others, the lateral extension of apical dendrites i
probably much too small to account for the tangential spreads o
the response to 5 mm and more.   Eccles (1951) suggested that thi

rtical response is an excitatory postsynaptic potential (EPSP) of
1e apical dendrites excited by tangential axons in the molecular
yer. This interpretation has been followed by Purpura and
rundfest (1956). If this cortical response is a synaptic potential,
1en it should summate upon repetitive excitation as do the EPSPs
1 the motoneuron (Chapter 16). The long-lasting EEG waves
uld then be composed of 'units' of these synaptic potentials
1mming together (Bremer, 1958). However, temporal and spatio-

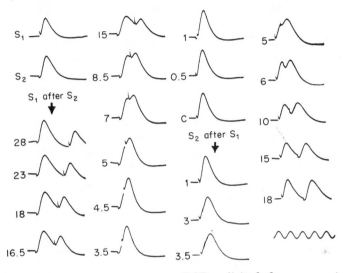

Fig. 18.15. The negative wave DCRs elicited from separate
stimulated sites S_1 and S_2 and recorded at an intermediate point.
The occlusive-like interaction of the responses is shown by
stimulation of S_1 at different times after that of S_2, the times
in msec given by the numbers at the left of each trace. Similar
interaction is seen with stimulation of S_2 at different times
after S_1. (Ochs and Booker, *Exptl. Neurol.*, **4**: 70, 1961.)

emporal interaction studies have not shown the summating behavior
expected of an EPSP mechanism (Ochs, 1962a). When two waves
were excited in close succession from two different points on the
cortex, the later-appearing response was diminished in amplitude
(Fig. 18.15). The amplitude gradually returned to its original
size at intervals between the two stimuli of 10–30 msec but even
longer depressed intervals are seen in such studies of the *excitability cycle*. In some respects the pattern is similar to the
occlusive interaction seen in other studies (Chapters 9, 14) where
a common element is excited to respond from each of two sources

of stimulation. Therefore, the response appears to act like a all-or-none action potential as Tasaki, Polley and Orrego (1954) ha previously concluded from their microelectrode studies. Burns an Grafstein (1952) suggested that the surface response is generate in axons passing tangentially in the outermost layer of the corte A transmission link in the outermost layer was also observed i experiments where layers below the uppermost one were cut and tran mission of the response still occurred (Ochs, 1962a). The occlusi interaction of the response however indicates that the response postsynaptic, i.e. it is generated in apical dendrites after a synaps The transmission of DCRs to greater lateral distances (Brooks an Enger, 1959) could be accomplished by cortico-cortical axor passing in the underlying white substance.

The type of DCR obtained will depend on the cortical regio stimulated and on the neuronal elements within the depths of cortical region (Adrian, 1936; Bishop and Clare, 1953). This w shown by the use of fine microelectrodes whereby a small populatio of neurons around the tip of the electrode is excited. Microelectrode were passed down into the cortex to stimulate at different deptl (Suzuki and Ochs, 1964). In sensory cortical regions (Chapter 21) number of different DCR patterns were obtained from the differer depths (Fig. 18.16). At the surface the usual negative wave DCR wa found. In the middle portions of the cortex a positive–negativ sequence was obtained similar in form to the specific cortical response to be discussed in Chapter 21.

Laminar recording of responses with microelectrodes inserted t various depths of the cortex shows that the negative wave DCR i localized in the upper layers of the cortex, consistent with its origi from the upper dendritic layers. Synaptic terminations on th upper reaches of the apical dendrites would, on usual consideration of electrotonic spread, be too small in amplitude at the initial seg ment of the cell and therefore ineffective. Some kind of activ propagation down to the initial segment seems to be required perhaps a mechanism similar to the decrementing type of conductio discussed by Lorente de Nó and Condouris (1959). The sam problem exists with regard to the synapses made on the remot dendritic branches of the spinal cord motoneurons (Chapter 12 where some kind of an active mechanism of spread is required t sufficiently depolarize the initial segment.

Where a positive–negative sequence of surface waves has bee excited, laminar recording reveals that in the middle layers o the responding site a negative slow wave is seen correspondin

phase with the surface positive wave. This result can be
terpreted on volume conductor principles with the neuronal
tivity in the deeper layers giving rise by electrical current flow
the surface positive phase of slow wave potential.

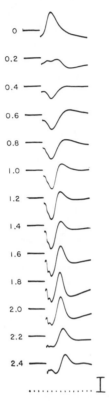

Fig. 18.16. A semi-microelectrode is used to stimulate the cerebral
cortex at various depths in millimeters indicated by the numbers
at the left of each trace. A simple negative wave DCR is excited
from the surface; a positive–negative sequence of waves in the
middle depths of the cortex. Time intervals 2 msec, amplitude
2 mv. (Suzuki and Ochs, 1964.)

Transcallosal responses

Electrical stimulation of one site on the cortex can excite distant
sites via the tracts of fibers in the underlying white matter. This
occurs also with respect to the large bundle of fibers, the *corpus
callosum*, connecting corresponding regions of the two hemispheres.

Curtis (1940) showed that on stimulation of one hemisphere th homologous site on the other hemisphere gave rise to a positive negative sequence of slow waves (Fig. 18.17). At first it was believe that the positive phase of potential represented afferent activity in th corpus callosum fibers followed after a synapse by the negative pan of the response in apical dendrites. However, small spike-like dis charges are found at the onset of the slow waves (Peacock, 1957 These spike-like waves are most likely the electrical sign of activity i the callosal fibers. The two slow wave components are both post synaptic, and represent the separate terminations of different fiber

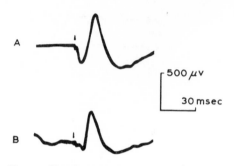

Fig. 18.17. Transcallosal response in absence of concurrent spontaneous activity (A) has a large preceding positive phase followed by the negative part of the response. When spontaneous activity is greater the positive phase is smaller in amplitude (B). (Grafstein, 1959.)

on different groups of cells giving rise to the positive–negativ sequence (Grafstein, 1959). The negative wave most likely i generated in the apical dendrites and the surface positive phase du to depolarization deeper in the cortex. The terminations of thes transcallosal fibers are, as indicated by Grafstein, as yet unresolved

Convulsive waves

An insight into the mechanism of synchronization is afforded by th abnormal synchronization seen in *convulsive spike* discharges Many years ago Jackson (1875) surmised that the fearful moto display of a *Grand Mal* epileptic seizure was caused by an exaggerated synchronous discharge of cortical neurons. During an attack th epileptic in the *tonic stage* will show a rigid extension of the legs and flexed arms. The rigidity is somewhat like decerebrate rigidity This is followed by a number of repeated jerks of the limbs in th *onic phase.* Jackson's hypothesis has been thoroughly verified by means of EEG recording (Penfield and Jasper, 1954). An EEG taken during a Grand Mal epileptic attack (Fig. 18.18) shows a rythmic series of high voltage spike discharges widely distributed in the cortex. Such abnormal synchronization sweeps a large number of neurons into this exaggerated kind of activity and prevents their normal differentiated activity.

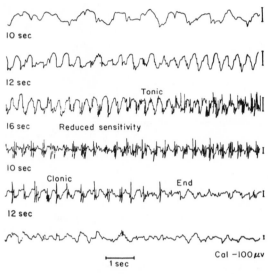

Fig. 18.18. The gradual onset of a convulsive seizure is seen in the upper records. The patient was in a coma and slow delta waves were recorded. Then an increase in frequency develops into the high voltage spike-like activity of the convulsive discharge. After the seizure the record returned to the slow delta wave form. (Penfield and Jasper, 1954.)

In another type of convulsive discharge known as *Petit Mal*, a series of synchronized 'spike and dome' waves are found in all parts of the cortex (Fig. 18.19). This is associated with loss of consciousness with very little motor involvement. The behavioral signs of an epileptic (ictal) attack are determined by the location of the abnormal synchronous activity in the brain. In the case of Petit Mal a pathological 'over-driving' from the thalamus is implicated (Chapter 20). In other types of convulsions, a more restricted brain involvement occurs and the functional changes are determined by the area of involvement. *Temporal lobe* epilepsy for example is associated with peculiar emotional and behavioral changes (Chapter 24) with apparently normal motor behavior otherwise. If a tumor is present in a region of the brain outside a motor or sensory area there may be little evidence of brain malfunction except for the abnormally large convulsive spikes present in

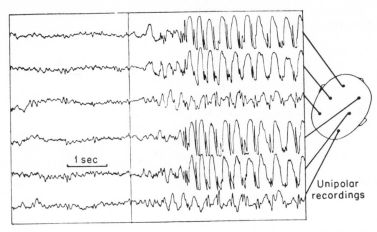

Fig. 18.19.   Recordings taken from various regions on the head shows the change of the EEG into the widespread spike and dome discharge of a Petit Mal convulsion.   (Brazier, *The Electrical Activity of the Nervous System.*   2nd Ed., Pitman, 1960.)

the EEG (Fig. 18.20). These convulsive wave discharges may be located by means of their electrical polarity. With a probe electrode placed close to the spike, the convulsive spike deflection is negative (sink). Further away the electrode records a positive (source) deflection. This method of searching with probe electrodes over the surface of the head is used to locate a tumor prior to surgery.

In an analysis of convulsive wave phenomena the following factors must be considered: (a) the source of the abnormal synchronization giving rise to the individual convulsive waves, (b) the triggering of trains of such waves, and (c) the spread of activity to other regions (Ajmone-Marsan, 1961). These aspects of convulsive wave activity can be experimentally studied.

When placed directly on the exposed surface of the cortex a number of pharmacological substances can elicit convulsive wave discharges. Strychnine has been classically used for this purpose. A series of mainly negative wave discharges appear, each wave of the group lasting 30–60 msec. The relatively large amplitude of these

pikes, of 2–6 mv, indicates that a large number of cells are syn-
hronized into each wave. The convulsive activity excited by
trychnine is not peculiar to this alkaloid. Other substances such as
netrazol, picrotoxin, acetylcholine in high concentration, mescaline,
▸enicillin, etc., can excite a similar convulsive discharge.

The convulsive agent appears to diffuse down into the cortex and
ensitize some neuronal 'aggregate' deeper in the cortex which

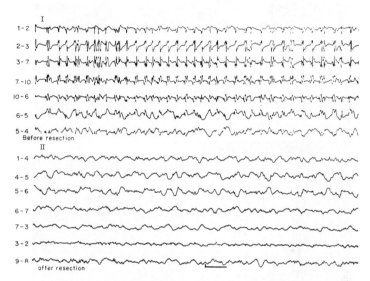

Fig. 18.20. Rhythmic convulsive spike discharges seen in the
upper group of EEG records (I) are most pronounced in leads
2–3, 3–7 and 7–10. After resection of the epileptic focus, a
more normal EEG pattern found in all leads as shown in the lower
group of traces (II). Calibration 1 sec; 50 uv. (Walker, *Electroenceph. Clin. Neurophysiol.* Suppl. 2: 30, 1949.)

▸ecomes hypersynchronized and then fires the response in other cells.
Microelectrode studies of single-cell discharge taken from cells in a
hronic epileptic focus (produced by injection of alumina cream into
he cortex) revealed a wide diversity of augmented neural discharges
Ward, 1961). Figure 18.21 shows an example of a spontaneous burst
▸f high frequency discharges of a single cell at the convulsive site.
Waxing and waning in the frequency of cell discharge is seen with
▸eriods of intense discharge during the active 'tonic phase' followed
▸y intermittent bursts during the 'clonic phase.'
Convulsive activity can also be elicited by intense electrical

stimulation directly applied to the cortex (*vide infra*).   During th
convulsive after-discharge, microelectrode recording of single-cel
activity has shown an increasing rate of discharge rising to a high
level during the tonic phase (Ajmone-Marsan, 1961).   This is followed

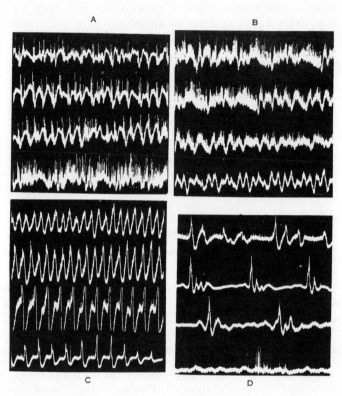

Fig. 18.21.   Microelectrode records taken from a cortical neuron
in an epileptogenic area shows (A) an increased spike discharge
along with slow waves during the onset of seizure.   Spikes appear
(B) with higher frequency.   Slow potentials increase (C) during
the tonic phase and merge into the clonic phase (D).   (Schmidt,
Thomas and Ward, *J. Neurophysiol.* **22**: 285, 1959.)

by intermittent activity in the clonic phase.   Ajmone-Marsan ha
pointed out that in his experience practically all neurons sampled
were found to be firing during convulsive activity.

It has been possible to record intracellularly from neurons in an
area sensitized by strychnine.   Convulsive activity in the neuron i
shown by high frequency bursts of spikes with a sustained level o
depolarization (Fig. 18.22).   In the period between repetitive spik

ring the membrane potential returns toward its usual value.   Small
uctuations of membrane potential present at this time suggest
ontinued synaptic bombardment from other cells or spontaneous
ariations of membrane potential.   In Ward's (1961) interpretation,
he critical step leading to epileptic discharge is a persistent
epolarization of the apical dendrites.   This causes flow of currents
cting on the rest of the cell to excite repetitive discharges.

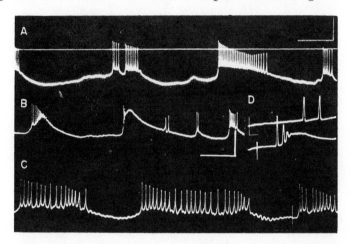

Fig.   18.22.   Intracellular   microelectrode   recording   from   a
neuron in a strychnine-treated region shows repetitive grouped
discharges.   Slow changes in the polarization level are seen associated with rhythmic bursts when depolarization reaches a critical
level.   A, 10 min after strychnization; B, 15 min; C, 40 min; D, 40
min afterwards.   In D a faster time sweep was used to show the
details of the spike.   Time calibration A and B, 250 msec; C, 20
msec; D, 5 msec.   Vertical line, 50 mv.   (Li, 1959.)

If a region is treated with a convulsive agent, electrical stimulation
nearby will give rise to large *driven convulsive waves* (Fig. 18.23).
Large convulsive spikes of constant amplitude driven at different
trengths of stimulation suggest that the convulsive wave is an
all-or-none' type of discharge.   An epileptic aggregate of cells
eep in the cortex could, by fibers which synapse on apical dendrites,
ive rise to the convulsive spike.   However, at present the organiza-
ion of this neuronal aggregate is unknown.
    The factors which control spread of activity from convulsive
ggregates to other regions causing convulsive wave activity appear
o be complex.   The topical application of strychnine to the
ortex not only gives rise to the large local strychnine spikes

which were referred to, but also to spike discharges in other cortical regions to which efferent fibers from the convulsive site project By methodically searching surrounding cortical areas after strych nizing one small cortical region, such cortical projections wer mapped out. Using this method of *strychnine neuronography*, th connections made between a number of cortical regions, some a great distances from the site of application, were determined. B

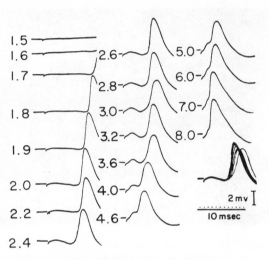

Fig. 18.23.   Single electrical pulses used to stimulate the cortex treated with a convulsant agent (mescaline) will trigger con- vulsive spikes. These have different latencies at the different relative strengths indicated by the numbers, but similar amplitudes. The negative wave DCRs preceding them are relatively small in size. Calibration 10 msec and 2 mv. (Ochs, Dowell and Russell, *Electroenceph. Clin. Neurophysiol.* **14:** 878, 1962.)

destroying the cortex between the excited site and the respondin site, the spread was shown to occur via the underlying cortico cortical axons connecting one area to another (McCulloch, 1944).

As has been mentioned, convulsive activity can also occur as result of direct tetanic stimulation of the cortex. Following a perio of tetanic stimulation a longer or shorter period of *after-discharg* consisting of a train of high voltage, fast frequency, convulsiv waves is found which can propagate in the cortex (Fig. 18.24).

An area receiving bombardment of activity from an epilepti area will after several hours or days in turn become epilepti (Morrell, 1961). Such *secondary foci* of epilepsy develop at th peripheral regions of an epileptic focus as is shown by continuation of epileptic activity there after the primary region is removed. A focus in one hemisphere by transmitting impulses to a homologous area on the contralateral hemisphere via callosal fibers for several days will also eventually cause that region to become a *mirror focus* of epileptic activity.

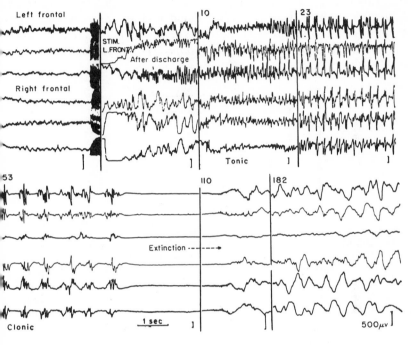

Fig. 18.24. Following intense electrical stimulation (left frontal cortex) a high voltage spike-like discharge of the EEG develops, the after-discharge. Then later a generalized seizure occurs. At the end of the convulsive discharge there is a period of depressed activity (extinction) before return of EEG activity. Time after stimulation indicated by numbers (10 sec, 23 sec, 53 sec, 110 sec, 182 sec). (Penfield and Jasper, 1954.)

Steady potential and electrical impedance of the cortex

The hypothesis of a relation between the polarization state of the cortex and apical dendritic function was developed with regard to the *steady potential* (*SP*) level of the cortex (Libet and Gerard, 1941; Gerard, 1941). One electrode was placed on the surface and the other electrode sub-cortically in the ventricle. A transcortical potential of several millivolts was measured between these electrodes with

the surface negative in polarity to the ventricle. The transcortical
potential was presumed due to a constant difference of potential
between the apical dendrites and the rest of the cell. The relation
of the SP to activity of the apical dendrites was supported by
O'Leary and Goldring (1964) who reviewed the effects of a variety of
different conditions which change neuronal activity and shift the SP
(cf. Libet and Gerard, 1962). A marked change is seen in the SP
following asphyxiation (van Harreveld and Stamm, 1953a). After
a latency of 2–5 minutes, the surface of the cortex becomes negative
in potential (Fig. 18.25). This *asphyxial potential* most likely

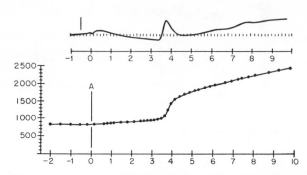

Fig. 18.25.   After onset of asphyxiation (A) there is a latent period
lasting several minutes and then as shown in the upper trace a
depolarization of the cortex.   During the depolarization a rapid
increase in the electrical impedance (resistivity) of the cortex
takes place as shown in the lower trace.   Impedance calibration
in ohms.   Voltage calibration, upper trace, 5 mv.   Time in
minutes.   (van Harreveld and Ochs, 1957.)

represents a greater sensitivity of the apical dendrites with respect to
other parts of the pyramidal cell to asphyxiation.   It is the loss of
normal semipermeable properties of the membranes of the apical
dendrites which gives rise to the surface negative swing (van
Harreveld and Ochs, 1956).   The negative wave DCR shows a slow
decline in amplitude during the latent period and after the asphyxial
change it can no longer be excited.   This is to be expected if the
negative wave DCR is an active response of the apical dendrites.
The connection of the SP level of polarization of these membranes to
their active responses is shown by the change of the amplitude of the
negative wave DCR with changes in the steady potential of the cortex
If the surface is depolarized by an applied current, the amplitude of
the negative wave DCR is decreased; if hyperpolarized, it is increased
(Caspers, 1959).

A marked increase in electrical impedance (resistivity) of the ortex is associated with the negative swing of the asphyxial potential Fig. 18.25). Electrical impedance measurement of the cortex is ssentially a measurement of the size of the extracellular space. This was shown for cell suspensions using an a.c. bridge technique o determine the volume concentration of the cells (Cole and Curtis, 944). At the relatively low frequency of 1000 cps the electrical mpedance of cell membranes is high and most of the measuring urrent passes between the cells. Application of this technique to ortex suggested an extracellular space amounting to approximately !5% of the cortical volume (van Harreveld and Ochs, 1956; van Iarreveld, Murphy and Nobel, 1963). This space is much larger han appears in electron micrographs. A discussion of the size of he extracellular space will be given in Chapter 19 where support for he larger value will be presented. The large *increase* of resistivity luring the asphyxial change was related to a movement of Na^+ and Cl$^-$ from the extracellular space into the cells, thereby decreasing the onductance which is determined by the electrolytes of the extra- ellular compartment. This interpretation was supported by an ncreased content of Cl^- present inside apical dendrites after the sphyxial change has occurred (van Harreveld and Schadé, 1959). The entrance of Cl^- into the apical dendrites indicates that the normal membrane permeability has been altered by the asphyxiation. Sodium ions present in the extracellular compartment will pre- umably also enter the cells as will water, as shown by a swelling of the pical dendrites in the asphyxiated cortex (van Harreveld, 1962).

Maturation of dendrites and dendritic function

The relation of dendrites to the cortical potentials is suggested by study of newborn rats, rabbits and cats. In these species the levelopment of apical dendrites is incomplete and during the first ew weeks of life the apical dendrites ramify and grow to their full ength and branch development. This ontological development is shown in a–e of Fig. 18.4. A 20-day maturation period is typical for he rat (Eayrs and Goodhead, 1960). Until the apical dendrites levelop in the first 15 days of life, the steady potential level of the ortex does not reach the usual levels typical of the adult (Bureš, 1957). There are differences in the time of maturation between he various species; for the rabbit the adult pattern is seen in 32–40 days. The EEG of the rabbit shows only high frequency, low mplitude waves with many silent periods early in maturation, at 8 to 10 days (Schadé, 1959). Higher amplitude waves of lower frequency and the adult pattern emerges at 10 to 1⅓ days. Superficial cortical responses (negative wave DCRs) can be obtained soon after birth. These responses, however, have a much longer duration (50–80 msec), and in the succeeding weeks the responses shorten to the 10–20 msec duration typical of the adult (Purpura, Carmichael and Housepian, 1960). Presumably these long-duration cortical responses do not require the development of the mechanisms giving rise to EEG rhythm and arise from the small-sized dendrites present at birth. Bishop (1950) had also found long-duration strychnine spike discharges present in the cortex of the newborn rabbit. The spikes gradually shorten in duration during the next few weeks of maturation.

The guinea pig offers a convenient check on the relation between dendrites and cortical function. In this species the apical dendrites increase to adult size *in utero*, at 40–50 days of gestation. Birth occurs at 66 days (Flexner, 1955). In this species an EEG of adult type is seen before birth at 40–50 days (Jasper, Bridgeman and Carmichael, 1937).

Spreading depression

Certain cortical regions termed *suppressor strips* were believed to have a special inhibitory function. Stimulation of these strip regions caused a decrease of activity in other areas for prolonged periods lasting one-half hour or more (Fulton, 1949). These suppressor strip actions are now considered to have been manifestations of a more generalized depressive condition known as *spreading depression* (*SD*) (Sloan and Jasper, 1950; Marshall, 1959; Ochs, 1962b). Spreading depression discovered by Leão (1944) occurs as a slow-moving wave of depression moving outward from its site of evocation at the rate of only 2–5 mm/min. Practically any stimulus which can strongly excite a population of neurons can excite SD—a burst of repetitive stimulation, d.c. current, application of KCl or mechanical stimulation. A more specific excitation is afforded by the use of metabolically active substances as shown by the studies of van Harreveld (1959) and Bureš, Burešová and Křivánek (1960). After it is initiated the wave of SD successively invades one area after another, the EEG is decreased and then there is a gradual recovery, starting in the region first depressed (Fig. 18.26).

Several indices of apical dendrite function show profound changes when a cortical area is occupied by SD. A large negative variation in the steady potential of the cortex takes place, indicating depolari zation of surface apical dendrites (Fig. 18.27).   This steady potential variation lasts 1–2 minutes and at this time an increase in electrical impedance is found present.   Freygang and Landau (1955) found the increase in impedance during SD to be slightly greater in the upper layers of the cortex.   The impedance increase appears to be due to

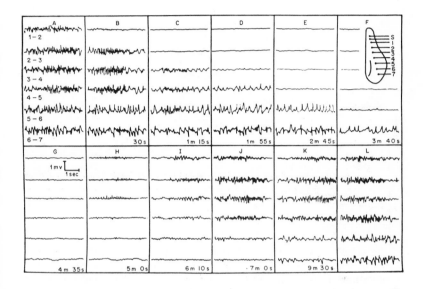

Fig. 18.26.   A series of electrodes along the cortical surface of the rabbit shown in column F from which the corresponding EEG traces are numbered.   Following a period of stimulation (S on diagram of the frontal pole), a decrease in EEG activity is seen to occur in the leads closest to the stimulus in column B and then at the times in minutes and seconds shown in the following columns C–K.   The spreading depression of EEG activity occurs successively in the leads connected to the next most posterior cortical region, etc.   A return of EEG activity then also takes place successively, first in the anterior and then in the posterior regions to resume the normal pattern in L.   (Leão, 1944.)

the movement of ions and water from the intercellular space of the cortex into apical dendrites (van Harreveld and Ochs, 1957; van Harreveld and Schadé, 1959).   This shift is smaller but similar to the movement of ions and water discussed with regard to the asphyxial change.   Recovery occurs after some scores of minutes, this recovery requiring expenditure of metabolic activity (Chapter 19).

That SD moves wholly within the cortex was shown when under-cutting connections to sub-cortical nuclei did not prevent its propagation. In the molecular layer the apical dendrites are dense and closely interdigitated, and shallow cuts through this layer can temporarily block transmission of SD. Conversely, all layers below the first can be cut and transmission of SD may occur in the remaining

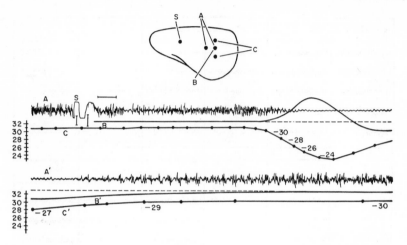

Fig. 18.27. When spreading depression propagates into a region of the cortex, the EEG becomes depressed as shown in the upper recording trace (A). The steady potential (B) shown by the continuous line becomes negative and then returns after a smaller but longer-lasting positive phase. The electrical conductivity (C) of the cerebrum (dotted continuous line) decreases and then gradually returns back to its original level in the continuation of the traces A', B', C'. Upper diagram shows placement of electrodes. (From van Harreveld and Ochs, 1957.)

molecular layer (Ochs, 1962b). Possibly the release of potassium (Grafstein, 1956) or glutamic acid (van Harreveld, 1959) from affected apical dendrites to nearby or contiguous dendrites is the agent of transmission. The mechanism envisioned is that when the permeability of the affected cells increases, some intracellular materials are released into the surrounding intercellular space to act on nearby cells. There is a high content of glutamic acid present in the cortex, most likely intracellular (Chapter 19). This and the low amount of glutamic acid which can excite SDs suggests that this substance may be the agent involved.

The non-specific nature of SD is indicated by the fact that it is excited in neuronal regions other than the cortex as, for example, in

the hippocampus, avian brain, frog retina, etc.   Species differences
are important.   SD is easier to excite in the rat or rabbit, but only by
use of facilitatory procedures can it be regularly obtained in the cat
and in primates (Marshall, 1959).   Some evidence suggests that it
may also occur in man in some convulsive disorders.

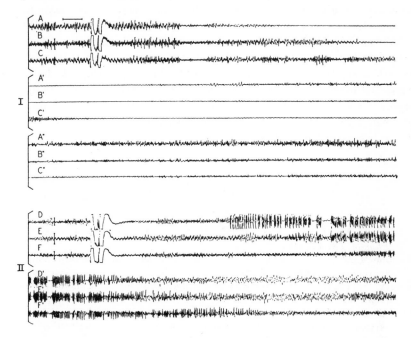

Fig. 18.28.   The EEG recorded at 3 stations along the cortex,
A, B, C, and records continued in traces A′, B′, C′, and later in
A″, B″ and C″.   After stimulation a spreading depression is
excited (I) and then gradual recovery occurs.   The EEG recorded
in stations D, E, F, and its continuation D′, E′, F′ shows (II) after
pre-treatment with acetylcholine, a similar successive spread of
convulsive wave activity.   (van Harreveld and Stamm, 1953b.)

Complete depression of cortical activity does not always occur as
suggested by the term SD.   A few bursts of large convulsive-like
spikes are often found during SD, and under certain conditions (e.g.
administration of CO_2) trains of spike discharges resembling convulsive wave discharges may be produced (van Harreveld and
Stamm, 1953b).   These *spreading convulsions* move in the cortex at
the same slow rate as SD, involving successive contiguous areas
(Fig. 18.28) and giving rise to the same SP and impedance changes.
It is possible that convulsions originate in the deeper layers of the

cortex when an inhibiting mechanism present in the upper layers is removed.

The connection of SD with changes in the state of apical dendrites was shown in the newborn rabbit (Schadé, 1959). As previously noted, the maturation period in this species is 32–40 days. The capacity to give rise to SDs develops between 24–30 days after birth. In the rat where maturation takes place sooner, Bureš (1957) could obtain SD in 15- and 20-day old animals. It is of interest that spreading convulsions were more commonly seen in Schadé's study in the immature cortex before 30 days than later when the mature pattern developed. At the earlier stages the upper layers were not fully developed and possibly these include the hypothetical mechanisms which act to suppress convulsions in the lower layers of the cortex.

REFERENCES

Adrian, E. D. (1936). The spread of activity in the cerebral cortex. *J. Physiol.* **88**: 127–161.

Ajmone-Marsan, C. (1961). Electrographic aspects of epileptic neuronal aggregates. *Epilepsia* **2**: 22–38.

Berger, H. (1929). Ueber das Elektrenkephalogram des Menschen. I. *Arch. Psychiat. Nevenkr.* **87**: 527–570.

Bishop, E. J. (1950). The strychnine spike as a physiological indicator of cortical maturity in the postnatal rabbit. *Electroencephalog. Clin. Neurophysiol.* **2**: 309–315.

Bishop, G. H. and Clare, M. H. (1953). Responses of cortex to direct electrical stimuli applied at different depths. *J. Neurophysiol.* **16**: 1–19.

Boycott, B. B., Gray, E. G. and Guillery, R. W. (1961). Synaptic structure and its alteration with environment temperature: a study by light and electron microscopy in the central nervous system of lizards. *Proc. Roy. Soc. B.* **154**: 151–172.

Brazier, M. A. B. (1961a). *A History of the Electrical Activity of the Brain. The First Half-Century.* Pitman Medical Publishing Co., London.

Brazier, M. A. B. (1961b) (Editor). Computer techniques in EEG analysis. *Electroencephalog. Clin. Neurophysiol. Suppl.* **20**. Elsevier, New York.

Brazier, M. A. B. and Finesinger, J. E. (1945). Action of barbiturates on the cerebral cortex. *Arch. Neurol. Psychiat.* **53**: 51–58.

Bremer, F. (1958). Cerebral and cerebellar potentials. *Physiol. Rev.* **38**: 357–388.

Brodmann, K. (1909). *Vergleichende Lokalisationslehre der Grosshirnrinde in ihren Prinzipien dergestellt auf Grund des Zellenbanes.* Reprinted 1925. Barth, Leipzig.

Brooks, V. B. and Enger, P. S. (1959). Spread of directly evoked responses in the cat's cerebral cortex. *J. Gen. Physiol.* **42**: 761–777.

Bureš, J. (1957).   The ontogenetic development of steady potential differences in the cerebral cortex in animals.   *Electroencephalog. Clin. Neurophysiol.* **9**: 121–130.

Bureš, J., Burešová, O. and Křivánek, J. (1960).   Some metabolic aspects of Leão's spreading cortical depression.   *Structure and Function of the Cerebral Cortex.*   Edited by D. B. Tower and J. P. Schadé.   Elsevier, New York.

Burns, B. D. (1951).   Some properties of the cat's isolated cerebral cortex. *J. Physiol.* **111**: 50–68.

Burns, B. D. (1958).   *The Mammalian Cerebral Cortex.*   Arnold, London.

Burns, B. D. and Grafstein, B. (1952).   The function and structure of some neurons in the cat's cerebral cortex.   *J. Physiol.* **118**: 412–433.

Caspers, H. (1959).   Über die Beziehungen zwischen Dendritenpotential und Gleichspannung an der Hirnrinde.   *Pflüg. Arch. Ges. Physiol.* **269**: 157–181.

Chang, H.-T. (1951).   Dendritic potential of cortical neurons produced by direct electrical stimulation of the cerebral cortex.   *J. Neurophysiol.* **14**: 1–23.

Cohn, R. (1949).   *Clinical Electroencephalography.*   McGraw-Hill, New York.

Cole, K. S. and Curtis, H. J. (1944).   Electrical physiology: electrical resistance and impedance of cells and tissues.   *Medical Physics.*   Edited by O. Glasser.   Year Book Publishing Co., Chicago.

Curtis, H. J. (1940).   An analysis of cortical potentials mediated by the corpus callosum.   *J. Neurophysiol.* **8**: 457–464.

Eayrs, J. T. and Goodhead, B. (1959).   Postnatal development of the cerebral cortex in the rat.   *J. Anat.* **93**: 385–402.

Eccles, J. C. (1951).   Interpretation of action potentials evoked in the cerebral cortex.   *Electroencephalog. Clin. Neurophysiol.* **3**: 449–464.

Flexner, L. B. (1955).   Events associated with the development of nerve and hepatic cells.   *Ann. N.Y. Acad. Sci.* **60**: 986–1001.

Freygang, W. H., Jr. and Landau, W. M. (1955).   Some relations between resistivity and electrical activity in the cerebral cortex of the cat.   *J. Cell. Comp. Physiol.* **45**: 377–392.

Fulton, J. F. (1949).   *Physiology of the Nervous System.*   3rd Edition. Oxford University Press, New York.

Gerard, R. W. (1941).   The interaction of neurons.   *Ohio J. Sci.* **41**: 160–172.

Gibbs, F. A. (1944).   Electroencephalography.   *Medical Physics.*   Edited by O. Glasser.   Pp. 361–371.   Year Book Publishing Co., Chicago.

Gibbs, F. A. and Gibbs, E. L. (1941).   *Atlas of Electroencephalography.* Cummings, Cambridge.

Grafstein, B. (1956).   Mechanism of spreading cortical depression.   *J. Neurophysiol.* **19**: 154–171.

Grafstein, B. (1959).   Organization of callosal connections in suprasylvian gyrus of cat.   *J. Neurophysiol.* **22**: 504–515.

Gray, E. G. (1959).   Axosomatic and axodendritic synapses of the cerebral cortex: an electron microscopic study.   *J. Anat.* **93**: 420–433.

Gray, E. G. and Guillery, R. W. (1961).   The basis for silver staining of synapses of the mammalian spinal cord; a light and electron microscope study.   *J. Physiol.* **157**: 581–588.

Hill, D. and Parr, G. (1963) (Editors).   *Electroencephalography.*   2nd Ed. MacDonald, London.

Jackson, J. H. (1875). On epilepsy and epileptiform convulsions. (Reprinted in *Selected Writings of John Hughling Jackson.* Vol. 1. 1931.) Hodder and Stoughton, London.

Jasper, H. H.(1941). Electroencephalography. *Epilepsy and Cerebral Localization.* Edited by W. Penfield and T. C. Erickson. Chapter 14. Charles C. Thomas, Springfield.

Jasper, H. H. (1949). Electroencephalography in man. *Electroencephalog. Clin. Neurophysiol. Suppl.* **2**: 16–29.

Jasper, H. H., Bridgeman, C. S. and Carmichael, L. (1937). An ontogenetic study of cerebral electrical potentials in the guinea pig. *J. Exptl. Psychol.* **21**: 63–71.

Kristiansen, K. and Courtois, B. (1949). Rhythmic electric activity from isolated cerebral cortex. *Electroencephalog. Clin. Neurophysiol.* **1**: 265–272.

Leão, A. A. P. (1944). Spreading depression of activity in the cerebral cortex. *J. Neurophysiol.* **7**: 359–390.

Li, C.-L. (1959). Cortical intracellular potentials and their responses to strychnine. *J. Neurophysiol.* **22**: 436–450.

Libet, B. and Gerard, R. W. (1941). Steady potential fields and neurone activity. *J. Neurophysiol.* **4**: 438–455.

Libet, B. and Gerard, R. W. (1962). An analysis of some correlates of steady potentials in mammalian cerebral cortex. *Electroencephalog. Clin. Neurophysiol.* **14**: 445–452.

Lorente de Nó, R. (1949). *Physiology of the Nervous System.* 3rd Ed., Edited by J. F. Fulton. Pp. 288–330. Oxford University Press, New York.

Lorente de Nó, R. and Condouris, G. A. (1959). Decremental conduction in peripheral nerve. Integration of stimuli in the neuron. *Proc. Natl. Acad. Sci. U.S.* **45**: 592–617.

Marshall, W. H. (1959). Spreading cortical depression of Leão. *Physiol. Rev.* **39**: 239–279.

McCulloch, W. S. (1944). Cortico-cortical connections. *The Precentral Motor Cortex.* Edited by P. C. Bucy. Chapter 8. University of Illinois Press, Urbana.

Morrell, F. (1961). Lasting changes in synaptic organization produced by continuous neuronal bombardment. *Brain Mechanisms and Learning.* Edited by A. Fessard, R. W. Gerard and J. Konorski. Pp. 375–392. Thomas, Springfield.

Ochs, S. (1962a). Analysis of cellular mechanisms of direct cortical responses. *Federation Proc.* **21**: 641–647.

Ochs, S. (1962b). The nature of spreading depression in neural networks. *Intern. Rev. Neurobiol.* **4**: 1–69.

O'Leary, J. L. and Goldring, S. (1964). D-C potentials in the brain. *Physiol. Rev.* **44**: 91–125.

Peacock, S. M., Jr. (1957). Activity of anterior suprasylvian gyrus in response to transcallosal afferent volleys. *J. Neurophysiol.* **20**: 140–155.

Penfield, W. and Jasper, H. (1954). *Epilepsy and the Functional Anatomy of the Human Brain.* Little, Brown and Co., Boston.

Purpura, D. P., Carmichael, M. W. and Housepian, E. M. (1960). Physiological and anatomical studies of development of superficial axodendritic synapse pathways in neocortex. *Exptl. Neurol.* **2**: 324–347.

Purpura, D. P. and Grundfest, H. (1956). Nature of dendritic potentials and synaptic mechanisms in cerebral cortex of cat. *J. Neurophysiol.* **19**: 573–595.

Ramón y Cajal, S. (1911). *Histologie du Système Nerveux de l'Homme et des Vertébrés.* Maloine, Paris (Republ. 1955). Instituto Ramón y Cajal, Madrid.

Schadé, J. P. (1959). Maturational aspects of EEG and of spreading depression in rabbit. *J. Neurophysiol.* **22**: 245–257.

Sholl, D. A. (1956). *The Organization of the Cerebral Cortex.* John Wiley and Sons, New York.

Sloan, N. and Jasper, H. (1950). The identity of spreading depression and 'suppression.' *Electroencephalog. Clin. Neurophysiol.* **2**: 59–78.

Sugar, O. and Gerard, R. W. (1938). Anoxia and brain potentials. *J. Neurophysiol.* **1**: 558–572.

Suzuki, H. and Ochs, S. (1964). Laminar stimulation for direct cortical responses from intact and chronically isolated cortex. *Electroencephalog. Clin. Neurophysiol.* **17**: 405–413.

Tasaki, I., Polley, E. H. and Orrego, F. (1954). Action potentials from individual elements in cat geniculate and striate cortex. *J. Neurophysiol.* **17**: 454–474.

van Harreveld, A. (1957). Changes in volume of cortical neuronal elements during asphyxiation. *Am. J. Physiol.* **191**: 233–242.

van Harreveld, A. (1959). Compounds in brain extracts causing spreading depression of cerebral cortical activity and contraction of crustacean muscle. *J. Neurochem.* **3**: 300–315.

van Harreveld, A., (1962). Water and electrolyte distribution in central nervous tissue. *Federation Proc.* **21**, 659–664.

van Harreveld, A., Murphy, T. and Nobel, K. W. (1963). Specific impedance of rabbits cortical tissue. *Am. J. Physiol.* **205**: 203–207.

van Harreveld, A. and Ochs, S. (1956). Cerebral impedance changes after circulatory arrest. *Am. J. Physiol.* **187**: 180–192.

van Harreveld, A. and Ochs, S. (1957). Electrical and vascular concomitants of spreading depression. *Am. J. Physiol.* **189**: 159–166.

van Harreveld, A. and Schadé, J. P. (1959). Chloride movements in cerebral cortex after circulatory arrest and during spreading depression. *J. Cell. Comp. Physiol.* **54**: 65–84.

van Harreveld, A. and Stamm, J. S. (1953a). Cerebral asphyxiation and spreading cortical depression. *Am. J. Physiol.* **173**: 171–175.

van Harreveld, A. and Stamm, J. S. (1953b). Spreading cortical convulsions and depressions. *J. Neurophysiol.* **16**: 352–366.

Ward, A. A., Jr. (1961). Epilepsy. *Intern. Rev. Neurobiol.* **3**: 137–186.

Whittaker, V. P. and Gray, E. G. (1962). The synapse: biology and morphology. *Brit. Med. Bull.* **18**: 223–228.

19

Metabolism of the Central Nervous System

Within the last few decades a greatly expanded interest in the biochemistry of the nervous system has established the discipline of neurochemistry (Richter, 1957; McIlwain, 1959; Quastel and Quastel, 1961; Elliot, Page and Quastel, 1962). Only a few aspects can be discussed here and emphasis will be placed on the cerebral cortex. As will be seen, the main source of energy is oxidative metabolism and this is relatively high in the brain. More recently the importance of particular amino acids and amines has been recognized with regard to neuronal excitability. We shall also in this chapter discuss the related subject of neurotransmitter substances in the central nervous system (CNS).

Circulation

The blood vessels of the brain are supplied by the carotid and vertebral arteries (Fig. 19.1). The cerebral arteries have connect-

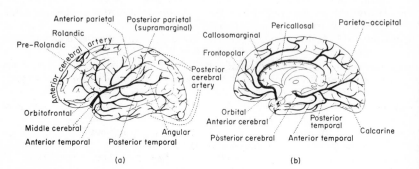

Fig. 19.1. Main arteries on the lateral surface of the human hemisphere (a). Main arteries on the medial surface (b). (From Strong and Elwyn, *Human Neuroanatomy*, Williams and Wilkins, 1943.)

ing branches at the base of the brain to form the *Circle of Willis* (Fig. 19.2). If one vessel is blocked, others may continue to supply the brain. In some species, such as the dog, occlusion of the carotids and the vertebrals can be compensated by the intervertebral vessels.   The sheep's blood supply to the brain is unique insofar as each carotid wholly supplies each half of the brain (Baldwin and Bell, 1963).

On the surface of the brain, blood vessels supplying the tissue branch to become the pial arterial supply.   From the pial vessels, intracortical arteries pass down vertically into the cortical substance (Fig. 19.3).   From these, still smaller vessels branch laterally to supply the capillaries across which the transport of O_2, CO_2, glucose,

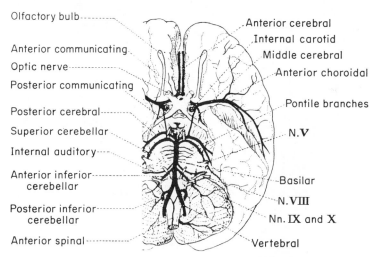

Olfactory bulb

Anterior communicating

Optic nerve

Posterior communicating

Posterior cerebral

Superior cerebellar

Internal auditory

Anterior inferior cerebellar

Posterior inferior cerebellar

Anterior spinal

Anterior cerebral

Internal carotid

Middle cerebral

Anterior choroidal

Pontile branches

N.V

Basilar

N.VIII

Nn. IX and X

Vertebral

Fig. 19.2.   Communicating vessels at the base of the human brain between the basilar artery and internal carotids forming the Circle of Willis.   (From Strong and Elwyn, *Human Neuroanatomy*, Williams and Wilkins, 1943.)

ions and other substances takes place.   These capillaries merge into small venules and veins which ascend vertically to reach the pial surface and become collected into the venous sinuses draining the brain.

Vasoconstriction and vasodilation of pial vessels seen on the surface of the cortex are indirect indices of the changes in blood flow taking place within the tissue itself.   Techniques have been developed so that the blood flow to the brain, or a part of the brain, can be studied in the human as well as in animals (Kety, 1960). Autonomic nerves supplying cortical vessels appear to have a minor effect on flow rates (Schmidt, 1950).   Blood flow is regulated intrinsically by local chemical changes.   Such *autoregulation* appears to be controlled by the CO_2 produced in the tissues as well as the lack of O_2 following a greater than normal utilization. This is shown by the vasodilator action of CO_2 and the effect of an increase in activity of a group of neurons to cause a vasodilation in that region (Serota and Gerard, 1938). This appears to act as a feedback system, i.e. the greater utilization of O_2 and production of CO_2 will bring more O_2 and glucose to that active region through dilation of the vessels.

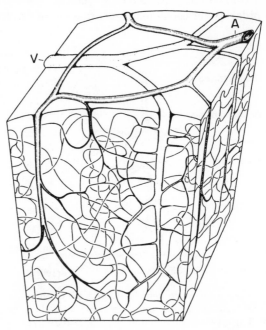

Fig. 19.3.   Diagrammatic illustration of the arterial (A) and venous (V) vessels of the cortex.   Branches extend down from the pial surface and communicate across the capillaries. (Scharrer, *Anat. Rec.*, **78**: 173, 1940.)

A special type of blood supply, the *choroid plexus* found in ventricles, is involved in the production of the *cerebrospinal fluid* filling the brain ventricles and the space between the brain and the skull (Davson, 1960). Isotope studies have shown that substances injected into the cerebrospinal fluid can readily enter the brain tissue. This is a point of some interest with respect to the subject of barriers to the transfer of substances into the CNS and it will be discussed in the next section. A supply of metabolites through the cerebrospinal fluid is not significant. The main function of cerebrospinal fluid is to act as a mechanical cushion for the brain, absorbing most of the shock of sudden head movements.

The blood-brain barrier and extracellular space

The *blood-brain barrier* is a controlling mechanism which only allows some substances from the blood to enter the brain rapidly while other substances either enter slowly or not at all. For instance, when injected into the blood the dye, trypan blue, will stain body tissues but not the brain or the spinal cord (Tschirgi, 1952, 1960).

The presence of the blood-brain barrier is shown by the fact that even Na^+ and Cl^- enters the brain tissue at a slow rate (Dobbing, 1961). Phosphate has an even lower rate of passage into the brain. However, as typical for a number of substances, once past the blood-brain barrier (by injection into the CNS or application to the pial surface) phosphate is readily incorporated by the cells into a variety of phosphorous compounds: phospholipids, phosphoprotein and inositol phosphate as well as into the energy-rich compounds, ATP and ADP.

After a stab wound in the brain, permeability of the barrier is increased as shown by the entrance of trypan blue from the blood. Vascular damage can change the permeability of the barrier. The possibility has been raised that some types of neural disorders, such as those following brain concussion or epilepsy, may be due primarily to vascular changes, i.e. the loss of the normal blood-brain barrier properties results in the entry of substances into the extracellular spaces of the brain which alter neuron properties (Aird, 1948).

During the first weeks of life the barrier is incompletely developed. Phosphate, K^+, sodium ferrocyanide and glutamic acid readily enter into the brain of the newborn rat until approximately 2 weeks after birth. However, trypan blue does not enter into the brain of the newborn rat, and this indicates that a barrier of some kind is present, at least to some substances if not to others (Himwich, 1962).

Difficulties of interpreting such data exist because the mechanism of the barrier is unknown. A permeability control by the capillaries of the blood vessels has been considered. Another hypothesis is that *glial cell* processes covering the blood vessels could perform this function (Tschirgi, 1952, 1960). The glia, or more properly neuroglia, are differentiated into astrocytes and oligodendrocytes (Glees, 1955), although a differentiation of various glial types is not always agreed upon. Glial cell processes have been observed around blood vessels with the electron microscope, a possible implication that they are involved in such a controlling mechanism.

The so-called 'ground substance' present between cells was at one time considered to act as a barrier. However, electron microscopic examination of neural tissue showed this 'ground substance' to be composed of axons and dendrites of neurons and finer processes of glial cells (Farquhar and Hartmann, 1957; Hortsmann and Meves, 1959). There are several times as many glial cells as there are neurons (Nurnberger and Gordon, 1957), and the neuroglia has long been considered to have some metabolic role in brain tissue. Taking into account the large number of glial cells and the electron microscope findings of a small extracellular space, the glia has been considered to perform this transfer function and act as an apparent barrier. The slow transfer of certain substances into the brain is explained by the slow rate of acceptance of them by the glia (Maynard, Schultz and Pease, 1957).

The presence of an appreciable extracellular space is supported by various physiological studies. In addition to the electrical impedance measurements suggesting an extracellular space of 25% (Chapter 18), further support for a space of this size comes from study of tissue Cl^-. If we assume that the Cl^- content inside cells is low, then by comparing the content of Cl^- present in a tissue with the Cl^- in the serum of the blood which is in equilibrium with the fluid in the extracellular space, an estimate may be made of the relative size of the extracellular space. The calculation is as follows:

% extracellular space (g H_2O/kg tissue)

$$= \frac{\text{total tissue } Cl^- \text{ (meq/kg)} \times 100}{\text{extracellular fluid } Cl^- \text{ (meq/l)}}$$

Using this approach, Manery and Hastings (1939), Aprison, Lukenbill and Segar (1960) and others have determined an extracellular space in the brain measuring approximately 30% or more.

A low Cl^- content inside neurons would be expected (Chapter 4) from the resting membrane potentials found in neurons of the cortex (Chapters 20, 22) as well as from the more extensive studies of spinal cord motoneurons previously discussed in Chapter 16. As has been noted, glial cells are larger in number than neurons and the possibility exists that a higher content of Cl^- is present inside glia to account for the high Cl^- content of brain tissue. In this regard the studies of Hild and Tasaki (1962) are of interest. In glial cells of tissue cultures they found that the resting membrane potentials were of the same order as that of neurons. Unless some other factors are present, it would appear from electrical potential studies that Cl^- is as low in glial cells as it is in neurons.

Studies of brain slices should show by the movement of ions into or from these tissues whether the glial cells still present in the slices function to decrease exchange, or whether with the removal of the vascular barriers in the slices a free diffusion into the extracellular spaces takes place.   Davson and Spaziani (1959) exposed brain slices to solutions containing either radioactive Na⁺, iodine, sucrose

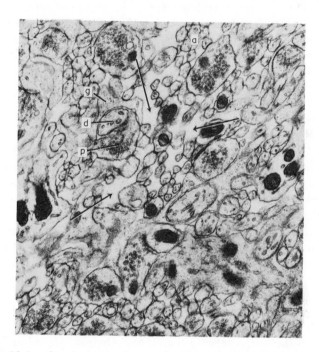

Fig. 19.4.   An electron micrograph of the molecular layer of the cerebellar vermis is shown using the technique of rapid freezing followed by substitution fixation at low temperature ($-85°C$) in acetone with 2% osmium tetroxide.   The tissue was cut at right angles to folia of the vermis, thus in the plane of the dendritic trees of the Purkinje cells.   Numerous presynaptic terminals are present containing synaptic vesicles.   A synapse between a presynaptic (p) and a postsynaptic structure (d) is seen.   The latter is probably a spine from the dendritic tree of a Purkinje cell.   Glia (g) surrounds these synaptic elements.   The small profiles are branches of axons (a) of the granular layer cells cut at right angles. A relatively large cellular space is present between these fibers (arrows).   The clefts between glia and the synaptic structures, and also the synaptic cleft itself are not greatly different from those seen in electron micrographs produced by the usual fixation procedures (stained with lead citrate, magnification 34,000 ×).
(Courtesy, A. van Harreveld.)

or p-aminohippurate. Their studies indicated a rapid communication with an extracellular space of 14–22%, depending on the molecule or ion used. In their studies of brain slices, Thomas and McIlwain (1956) found that of the 42 meq/kg of Cl^- present in slices only 2 meq/kg of Cl^- remained after soaking in low Cl^- solutions. For the most part the Cl^- diffuses freely from the slices as would be expected from an extracellular space in communication with the bath fluid around the slice. A space of 20–25% has been used for the extracellular space by the neurochemists to apportion the various chemical constituents of the cortex (McIlwain, 1959; Tower, 1960).

While physiological studies indicate an extracellular space in the cortex of 20–25% there remains to be explained the apparent absence of extracellular space seen in electron micrographs. This may very well be due to the asphyxial change (Chapter 18) which would be expected to occur upon removing the brain tissue to prepare it for electron microscopic examination. This change would occur in the tissue within a few minutes and before the fixation of cellular structures by osmium has taken place. The movement of ions and water into the cells from the extracellular space during this asphyxial change would give rise to the apparent lack of extracellular space (van Harreveld, 1962). Both neurons and glia may participate in an internal translocation of substance and fluid (van Harreveld, 1961). A further development in the technique of freeze-substitution for electron microscopy shows the presence of a large intercellular space before this asphyxial change takes place (Fig. 19.4). The brain tissue (cerebellum) was exposed and while in its functioning state the surface was rapidly frozen and then subjected to substitution-fixation with osmium–acetone. By this means the position of the cellular constituents was maintained during fixation and subsequent embedding for sectioning and electron microscopy (van Harreveld and Crowell, 1964). The anatomical evidence of a large extracellular space demonstrated by this means adds to the physiological evidence cited.

Oxidative metabolism

The energy requirements of the brain are met by the glucose and O_2 required for its utilization which are brought to it via the blood. The amount of O_2 taken up by the CNS is high with respect to other tissues. The measured rate of oxygen uptake is approximately 3.3 ml per 100 g per minute (Kety, 1957) amounting to 20% of the total oxygen uptake of the body. EEG activity and consciousness depend on a continuous supply of oxygen to the brain. EEG activity ceases within approximately 15 seconds after the blood supply to the head is interrupted (Sugar and Gerard, 1938). In man, consciousness is lost even sooner. Blood circulation to the brain of human subjects was abruptly arrested by a pressure cuff around the neck and this was followed, at a mean time of 6.8 sec, by loss of consciousness and delta waves in the EEG (Rossen, Kabat and Anderson, 1943). A revival of brain function without permanent damage occurs if the blood supply has not been interrupted for a period longer than approximately 5 min (Heymans, 1950). If asphyxiation is continued for longer periods, memory and intellectual functions are lost permanently. The brain stem neurons controlling respiration and vasomotor reflexes are more resistant to asphyxiation and can survive periods of anoxia lasting as long as 30 min. The short survival period of 5 min for which higher functions can last without oxygen is similar to the latent period before the onset of the asphyxial change (Chapter 18). A distinction can be made between the alteration of permeability of apical dendrites and translocation of ions and water which can survive long asphyxiation (54–60 min) and the enzyme mechanisms controlling the viability of neurons. The latter is more sensitive to lack of O_2 (van Harreveld and Tachibana, 1962). The survival period is temperature dependent and can be prolonged by cooling the brain (Schneider, 1957). This phenomenon is taken advantage of in cardiac surgery where cooling of the blood to the head is used to extend periods of operating time when circulation must necessarily be stopped. The newborn mammal is more resistant to oxygen lack and has a longer survival period, a feature of great value when circulation may be interrupted for scores of minutes during delivery.

The brain is almost as dependent on the glucose supplied to it by the blood as it is on oxygen. Practically all the oxygen consumed is eventually utilized in the oxidation of glucose which is consumed in the human brain at the rate of 5.4 mg per 100 g per minute (Kety, 1957). Glucose utilization is shown by a respiratory quotient close to unity. When the blood level of glucose is experimentally reduced by the administration of insulin, the EEG shows a shift to the lower frequencies until large slow rhythms of 2–3 per second become predominant (Dawson and Greville, 1963). Consciousness is lost at this stage. If the glucose level drops too low, even the visceral functions controlled by the brain stem may be interrupted (Himwich, 1951). Permanent damage to the cerebral cortex is produced if a low glucose level is maintained for too long a time.

Various carbohydrates and amino acids have been injected in such hypoglycemic animals to determine which of these substances could substitute for glucose. Fructose and glutamic acid can be metabolized but glucose is required for normal metabolic rates.

By surgically blocking all alternative paths of blood supply to the brain and then perfusing through the carotids (*vide supra*), Geiger (1958) and his associates were able to make metabolic studies in the isolated brain. In such preparations 'simplified' defibrinated blood is pumped through the brain at controlled pressures while flow rates and vascular resistance are measured. Oxygen consumption and uptake of glucose are found by the concentration differences at inflow and egress. The brain fails to utilize glucose after $1-1\frac{1}{2}$ hours unless the nucleotides, *uridine* and *cytidine*, are added to the perfusion fluid. Presumably these nucleotides are important factors controlling the normal uptake of glucose from the blood by the brain. Analysis of the isolated perfused brain after injection of isotopically labeled glucose indicates a complexity of metabolic pathways for the entering glucose. A portion of the glucose is built into proteins and other acid-insoluble components (Geiger, 1958).

Metabolic activity in neurons leads to the formation of high-energy phosphate bonds in ATP and creatine phosphate. We have already discussed the evidence that the high-energy phosphorus bonds in ATP are related to the sodium pump (Chapter 7). A number of metabolic alterations including a decrease in O_2 or glucose supply have as a common feature a reduction in the amount of phosphate compounds, particularly creatine phosphate (McIlwain, 1959). The ATP level may be kept near normal or show a transient fall when metabolic activity is greatly increased—creatine phosphate acts as a store and supplies the high-energy phosphate bonds to replenish ATP (McIlwain, 1963).

Mitochondria and oxidative metabolism in dendrites

In the mitochondria, oxidative metabolism proceeds by an ordered series of enzymatic steps and the energy derived from oxidative metabolism is channeled into the energy-rich phosphorous bonds of creatine phosphate and ATP (Chapter 7; Abood, 1960). There appears to be a large number of mitochondria in the dendrites. Lowry *et al.* (1954) developed micro-histochemical techniques so that the content of key metabolic enzymes in various layers of the cortex could be sampled. A core of cortex was punched out and thin sections sliced off so that enzymatic activity at different depths of the cortex could be determined.   They found a higher oxidative metabolism in the molecular layer which they have considered to have a high density of apical dendrites.   Their conclusion was that a large part of cerebral metabolism is neuronal and probably mainly within the apical dendrites of pyramidal cells.   This point is, however, not secured because it is as yet difficult to determine the density of the finer terminations of the dendrites in any region.   The difficulty comes in distinguishing in electron micrographs the dendritic terminals from the fine endings of glial cells.

Maturation studies of the cortex (Chapter 18) suggest a relationship of apical dendrites to mitochondria and oxidative metabolism. During the proliferation of dendrites within the first several weeks after birth, a number of important enzymes begin to appear and increase in activity (Himwich, 1962).   There is also a corresponding increase in the concentration of mitochondria in the brain (Samson, Balfour and Jacobs, 1960).   A large number of mitochondria in the apical dendrites was shown in the recent electron micrographs of Pappas and Purpura (1961).   The mitochondria were described as slender and exceptionally long, extending for considerable lengths along the inside of the dendrites.   Hydén and Lange (1961) studied the metabolism of single isolated cell bodies of neurons and glia. Cytochrome oxidase and succinoxidase were found to be lower in neurons than in the glial cells.   We might expect that in the removal of neurons from the matrix of the neural tissues, most of the finer dendritic branches are severed from the cell body, these branches having the higher oxidative metabolic rates.

A useful preparation for study of metabolic activity of neuron is that of thin slices of brain cortex placed in Warburg flasks in a balanced ion medium with glucose or other substrates present (McIlwain, 1959).   The metabolic rate of these brain tissue slices is determined by their O_2 uptake, CO_2 production and by chemical balance determinations showing an accumulation of energy-rich phosphate compounds.   It is possible to stimulate electrically these brain cortex slices *in vitro* and increase their oxidative metabolism as much as 100% (McIlwain, 1959; Heald, McIlwain and Sloane-Stanley, 1960).   In addition to electrical stimulation, increased K^+ present in the medium can also increase oxidative metabolism. Stimulation of metabolic activity by adding K^+ does not occur if the tissues have been minced (Quastel and Quastel, 1961) and it would appear that the stimulation of metabolism by K^+ or electrical currents follows upon depolarization of cell membranes present in the slices.   Microelectrode studies have shown resting membrane potentials and spike discharges present in the slices (Hillman, Campbell and McIlwain, 1963).

Metabolic changes are found during spreading depression which has been regarded as affecting especially the apical dendrites (Chapter 18). A number of agents known to interfere with oxidative metabolism, such as DNP, NaCN, azide and iodo-acetic acid are effective in exciting SD (Bureš, Burešová and Křivánek, 1960). After SD is elicited, an expenditure of metabolic energy is required to pump Na^+, Cl^- and water back out of the cells during the recovery phase. This accounts for the reduced content of glucose, glycogen and phosphocreatine found in an area which has been occupied by SD. Possibly it is the increased Na^+ inside the cell which stimulates the sodium pump (Chapters 4, 7) and the removal of ions and water.

Glutamic acid and GABA

The presence of an active amino acid metabolism in neurons has been recognized in recent years (Waelsch, 1962). As in other tissues, a number of amino acids are synthesized from intermediates arising from the aerobic breakdown of glucose via the citric acid cycle (Chapter 7). The *essential* amino acids (those which cannot be synthesized and must be obtained from the diet) are supplied by the blood and their passage across the blood-brain barrier into the brain was shown by the use of labeled amino acids.

An aspect of amino acid metabolism in the neuron which is of signal importance is the unique position of glutamic acid and the closely related substance gamma-aminobutyric acid (GABA). Together they account for half the total α-amino nitrogen present. In mammals, GABA appears to be present only in nervous tissue (Roberts, 1961).

Of a number of amino acids, only glutamic acid was found to be a substrate for oxidative metabolism in brain slices. Glutamic acid enters the citric acid cycle after its conversion either by a *deamination* or a *transamination* reaction to α-ketoglutarate, an intermediate in the citric acid cycle (Fig. 19.5) (Tower, 1959). It must be stressed, however, that glucose is the major energy source in the brain (Chapter 7).

Another important reaction is the conversion of glutamic acid to GABA by a *decarboxylation* reaction. This reaction requires as a coenzyme pyridoxal phosphate, which is synthesized from *pyridoxine (vitamin B_6)*. As will be seen, neurological disorders caused by a deficiency in this vitamin in the diet may be due to its metabolic role in decarboxylation.

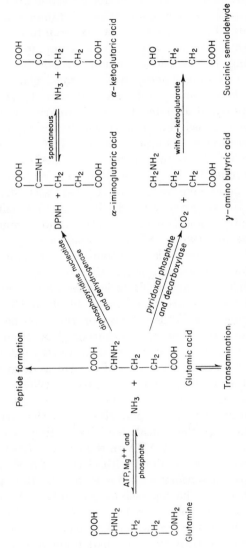

Fig. 19.5. The metabolic interrelations between glutamic acid and γ-aminobutyric acid (GABA) are shown. From GABA the conversion to succinic semialdehyde leads into the Krebs citric acid cycle. (McIlwain, 1959.)

The metabolic interrelation between glutamic acid and *glutamine* is also of interest.   Glutamine can more readily pass the blood-brain barrier than glutamic acid and once in the brain it may enter the metabolic pathways described above for glutamic acid.

In addition to these metabolic roles, glutamic acid and GABA change the excitability of neurons.   A first step in this concept was the discovery that administration of the compound *semicarbazide* results in prolonged convulsions.   Semicarbazide blocks the action of the coenzyme pyridoxal phosphate and these convulsions can be antidoted with the vitamin pyridoxine (vitamin B_6) (Pfeiffer, 1960; Killam, Dasgupta and Killam, 1960).   Similarly, a diet deficient in pyridoxine can cause convulsions which are rapidly antidoted by feeding pyridoxine (Coursin, 1960).   The interference with pyridoxal phosphate leads to a deficiency of GABA which leads to increased excitability in the neuron (Bain and Williams, 1960).

A neuronal depressive action of GABA was shown by the rapid block of the negative wave DCR (Fig. 19.6) within seconds after topical application (Purpura, Girado and Grundfest, 1957; Iwama and Jasper, 1957).   Such a rapid action of GABA is additional evidence that this negative wave response originates from the superficial apical dendrites (Chapter 18).   During GABA block of the negative wave DCR, a smaller positive wave is seen. Purpura (1960) has interpreted this as a block of EPSP responses with an uncovering of an IPSP.   However, the hypothesis that these surface responses are synaptic potentials has been questioned (Chapter 18) and an alternative view is that GABA has a generalized depressive action on the membranes of the apical dendrites to cause this block of the DCR (Elliot and Jasper, 1959).   The surface positive wave seen during GABA block would reflect remaining sinks of activity in parts of the dendrites below the surface with the uppermost portions of the apical dendrites acting as a source.   A general depressive action of GABA on the neurons has been taken to account for the decrease obtained with GABA of both positive and negative phases of the sensory evoked responses by Bindman, Lippold and Redfearn (1962).   The depressive effect of GABA has associated with it a small permeability increase to K^+.   This was shown by radioisotope studies using ^{42}K which had been allowed to soak into the cortex.   After cortical elements had taken up the isotope, its efflux was measured.   Application of GABA caused an increased efflux of ^{42}K (Brinley *et al.*, 1960).

A general action of GABA to decrease neuronal excitability was shown earlier on spinal cord motoneurons by Curtis, Phillis and

Watkins (1959, 1960) using electrophoresis from coaxial microelectrodes. An outside barrel permitted the release of GABA and
other test substances in the near vicinity of the membrane of the cell

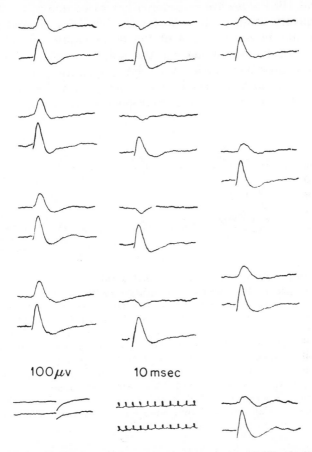

100μv   10 msec

Fig. 19.6.   Effect of GABA on the negative wave DCR (dendritic
potential).   Four consecutive pairs of sweeps in each column.
Upper trace recorded at a distant point (3 mm) from the stimulating electrodes, lower trace at stimulated point.   Left column,
control responses.   Middle column, after 1% GABA applied to
distant point (3 mm) and those responses reversed.   Right column,
recovery 11 min after washing.   (Iwama and Jasper, 1957.)

which is entered into by the inner microelectrode used to record cell
potentials (Chapter 16).   The release of GABA near the cell increased
its threshold to direct electrical excitation 2–3 times.   Both the
EPSP and IPSP were found present but diminished in size (Fig.

19.7). From their studies Curtis and Watkins (1960) concluded that GABA acts to produce an increase of membrane threshold without altering the resting membrane potential. The decrease of EPSP and IPSP sizes are considered not to be due to the block of their respective transmitter substances, but to a general increase in the membrane conductance of the postsynaptic cell membrane. GABA is considered to act on the spike-generating mechanism and not on those mechanisms underlying synaptic potential *per se*. The evidence is however still indirect. Krnjević and Phillis (1963a), using a multiple microelectrode electrophoretic technique and extra-

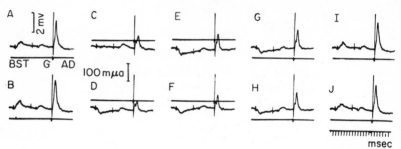

Fig. 19.7. Focal potentials recorded within a spinal cord moto-neuron group, the biceps-semitendinosus (BST). Responses to orthodromic stimulation (BST), gastrocnemius (G) stimulation, and antidromic stimulation of fibers of the ventral root (AD) are shown. A and B, control responses. The effect of the GABA ion-tophoretically perfusing the nuclear group locally through another barrel of the electrode is shown in C, D, E, F, at respectively 1, 2, 5 and 6 sec after injection. All three responses show diminution of amplitude. The ejection of GABA was stopped, and G, H, I, J, recorded respectively at 1, 2, 9 and 10 sec later shows recovery of responses. Calibration 2 mv, time 1 msec. (Curtis, Phillis and Watkins, 1959.)

cellular recording of single-cell discharge, found a remarkably rapid depression of spontaneous or induced repetitive discharge of cortical cells by GABA. An amount as small as 10^{-14} moles was effective. The rapidity of the process, as in the rapid block of the surface negative DCRs, suggests an action on the cell membranes rather than on metabolic processes involving the glutamic acid–GABA system.

Because of their metabolic relationship an accumulation of glu-tamic acid rather than a decrease of GABA level may cause an increased excitability and convulsive waves when decarboxylation of glutamic acid to GABA is blocked. In the spinal cord moto-neuron, electrophoretic release of glutamic acid near the cell causes

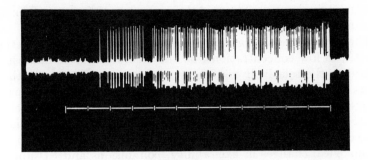

Fig. 19.8.   A single unit in the cortex of the cat is recorded from one barrel of a multiple-barrel microelectrode excited by iontophoretic application of L-glutamate through another nearby barrel at the time indicated by the lower line.   The cell shows a large increase of spike discharges.   Time signals on line, 1 sec.   (Courtesy, K. Krnjević.)

an increased discharge of motoneurons.   Similarly, in the cerebral cortex glutamic acid is a potent excitant (Fig. 19.8).   Like GABA's depressant action, the excitation produced by glutamic acid appears rapidly and ceases soon after stopping the electrophoretic release of the substance.   Glutamic acid and GABA appear to have reciprocal actions on excitability as shown in Fig. 19.9.   Glutamic acid released from one barrel of a multiple micropipette excites a rapid

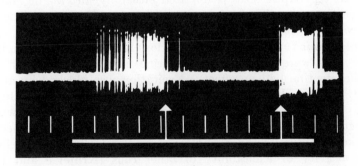

Fig. 19.9.   During the time of release of L-glutamate indicated by the lower line, a discharge of spikes is recorded from the unit in the cat cortex (cf. Fig. 19.8).   GABA released from another barrel at the first vertical arrow.   During the release of GABA the neuronal discharge produced by L-glutamate was blocked.   At second arrow GABA release was stopped and the cell resumed firing in response to L-glutamate.   Time signals on line, 1 sec.   (Courtesy, K. Krnjević.)

sustained discharge.   Then GABA was released from another barrel
causing a rapid block of the discharge.

The rapid action of glutamic acid and the depressant action of
GABA, in low concentrations, on the membrane is of interest with
regard to the relatively high content of these substances in the cell.
If, as appears from the discussion, they are not synaptic transmitter
substances, then these substances and the other amines structurally
related to them (Curtis and Watkins, 1963) represent a relatively
new class of substances, the *excitability modulators*.   In any case,
pathological changes in excitability, convulsions and SD appear to
involve this system.

Neurotransmitters

The operation of the transmitter substance ACh at the synapse
between the spinal cord motoneuron collateral and Renshaw cells
has been shown (Chapter 16).   Components of an ACh system
also appear to be present in the cortex (Hebb, 1957).   By the use
of the iontophoretic injection technique applied to single cells
within the cortex, approximately 15% of the cells were found to
respond to ACh with increased rates of discharge (Krnjević and
Phillis, 1963b).   The distribution of the cells is highest between
0.8 and 1.3 mm below the surface.   These cells were identified by
antidromic stimulation of the pyramidal tract as Betz cells (Chapter
22) and shown to be sensitive to ACh.   The action of ACh at
different synaptic sites is imitated either by *nicotine* or *muscarine*
suggesting two different synaptic receptor substances.   The pharmacological properties of the ACh-sensitive Betz cells showed
a *muscarinic* type of transmitter action (Krnjević and Phillis, 1963c).
The cells were excited by muscarine and acetyl-β-methylcholine
while nicotine had no effect.   Excitation was blocked by atropine
and hyocine while both D-tubocurarine and dihydro-β-erythroidine
had no blocking effect.   Atropine injected systemically was also
effective in producing a great reduction in the spontaneous or
evoked activity of these ACh-sensitive Betz cells without effecting
the activity or excitability of other cells (Krnjević and Phillis,
1963c).   These results give a rationale for the known central action
of atropine and hyocine and the earlier indirect evidence of a central
excitatory effect of muscarinic substances (Pfeiffer, 1959; Riehl and
Unna, 1960).

Further evidence for a role of ACh in the cortex was shown by
Mitchell (1963) in that a low level of ACh spontaneously released
was correlated with the electrical activity of the brain.   Upon

direct electrical stimulation of the cortex or excitation by transcallosal or sensory stimulation of the somatosensory area, ACh
release was increased, the amount depending on the rate of
stimulation.

Marrazzi (1957), injecting substances into the carotid supply to
the brain, found that catecholamines (adrenalin) and indoles (serotonin) depressed the amplitude of transcallosal responses (Chapter

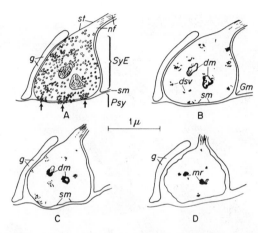

Fig. 19.10.   A diagrammatic representation of nerve terminals
at a synaptic ending in the acoustic ganglion is shown.   A, normal.
The cochlea was destroyed to cause nerve degeneration.   B shows
a terminal 22 hours later; C and D are endings 44 hours later showing decreased content of vesicles and mitochondria.   Stalk of synaptic ending (st), neurofibril (nf), glia (g), synaptic ending (SyE),
synaptic membrane (sm), postsynaptic ending (Psy), degenerating
mitochondria (dm), degenerated synaptic vesicles (dv), glial membrane (Gm), mitochondrial remnants (mr).   (de Robertis, *Exptl.
Cell Res. Suppl.* 5, 1958.)

8).   Injections into blood may result in changes in cortical excitability indirectly through an effect on other brain regions, particu-
arly the reticular formation, as will be discussed in Chapter 20.
It was, therefore, of interest that a direct depressant effect of adrenalin and serotonin (5-hydroxytryptamine) on some cortical cells was
shown by electrophoretic studies (Krnjević and Phillis, 1963a).

The electrophoretic technique holds promise of discovering the
nature of transmitter substances other than ACh.   The inhibitory
effects of GABA were first found through the inhibitory action

of brain extracts, Florey's Factor I (Florey, 1954; Florey and McLennan, 1955). McLennan (1963) believes that inhibitory actions are not accounted for entirely by GABA in the extracts and it is possible that other transmitter substances may be discovered in brain extracts. In electron micrographs, vesicles are seen in the nerve terminals similar in form to those seen in the nerve terminals of the neuromuscular junction. These are therefore believed also to contain transmitter substance. A decreased number of

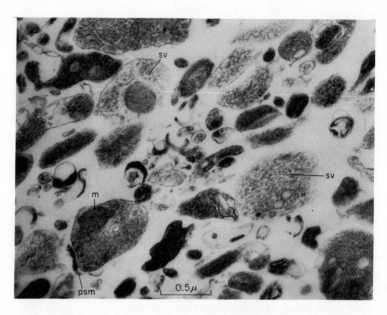

Fig. 19.11.   Nerve endings in centrifuged brain extracts identified with electron microscope.   Pinched-off synaptic endings contain synaptic vesicles (sv) and mitochondria (mo).   Also present are the thickened postsynaptic membranes (psm) seen at some synaptic junctions.   × 53,000.   (Courtesy, E. G. Gray.)

vesicles in the nerve terminals of CNS synapses during degeneration has been noted (Fig. 19.10).

Using high-speed centrifugation of homogenates of brain it is possible to separate fractions containing various particulates such as nuclei, mitochondria, and microsomes.   One fraction was shown to be composed of membranes encircling typical appearing synaptic vesicles (de Robertis, de Iraldi, Rodriguez and Gomez, 1961; Gray and Whittaker, 1962).   The centrifuged fraction which Gray and Whittaker have called Fraction B appears in electron micrographs to be pinched or torn off fragments of the nerve terminals (Fig. 19–11). They are packed with synaptic vesicles and a few mitochondria, and in places the characteristic thickened postsynaptic membrane has been torn off along with the presynaptic portion. This thickened membrane at the synapse is a characteristic feature of the type 1 synapses of the CNS (Chapter 18). Of particular interest with regard to transmitter function is the presence of ACh in these fractions of nerve endings. There is also evidence of other transmitter substances present in such fractions (Whittaker, 1961; de Robertis *et al.*, 1963) and this type of investigation holds promise of the identification of the transmitter substances of the CNS.

REFERENCES

Abood, L. G. (1960). Neuronal metabolism. *Handbook of Physiology—Neurophysiology.* Vol. 3, pp. 1815–1826. American Physiological Society, Washington, D.C.

Aird, R. B. (1948). The role of tissue permeability with particular reference to the blood-brain barrier in diseases of the central nervous system. *Calif. Med.* **69**: 5. Chairman's address.

Aprison, M. H., Lukenbill, A. and Segar, W. E. (1960). Sodium, potassium, chloride and water content of six discrete parts of the mammalian brain. *J. Neurochem.* **5**: 150–155.

Bain, J. A. and Williams, H. L. (1960). Concentrations of B6 vitamers in tissue and tissue fluids. *Inhibition in the Nervous System and Gamma-aminobutyric Acid. An International Symposium.* Pp. 275–293. Pergamon Press, New York.

Baldwin, B. A. and Bell, F. R. (1963). Blood flow in the carotid and vertebral arteries of the sheep and calf. *J. Physiol.* **167**: 448–462. The effect on blood pressure in the sheep and calf of clamping some of the arteries contributing to the cephalic circulation. *Ibid.*, 463–479.

Bindman, L. J., Lippold, O. C. J. and Redfearn, J. W. T. (1962). The non-selective blocking action of γ-aminobutyric acid on the sensory cerebral cortex of the rat. *J. Physiol.* **162**: 105–120.

Brinley, F. J., Jr., Kandel, E. R. and Marshall, W. H. (1960). Effect of gamma-aminobutyric acid (GABA) on ^{42}K outflux from the rabbit cortex. *J. Neurophysiol.* **22**: 237–256.

Bureš, J., Burešová, O. and Křivánek, J. (1960). Some metabolic aspects of Leão's spreading cortical depression. *Structure and Function of the Cerebral Cortex.* Edited by D. B. Tower and J. P. Schadé. Pp. 257–265. Elsevier, New York.

Coursin, D. B. (1960). Seizures in vitamin B6 deficiency. *Inhibition in the Nervous System and Gamma-aminobutyric Acid. An International Symposium.* Pp. 294–301. Pergamon Press, New York.

Curtis, D. R. and Watkins, J. C. (1960). Investigations upon the possible synaptic transmitter function of gamma-aminobutyric acid and naturally occurring amino acids. *Inhibition in the Nervous System and Gamma-aminobutyric Acid. An International Symposium.* Pp. 424–444. Pergamon Press, New York.

Curtis, D. R. and Watkins, J. C. (1963).   Acidic amino acids with strong excitatory actions on mammalian neurones.   *J. Physiol.* **166**: 1–14.

Curtis, D. R., Phillis, J. W. and Watkins, J. C. (1959).   The depression of spinal neurones by γ-amino-*n*-butyric acid and β-alanine.   *J. Physiol.* **146**: 185–203.

Curtis, D. R., Phillis, J. W. and Watkins, J. C. (1960).   The chemical excitation of spinal neurones by certain acidic amino acids.   *J. Physiol.* **150** 656–682.

Davson, H. (1960).   Intracranial and intraocular fluids.   *Handbook of Physiology—Neurophysiology.* Vol. 3, pp. 1761–1788.   American Physiological Society, Washington, D.C.

Davson, H. and Spaziani, E. (1959).   Blood-brain barrier and the extra cellular space of brain.   *J. Physiol.* **149**: 135–143.

Dawson, M. E. and Greville, G. D. (1963).   Biochemistry (with Revisions and Additions by H. McIlwain).   *Electroencephalography.* Edited by D. Hil and G. Parr.   2nd Ed.   Chapter 5.   Macdonald, London.

de Robertis, E., de Iraldi, A. P., Rodriguez, G. and Gomez, J. (1961).   On the isolation of nerve endings and synaptic vesicles.   *J. Biophys. Biochem Cytol.* **9**: 229–235.

de Robertis, E., Rodriguez de Lores Amaiz, G., Salgmcoff, L., de Iraldi, A. P and Ziehes, L. M. (1963).   Isolation of synaptic vesicles and structura organization of the acetylcholine system within the brain nerve end ings.   *J. Neurochem.* **10**: 225–235.

Dobbing, J. (1961).   The blood-brain barrier.   *Physiol. Rev.* **41**: 130–188.

Elliott, K. A. C. and Jasper, H. H. (1959).   Gamma-aminobutyric acid *Physiol. Rev.* **39**: 383–406.

Elliott, K. A. C., Page, I. H. and Quastel, J. H. (1962) (Editors).   *Neuro chemistry.*   2nd Ed.   Thomas, Springfield.

Farquhar, M. G. and Hartmann, J. F. (1957).   Neuroglial structure and relationships as revealed by electron microscopy.   *J. Neuropath. Exptl Neurol.* **16**: 18–39.

Florey, E. (1954).   An inhibitory and an excitatory factor of mammalian central nervous system, and their action on single sensory neuron.   *Arch Intern. Physiol.* **62**: 33–53.

Florey, E. and McLennan, H. (1955).   The release of an inhibitory substance from mammalian brain, and its effect on peripheral synaptic transmission *J. Physiol.* **129**: 384–392.

Geiger, A. (1958).   Correlation of brain metabolism and function by the use of a brain perfusion method *in situ.*   *Physiol. Rev.* **38**: 1–20.

Glees, P. (1955).   *Neuroglia: Morphology and Function.*   Charles Thomas Springfield.

Gray, E. G. and Whittaker, V. P. (1962).   The isolation of nerve ending from brain: An electron microscopic study of cell fragments derived by homogenization and centrifugation.   *J. Anat.* **96**: 79–88.

Heald, P. J., McIlwain, H. and Sloane-Stanley, G. H. (1960).   Centra nervous system metabolism *in vitro.*   *Handbook of Physiology—Neuro physiology.*   Vol. 3, pp. 1827–1842.   American Physiological Society Washington, D.C.

Hebb, C. O. (1957).   Biochemical evidence for the neural function of acetyl choline.   *Physiol. Rev.* **37**: 196–220.

Heymans, C. (1950). Survival and revival of nervous tissues after arrest of circulation. *Physiol. Rev.* **30**: 375–392.

Hild, W. and Tasaki, I. (1962). Morphological and physiological properties of neurons and glial cells in tissue culture. *J. Neurophysiol.* **25**: 277–304.

Hillman, H. H., Campbell, W. J. and McIlwain, H. (1963). Membrane potentials in isolated and electrically stimulated mammalian cerebral cortex. *J. Neurochem.* **10**: 325–339.

Himwich, H. E. (1951). *Brain Metabolism and Cerebral Disorders*. Williams and Wilkins, Baltimore.

Himwich, W. A. (1962). Biochemical and neurophysiological development of the brain in the neonatal period. *Intern. Rev. Neurobiol.* **4**: 117–158.

Horstmann, E. and Meves, H. (1959). Die Feinstruktur des Molakularen Rindengraves und ihre physiologische bedeutung. *Z. Zellforsch. Mikroskop. Anat.* **49**: 569–604.

Hydén, H. and Lange, P. (1961). Differences in the metabolism of oligo-dendroglia and nerve cells in the vestibular area. *Regional Neuro-chemistry*. Edited by S. S. Kety and J. Elkes. Pp. 190–199. Pergamon Press, New York.

Iwama, K. and Jasper, H. H. (1957). The action of gamma-aminobutyric acid upon cortical electrical activity in the cat. *J. Physiol.* **138**: 365–380.

Kety, S. S. (1957). General metabolism of the brain *in vivo*. *Metabolism of the Nervous System*. Edited by D. Richter. Pp. 221–237. Pergamon Press, New York.

Kety, S. S. (1960). The cerebral circulation. *Handbook of Physiology—Neurophysiology*. Vol. 3, pp. 1751–1760. American Physiological Society, Washington, D.C.

Killam, K. F., Dasgupta, S. R. and Killam, E. K. (1960). Studies in the action of convulsant hydrazides as vitamin B_6 antagonists in the central nervous system. *Inhibition in the Nervous System and Gamma-amino-butyric acid. An International Symposium*. Pp. 302–316. Pergamon Press, New York.

Krnjević, K. and Phillis, J. W. (1963a). Iontophoretic studies of neurones in the mammalian cerebral cortex. *J. Physiol.* **165**: 274–304.

Krnjević, K. and Phillis, J. W. (1963b). Acetylcholine-sensitive cells in the cerebral cortex. *J. Physiol.* **166**: 296–327.

Krnjević, K. and Phillis, J. W. (1963c). Pharmacological properties of acetyl-choline-sensitive cells in the cerebral cortex. *J. Physiol.* **166**: 328–350.

Lowry, O. H., Roberts, N. R., Leiner, K. Y., Wu, M.-L., Farr, A. L. and Albers, R. W. (1954). The quantitative histochemistry of brain, III. Ammon's horn. *J. Biol. Chem.* **107**: 39–49.

Manery, J. F. and Hastings, A. B. (1939). The distribution of electrolytes in mammalian tissues. *J. Biol. Chem.* **127**: 657–676.

Marrazzi, A. S. (1957). The effects of certain drugs on cerebral synapses. *Ann. N.Y. Acad. Sci.* **66**: 496–507.

Maynard, E. A., Schultz, R. L. and Pease, D. C. (1957). Electron microscopy of the vascular bed of rat cerebral cortex. *Am. J. Anat.* **100**: 409–422.

McIlwain, H. (1959). *Biochemistry and the Central Nervous System*. 2nd Ed. Churchill, London.

McIlwain, H. (1963). *Chemical Exploration of the Brain. A Study of Cerebral Excitability and Ion Movements*. Elsevier, New York.

McLennan, H. (1963). *Synaptic Transmission.* Saunders, Philadelphia.

Mitchell, J. F. (1963). The spontaneous and evoked release of acetylcholine from the cerebral cortex. *J. Physiol.* **165**: 98–116.

Nurnberger, J. I. and Gordon, M. W. (1957). The cell density of neural tissues: direct counting method and possible applications as a biological referent. *Progr. Neurobiol.* **2**: 100–138.

Pappas, G. D. and Purpura, D. P. (1961). Fine structure of dendrites in the superficial neocortical neuropil. *Exptl. Neurol.* **4**: 507–530.

Pfeiffer, C. C. (1959). Parasympathetic neurohumors; possible precursors and effect on behavior. *Intern. Rev. Neurobiol.* **1**: 195–244.

Pfeiffer, C. C. (1960). Chairman's introduction. *Inhibition in the Nervous System and Gamma-aminobutyric Acid. An International Symposium.* Pp. 273–274. Pergamon Press, New York.

Purpura, D. P. (1960). Pharmacological aspects of ω-amino acid drugs on different cortical synaptic organizations. *Inhibition in the Nervous System and Gamma-aminobutyric acid. An International Symposium.* Pp. 495–514. Pergamon Press, New York.

Purpura, D. P., Girado, M. and Grundfest, H. (1957). Selective blockade of excitatory synapses in the cat brain by γ-aminobutyric acid. *Science* **125**: 1200–1202.

Quastel, J. H. and Quastel, D. M. J. (1961). *The Chemistry of Brain Metabolism in Health and Disease.* Charles C. Thomas, Springfield.

Richter, D. (1957). *Metabolism of the Nervous System.* Pergamon Press, New York.

Riehl, J. L. and Unna, K. R. (1960). Effects of muscarine on the central nervous system. *Rec. Advan. Biol. Psychiat.* **2**: 345–361.

Roberts, E. (1961). Metabolism of γ-aminobutyric acid in various areas of brain. *Regional Neurochemistry.* Edited by S. S. Kety and J. Elkes. Pp. 324–339. Pergamon Press, New York.

Rossen, R., Kabat, H. and Anderson, J. P. (1943). Acute arrest of cerebral circulation in man. *Arch. Neurol. Psychiat.* **50**: 510–528.

Samson, F. E., Balfour, W. M. and Jacobs, R. J. (1960). Mitochondrial changes in developing rat brain. *Federation Proc.* **19**: 286.

Schmidt, C. F. (1950). *The Cerebral Circulation in Health and Disease.* Charles C. Thomas, Springfield.

Schneider, M. (1957). The metabolism of the brain in ischaemia and hypothermia. *Metabolism of the Nervous System.* Edited by D. Richter. Pp. 238–244. Pergamon Press, New York.

Serota, H. M. and Gerard, R. W. (1938). Localized thermal changes in the cat's brain. *J. Neurophysiol.* **1**: 115–124.

Sugar, O. and Gerard, R. W. (1938). Anoxia and brain potentials. *J. Neurophysiol.* **1**: 558–570.

Thomas, J. and McIlwain, H. (1956). Chloride content and metabolism of cerebral tissues in fluids low in chlorides. *J. Neurochem.* **1**: 1–7.

Tower, D. B. (1959). Glutamic acid metabolism in the mammalian central nervous system. *Biochemistry of the Central Nervous System.* Edited by F. Brücke. Pp. 213–250. Pergamon Press, New York.

Tower, D. B. (1960). Chemical architecture of the central nervous system. *Handbook of Physiology—Neurophysiology.* Vol. 3, pp. 1793–1813. American Physiological Society, Washington, D.C.

Tschirgi, R. D. (1952). Blood-brain barrier. *Biology of Mental Health and Disease*. Hoeber, New York.

Tschirgi, R. D. (1960). Chemical environment of the central nervous system. *Handbook of Physiology—Neurophysiology*. Vol. 3, pp. 1865–1890. American Physiological Society, Washington, D.C.

van Harreveld, A. (1961). Asphyxial changes in the cerebellar cortex. *J. Cell. Comp. Physiol.* **57**: 101–110.

van Harreveld, A. (1962). Water and electrolyte distribution in central nervous tissue. *Federation Proc.* **21**: 659–664.

van Harreveld, A. and Crowell, J. (1964). Extracellular space in central nervous tissue. *Federation Proc.* **23**: 304.

van Harreveld, A. and Tachibana, S. (1962). Recovery of cerebral cortex from asphyxiation. *Am. J. Physiol.* **202**: 59–65.

Waelsch, H. (1962). Amino acid and protein metabolism. *Neurochemistry*. Edited by K. A. C. Elliott, I. H. Page and J. H. Quastel. Chapter 14. Thomas, Springfield.

Whittaker, V. P. (1961). The binding of neurohormones by subcellular particles of brain tissue. *Regional Neurochemistry*. Edited by S. S. Kety and J. Elkes. Pp. 259–263. Pergamon Press, New York.

20

Non-Specific Sensory Mechanisms —Sleep and Wakefulness

Animals show a marked cyclic alteration in their activities in their waking and sleeping states. The obvious differences are well known, namely, the loss of motor tone and consciousness during sleep as compared with the wakeful state. Experimental studies of sleep deprivation in man have shown that only a few days of sleeplessness can be tolerated without mental and physical deterioration. The urge to sleep becomes almost irresistible and activity is required to keep awake. Longer periods of sleep deprivation lead to impaired emotional states, hallucinations, increased sensitivity to pain and extreme muscular weakness (Kleitman, 1963).

A number of theories have been advanced in the past to explain the onset of sleep (Economo, 1929; Kleitman, 1963). These include a constriction of blood vessels of the brain, a 'hypnotoxin' or substance produced by the body acting on the brain, shifts in parasympathetic–sympathetic balance, etc. These have been replaced by a neural theory resulting from EEG studies in which mechanisms of the brain stem have been shown to be crucially involved in a control of sleep and waking states. As has been previously noted (Chapter 18), the EEG in the relaxed waking state is composed of alpha and beta waves. During sleep delta waves are predominant. This has served as a guide in the studies of the effect of various brain stem transections on sleep and waking mechanisms which will be discussed later in this chapter. Recent EEG studies in man and animals have also revealed that sleep is not a uniform state. Periodic changes in the EEG occur during the sleep period and in man these are associated with dreaming. We shall discuss this phenomenon in a later section of this chapter. The close connection of sleep to EEG activity requires that we first discuss the mechanisms by which EEG rhythms are controlled.

Thalamic pacemaker for EEG

As described in Chapter 18 isolated islands of the cortex have low spontaneous rhythmicity, but a stimulation will excite rhythmic discharges. Therefore, the cortex is inherently rhythmic, but requires a pacemaker to trigger it. Certain regions in the thalamus appear to perform this pacemaker function. Sensory tracts to the cortex have their relays in the *specific thalamic* nuclear groups (Chapter 21). Also present are the *non-specific* nuclei (Fig. 20.1). Fibers from these nuclei have a diffuse distribution in the cortex. Morison and Dempsey (1942) used the *stereotaxic apparatus* of Horsley and Clark to carry needle electrodes into selected parts of the thalamus. They discovered that stimulation of the non-specific nuclei at pulse rates of 5–10/sec could trigger wave discharges in the cerebral cortex which were recorded from all cortical areas. The repetitive waves so evoked in the cortex were similar to the bursts of 8–12/sec EEG waves which appear spontaneously (Fig. 20.2). The triggered waves are negative in polarity at the cortical surface. With successive discharges, the waves increase in size. This is due to the successive recruitment of more neurons into the group giving rise to the discharge, and the waves are referred to as *recruiting waves*. The triggering action of the non-specific thalamic nuclei was demonstrated by the finding that stimulation with only a single shock can excite a train of recruiting waves in the cortex (Dempsey and Morison, 1942a). A common origin for the spontaneous cortical waves and the thalamically triggered recruiting waves was shown by their occlusive interaction. While a spontaneously occurring cortical rhythm was in progress, recruiting waves were produced. When recruiting waves preceded or coincided with the spontaneous waves, the latter were smaller in amplitude. This also occurred in the reverse direction when the driven recruiting wave was produced soon after a spontaneously appearing wave. This occlusive interaction of recruiting and spontaneous cortical waves shows that they have a common neural origin in the cortex (Dempsey and Morison, 1942b).

While stimulation of the non-specific thalamic nuclei of the cat evokes recruiting waves in all parts of the cortex they are larger in sensorimotor cortex and middle suprasylvian gyri. Ablation of all but a small region of the cortex showed the recruiting response still present within that remaining cortical region. This was the case whether such cortical islands were made in frontal, posterior or medial sites (Dempsey and Morison, 1942a). Non-specific afferent fibers arising from the non-specific thalamic nuclei terminate widely within the cortex (Chapter 18). These fibers appear to carry recruiting impulses to the cortex. That the fibers

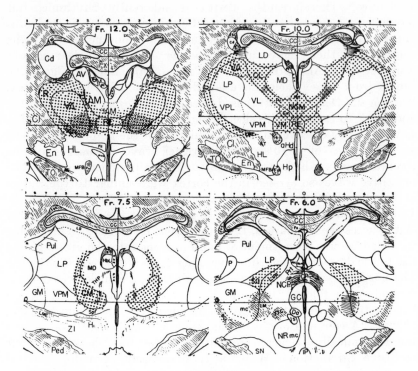

Fig. 20.1.   Diagram of thalamic reticular system of the cat.
Stereotaxic frontal plans (Fr.) 12, 10, 7.5 and 6.   Shown by the
stippling are areas in which stimulation gives recruiting responses.   The double stippling in the ventral portion of the nucleus
ventralis anterior indicates region where rostrally conducting
paths are most dense.   Some of the nuclei shown in these figures
are: AD, anterodorsal nucleus; AM, anteromedial nucleus; AV,
anteroventral nucleus; CC, corpus callosum; Cd, caudate nucleus;
CI, internal capsule; CM, centromedian nucleus; LD, lateral
dorsal nucleus; CP, posterior commisure; En, enteropenduncular
nucleus; Fx, fornix; GM, medial geniculate body; HL, lateral
hypothalamic area; LIM, nucleus limitans; LP, lateral posterior nucleus; MD, medial dorsal nucleus; NCP, nucleus of
the posterior commisure; NR, red nucleus; Pul, pulvinar; R,
reticular nucleus; RE, nucleus reuniens; SN, substantia nigra;
VA, ventral anterior nucleus; VL, ventral lateral nucleus; VM,
ventral medial nucleus; VPL, ventral posterolateral nucleus; VPM,
ventral posteromedial nucleus; Zi, zona incerta.   (Jasper, 1960.)

lo not gain access to the cortex via the specific sensory pathways was shown by the destruction of specific sensory nuclei in the thalamus without interfering with recruiting responses elicited from the non-specific nuclei (Hanbery and Jasper, 1953). The non-specific thalamic outflow apparently is distributed in the cortex via the internal capsule after funneling through a common non-specific nuclear group, the *nucleus reticularis* (Hanbery, Ajmone-Marsan and Dilworth, 1954). This was suggested by the shorter latency of recruiting waves excited from this region. The long latency of the recruiting waves (15–30 msec) could be explained by a low conduction velocity in the thalamocortical fibers. However, no differences in latency with stimulation closer or further from the cortex within

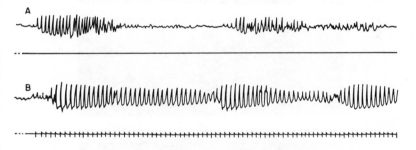

Fig. 20.2.   Records taken from suprasylvian gyrus of the cortex: (A) a series of spontaneous 8 to 12 per sec bursts; (B) repetitive stimulation within the intralaminar thalamic nuclei (at rate shown by signal marks in lowest line) producing a recruiting response which typically shows a waxing and waning in the amplitudes of the waves.   (Dempsey and Morison, 1942a.)

this system was found (Ajmone-Marsan, 1958). Other cortical responses have very little intracortical delay. A negative wave DCR starts with a delay of only a few milliseconds (Chapter 18) and the cortical response evoked from the specific thalamic nuclei also has a latency of a few milliseconds (Chapter 21). The long latency of the recruiting response appears to be due to a delay in the thalamus; most likely a polysynaptic system is excited in this region which, after an interval, transmits impulses to the cortex.

The properties of the thalamic polysynaptic system change with repeated stimulation to give rise to the 'waxing' phase of recruiting. The first wave excited in the train is small. Successive waves increase in amplitude and they also show a tendency to decrease in latency. During the 'waning' phase when amplitudes diminish, the latency tends to increase (Ajmone-Marsan, 1958).

The non-specific fibers from the thalamus appear to terminate on apical dendrites. The negative waves of the recruiting response have a similarity to the negative wave DCRs. When recruiting waves were elicited simultaneously with DCRs, the result was an occlusive type of interaction (Landau, Bishop and Clare, 1961),

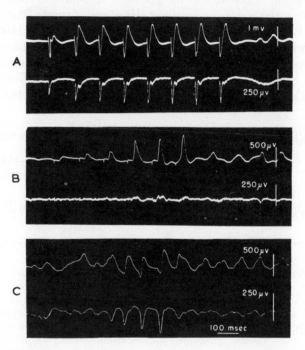

Fig. 20.3. The augmenting responses (A) recorded in the anterior sigmoid gyrus of the cortex to repetitive stimulation of the nucleus ventralis lateralis are shown in the upper trace and recordings from the medullary pyramids in the lower trace. The recruiting responses (B) recorded from the cortex upon stimulation of the nucleus reuniens is shown without a corresponding discharge found in the pyramidal trace (lower trace). The spontaneous spindle discharge (C) recorded from the cortex gives rise to some pyramidal tract discharge as seen in the lower trace. (Brookhart and Zanchetti, *Electroencephalog. Clin. Neurophysiol.*, 8: 427, 1956.)

a behavior expected if both the recruiting responses and negative wave DCRs are due to the activity of a common group of apical dendrites. The interaction is similar to that described for negative wave DCRs elicited from two cortical sites (Chapter 18). Recording from the cortical layers shows the negative waves of the recruiting response to be located in the upper cortical layers, most likely in the apical dendrites (Li, Cullen and Jasper, 1956).

Another type of cortical response excited by thalamic stimulation (Dempsey and Morison, 1943) is the *augmenting response* (A, Fig. 20.3). The augmenting response has some similarity to the recruiting response (B, Fig. 20.3). In each type of response the waves increase in amplitude with each repeated shock. They differ in that the augmenting waves have a short latency compared to the 15–30 msec latency of the recruiting waves (Starzl and Magoun, 1951; Bishop, Clare and Landau, 1961). The augmenting wave typically also has a positive phase preceding the negative wave. Associated with this surface positive potential is a sink of negativity found in the deeper cortical layers on laminar recording (Spencer and Brookhart, 1961a) and a motor discharge into the pyramidal tract (Fig. 20.3). Spontaneous electrical waves (C, Fig. 20.3) appear to be a mixture of augmenting and recruiting types of thalamic control (Spencer and Brookhart, 1961b).

In addition to a pacemaker action of thalamic regions on the cortex, corticothalamic impulses from the cortex terminate back on the thalamus and have an effect to modify rhythmic patterns. This interaction is not indispensable as shown by the finding (*vide supra*) that rhythmic discharges can be excited in isolated islands of cortex. Similarly, it has been found that the thalamus of decorticated preparations has similar rhythmic discharge. A theory for the production of such thalamic rhythms which in turn excite EEG rhythms has recently been proposed by Andersen and Eccles (1962). Recordings from individual thalamic cells show the presence of a long phase of hyperpolarization after a recruiting discharge (Purpura and Shofer, 1963). Similar long-lasting hyperpolarizations are seen in intracellular recordings taken from Betz cells (Chapter 22) and other CNS cells (Chapter 24). Andersen and Eccles (1962) believe that inhibitory interneurons are excited by axon collaterals (Fig. 20.4) so that when the thalamic cell discharges, the inhibitory cells are excited and the resulting hyperpolarization maintains an inhibition of thalamic cells for the duration of one wave of an EEG rhythm. This mechanism therefore is considered to control the cortical rhythm much as spinal cord motoneuron rhythmicity is controlled by the duration of the hyperpolarization phase (Chapter 16).

Arousal from the reticular formation

The identification of regions in the brain initiating the state of sleep or alternatively producing the waking state was greatly advanced

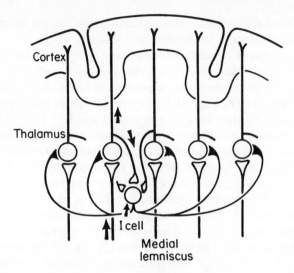

Cortex

Thalamus

I cell

Medial
lemniscus

Fig. 20.4.   Diagram of an hypothesis of EEG pacemaker arising
from the thalamus.   Thalamic cells have collaterals ending on
inhibitory (I cells) which act on other thalamic cells.   The
duration of inhibitory cell activity determines the duration of the
EEG wave.   (Andersen and Eccles, 1962.)

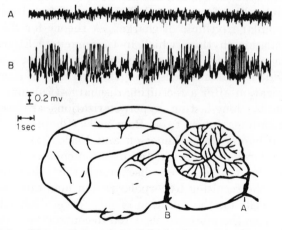

A

B

0.2 mv

1 sec

Fig. 20.5.   The medial surface of the brain stem is shown with cut
A behind the medulla to produce an *encephalé isolé* preparation.
Cut B at the intercollicular level produces a *cerveau isolé* preparation.   The encephalé isolé preparation shows in trace A
above, a low amplitude activated EEG.   The cerveau isolé
preparation shows in trace B above, a sleep-like pattern of the
EEG.   (From Bremer, 1937.)

by Bremer's (1937) first studies of the EEG of the brain of cats after mid-collicular decerebration. This *cerveau isolé* preparation (as the remaining anterior part of the brain is called) shows an EEG pattern of slow wave activity typical of drowsiness or sleep (B, Fig. 20.5). Furthermore, the pupils are constricted and the nictitating membranes cover the eye as in the normal sleep of the cat. Only the first three cranial nerves (olfactory, optic and oculomotor) remain connected with the brain. Bremer showed that sensory stimulation with strong odors via the olfactory nerves could transform the sleep pattern to a wakeful pattern. If more of the brain stem was included by a transection made through the lower part of the medulla to produce an *encephalé isolé* preparation (A, Fig. 20.5), then a wakeful pattern of the EEG was seen. Bremer concluded that the wakeful pattern is due to the greater number of sensory inputs connected with the brain stem of the encephalé isolé preparation, and that this activity constituted a tonic excitatory condition required for wakefulness. The specific sensory pathways to the cortex were considered to carry these excitatory impulses to the cortex.

Present in the brain stem is a structure known as the *reticular formation*. The term derives from its characteristic appearance of cells interposed between bands of fibers, an arrangement suggesting that it performs an integrating function (Rossi and Zanchetti, 1957). The reticular formation is found in the medulla and pons, extending forward into the non-specific thalamic nuclei and caudally along the dorsal horns of the spinal cord. A number of important vital functions are controlled from the reticular regions of the brain, e.g. circulation and respiration to be discussed in Chapter 23. The somatic motor control functions of this region will be discussed in Chapter 22.

By means of electrodes stereotaxically placed in the reticular formation of the brain stem, Moruzzi and Magoun (1949) were able to show that repetitive stimulation was effective in transforming a slow wave sleep pattern to a low amplitude, fast wave pattern typical of the wakeful state (Fig. 20.6). This EEG change has been called *arousal, alerting* or *desynchronization*. The period of EEG activation so obtained usually outlasts the period of stimulation before the return of the slow wave sleep pattern. The duration and degree of arousal varies. Some of the variability is due to an habituation of arousal to repeated elicitations which will be discussed in Chapter 25.

Arousal can also be obtained from the lightly anesthetized animal or in drowsing animals in which electrodes have been chronically implanted in the reticular formation. When these animals show signs of drowsiness, stimulation of the reticular formation causes them to raise their heads and look around; they show *behavioral arousal* at the time their EEG shows a wakeful pattern.

The stimulation studies of the reticular formation showing arousal are complemented by the prolonged sleep states which follow damage to those parts of the brain stem where the reticular formation is present. Such lesions occur in the sleeping disease *encephalitis*

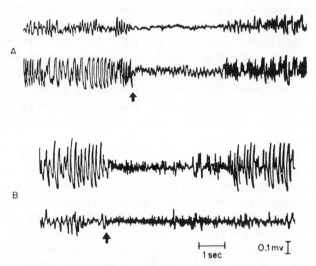

Fig. 20.6.   The EEGs obtained from motor and visual cortex show that upon sensory stimulation (A) at the arrow, the EEG changes temporarily to the activated pattern.   A similar activation occurs in response to a brief electrical stimulation (arrow) of the reticular formation.   (Bremer, 1961.)

lethargica (Economo, 1918).   For the most part the lesion in this disease is found in the central gray of the midbrain.   Tumors in this region also produce prolonged states of somnolence (Fulton and Bailey, 1929).   Experimental lesions have been produced in this central region and these also cause a prolonged somnolent state (Lindsley, Bowden and Magoun, 1949).   As can be seen in Fig. 20.7, lesions of the dorsal portion of the midbrain or laterally to include the specific sensory pathways do not produce the sleep state.   However, lesions placed centrally and low to include the reticular formation produce the high voltage, low frequency EEG pattern associated with sleep. The behavior of these animals also corresponds to the EEG signs. Animals prepared with lateral destructions including the specific sensory pathways appear alert and awake. Those animals with midline destructions of the reticular formation are comatose, lying limply on their sides (French and Magoun, 1952) (Fig. 20.8).

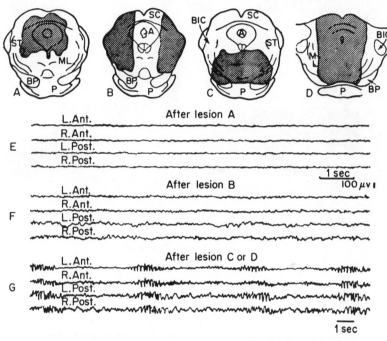

Fig. 20.7. Transverse sections of the brain stem shown diagrammatically with lesions indicated by cross-hatching. A lesion involving the upper medial part of the brainstem (A) or of the lateral parts of the brainstem (B) does not interfere with activation pattern of the EEG, as shown in EEG records E and F. Lesions involving the medial part of the brain stem (C, D) do, as shown in EEG traces G. (Lindsley, Bowden and Magoun, 1949.)

Therefore, the reticular formation acts as a second type of sensory system in parallel with that of the specific sensory system and the integrity of the reticular formation is required to maintain the wakeful state. The reticular formation activation system receives collaterals from the various specific afferent tracts passing alongside it. These collaterals serve as an afferent source of excitation to the reticular formation which then passes its tonic excitation upward

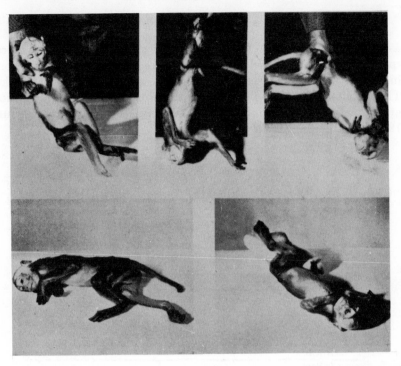

Fig. 20.8.   A monkey prepared with lesions in the brain stem region
(D of Fig. 20.7) has an appearance akin to deep sleep or coma.
(French and Magoun, 1952.)

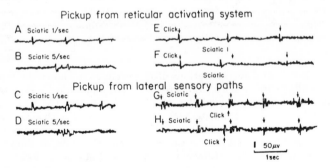

Fig. 20.9.   Evoked responses to a brief sciatic nerve stimulation
(A, B) or to a click of sound (E, F) are shown recorded from the
reticular formation.   When the responses follow one another
at close intervals, the second evoked response is diminished in
amplitude, an occlusive-like interaction of common responding
elements.   A similar presentation of sound stimulation in the
lateral sensory paths (C, D) does not show this type of occlusive-
like interaction (G, H).   (Modified from French, von Amerongen
and Magoun, *Arch. Neurol and Psychiat.*, **68**: 577, 1952.)

o the cerebral cortex (*vide infra*). The action of collaterals on neurons of the reticular formation was shown by the evoked responses recorded within the reticular formation following a brief stimulation of specific sensory channels. These evoked responses were obtained in response to clicks, light flashes, touches or an electrical shock to the sciatic nerve. The evoked responses within the reticular formation have the same form regardless of which of these different sensory modalities have been excited. When responses to different

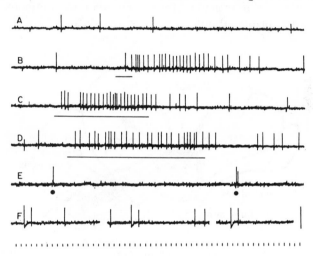

Fig. 20.10. The spontaneous discharge of a neuron of the reticular formation shown in A. Tapping the ipsilateral forelimb (B) as shown by the bar under the trace of B is followed by a discharge of the unit. Similarly rubbing the back (C), touching whiskers (D), a sudden sound (hand clap) (E) or single electrical shocks to the ipsilateral sensory motor cortex (F), will all cause a discharge of this same cell. Calibration, 10 msec, 0.5 mv. (From Palestini, Rossi and Zanchetti, 1957.)

ense modalities are presented close together in time, an occlusive interaction of the reticular responses occurs (Fig. 20.9). This occlusion indicates that the collaterals feed into a common cell population in the reticular formation which then gives rise to the response. Microelectrode recordings of units within the reticular formation shows that diverse sensory inputs can excite discharges in the same cells (Palestini, Rossi and Zanchetti, 1957; Bradley and Mollica, 1958). This is indicated in Fig. 20.10 where a cell is shown responding to tapping of the foreleg, rubbing the back, touching whiskers, hand clap (sound) as well as to single shocks to the sensorimotor cortex. About 49% of the reticular formation cells in the medial region showed such convergence of input, while 7% could only be driven by a single sensory modality.

The non-specificity of cells in their response to different sensory modalities shown by evoked responses and by unit-cell studies suggests that the general level of sensory activity is abstracted in the reticular formation from the various specific sensory inputs ascending in the brain (Fig. 20.11). In turn this increased level of activity within the reticular formation acts to augment cortical activity and bring about the waking state. The generalized

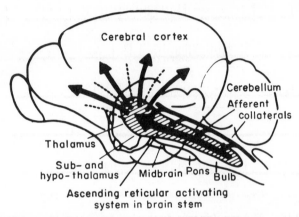

Ascending reticular activating
system in brain stem

Fig. 20.11. The simplest version of the ascending reticular activating system is shown. Collateral sensory impulses converge into the reticular formation shown by the hatched area. Impulses from the reticular formation are, in turn, relayed to the cerebral cortex where activation is produced. (Starzl, Taylor and Magoun, *J. Neurophysiol.* 14: 479, 1951.)

function of this region has been viewed as a *tonic* sensory system, one which increases cortical excitability. The unit studies also have shown that a more specific type of organization is found in the reticular formation by the fact that some cells respond to one type of sensory input and not others. The significance of such sub-systems within the reticular formation is at present little understood (Rossi and Zanchetti, 1957). A more recently discovered division of function between upper and lower parts of the reticular system will be discussed in the next section.

In their original study, Moruzzi and Magoun (1949) suggested that the ascending influence from reticular formation acted on the non specific thalamic nuclei to interfere with their pacemaker activity (*vide supra*). This was shown by the fact that recruiting waves excited from the thalamus could be blocked by reticular formation stimulation. Similarly, the negative phase of augmenting potentials have been shown to be blocked by reticular formation stimulation (Gauthier, Parma and Zanchetti, 1956). However, alternatively we can consider the possibility that fibers from the reticular formation terminating on the apical dendrites of pyramidal cells block at this common site of response by occlusive interaction. This was indicated by the effect of reticular formation stimulation to decrease negative wave DCRs (Purpura, 1956) interpreted by Purpura, however, as an IPSP action on apical dendrites (Chapters 18, 19). However, an inhibitory action of reticular formation activation is hard to reconcile with a variety of evidence showing that the effect of reticular formation is to increase cortical excitability (Magoun, 1963). At a low level of reticular formation activation, synaptic activation will result in a subliminal excitability increase. With increased excitation of the reticular formation, the result is the discharge of the apical dendrites and the occlusive interaction of responses engaging the apical dendrites (Bremer, 1961; cf. Chapter 18). This interpretation of the data seems to account for the main features of activation and it overcomes the apparent discrepancy of decreased cortical responses during states associated with activation. However, the evoked responses are mass discharges, representing an averaging of a large number of cortical cells (Chapters 18, 21). The discharge of individual units may be recorded with microelectrodes from the cortex during states of sleep and wakefulness (Creutzfeldt and Jung, 1961). The irregular discharges found in the waking state become grouped during sleep into bursts with long periods of suppression, possibly due to an inhibitory mechanism. A prolonged suppression or inhibition of unit responses is found following an evoked response and the period of suppression is longer-lasting in the waking state. This, and the greater synchronization of units in the sleep state led Evarts (1961) to consider that inhibitory mechanisms are present in the waking state causing cells to become differentiated in their activities. Further studies of unit responses should reveal those special mechanisms present in the cortex to give rise to sleep and wakefulness.

There is anatomical evidence that the reticular formation fibers gain entry to the cortex other than via the non-specific thalamic nuclei. Indeed Starzl, Taylor and Magoun (1951) found that destruction of the non-specific thalamic regions did not block EEG arousal produced by reticular formation stimulation. However, other evidence indicates that there is an action of the reticular formation on the non-specific thalamic nuclei. Stimulation of non-specific thalamic nuclei on one side of the brain stem excites recruiting-like waves recorded from the non-specific thalamic nuclei on the other side. Stimulation of the reticular formation blocks these crossed thalamic recruiting responses demonstrating the effect of the reticular formation on the non-specific thalamic nuclei (Moruzzi and Magoun 1949). Therefore, the evidence suggests two ascending influences from the reticular formation, one via the thalamus, the other by passing it.

In addition to ascending reticulo-cortical influences, there are also corticofugal actions on the reticular formation. Some regions of the cortex when stimulated are able to evoke responses in the reticular

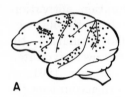 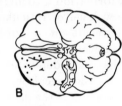 

A   B   C

Fig. 20.12. Dots on the cortical surface represent sites on the monkey brain where stimulation gave rise to evoked potentials recorded in the central cephalic part of the brain stem. A, lateral surface; B, base of brain; C, medial surface. Inactive zones are left blank. (French, Hernández-Peón and Livingston, 1955.)

formation (French, Hernández-Peón and Livingston, 1955). The distribution of those cortical sites are shown in Fig. 20.12. It is quite likely that arousal may be brought about by such corticofugal pathways.

Corticofugal mechanisms acting back on the reticular formation in feedback fashion appear to be the basis of a reflex response of animal to a novel stimulation first described by Pavlov as the *orienting reflex* (Sokolev, 1960). In response to a sudden sound the eyes and head are turned in that direction, and shifts in body tonus may occur with flexion on the side of the sound and extension on the opposite side. The alpha rhythm is blocked, i.e., alerting is seen in the EEG. A novel stimulus is required to excite the orienting reflex. On repetition of the stimulus the reflex effects become adapted or habituated (Chapter 25). An absence of one of a series of repeated stimulations to which the animal has adapted is novel and this may excite the reflex anew (Sokolev, 1960). This mechanism appears to account for a mother's sudden awakening from an apparently deep sleep in response to her baby's cry or a sudden sound (Oswald, 1962). This corticoreticular mechanism is one of a number of feedback systems found present in the sensory system whereby a higher center exerts a control over sensory input—in this case the non-specific effects of the arousal system (Chapters 17, 22).

Hypnogenic systems

It appears that sleep can come about not only by the reduction of activity in a tonic activating system but also by the influence of an active sleep-producing system. Evidence for such an active sleep-producing mechanism was obtained by Hess (1944) using electrodes chronically implanted in the thalamus of cats. These animals were not otherwise restrained except by the connecting cable. Electrical stimulation of alert animals in the region of the massa intermedia of the thalamus with low rate, long duration pulses caused the animals to select a likely place to sleep in which they curled up and then proceeded to go to sleep much as a normal animal would. And like the normally drowsing animal, noises or food smells aroused it in the early stages of sleep. Therefore, Hess believed that stimulation in this region of the diencephalon produced true sleep by an active process rather than as a loss of excitatory influences arising from the reticular formation. Hess, Koella and Akert (1953) and Akimoto et al. (1956) have shown that these behavioral signs of sleep are accompanied by slow EEG waves typical of the sleeping animal. Also noted was a transformation to an arousal by a changed rate of stimulation. Stimulation at 8/sec was effective in inducing sleep, 40/sec in causing arousal.

Another part of the diencephalon, the sub- and hypothalamic region, has been implicated by Ranson (1939) as a waking center. Lesions in these regions could produce somnolence by the elimination of impulses in a system of fibers passing down into the brain stem. In a study of the hypothalamic region of rats, Nauta (1946) found that lesions of the posterior portion produced prolonged somnolence. Lesions more forward in the preoptic region produced a state of sleeplessness. This suggested to him that a sleep center was present in this part of the brain. These studies fitted with those of Economo (1918) who found, in some of his encephalitic patients, prolonged sleeplessness associated with lesions in forward parts of the hypothalamic region.

The connection of areas within the hypothalamus and limbic brain stem to sleep and wakefulness was more recently investigated (Hernández-Peón and Ibarra, 1963; Hernández-Peón *et al.*, 1963). Positive sleep-producing areas were found as well as arousal areas. Electrodes were chronically implanted into hypothalamic and nearby basal brain structures and cannulae were also inserted in these regions so that the action of locally injected ACh, or noradrenalin as well as electrical stimulation could be studied in the relatively un-restrained cat. Electrical stimulation of these brain areas could produce both behavioral signs of sleep and large amplitude, slow

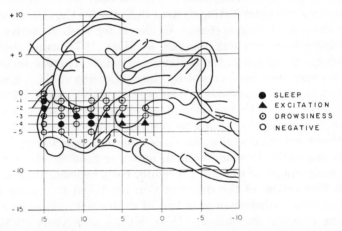

Fig. 20.13. A sagittal section of the brain stem shows those regions where acetylcholine injections into free-moving awake animals via chronically implanted cannulae will produce a state resembling sleep, both behaviorally and in the EEG records. Other sites give excitation, drowsiness, or have no effect. (Hernández-Peón and Ibarra, 1963.)

waves in the EEG typical of sleep. The effect was most readily obtained from the preoptic area of the hypothalamus using stimulating frequencies of 1–8 sec. The animal relaxed and curled up; sleep ensued 45 seconds after the onset of stimulation. The animal could be aroused from this state of sleep by stimulation in the reticular formation. Injection of ACh into the medial posterior hypothalamus area (Fig. 20.13) also caused the usual signs of sleep. The animal settled itself by curling up and the EEG showed the sleep pattern. The latency was 2–5 minutes and lasted 2–3 hours. Unless sleep was very deep, sensory stimulation was effective in arousing the animal. Atropine blocked the effect of ACh-induced sleep and it also blocked electrical stimulations in these hypnogenic regions.

Cholinergic substances injected into parts of the limbic brain regions were shown to be effective in inducing sleep. In other regions, injection of cholinergic agents gave rise to arousal. Of interest was the fact that injections of noradrenalin elicited alertness from the same points in the preoptic area where cholinergic stimulation evoked sleep (Hernández-Peón et al., 1963).

A hypnogenic role for ACh in the reticular formation was shown. When Ach was injected into this region via chronically implanted cannulae, the animals would curl up rapidly, showing the behavior seen in normal onset of sleep (Cordeau, Moreau, Beaulnes and Laurin, 1963). These animals could be aroused by external stimuli early in the sleep so produced, and the EEG showed a sleep pattern. The injection of adrenalin into the reticular formation produced the opposite effect—behavioral arousal and desynchronization of the EEG. Such actions of adrenalin complement the studies of Dell, Bonvallet and Hugelin (1955), Sigg, Ochs and Gerard (1955) and Rothballer (1956) in that small amounts of adrenalin injected into the blood supply appear to have an excitant effect on the reticular formation. The amounts involved approach that of the adrenalin circulating in the blood during stress and may be part of a hormonal action of adrenalin to stimulate the CNS through this route during stress. However, adrenalin electrophoretically released near single cells of the reticular formation failed to excite them (Curtis and Koizumi, 1961) making the mechanism of adrenalin action unclear at the present time.

In addition to the evidence of hypnogenic regions in the thalamus and hypothalamus, an active suppression of the reticular activating system arising from the lower brain stem has been shown in the studies of Batissi, Moruzzi, Palestini, Rossi and Zanchetti (1959). Lesions made in the rostropontile part of the brain stem (A, Fig. 20.14) gave rise to an EEG picture of arousal while lesions a few millimeters lower, at the midpontile level (B, Fig. 20.14), resulted in the EEG pattern typical of sleep. The inference was that a mechanism present in the lower part of the reticular formation brings about sleep by inhibiting the upper reticular formation (Moruzzi, 1960). This was further indicated by the experiments of Magni, Moruzzi, Rossi and Zanchetti (1959) using a method of separately blocking the activity of upper and caudal parts of the brain stem by perfusion of barbiturates through their different respective blood supplies, carotid and vertebral (Fig. 20.15). Barbiturates have been shown to exert their

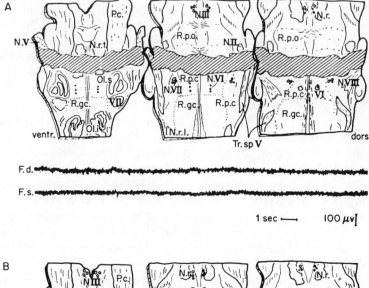

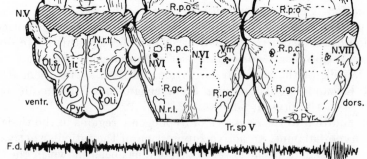

Fig. 20.14. Horizontal sections of the brain stem in the anterior-posterior plane of the cat with lesions transecting the brain stem shown in cross-hatching. Transection at the midpontile level (A) gives rise as shown in the EEG traces below to an activated EEG pattern. Transection higher in the brain stem, at the rostropontile level (B), gives rise to sleep-like pattern of EEG. Right (F.d.) and left (F.s.) frontal area recorded in EEG. (Batini *et al.*, 1959.)

ypnotic action via a block of the reticular formation (Arduini and Arduini, 1954). Upon perfusion of the caudal half of the brain tem through the vertebral vessels with the barbiturate *thiopental*, ctivation of the EEG was found (Fig. 20.16). This would be due to a block of the lower brain stem and a release of tonic activation produced by the rostral reticular formation (rostropontile region).

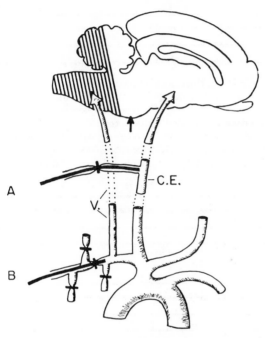

Fig. 20.15.   The midbrain and upper cerebrum are perfused (A) via the carotid blood supply through a cannula inserted in the external carotid (C.E.) blood vessel.   Perfusion of the medulla and caudal pons (B) shown cross-hatched, is achieved by a cannula inserted into the vertebral artery (V.).   (From Magni *et al.*, 1959.)

Similarly, barbiturate perfusion of the upper portion via the carotids will bring about the sleep-like EEG pattern (Fig. 20.17).

It appears that two systems are involved in both limbic and reticular formation structures, a sleep-inducing or hypnogenic system and an awakening or arousal system.   These may be reciprocally connected so that activity in the one will suppress the other, and vice-versa thereby giving rise to the sleep–waking cycle (Hernández-Peón, 1963).

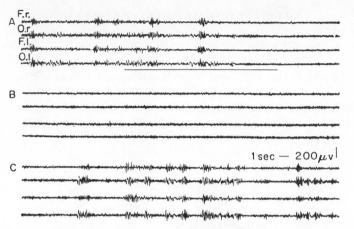

Fig. 20.16. Using the injection route B of Fig. 20.15, thiopental injected into lower part of the brain stem to block its activity at the time shown by the bar (A) causes the sleep pattern to become replaced with an activated EEG pattern. The records are continued (B, C) showing recovery from the effect of the injection. Traces in A and its continuation B, C are: F.r., frontal right; O.r., occipital right; F.l., frontal left; O.l., occipital left. (Magni *et al.*, 1959.)

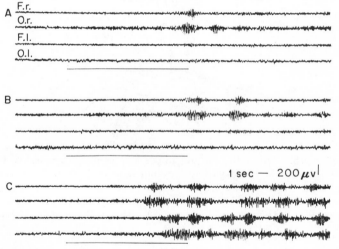

Fig. 20.17. Using the injection route shown in A of Fig. 20.15, thiopental injected into the upper part of the brain stem to block its activity at the time under the EEG traces shown by the bar causes soon afterwards a change toward a sleep pattern. In A, B and C, 0.1, 0.3 and 0.6 mg respectively, of thiopental was injected. A unilateral effect is seen at the weaker dose levels (A, B) where injections into the right carotid gave the effect on the EEG recorded on that side, not on the left. With a larger dose, C showed a bilateral effect. Traces as in Fig. 20.16. (Magni *et al.*, 1959.)

Rhombencephalic sleep (paradoxical phase of sleep)

So far we have been considering sleep simply as a uniform state of the organism characterized by the slow wave activity of the EEG and motor relaxation. More recently the investigations of human sleep by Aserinsky and Kleitman (1955) and Dement and Wolpert 1958) have shown that during sleep periods of paradoxical low amplitude, fast wave activity appears in the EEG. During these

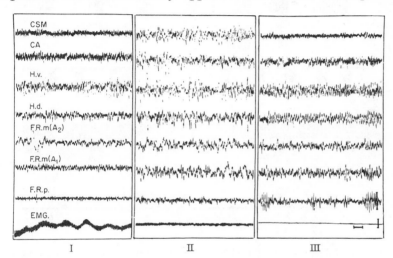

Fig. 20.18. Columns show EEG of the cat in (I), arousal; (II), slow phase of sleep; (III), rhombencephalic (paradoxical) phase of sleep. EEG records taken from various sites; sensorimotor (CSM), auditory (CA), hippocampal (H.v., H.d.) pontile and mesencephalic reticular formation (F.R.p., F.R.m.) shows in the slow phase of sleep slow waves and spindles. In rhombencephalic sleep there is an activated EEG pattern in the cortex and larger wave rhythms in the hippocampus and pontile reticular formation. The electromyogram taken from the neck muscles (EMG) shows a disappearance of activity during the rhombencephalic phase of sleep. (Disregard wave-like shifts in EEG base-line in I). Calibration 1 sec., 50 μv. (Courtesy M. Jouvet, from Jouvet, 1960.)

periods *rapid eyeball movements* often occur, and when the subject is awakened he reports that he has been dreaming. No dreams are reported present when the subject is awakened at other times. These dreams occur periodically at 80–90 min intervals giving rise to 5 or 6 dreaming sessions. Using the rapid eye movements and low amplitude EEG as an index of dreaming, it was possible to incorporate external stimuli into a dream sequence (Kleitman, 1960).

A light shined in the face or a water spray from a hypodermic syringe would elicit dreams in which light or water became part of the dream. Furthermore, a dream may be continued from one period to another period. Upon awakening, the subject may remember little of his

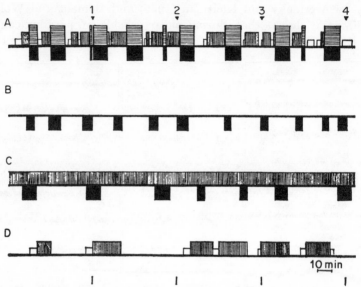

Fig. 20.19. Bar graph showing extent and duration of signs of sleep and wakefulness in cats: (A), intact; (B), decorticate preparation; (C), mesencephalic preparation and (D), animals with coagulation of the pontine reticular formation. Numbers represent hours of recording. Black rectangles indicate the appearance of the rhombencephalic stage of sleep. White rectangles represent spindling activity found in the cortex; vertical hatched rectangles indicate the presence of slow waves and spindles at the cortical and diencephalic level. The horizontally hatched rectangles represent periods of arousal. Note absence of slow wave and sleep spindles in decorticated cats; absence of rhombencephalic phase of sleep in cats with pontine lesions, suggesting an origin of the rhombencephalic phase of sleep from the pons. (Jouvet, 1960.)

dreams. Therefore, it appears that normally we dream but usually remember little of them (Oswald, 1962).

When studied continuously throughout their sleeping time, animals will show a similar periodic activation of their EEG. In the cat Jouvet (1960) found that the tonus of the neck muscles was correlated with these paradoxical phases of EEG activation, the muscle EMG showing a total lack of discharge at this time (Fig.

20.18). Using the reduction of EMG activity as an index of the presence of this periodical activation, it was found that decortication did not block it, nor did cuts of the brain stem producing a mesencephalic animal. However, it was blocked by a lower pontile level transection (Fig. 20.19). Jouvet believes that a mechanism in the pons (rhombencephalon) region brings about these periodic changes during sleep. Stimulation of this area of the brain either electrically or with drugs may excite or increase the duration of the paradoxical phase. Cholinergic drugs such as eserine can prolong its duration, and atropine can reduce its duration or stop it from appearing. Further study may very well reveal other interesting connections between biochemical sensitivity and phases of sleep.

REFERENCES

Ajmone-Marsan, C. (1958). Recruiting response in cortical and subcortical structures. *Arch. Ital. Biol.* **96**: 1–16.

Akimoto, H., Yamaguchi, N., Okabi, K., Nakagawa, T., Nakamura, I., Abe, K., Horli, T. and Masahashi, K. (1956). On the sleep induced through electrical stimulation of dog thalamus. *Folia Psych. Neurol. Jap.* **10**: 117–146.

Andersen, P. and Eccles, J. C. (1962). Inhibitory phasing of neuronal discharge. *Nature* **196**: 645–647.

Arduini, A. and Arduini, M. G. (1954). Effects of drugs and metabolic alterations on brain stem arousal mechanism. *J. Pharmacol. Exptl. Therap.* **110**: 76–85.

Aserinsky, E. and Kleitman, N. (1955). Two types of ocular motility occurring in sleep. *J. Appl. Physiol.* **8**: 1–10; and A motility cycle in sleeping infants as manifested by ocular and gross bodily activity. *Ibid.*, 11–18.

Batini, C., Moruzzi, G., Palestini, M., Rossi, G. F. and Zanchetti, A. (1959). Effects of complete pontine transections on the sleep-wakefulness rhythm: the midpontine pretrigeminal preparation. *Arch. Ital. Biol.* **97**: 1–12.

Bishop, G. H., Clare, M. H. and Landau, W. M. (1961). The equivalence of recruiting and augmenting phenomena in the visual cortex of the cat. *Electroencephalog. Clin. Neurophysiol.* **13**: 34–42.

Bradley, P. B. and Mollica, A. (1958). The effect of adrenaline and acetylcholine on single unit activity in the reticular formation of the decerebrate cat. *Arch. Ital. Biol.* **96**: 168–186.

Bremer, F. (1937). L'activité cérébrale au cours du sommeil et de la narcose. Contribution à l'étude du mécanisme du sommeil. *Bull. Acad. Roy. Med. Belg.* **2**: 68–86.

Bremer, F. (1961). Neurophysiological mechanisms in cerebral arousal. *The Nature of Sleep*. Edited by G. E. W. Wolstenholme and M. O'Connor. Pp. 30–56. Ciba Foundation Symposium. Little, Brown and Co., Boston.

Cordeau, J. P., Moreau, A., Beaulnes, A. and Laurin, C. (1963). EEC and behavioral changes following microinjections of acetylcholine and adrenaline in the brain stem of cats. *Arch. Ital. Biol.* **101** 30–47.

Creutzfeldt, O. and Jung, R. (1961). Neuronal discharge in the cat's motoi cortex during sleep and arousal. *The Nature of Sleep*. Edited by G. E W. Wolstenholme and M. O'Connor. Pp. 131–170. Ciba Foundatior Symposium. Little, Brown and Co., Boston.

Curtis, D. R. and Koizumi, K. (1961). Chemical transmitter substances ir brain stem of cat. *J. Neurophysiol.* **24**: 80–90.

Dell, P., Bonvallet, M. and Hugelin, A. (1955). Tonus sympathique adrénaline et contrôle réticulaire de la motricité spinale. *Electroenceph alog. Clin. Neurophysiol.* **6**: 599–618.

Dement, W. and Wolpert, E. (1958). The relation of eye movements, bodɣ motility and external stimuli to dream content. *J. Exptl. Psychol.* **55** 543–553; and Relationships in the manifest content of dreams occurring on the same night. *J. Nervous Mental Disease* **126**: 568–578.

Dempsey, E. W. and Morison, R. S. (1942a). The production of rhythmicallɣ recurrent cortical potentials after localized thalamic stimulation. *Am J. Physiol.* **135**: 293–300.

Dempsey, E. W. and Morison, R. S. (1942b). The interaction of certair spontaneous and induced cortical potentials. *Am. J. Physiol.* **135** 301–308.

Dempsey, E. W. and Morison, R. S. (1943). The electrical activity of a thalamocortical relay system. *Am. J. Physiol.* **138**: 283–296.

Economo, C. von (1918). *Die Encephalitis Lethargica*. Deuticke, Vienna.

Economo, C. von (1929). Schlaftheorie. *Ergeb. Physiol.* **28**: 312–339.

Evarts, E. V. (1961). Effects of sleep and waking on activity of single units in the unrestrained cat. *The Nature of Sleep*. Edited by G. E. W. Wolstenholme and M. O'Connor. Pp. 171–187. Ciba Foundation Symposium. Little, Brown and Co., Boston.

French, J. D. and Magoun, H. W. (1952). Effects of chronic lesions in central cephalic brain stem of monkeys. *Arch. Neurol. Psychiat.* **68**: 591–604.

French, J. D., Hernández-Peón, R. and Livingston, R. B. (1955). Projections from cortex to cephalic brain stem (reticular formation) in monkey. *J. Neurophysiol.* **18**: 74–95.

Fulton, J. F. and Bailey, P. (1929). Tumors in the region of the third ventricle: their diagnosis and relation to pathological sleep. *J. Nervous Mental Disease* **69**: 1–25, 145–164, 261–272.

Gauthier, C., Parma, M. and Zanchetti, A. (1956). Effect of electrocortical arousal upon development and configuration of specific evoked potentials. *Electroencephalog. Clin. Neurophysiol.* **8**: 237–243.

Hanbery, J., Ajmone-Marsan, C. and Dilworth, M. (1954). Pathways of non-specific thalamocortical projection system. *Electroencephalog. Clin. Neurophysiol.* **6**: 103–118.

Hanbery, J. and Jasper, H. H. (1953). Independence of diffuse thalamocortical projection system shown by specific nuclear destructions. *J. Neurophysiol.* **16**: 252–271.

Hernández-Peón, R. and Ibarra G. C. (1963). Sleep induced by electrical or chemical stimulation of the forebrain. *The Physiological Basis of Mental Activity*. Edited by R. Hernández-Peón. *Electroencephalog. Clin. Neurophysiol. Suppl.* **24**: 188–198.

Hernández-Peón, R., Chávez-Ibarra, G., Morgane, P. J. and Timo-Iaria, C. (1963). Limbic cholinergic pathways involved in sleep and emotional behavior. *Exptl. Neurol.* **8**: 93–111.

Hess, W. R. (1944). Das Schlafsyndrom als Folge dienzephaler Reizung. *Helv. Physiol. Acta.* **2**: 305–344.

Hess, R., Jr., Koella, W. P. and Akert, K. (1953). Cortical and subcortical recordings in natural and artificially induced sleep in cats. *Electroencephalog. Clin. Neurophysiol.* **5**: 75–90.

Jasper, H. H. (1960). Unspecific thalamocortical relations. *Handbook of Physiology–Neurophysiology*. Vol. 2, pp. 1307–1321. American Physiological Society, Washington, D.C.

Jouvet, M. (1960). Telencephalic and rhombencephalic sleep in the cat. *The Nature of Sleep*. Edited by G. E. W. Wolstenholme and M. O'Connor. Pp. 188–208. Ciba Foundation Symposium. Little, Brown and Co., Boston.

Kleitman, N. (1960). The nature of dreaming. *The Nature of Sleep*. Edited by G. E. W. Wolstenholme and M. O'Connor. Pp. 349–374. Ciba Foundation Symposium. Little, Brown and Co., Boston.

Kleitman, N. (1963). *Sleep and Wakefulness*. Revised and enlarged edition. University of Chicago Press, Chicago.

Landau, W. M., Bishop, G. H. and Clare, M. H. (1961). The interactions of several varieties of evoked response in visual and association cortex of the cat. *Electroencephalog Clin. Neurophysiol.* **13**: 43–53.

Li, C.-L., Cullen, C. and Jasper, H. H. (1956). Laminar microelectrode analysis of cortical unspecific recruiting responses and spontaneous rhythms. *J. Neurophysiol.* **19**: 131–143.

Lindsley, D. B., Bowden, J. W. and Magoun, H. W. (1949). Effect upon the EEG of acute injury to the brain stem activating system. *Electroencephalog. Clin. Neurophysiol.* **1**: 475–486.

Magni, F., Moruzzi, G., Rossi, G. F. and Zanchetti, A. (1959). EEG arousal following inactivation of the lower brain stem by selective injection of barbiturate into lower brain stem circulation. *Arch. Ital. Biol.* **97**: 33–46.

Magoun, H. W. (1963). *The Waking Brain*. (2nd Ed.) Charles C. Thomas, Springfield.

Morison, R. S. and Dempsey, E. W. (1942). A study of thalamo-cortical relations. *Am. J. Physiol.* **135**: 281–292.

Moruzzi, G. (1960). Synchronizing influences of the brain stem and the inhibitory mechanisms underlying the production of sleep by sensory stimulation. *The Moscow Colloqium on Electroencephalography of Higher Nervous Activity*. Edited by H. H. Jasper and G. D. Smirnov. *Electroencephalog. Clin. Neurophysiol. Suppl.* **13**: 231–256.

Moruzzi, G. and Magoun, H. W. (1949). Brain stem reticular formation and activation of the EEG. *Electroencephalog. Clin. Neurophysiol.* **1**: 455–473.

Nauta, W. J. H. (1946). Hypothalamic regulation of sleep in rats. Ar experimental study. *J. Neurophysiol.* **9**: 285–316.

Oswald, I. (1962). *Sleeping and Waking: Physiology and Psychology.* Elsevier New York.

Palestini, M., Rossi, G. F. and Zanchetti, A. (1957). An electrophysiologica analysis of pontine reticular regions showing different anatomica organization. *Arch. Ital. Biol.* **95**: 97–109.

Purpura, D. P. (1956). Observations on the cortical mechanism of EEC activation accompanying behavioral arousal. *Science* **123**: 804.

Purpura, D. P. and Shofer, R. J. (1963). Intracellular recording from tha lamic neurons during reticulocortical activation. *J. Neurophysiol.* **26** 494–505.

Ranson, S. W. (1939). Somnolence caused by hypothalamic lesions in the monkey. *Arch. Neurol. Psychiat.* **41**: 1–23.

Rossi, G. F. and Zanchetti, A. (1957). The brain stem reticular formation Anatomy and physiology. *Arch. Ital. Biol.* **95**: 199–438.

Rothballer, A. B. (1956). Studies on the adrenalin-sensitive components o the reticular activating system. *Electroencephalog. Clin. Neurophysiol* **8**: 603–621.

Sigg, E., Ochs, S. and Gerard, R. W. (1955). Effects of the medullary hor mones on the somatic nervous system in the cat. *Am. J. Physiol.* **183** 419–426.

Sokolev, E. N. (1960). Neuronal models and the orienting reflex. *CNS ana Behavior.* Vol. III. Edited by M. A. B. Brazier. Pp. 187–276. Macy Foundation, New York.

Spencer, W. A. and Brookhart, J. M. (1961a). Electrical patterns of aug menting and recruiting waves in depths of sensorimotor cortex of cat *J. Neurophysiol.* **24**: 26–49.

Spencer, W. A. and Brookhart, J. M. (1961b). A study of spontaneous spindle waves in sensorimotor cortex of cat. *J. Neurophysiol.* **24** 50–65.

Starzl, T. E. and Magoun, H. W. (1951). Organization of the diffuse thalamic projection system. *J. Neurophysiol.* **14**: 133–146.

Starzl, T. E., Taylor, C. W. and Magoun, H. W. (1951). Ascending conduction in reticular activating system, with special reference to the diencephalon *J. Neurophysiol.* **14**: 461–477.

21

Higher Sensory Mechanism

The repetitive discharge from the receptor organs (the sensory code described in Chapter 11) will be traced through pathways in the spinal cord and thalamus to the sensory regions of the cortex. A term used by Pavlov (Chapter 25) is particularly apt with regard to the whole of a specific sensory pathway—the *first signalling system*. For example, with regard to the visual system (*vide infra*) this would involve the optic nerve, optic tract, lateral geniculate body, optic radiations and striate cortex. The sensory mechanisms and their relation to sensation and perception to be described in this chapter requires attention to the complex anatomical relationships of sensory fibers and tracts present in the CNS. It is likely that study of the simpler arthropod CNS will one day reveal general principles of sensory transformations (Wiersma, 1962).

Specific sensory areas in the cortex

The specific sensory areas of the cortex for visual, somesthetic and auditory reception are shown for several species in Fig. 21.1. The afferent fibers of ascending sensory pathways terminate within these sensory areas of the cortex. The cytoarchitectural organization of the primary receptor areas is in part determined by the entry of afferent fibers of large diameter into that part of the cortex with an extensive proliferation of their terminals. In the case of the visual cortex, the presence of terminals in the fourth layer produces a striped appearance and it is designated the *striate cortex* (O'Leary, 1941). A similar though not so pronounced cytoarchitectural appearance is found for the other primary sensory areas, i.e. auditory and somesthetic (Chapter 18). Too much emphasis should not be placed on the horizontal layering of the cortex. Physiological evidence of an important vertical organization of cortical cells will be presented later in this chapter.

The sensory function of these primary areas was shown by various techniques. One of the earliest proofs was behavioral. Dogs were trained to respond to food signals (Chapter 25). Then various parts of the cortex were removed and the retention of the response was determined.   Minkowski (1911) showed by this means that a region in the occipital area was essential for visual apprehension.   Another technique was the use of strychnine for the localization of the somesthetic area by Dusser de Barenne (1916).   Strychnine was applied to various regions of the cortex, making those regions hyperexcitable (Chapter 18).   When strychnine was applied to the somesthetic region, a previously innocuous touch to the skin caused altered

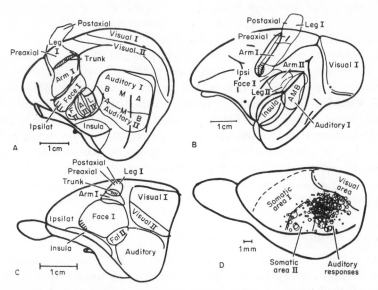

Fig. 21.1.   Sensory areas of the cortex are shown for: A, cat; B, monkey; C, rabbit; D, rat.   Primary and secondary sensory areas are labelled I and II for the different sensory modalities. (From Bard, *Medical Physiology* (10th Ed.).   C. V. Mosby, 1956.)

sensations as judged from the animal's reaction.   Other cortical regions so treated were without effect.

Sensory areas in the cerebral cortex have been identified in man (Fig. 21.2).   An area of the cortex is exposed under local anesthesia in patients requiring neurosurgical intervention (e.g., for the removal of scar tissue).   The patient is conscious and able to report the effects of electrical stimulation in the various cortical regions tested. Penfield and Jasper (1954) have summarized the results of extensive studies on such patients made at the Montreal Neurological Institute. Stimulation of the somesthetic cortex (the Rolandic cortex—postcentral areas 3, 1, 2) gives rise to sensations characterized as 'numbness, tingling, or a feeling of electricity.' The numbness may be produced by local depression of cortical excitability following strong stimuli. Less frequently, other sensations are reported, i.e. a sense of movement without the patient actually moving. The

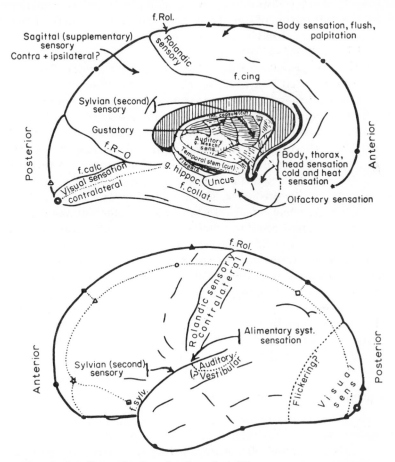

Fig. 21.2. Somesthetic, visual and auditory sensory areas are indicated as found in the cortex of the human by electrical stimulation. The medial surface of the brain is shown above; the lateral surface below. (From Penfield and Jasper, 1954.)

area of the skin surface in which such sensations are evoked is related to a part of the somesthetic cortex which is electrically stimulated. This *somatotopic* relationship will be discussed in a later section.

Auditory sensations were found localized in a narrow zone on the posterior part of the fissure of Sylvius (Fig. 21.2) in areas 41 and 42 and deeper in the fissure known as Heschl's transverse gyrus. The auditory sensations elicited by electrical stimulation were described by the patients as 'ringing, humming, clicking, rushing, chirping, buzzing, knocking, rumbling.' Occasionally deafness was experienced or an alteration of sound quality. The deafness may have been produced by a localized cortical depression of the auditory region by strong stimulation.

In man the primary visual cortex is mainly hidden from direct view. It is located in area 17 on the medial surface of the occipital part of the brain in the cortex around the calcarine fissure (Fig. 21.2). The more readily accessible visual areas 18 and 19 around area 17 gave rise to visual sensations upon stimulation. These were described by the patients as 'flickering lights, dancing lights, bright lights, stars, wheels, blue-green and red-colored discs, fawn and blue lights, colored balls whirling, radiating gray spots becoming pink and blue, a long white mark, shadow moving up and down, brown squares, black wheel, colorless star.' The images appeared simple and unreal. Upon re-stimulation of the same point on the cortex, the image might appear in the same place or be changed with regard to its apparent position. Movement of the image was common, either moving smoothly or more often dancing, flickering or whirling. With strong stimulations a shadow instead of lights might be experienced. This may be a local cortical depressive effect probably similar to the numbness experienced when the somesthetic cortex was strongly stimulated, or the deafness when the auditory cortex was strongly stimulated.

The primary sensory response

A flash of light, a click or a brief touch of the skin gives rise to a characteristic response evoked in the corresponding visual, auditory or somesthetic cortex. The form of these *primary sensory responses* may be either a positive wave lasting 10–20 msec or a positive–negative sequence similar to those excited from middle cortical layers by laminar stimulation (Fig. 18.16). The sensory-evoked responses show variability in their latency and form as would be expected from interactions occurring from various sensory inputs and non-specific activity of the reticular formation. The variability is reduced, particularly the latency of the response, and a pattern obtained which is more amenable to analysis if the sensory-evoked response is elicited by electrical stimulation of the sensory tracts

eading to the cortex. For this purpose electrodes have been stereotaxically placed within the various specific nuclear groups of the
thalamus where a relay of fibers to the primary cortical areas
(somesthetic, auditory and optic) is situated. On stimulation of any
one of the nuclear groups by a single brief shock, a characteristic
response (Fig. 21.3) is obtained in the corresponding primary

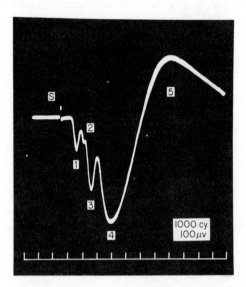

Fig. 21.3. Evoked response recorded from the visual cortex of the
cat. The electrical waves following stimulation (S) of the visual
pathway are numbered, downward deflections positive in polarity.
Calibration 1 msec, 100 μv. (From Malis and Kruger, *J. Neurophysiol.* **19**: 172, 1956.)

receptor cortical area (Bremer and Stoupel, 1956; Landau and
Clare, 1956). This evoked response has in addition to the slow
positive and negative waves characteristic of a natural stimulus, a
series of fast spike-like waves beginning at the onset and continuing
through part of the slow positive wave. Numbers are used to
designate these components (Fig. 21.3). With the cortex ablated
and recordings taken from the underlying white matter, a small
spike-like wave is found coinciding in time with the fast wave
labeled Component 1 in the evoked response (Bremer and Stoupel,
1956). This suggests that this spike-like wave represents the
volley of activity in the entering specific afferent fibers. The conduction velocity of the spike computed from stimulation at different
places along the path from the specific thalamic nucleus to the cortex

also indicated that the first wave is the sign of activity in the specific afferent fibers terminating in the cortex (Marshall, Talbot and Ades, 1943). Further evidence is its relative resistance to cortical asphyxiation, drugs and spreading depression (Marshall, 1950). The origin of the later series of spike-like waves is as yet unknown (Bremer, 1958). There is some evidence that the fast wave designated Component 2 in Fig. 21.3 is the sign of activity in a slower conducting group of afferent sensory fibers. The later fast wave (Component 3) appears to be intracortical in its origin. These spike-like waves may be arising from pyramidal and stellate cells by a series of synaptic relays (Bishop and Clare, 1953). However, fast waves may occasionally appear in a long train suggesting that they are actually a rhythmic discharge of the specific afferent fibers.

On a volume conductor basis, the slow positive phase (Component 4) is considered to be due to activity in the lower layers of the cortex. This was shown by laminar recording of the evoked responses at different levels in the cortex (Li, Cullen and Jasper, 1956; von Euler and Ricci, 1958). When this is done the surface positive wave becomes inverted to a negative wave in the middle layer of the cortex (Fig. 21.4). The surface positive potential is the result of the polarized upper portion of the dendrites acting as a source to these sinks of activity deeper in the cortex.

The negative wave (Component 5) of the surface response appears to be a depolarization of the upper apical dendrites, as is the negative wave DCR (Chapter 18). This was shown for the auditory response and somesthetic responses by the occlusive interaction of this phase of the primary response with the negative wave DCR (von Euler and Ricci, 1958; Nakahama, 1959).

Bishop (1956) considered the positive–negative sequence of slow waves to arise as an ascending depolarization of the apical dendrites, a propagation which on this theory would take place in the antidromic direction. The propagation velocity required of this antidromic propagation would be low, considering the duration of these waves and the average length of the dendrites in their vertically oriented direction as 0.5–1.0 mm. Roughly a velocity of 0.5–1.0 m/sec may be estimated. From a study of the propagation along the apical dendrites in the oculomotor nucleus, Lorente de Nó (1953) determined the conduction velocity for dendrites as 2 m/sec. Hild and Tasaki (1962) using microelectrodes found a much lower conduction velocity present in the larger dendritic branches of neurons in tissue culture, 0.02–0.05 m/sec at 26°C. Such a low velocity could fit with Bishop's theory. However, laminar recordings of the

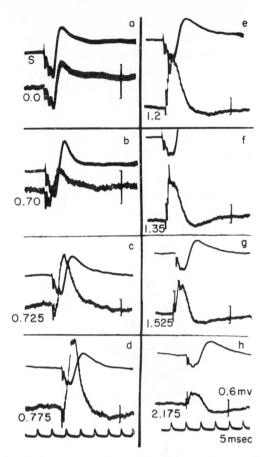

Fig. 21.4. Laminar recording of evoked response. In each of the pair of traces (a–h) the upper trace is the evoked response recorded from the surface of the cortex consisting of a slow positive wave with fast spikes followed by a slow negative wave. The lower trace is recorded at different distances below the surface with the depth in millimeters noted by the numbers at the left. Notice the large negative phase recorded at deeper levels (0.7–1.2 mm) coinciding with the surface positive phase. (Li, Cullen and Jasper, 1956.)

evoked responses taken at successively deeper levels of the cortex did not show a progressively lengthening latency of the negative part of positive–negative sequence as would be expected from a slow upward propagation in apical dendrites (von Euler and Ricci, 1958). It appears likely that the surface positive wave and the surface negative wave are each due to activity in separate groups of neurons.

In this view, activation of the deeper cortical group gives rise to the surface positive phase which is followed, after activation of the apical dendrites, by the surface negative component. This accounts for the dissociation of the two phases of the evoked responses so often seen—large negative waves along with small positive waves, or large positive waves with small negative waves.

By the use of evoked-response techniques, secondary (Fig. 21.1) and even tertiary sensory areas have been found. The significance of such multiple representation of sensory areas in the cortex is not clearly understood.

Point-to-point localization

If the skin surface is excited by a brief punctate touch stimulation, the primary response evoked in the somesthetic cortex is found to be localized in a small region of that primary sensory area. By

Fig. 21.5. A homuncular representation of the somesthetic sensory areas I and II of the dog shows those regions of the body giving rise to evoked responses in the various parts of the sensory region. In this way the body surface is shown to be represented on the surface of the cortex. (From Bard, *Medical Physiology* (10th. Ed.). C. V. Mosby, 1956.)

comparing the point stimulated on the skin surface to the point on the cortex giving the response, a *point-to-point* localization may be made of the body surface mapped onto the somesthetic cortex (Woolsey, Marshall and Bard, 1942). The spatial arrangement of sensory regions is indicated in Fig. 21.5 where a detailed representation of the skin surface onto the cortex is shown by means of a *figurine.* The extent of the cortex representing any particular portion of the receptor field depends on the use each species has for that modality in a given part of the body. For example, the toe representation in the cortex of the dog is small, while in the monkey the thumb area takes a very large area and the other digits are also represented by fairly large areas. The greatly increased area representing the thumb and digit in the monkey becomes so large that the head area becomes split, with the face and occiput representations to either side of the hand representation (Woolsey, 1958). The large area given over to sensory representation of the snout in the cortex of the pig is another example of this relationship of the size of a sensory area to the importance that sensory function has for a species' behavior.

When a brief punctate light flash is presented at one point in the visual field, an evoked response is found localized at a small point within the primary visual cortex (Marshall and Talbot, 1942). A correspondence of the points within the visual field to the points mapped by the evoked response on the visual cortex was found. Localization of the evoked electrical response in the visual cortex to punctate stimulation has been described as localizable to within less than a millimeter, falling off sharply in all directions from a central focus of activity. Such findings suggest that a somesthetic or visual representation is first laid down in point-to-point fashion in the primary receptor area (Poljak, 1957). While it is difficult to determine the actual volume of the cortex and the number of cortical neurons engaged in an evoked response, the number of cells must be very large. The specific afferent fibers entering the cortex extend as far as 100 to 200 micra laterally in the cortex and, by means of their multiple branches, synapse with a considerable number of cells (Fig. 21.6). Engagement of such very large numbers of neurons by each afferent fiber makes for too coarse a 'grain' representing a point within the visual cortex—a factor incompatible with detailed vision. Furthermore, there is a divergence of activity within the retina and along the sensory pathway which would tend to diffuse the neural area excited by a point of light (Chapter 11). To account for a finer 'grain of representation,' mechanisms of *convergence* must be invoked, i.e. neurons excited by excitation from several afferent fibers give rise to a greater density of synaptic activity in a smaller group of cells (Marshall and Talbot, 1942; Lorente de Nó, 1934). A surrounding inhibitory field would act to cause such a sharpening. Within recent years single-cell analysis has permitted an examination of the response properties of a population of sensory cells excited by sensory inputs. The results obtained by single-unit study will be discussed in the following sections in relation to the sensory modalities of vision, somesthesis and audition. In general, as will be exemplified in those sections, the present indications are that sensory information is not to be compressed into the formula of a simple point-to-point localization. As will be seen, mechanisms have been discovered which require a new way of thinking of sensory impulse transformation within the higher neural centers.

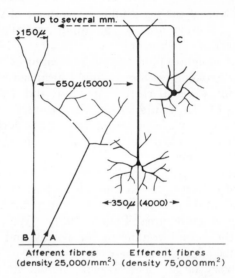

Fig. 21.6. The terminations of the specific afferent fibers (A) are shown entering the cortex at an angle. They branch and have a wide lateral extension—650 μ. The number of cells influenced by a specific sensory fiber is relatively large—5000 as given in the brackets. Other quantitative features of the visual cortex are shown; non-specific afferents (B), stellate cells (C) and pyramidal cells. (Scholl, *The Organizaton of the Cerebral Cortex*, Wiley, 1956.)

Visual sensory mechanisms

The fibers passing from the ganglion cells of the retina of mammals are collected in the optic nerve with a divergence taking place at the *optic chiasma* (Fig. 21.7). As can be seen in this figure, the fibers from the medial half of the eye cross at the optic chiasma, the other half remaining uncrossed. Each half of the retina receives light rays from half of the visual field. The fibers of each eye corresponding to the same visual field are collected together to pass to the lateral geniculate body and then to the visual cortex. The result of such channeling is that half of the visual field is represented in one hemisphere of the brain, the other half in the other hemisphere. The effect on visual reception of cutting the pathway is shown in Fig. 21.7. An apparent failure to affect central vision on cutting the radiation fibers is known as *macular sparing*. One explanation of this phenomenon is that a duplication of the connections of each of the visual tracts leading to the visual areas of the cortex will allow central vision to be retained when one side is destroyed. However, Putnam and Liebman (1942) found little evidence for such a mechanism, and it now appears on adequate study that macular sparing is due to the escape of some of the radiation fibers from the lesion.

The lateral geniculate is not a simple relay station for impulses passing from the retina to the cortex. It has a 6-layered structure in primates with layers 1, 4 and 6 receiving fibers from the contralateral eye and layers 2, 3 and 5 receiving fibers from the ipsilateral eye. The possibility was raised by LeGros Clark (1940) that there are three sets of afferent optic fibers representing the primary colors and these are distributed into the laminae for color reception. However, there is anatomical and physiological evidence difficult to reconcile with this theory (Chow, 1955; de Valois, 1960).

The topographic organization of the geniculate has been studied. Fibers from each small retinal area are found by means of localized degeneration following a punctate retinal lesion, to project to a small region of the lateral geniculate. The relationship is not organized as previously indicated, in a strict point-to-point fashion. One optic nerve fiber can terminate on several cells (Glees and LeGros Clark, 1941), but there is little interaction and the individual geniculate cells probably respond as do the retinal ganglion cells.

Microelectrode recordings were made from cells of the lateral geniculate while a small point of light was presented to the visual field of cats (Hubel, 1959). The point of light was moved around within the visual field, producing either an 'on' response or an 'off' response of that cell (Chapter 11). By this means it has been found that an 'on' response which was excited in a unit by a spot in the visual field was inhibited and gave an 'off' response to light in an annular region around that spot as shown in Fig. 21.8. In A to the right, opposite the diagram showing the spot stimulus, the thin line shows the flash of light giving rise to an 'on' response in the trace below it. An annular light made to excite the retina around the spot, as shown in B, gave rise to discharges at the

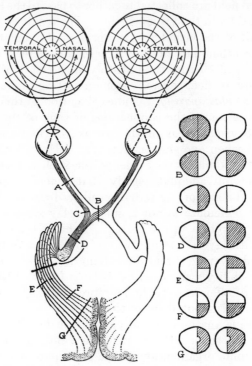

Fig. 21.7.   At the top are the visual fields with light rays focused onto the retinae of the eyes.   The retinal fibers corresponding to the left halves of each retina are gathered together in the optic nerve (A) and optic tract (D) passing to the left geniculate nucleus and there to the left visual cortex.   (A similar crossing at the optic chiasm (B) for the fibers from the right half of the retinae is not shown.)   The effect of lesions at different points along the visual pathways are indicated by the letters and the corresponding defects for the visual fields of the two eyes are given by the diagrams A–G on the right. A, complete blindness left eye; B, bitemporal hemianopsia; C, unilateral nasal hemianopsia; D, right homonymous hemianopsia— interruption of either optic tract or geniculocalarine projection; E and F, right upper and lower quadrant heminopsias; G, right homonymous hemianopsia from a large lesion of occipital lobe. (After Homans; from Ruch and Fulton, *Medical Physiology and Biophysics*, 17th Ed., Saunders, 1960.)

cessation of the light, i.e. an 'off' discharge.   A movement of the spot is a particularly effective stimulus.   This is shown in C of Fig. 21.8 where the arrow indicates the effective direction of movement of the spot in the visual field.   Another finding is that the activity of the lateral geniculate neurons is readily augmented by increasing the overall illumination presented to the animal, as shown in D of Fig. 21.8.

Transmission of evoked responses through the lateral geniculate in the cat was studied by recording evoked responses of the lateral geniculate cell to optic nerve stimulation. A paired shock technique was used to study the *recovery cycle* of transmission of the second response. In such studies Marshall (1949) found a complex change in excitability with a summation interval of 30 msec followed by a subnormality which lasted several seconds. Responses of the cat

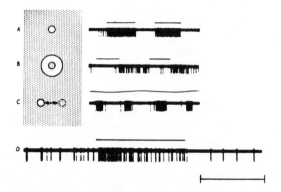

Fig. 21.8. The visual stimulus in the visual field is a small light spot shown to the left at A. The spot is positioned for a maximum 'on' response of a geniculate cell to a flash which is indicated by the upper line over the trace at the right. A large number of spike discharges is seen to occur at the time of the stimulus. An annular light stimulus concentric around the maximum position occupied by the spot of A gives rise to a decrease in unit responses as shown in B by decreased unit discharge during illumination. In C, movement of the spot across the receptive field gives rise to a discharge when it passes through the maximum response position. In D, the line above the unit recording trace indicates the time of presentation of a diffuse light stimulation with an increase of neural spike discharges. Time calibration, 1 sec. (Hubel, 1960.)

lateral geniculate cells were further studied by Bishop and Davis (1960). The field response recorded by a microelectrode placed within the lateral geniculate is shown in Fig. 21.9. The response labeled t_1 is the sign of focal activity in the optic nerves entering the geniculate, and r_1 is the responses of geniculate cell bodies on which they synapse. At a higher strength of optic nerve stimulation, a slower conducting group of optic nerve fibers t_2 is excited with its corresponding geniculate cell body response r_2. In their study of the recovery cycle, they found, as did Marshall, a prolonged subnormality. The second response attained 87% of control amplitude at a shock interval of 220 msec, and only after 2 seconds returned to control levels. Such prolonged depressions of excitability are not due to events taking place in the postsynaptic cells as shown by antidromic excitation following stimulation of the radiation fibers (Vastola, 1959). This will produce a short refractoriness and a depression period lasting at most approximately 100–200 msec. The longer periods of decreased excitability on orthodromic excitation appear therefore

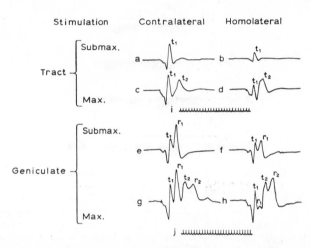

Fig. 21.9.   Evoked responses recorded from the geniculate nucleus and optic tract to contralateral and homolateral volleys.   Submaximal stimulation gives rise to a t_1 response signifying activity of the optic nerves.   This is followed by a geniculate cell response, r_1.   At maximal stimulation a second afferent fiber group t_2 is excited and also its geniculate response r_2.   Time intervals 0.2 msec.   (Bishop and McLeod, *J. Neurophysiol.* **17**: 387, 1954.)

to be located in the presynaptic optic nerve terminals synapsing on geniculate neurons.   Possibly a presynaptic inhibition mechanism is present at the terminals similar to the presynaptic inhibition described for the spinal cord (Chapter 17).

Using responses of single units and the focally recorded evoked responses from the lateral geniculate, Curtis and Davis (1962) found that 5-hydroxytryptamine electrophoretically applied to single cells depressed synaptic firing of these cells.   Their studies suggest that the transmitter substance acting at this synapse is related to 5-hydroxytryptamine. Lysergic acid diethylamide (LSD) can in very small amounts produce visual hallucinations in human subjects. Peculiar shapes and colors are seen. These effects appear to be due to the action of LSD to depress geniculate transmission (Evarts, Landau, Freygang and Marshall, 1955).

Hubel (1959) and Hubel and Wiesel (1962) were able to record the activity of single neurons in the visual cortex of unrestrained mobile animals or lightly anesthetized animals. Recordings were generally made from cells located in the posterior lateral gyrus of the brain

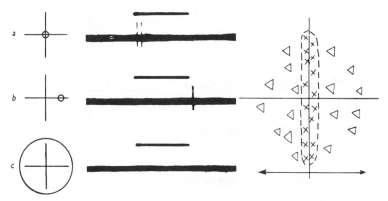

Fig. 21.10. Positions of a spot of light in the visual field shown at the left give rise to responses of a visual cortex neuron in the traces shown in the center of this figure. Stimulus located at (a) gives rise to a plural discharge at the onset of the light indicated by the upper bar. Two spikes are seen in the trace. With the spot to the side of the maximal position (b) the neuron responds at the 'off' of the light stimulus. In (c) a diffuse illumination of the area gives no response. The diagram at the right shows by the crosses an elongated receptive area giving rise to 'on' responses with a surrounding area indicated by the triangles which was found to give 'off' responses. (Hubel and Wiesel, 1959.)

which is the receptive field for central vision in the cat. One outstanding difference between unit response behavior of cortical neurons compared to those of the lateral geniculate is that the activity of the cortical neurons was not increased with increased background illumination or light stimulations of a large area of the visual field (Hubel, 1960). Cortical neurons were found to respond to small spots of light with an inhibitory response to stimulation of the surrounding field. This is shown in Fig. 21.10 where the crosses on the right show various excitatory

positions of the spot within the visual field while recording from
a single neuron in the visual cortex. Flashes of light at these
positions cause an 'on' response (a), while on both sides of this
area inhibitory 'off' responses were obtained (b). A slit of light
which covers both excitatory and inhibitory parts of the visual
field was ineffective (c). Conversely, there are other neurons which
were found to have a centrally located receptive region giving an

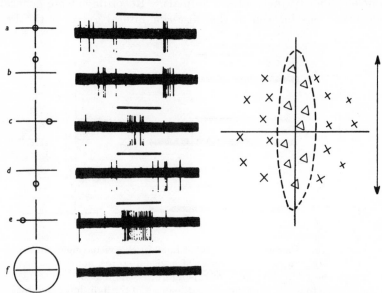

Fig. 21.11. The positions of a small spot in the visual field giving
rise to 'off' discharges in a visual cortex neuron are shown at the
left in a, b and d with their corresponding recorded traces as in
Fig. 21.10. 'On' responses were found at positions c and e. The
inhibitory 'off' responses are distributed in elongated fashion as
shown by the triangles in the diagram at the right. It is surrounded
by excitatory 'on' responses as indicated by the crosses. No
response was seen to a large diffused light stimulus as shown in f.
(Hubel and Wiesel, 1959.)

'off' response surrounded by a region giving 'on' responses (Fig. 21.11).

In general, the central responsive region is ellipsoidal. Therefore
a light stimulus of slit form is most effective if it is oriented over
only the excitatory region of the visual field of a cell without including
the inhibitory surround (Fig. 21.12).

The slit exciting a given cell has a particular orientation which may
be horizontal, vertical or oblique with respect to the vertical axis
of the visual field. This orientation of a slit stimulus appears to be

specifically defined for a given cell recorded from, and the term 'receptive-field axis orientation' is used to show this relation of a given type of light stimulus to the responding cell. The size of the excitatory or inhibitory surrounding territories may be larger for some cells than for others, e.g. a large excitatory area may be surrounded by only a thin strip of inhibitory territory and vice versa.

Movement back and forth across the boundary of excitatory and

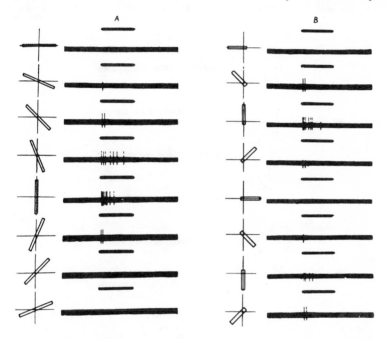

Fig. 21.12. The orientation of a slit of light in the visual field used for stimulation of visual cortex neuron responses shown to the left of columns A and B. Excitatory responses recorded in the traces at the right of the slit figure are seen to be maximal for this cell when the slit is close to the vertical orientation. Horizontal positions gave no response and partial responses were found at intermediate angles. (Hubel and Wiesel, 1959.)

inhibitory regions of a spot or slit is generally more effective than a stationary stimulus. The cell appears to respond to the contrast between light and dark regions. For some cells movement in one direction was excitatory while no effect was found with movement in the reverse direction. This is indicated in Fig 21.13 where a movement of the slit stimulus in the direction upward and to the right was most effective.

Binocular vision results in a single unified visual experience and the perception of depth of vision.   Convergence of the eyeballs is required so that the fovea of both eyes are focused on the same object.   A defect of convergence at distances less than 20 feet, generally by failure of the muscles moving one of the eyes, gives rise to *diplopia* (double vision).   Single-cell studies have shown that there are a relatively large number of neurons in the visual cortex excited by stimuli coming from corresponding spots in the

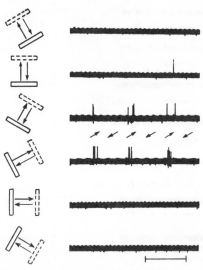

Fig. 21.13.   The orientation and the direction of movement of a slit light stimulus in the visual field is shown on the left.   Original position is shown by the solid slit; movement direction by arrows and the position it is moved to by the dashed slit.   Movements up and to the right were effective to excite responses as shown by the traces at the right.   Movement back to the original position was ineffective.   Time, 1 sec.   (Hubel and Wiesel, 1959.)

retina of both eyes (Hubel and Wiesel, 1959, 1962).   As many as 84% of the cells studied were found to show such binocular representation.   If the effective stimulation was a strip of light presented to one eye at a certain angle, stimulation of the same place in the visual field of the other eye excited that cell.   Not only synergistic actions but antagonistic actions as well were found.   A slit stimulation presented to the comparable site of the other eye might well inhibit an excitatory response and vice versa.

These unit-cell studies made in the visual cortex of the cat show response to unique aspects of objects in the visual field—to strips, bars, edges and to movements. The question arises as to what relationship the various cells have to one another. By systematic recording along a tract perpendicular to the surface, a vertical organization of the cells in the cortex was found. On gradual penetration of the cortex, successive units were found to respond to the same kind of visual stimulus, e.g., to a strip of light at a given orientation. On a slanted entry of the electrode into the cortex, a number of different types of responding units were found. First a number of cells

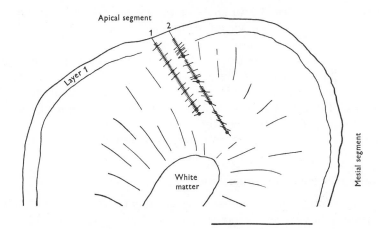

Fig. 21.14. Two recording penetrations of microelectrodes (1 and 2) into the visual cortex are shown along with responses from neurons recorded at different distances from the surface. The lines intersecting the tracks represent the orientation of the light slits used for stimulation of the visual field which gave maximal neural responses. Notice the similarity of orientations for the cells along track 1 which is nearly perpendicular to the surface compared to the changes in orientation of responsivity of the cells along track 2. Horizontal line, 1 mm. (Hubel and Wiesel, *J. Physiol.* **165**: 559, 1963.)

showing one type of response to a stimulus type was found, then a response to another kind of stimulus as shown in Fig. 21.14. The lines numbered 1 and 2 signify the passage of the recording electrode down through the cortex, while the short lines along those lines represent the receptive-field axis orientation to a slit light stimulus of neurons recorded at those depths. Track 1 is closer to a perpendicular penetration, and most cells have the same receptive-field axis orientation. Track 2, which is at a greater angle to the vertical shows cells falling into small groups of different receptive-field axis orientations.   The findings suggest that with directions closest to the vertical the cells will all be stimulated by the same type of slit light stimulus in the visual field.   This similarity of the receptive fields of a small vertical core of cortical neurons is referred to as a vertical *module*.   It indicates some functional importance of the vertical organization in the cortex, which is as yet not understood.

In the frog, similar complex receptive properties were found in single fibers of optic nerves (Maturana, Lettvin, McCulloch and Pitts, 1960).   In this animal, the axons of ganglion cells were seen to respond asymmetrically to spots in the visual field, to edges and to special contours of the visual stimulus.   It would appear that in this species a more complex visual organization is present in the retina.   An explanation may be found in the anatomical differences in the visual systems of these two species; in the frog the retinal fibers terminate directly in the optic lobes.   In any event, single-cell analysis of the visual system has shown that the sensory system is organized to receive certain aspects of the form of the visual object, and movement, and not simply points of light.

Somesthetic sensory mechanisms

Two ascending systems subserving cutaneous and fascial and joint movement have been recognized.   The first system is that of the fibers of large diameter subserving touch and joint movements signifying limb position.   These fibers enter the cord and ascend in the dorsal columns to synapse in the *nucleus gracilus* and *cuneatus* of the upper medullary region of the brain stem (A, Fig. 21.15). From the gracilus and cuneatus nuclei, fibers arise which form the *medial lemniscus* tract.   This tract swings across to the other side of the brain to terminate in the specific nuclear groups of the thalamus. From the specific thalamic nuclei, as has been previously noted, electrical stimulation can evoke via the ascending fibers, specific sensory responses in the somesthetic sensory region of the cortex.

Single cells of the gracilus and cuneatus were found to respond to light pressure of the skin.   In addition, a small number of cells responded to joint movement of the limbs; none of these units responded to temperature, skin damage or itch-producing stimuli (Wall, 1961).   A technique used to show that the fibers of the dorsal column represent mainly skin afferents and to a smaller extent fibers from muscle receptors was the recording of antidromic volleys to skin and muscle nerves upon dorsal column stimulation.

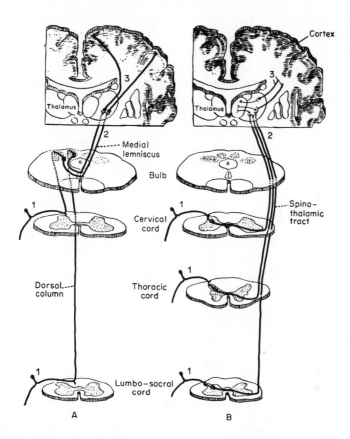

Fig. 21.15.   In A, sensory fibers of the lemniscal system are shown
passing upward to synapse in the nucleus gracilus and cuneatus.
These cells in turn give rise to the medial lemniscus fibers which
synapse on thalamic cells and these in turn ascend to terminate
in the cortex.   The numbers indicate the first, second and third
order neurons.   In B, afferent fibers of the spinothalamic system
synapsing in the dorsal horn of the cord give rise to fibers which
cross to the other side of the cord and then ascend in the spinothalamic tract to synapse on cells in the thalamus.   Third order
neurons reach the cortex in some as yet unspecified location.
(Strong and Elwyn, *Human Neuroanatomy*, Williams and Wilkins,
1943.)

It was clearly seen that only small volleys passed back into muscle nerves while large action potentials were recorded from the skin nerves. The fibers carrying these discharges were those of large diameter. The lemniscal system is selective with regard to the range of various sensory inputs to the cord. For all parts of the system—the dorsal columns, the gracilus and cuneatus nuclei, the medial lemniscus and the thalamic region—a topographical representation of the skin surface was found. This topographical represen-

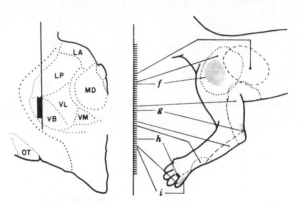

Fig. 21.16. The vertical line in the cross-section diagram of the thalamus at the left indicates the track of a recording microelectrode into the thalamus. The thick black section is from neurons within VB, the ventrobasal nuclear complex, shown in the middle on an expanded scale. This part of the thalamus has cells receptive to stimulation within restricted areas of the skin. Areas f, g and i of the cat were stimulated by light mechanical touch. A cell responding to gentle rotation of the toe joint was found at position h. Other nuclear groups: LA, lateral anterior nucleus; LP, lateral posterior nucleus; MD, mediodorsal nucleus; VM, ventromedial nucleus. OT represents the optic tract. (Poggio and Mountcastle, 1960.)

tation is further carried out in the post-central gyrus of the receptor area in the cortex (cf. Fig. 21.5).

The second ascending tract system to be considered is the *spinothalamic tract* carrying sensations of pain and temperature. On entering the cord these fibers of smaller diameter terminate on cells in the *substantia gelatinosa* (B, Fig. 21.15). The axons of these cells cross over to the other side of the cord and then ascend in the ventrolateral columns of the cord to terminate in the thalamus.

The thalamic relay of the two somatic afferent systems, the dorsal column-lemniscal and the spinothalamic, have different locations

within the thalamus.   The lemniscal system terminates on cells of
the *ventrobasal nuclear complex* of the thalamus.   This is the
region of the thalamus which sends fibers to the post-central gyrus

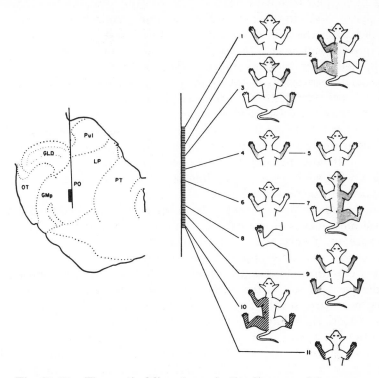

Fig. 21.17.   The vertical line shows in the diagram of the cross-
section of the thalamus at the left, the penetration of a recording
microelectrode in PO, the posterior nuclear thalamic group.
At the right on an expanded scale is shown the responses of the
cells in this PO group to stimulation of various regions in the body
surface of the cat.   These neurons, in contrast to the ventrobasal
group, have large receptive fields on the surface of the body as
shown by the figures at the right.   Other abbreviations: Pul,
pulvinar; GLD, dorsal nucleus of the lateral geniculate body;
GMp, magnocellular division of medial geniculate body; LP,
lateral posterior nucleus; PT, pretectal region; OT, optic tract.
(Poggio and Mountcastle, 1960.)

as shown by degeneration in this thalamic region when that part
of the cortex is removed (Rose and Mountcastle, 1952).   The spinothalamic tract terminates in the *posterior nuclear group* of the dorsal
thalamus (cf. Fig. 21.6 and Fig. 21.7).

The response behavior of cells in these two parts of the thalamus has been summarized by Mountcastle (1961). At 50 μ intervals along the vertical track shown in Fig. 21.16, a number of thalamic cells have their receptive fields on the contralateral side as shown at the right. Cells in this part of the thalamus were activated by a light touch within the skin regions shown by f, g and i. The cell h gave responses upon a gentle rotation of the joint of the third toe. Other field territories are shown without letters. In contrast to the restricted territories of touch or joint movement of cells in the ventrobasal complex units, the peripheral fields exciting posterior nuclear thalamic cells are more widespread (Fig. 21.17). Cells within this part of the thalamus not only have larger sensory fields but they also respond to excitation from both sides of the body. Auditory, nociceptive and mechanoreceptive cells are found present in this region with some cells responding to all of these different sensory modalities (Poggio and Mountcastle, 1960).

Single-unit analysis reveals cells in the cortex responding to somesthetic movements of the hairs of the skin and pressure on skin, deep pressure on fascia and joint rotation (Mountcastle, 1957). Each cell responds to only one of these sensory modalities and very few cells were unresponsive to stimulation of one of the somesthetic modalities. A cell in the cortex responding to skin pressure might show a resting level of discharge of several impulses/sec. Upon stimulation this may rise to over 100 impulses/sec with a rapid cessation on removal of pressure. The skin territories giving rise to these cortical unit excitations are contralateral and generally small in area. The size of the territory exciting a cortical unit is larger on more proximal parts of the limb surface. Cortical units may show either an increase or a decrease of response rate on light mechanical stimulation. On occasion a nearby cell having a limited territory of excitation was found to have a reciprocal relationship in its discharge to mechanical activation of a larger surrounding peripheral territory giving inhibition. The two cells shown in Fig. 21.18 respond to their peripheral stimulations with a reciprocal discharge rate. Similar reciprocal interaction may be observed with respect to other sensory modalities such as rotation of a joint.

Making use of these various sensory modalities of response, Mountcastle (1957) first discovered a vertical modular arrangement in the somesthetic cortex. The units along a track vertical to the surface all gave rise to the same sensory discharge, e.g. the successive cells along one track respond to skin touch-pressure, the cells along another track to joint rotation (Powell and Mountcastle, 1959).

The major ascending pathway for the sensation of pain appears to be within the spinothalamic tract terminating in the posterior dorsal group of thalamic cells (Whitlock and Perl, 1959; Poggio and Mountcastle, 1960). The further course of distribution of pain impulses from the thalamus to the cortex is unknown. There is a projection to the second somatic area of the cortex. Terminations in other regions are present (Rose and Mountcastle, 1959). After destruction of the cortex of one cerebral hemisphere patients may

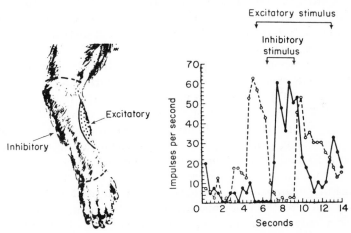

Fig. 21.18. A neuron recorded from the sensory cortex in the post-central gyrus of the monkey was excited by stimulation of the excitatory skin field shown diagrammatically on the arm at the left. Mechanical stimulation in the (inhibitory) skin area around it inhibited the discharge. The inhibitory stimulation excited a second neuron whose discharge was also recorded and shown plotted in the graph at the right (solid line). A reciprocal rate of discharge of the inhibitory cell is shown with respect to the activity of the cell which is stimulated from within the excitatory field (dashed line). (From Mountcastle and Powell, after Mountcastle, 1961).

have a remaining sensation of pain of a protopathic nature on both sides of the body. This may be due to a bilateral representation of pain terminations in both hemispheres (Walker, 1943). However, it is also well known that cortical stimulation in the conscious human is not painful and appreciation of pain may be sub-cortical.

One of the difficulties in analysing pain mechanisms is the inter-action between pain and other sensory modalities. This is exemplified by the phenomenon known as *referred pain* (MacKenzie, 1920). Examples of referred pain are: pain in the left shoulder and in the ulnar nerve distribution along the left arm following certain heart disease; a stone in the ureter which gives rise to pain in the lumbar region radiating into the groin; gall bladder distension experienced as pain localized between the scapulae. In all these examples a nociceptive lesion in a visceral organ excites visceral afferent fibers which appear to terminate on interneurons in the spinal cord or brain stem on which afferent terminations from cutaneous receptor fibers also converge. The effect of increased sensory activity on these interneurons from the visceral afferents lowers their threshold so that sensory excitation in the cutaneous field will also cause pain which is 'referred' to the cutaneous field of distribution of those fibers (Sweet, 1959).

A similar mechanism appears to underlie the phenomenon of *phantom limb* which is often associated with excruciating pain (Livingston, 1943). Upon loss of a limb a patient may feel that the limb is still present. In one such case vividly described by Livingston, the missing hand and fingers were felt to be tightly clenched. The excruciating pain this patient experienced can be approximated by trying to hold the fist clenched for several minutes. The stimulus for phantom limb may arise from the nerve fibers which grow into a whorl-like *neuroma* at the stump of an amputated limb. Injection of procaine into the neuroma will relieve the pain. However, this is usually only temporary. It would appear that the bombardment of central neurons by continuous pain impulses may, like convulsive activity (Chapter 18), change them and make them permanently pain sensitive (Gerard, 1951). Surgical intervention by cutting the spinothalamic tract in an attempt to relieve severe pain may only be temporary if the cut does not transect all of the pathway. In some cases of intractable pain, frontal cortex ablations are resorted to, not so much to relieve pain as to make the patient less disturbed by the pain (Fulton, 1951; cf. Chapter 25).

Auditory sensory mechanisms

From the peripheral auditory receptor in the organ of Corti, auditory impulses are carried to the cortex in a complex series of relay nuclei (Fig. 21.19). Microelectrode recording from cells at different levels of the auditory pathway show that they have a peak sensitivity for a given frequency when a range of sound waves are presented to the ear (Fig. 21.20). The peak sensitivity is the *best* or *characteristic* frequency of that neuron. At all neural stations, a *tonotopic* organization (orderly representation of tones within the CNS) can be demonstrated. This was shown by Rose (1960)

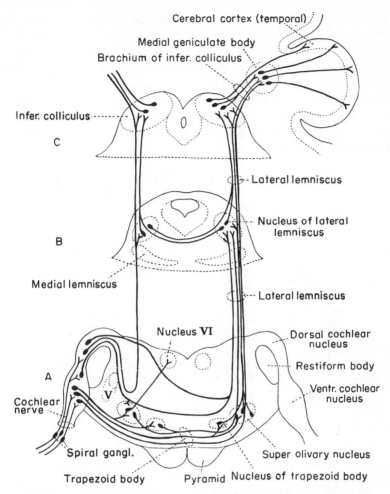

Fig. 21.19. The ascending pathways of neurons of the auditory system is shown with its various connections in the brain stem. A relay occurs in the medial geniculate body with fibers passing upward to end in the auditory cortex. Numerous collateral terminations are found at: A, medulla; B, isthmus; C, midbrain levels of the brain stem. (From Strong and Elwyn, *Human Neuroanatomy*, Williams and Wilkins, 1943.)

for the cochlear nuclear complex (dorsal and ventral cochlear nuclei) in the cat. The ear was stimulated at various frequencies and strengths while a microelectrode was positioned at different depths. Upon penetration at small increments a stepwise change in the characteristic frequency was found for a series of cells along the tract of passage through the cochlear nuclear complex (Fig. 21.21).

Within the cortex a tonotopic organization was found in the auditory cortex. Some of the difficulties encountered in assigning a tonotopic organization to the auditory cortex in the past became clear only recently when the multiplicity of separate cortical areas for audition finally became recognized. An earlier concept of two such areas (labeled I and II, Fig. 21.1) has been resolved into four tonotopically organized auditory areas as shown by Woolsey (1960) for the cat in Fig. 21.22.

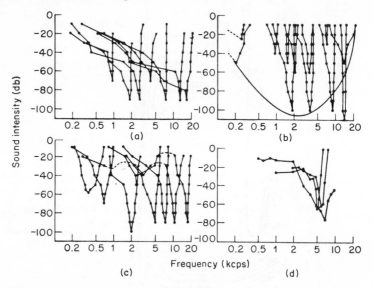

Fig. 21.20. The plots of sound frequency against intensity (db). Tones giving rise to spike discharges in individual neurons of the auditory system show a peak sensitivity at a given frequency for cells in: (a) cochlear nerve, (b) inferior colliculus, (c) trapezoid body, (d) medial geniculate body. (From Katsuki, 1961.)

The first auditory area in black is AI on the ectosylvian cortex. Below it in stippling is the secondary region AII. Another auditory region shown by slanted lines is EP on the posterior ectosylvian gyrus. Yet another area is SF shown cross-hatched. It begins on the anterior ectosylvian gyrus, disappearing in the suprasylvian sulcus and emerging above the posterior ectosylvian gyrus. These auditory areas have a general relationship to cytoarchitecturally differentiated regions which had earlier been delineated by Rose (1949).

In addition to this central auditory area there is a region on the insular cortex termed Ins and above it *Tunturi's third auditory area* responding to all frequencies with no tonotopic localization. All of these give short-latency responses. The remaining areas shown in this figure receive long-latency evoked responses to sound stimulation. These areas are part of the associational projections to be discussed in a later section of this chapter.

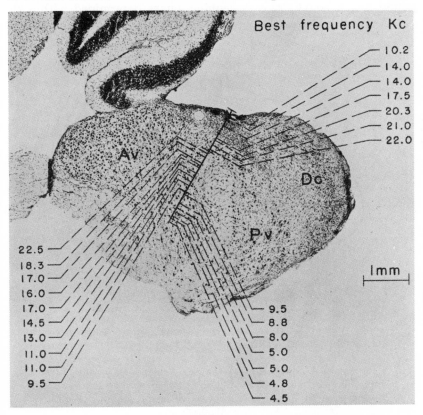

Fig. 21.21. Path of recording microelectrode through the cochlear nuclear complex is shown with the best (characteristic frequency) in kilocycles (Kc) given for the individual cells along the track. There is a progressive shift of the characteristic frequencies, i.e. a tonotopic arrangement. (Rose, 1960.)

Of the auditory areas, the only one receiving direct projections from the thalamus is AI (Rose and Woolsey, 1958). A small lesion in the cortex will produce a sharply defined focus of retrograde degeneration in a part of the medial geniculate. AII and EP also receive afferent inputs from sub-cortical inputs as shown by evoked responses remaining when AI was ablated. A cortico-cortical transmission between these auditory areas is also present (Downman, Woolsey and Lende, 1960).

A tonotopic organization within the receptor area AI was first shown by Tunturi (1950). Strychnine was applied in small areas on the middle ectosylvian gyrus of the cortex and the frequency of sound which could drive strychnine spikes determined within the area. By this means the tonotopic representation of frequencies in

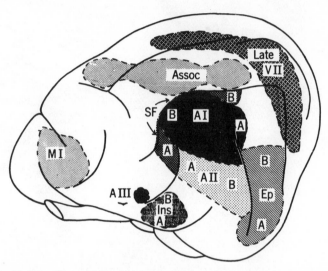

Fig. 21.22.   The cochlear is represented on the cortex of the cat with apex (A) and base (B) shown in the various auditory receptor areas: AI, black; second auditory area AII, stippled; AIII, Tunturi's third auditory area; area Ep, shown by slanted lines; area SF, has two sectors A and B hooked around AI, and the insular area, Ins.   The associative areas (cf. Fig. 21.25) shown also give auditory responses with longer latencies to clicks of sound. (Woolsey, 1960.)

AI shown by Fig. 21.23 was found. Localization is best when 'P' pulses are used. These are trains of a pure sound frequency which are designed to rapidly rise and fall in amplitude over approximately 5 cycles of the particular sound frequency investigated. This form for a short period of sound stimulation has been identified as the elementary type of a sound frequency; any other would contain additional sound frequencies (Tunturi, 1960). A unit analysis of auditory neurons has in general confirmed this tonotopic organization within the cortex (Hind, 1960; Katsuki, 1961).

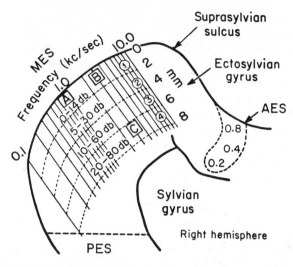

Fig. 21.23. Frequency responses tonotopically distributed in the middle ectosylvian (MES) gyrus with the low frequencies represented posteriorly and high frequencies anteriorly. An intensity distribution (db) is found in the mediolateral direction. (AES) anterior ectosylvian sulcus. (PES) posterior ectosylvian sulcus. (Tunturi, *Am. J. Physiol.* **168**: 712, 1952.)

Perceptual mechanisms

The classical view is that sensations are received in the primary receptor areas as simple patches of light, tones or touches. Elsewhere in the cortex they are combined to form the more complex pattern required for the perception of objects. As we have seen, the fundamental elements for vision and somesthesis in the primary areas are not just simple point-to-point arrangements for excitation of light or of tactile stimulation but rather are certain aspects of the sensory object, its shape, orientation, movement and direction of movement, and this requires a new concept of sensory organization which as yet is not at hand.

There are other observations which indicate that sensory organization within the primary receptor area is complex. The studies of Lashley (1942) indicate a *reduplication* phenomenon in a primary receptor site. Animals were trained to respond to visual patterns (Chapter 25) and then large ablations of the primary visual area were made. As long as a small remnant of the primary area was spared, visual responses remained. Of interest was the lack of specificity in the location of the remnant suggesting that in some fashion many parts of the visual cortex can receive sensory input. However, if the whole of the specific sensory area is destroyed, then its function of pattern discrimination is lost. In lower organisms such as the rat, remaining vision may be limited to the perception of shades of light. Sounds may still be sensed as shown after bilateral auditory cortex ablations in animals trained to respond to sound. However, a pattern of sounds can no longer be perceived after such ablations (Diamond and Neff, 1957; Neff, 1960). Therefore, perception requires the presence of the specific sensory areas of the cerebral cortex.

Cortical areas around the primary receptive areas are also

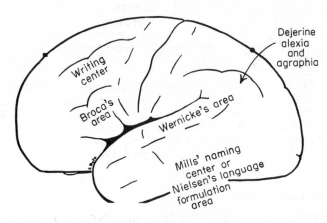

Fig. 21.24. The areas in the human brain related to speech and writing as indicated from pathological studies. Difficulties in recognition or expression of spoken and written words are found with lesions in the various named regions. (Penfield and Roberts, 1954.)

involved in perception. The basis for this view was derived from clinical studies of patients with brain lesions (Penfield and Roberts, 1959). When lesions were present in or near the primary receptor areas, there is a disturbance or a loss of perception, an *agnosia* (Fig. 21.24). With lesions near the somesthetic area the sense of touch may remain, but a complex tactile pattern cannot be recognized. For example a house-key placed in the hand is not recognized as such until looked at. Patients with lesions near the visual area may be able to make out individual letters but not to read words. They are said to have *word-blindness*. Or, the individual by a reaction to a sudden sound is shown not to be deaf, yet not be able to recognize spoken words. This is called *word-deafness*.

Memory and intelligence may remain relatively normal in the face of such apparently highly disturbed perceptual losses.

Rarely are these agnosias so purely relegated to one sensory modality. There is almost always an involvement of several sensory modalities. Recognition of an object usually involves more than one sensory modality and the term *associational* cortex was applied to regions between the sensory cortex where such a merging of sensory functions was assumed to take place. Recently, the merging of several sensory inputs in the cortex has been shown in a

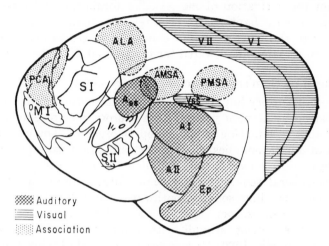

Auditory
Visual
Association

Fig. 21.25. Primary sensory and associational areas of the cortex: AI, auditory area I; AII, auditory area II; Ep, ectosylvian auditory area; Asg, auditory area of anterior suprasylvian gyrus; SI, somatic sensory area I; SII, somatic sensory area II; MI, somatic motor area I; VI, visual area, I; VII visual area II; Vss, visual area of syprasylvian sulcus; PMSA, posterior middle suprasylvian associational area; AMSA, anterior middle suprasylvian associa- tion area; ALA, anterior lateral association area; PCA, pericruciate association area. (Thompson, *et al.*, 1963.)

somewhat different manner. Using the evoked response technique Amassian (1954) found that both auditory and somesthetic responses were present in an area in the anterior lateral gyrus of cats, in an associational cortical region outside the specific sensory areas. These 'associational' responses were subsequently discovered in other places and Thompson, Johnson and Hoopes (1963) have shown four such associational areas for the cat (Fig. 21.25). The associa- tional areas of the cat brain fall into regions between specific sensory areas, except for a small overlap on part of the somesthetic area and a large overlap of one region onto the primary somatic-motor area. Each of these associational areas responds equally well to auditory, visual and tactile stimulation. The evoked responses although similar in appearance, differ from specific evoked responses in that they have a longer latency, duration and a greater sensitivity to depression by anesthesia. The responses are not relayed from specific receptor cortical areas as shown by their presence in the associational regions after removal of all the rest of the cortex including the primary sensory areas. The responses appear to represent the activation of the reticular formation and non-specific thalamic nuclei (Chapter 20). The relation of these 'associational' responses to the mechanisms of coherence of sensory modalities in perception remains unanswered for the present (Chapter 25).

Centrifugal mechanisms controlling sensory input

A control of sensory impulses by mechanisms acting on the receptors was inferred by Ramón y Cajal from the presence of efferent nerve fibers found terminating within receptor organs. The gamma loop control of muscle spindles (Chapter 17) is the best example of such a *centrifugal control mechanism*. Similar control mechanisms at the other peripheral sensory organs or at intermediate nuclear relays along the ascending sensory pathways could be the basis for a discrimination of sensory input to the cortex. Attention could be focused on pertinent stimuli with a decrease of 'non-essential' stimuli (Hagbarth, 1960; Hernández-Peón, 1961; Livingston, 1959). Such a corticofugal 'gating' effect was suggested by Hernández-Peón, Scherrer and Jouvet (1956). They used a click as a sound stimulation to excite evoked responses in the lateral geniculate body. When the sight of a mouse suddenly attracted the attention of the animal, the evoked response amplitudes became decreased. The mechanism suggested was an inhibition of impulses ascending in the auditory system although a number of different mechanisms could account for amplitude changes of evoked responses (Chapters 18, 20). Evidence for a corticofugal 'gating' effect was found in the cochlear nucleus on stimulation of a descending efferent path by Desmedt (1960) most likely via the efferent fibers terminating in the cochlear nucleus (Rasmussen, 1960), and found present in the cochlear nerve proceeding to the organ of Corti.

A descending inhibitory 'gating' effect on somesthetic transmission was shown by Hagbarth and Kerr (1954). They stimulated the dorsal roots of curarized cats and recorded the ascending discharge in the dorsal columns. Upon stimulation of the reticular formation, cerebellum or sensorimotor cortex, the size of the ascending volley was decreased (Fig. 21.26). The descending impulses therefore appear to have an inhibitory influence acting at the lower spinal level where afferent fibers enter the cord to synapse on ascending neurons. Anderson, Eccles and Sears (1962) have shown that on

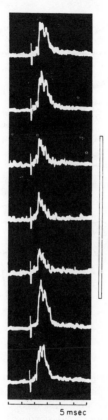

5 msec

Fig. 21.26. Dorsal root reflexes are shown before and during stimulation of the contralateral sensory cortex at time indicated by the bar to the right. A reduction in the size of the dorsal root reflex is seen during cortical stimulation. (Hagbarth and Kerr, 1954.)

stimulation descending fibers from the sensorimotor cortex excite the same interneurons of the spinal cord which mediate presynaptic inhibition for local spinal and transmission (Chapter 17). These terminate on dorsal root afferent fibers as shown by the dorsal root potentials (Fig. 21.27). The major effect of the presynaptic inhibitory system was on group Ib and cutaneous afferents entering the cord.

In addition, Towe and Jabbur (1961) showed that descending fibers from the sensorimotor cortex could inhibit transmission through the gracilus and cuneate nuclear relays of the lemniscal system. Marshall (1941) had earlier shown that transmission through

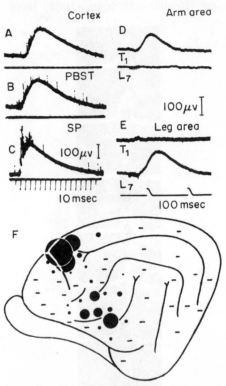

Fig. 21.27. Dorsal root potential responses shown in traces A–C following: A, electrical stimulation of the contralateral cortex of the cat; B, stimulation of the posterior biceps semitendinosis (PBST); C, a single volley in superficial peroneal (SP) nerve. Trace D shows response in dorsal roots (arm) of thoracic (T_1) and none in lumbar (leg) dorsal routes L_7 after stimulating cortical arm region. A reversed effect on stimulating cortical leg area is shown in E. The most effective region of cortical stimulation is shown by the layer black spots in F located in the sensorimotor area I, the next most effective in sensorimotor area II. (Andersen, Eccles and Sears, 1962.)

this nuclear region was followed by a prolonged decrease in excitability. Recordings taken from the surface showed a prolonged surface positive phase present in the cuneate nucleus corresponding to the prolonged depressed excitability (Therman, 1941). This behavior is similar to the prolonged depressed excitability and the associated cord and root potentials explained by the mechanism of presynaptic inhibition. Anderson, Eccles and Schmidt (1962) showed this by recording a depolarization of the terminals of the presynaptic fibers during the prolonged diminished excitability. The depolarization of the presynaptic fibers below the surface gives rise, on conductor volume

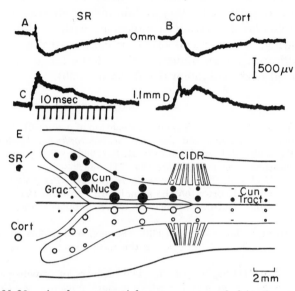

Fig. 21.28. A, slow potential response recorded in the cuneate nucleus following superficial radial (SR) nerve stimulation. B, similar slow potential response upon sensorimotor cortex (Cort) stimulation. C and D, responses to the same two different stimuli but recording at a depth of 1.1 mm below the surface, at positions shown in E. The relation amplitudes of the slow potential responses are indicated by the sizes of the spots. Filled spots represent superficial radial; open spots, cortical stimulation. Other abbreviations: cuneate nucleus (Cun Nuc), cuneate tract (Cun Tract), first cervicle root (CIDR). (Andersen, Eccles and Schmidt, 1962.)

principles, to the long-lasting positive potential recorded from the surface of the cuneate nucleus (Fig. 21.28).

Not all the corticofugal influences on transmission through the cuneate and gracilus nuclei can be explained by presynaptic inhibitory action. Cortical facilitating descending effects were also found by Jabbur and Towe (1961). Bremer and Stoupel (1959) found a facilitation of primary sensory responses evoked in the visual cortex upon reticular formation stimulation. This could be brought about either by cortical or sub-cortical mechanisms. An effect of reticular formation stimulation to alter transmission within the lateral geniculate ganglion itself was shown by an augmentation of geniculate postsynaptic potentials following reticular formation stimulation (Suzuki and Taira, 1961). In addition, Suzuki and Taira showed by a single-cell analysis of the radiation fibers coming from the lateral geniculate that both facilitatory and inhibitory effects were produced by such reticular formation stimulation, with facilitatory effects predominating. Mechanisms of centrifugal control appear to have great significance for an understanding of the integrative processes of the central nervous system (Livingston, 1959).

REFERENCES

Amassian, V. E. (1954). Studies on organization of a somesthetic association area, including a single unit analysis. *J. Neurophysiol.* **17**: 39–58.

Andersen, P., Eccles, J. C. and Schmidt, R. F. (1962). Presynaptic inhibition in the cuneate nucleus. *Nature* **194**: 741–743.

Andersen, P., Eccles, J. C. and Sears, T. A. (1962). Presynaptic inhibitory action of cerebral cortex on the spinal cord. *Nature* **194**: 740–741.

Bishop, G. (1956). Natural history of nerve impulse. *Physiol. Rev.* **36**: 376–399.

Bishop, G. H. and Clare, M. H. (1953). Sequence of events in optic cortex response to volleys of impulses in the radiations. *J. Neurophysiol.* **16**: 490–498.

Bishop, P. O. and Davis, R. (1960). The recovery of responsiveness of the sensory synapses in the lateral geniculate nucleus. *J. Physiol.* **150**: 214–238.

Bremer, F. (1958). Cerebral and cerebellar potential. *Physiol. Rev.* **38**: 357–388.

Bremer, F. and Stoupel, N. (1956). Interpretation de la réponse de l'aire visuelle corticale a une voleé d'influx sensoriels. *Arch. Intern. Physiol.* **64**: 234–250.

Bremer, F. and Stoupel, N. (1959). Facilitation et inhibition des potentiels evoqués corticaux dans l'eveil cérébral. *Arch. Intern. Physiol. Biochem.* **67**: 240–275.

Chow, K. L. (1955). Failure to demonstrate changes in the visual system of monkeys kept in darkness or colored lights. *J. Comp. Neurol.* **102**: 597–606.

Curtis, D. R. and Davis, R. (1962). Pharmacological studies upon neurons of the lateral geniculate nucleus of the cat. *Brit. J. Pharmacol.* **18**: 217–246.

Desmedt, J. E. (1960). Neurophysiological mechanisms controlling acoustic input. *Neural Mechanisms of the Auditory and Vestibular Systems.* Edited by G. L. Rasmussen and W. F. Windle. Chapter 11. Thomas, Springfield.

de Valois, R. (1960). Color vision mechanisms in the monkey. *J. Gen. Physiol.* **43**: Suppl., part 2, 115–128.

Diamond, J. T. and Neff, W. D. (1957). Ablation of temporal cortex and discrimination of auditory patterns. *J. Neurophysiol.* **20**: 300–315.

Downman, C. B. B., Woolsey, C. N. and Lende, R. A. (1960). Auditory areas I, II and EP; cochlear representation, afferent paths and interconnections. *Bull. Johns Hopkins Hosp.* **106**: 127–142.

Dusser de Barenne, J. G. (1916). Experimental researches on sensory localisations in the cerebral cortex. *Quart. J. Exptl. Physiol.* **9**: 355–390.

Evarts, E. V., Landau, W., Freygang, W. and Marshall, W. H. (1955). Some effects of lysergic acid diethylamide and bufotenine on electrical activity in the cat's visual system. *Am. J. Physiol.* **182**: 594–598

Fulton, J. F. (1951). *Frontal Lobotomy and Affective Behavior.* Norton, New York.

Gerard, R. W. (1951). The physiology of pain; abnormal neuron states in causalgia and related phenomena. *Anesthesiology* **12**: 1–13.

Glees, P. and LeGros Clark, W. F. (1941). The termination of optic fibers in the lateral geniculate body of the monkey. *J. Anat.* **75**: 295–308.

Hagbarth, K. E. (1960). Centrifugal mechanisms of sensory control. *Ergeb. Biol.* **22**: 47–66.

Hagbarth, K. E. and Kerr, D. I. B. (1954). Central influences on spinal afferent conduction. *J. Neurophysiol.* **17**: 295–307.

Hernández-Peón, R. (1961). Reticular mechanisms of sensory control. *Sensory Communication.* Edited by W. A. Rosenblith. Chapter 26. John Wiley and Sons, New York.

Hernández-Peón, R., Scherrer, H. and Jouvet, M. (1956). Modification of electrical activity in cochlear nucleus during 'attention' in unanesthetized cats. *Science* **123**: 331–332.

Hild, W. and Tasaki, J. (1962). Morphological and physiological properties of neurons and glial cells in tissue culture. *J. Neurophysiol.* **25**: 277–304.

Hind, J. E. (1960). Unit activity in the auditory cortex. *Neural Mechanisms of the Auditory and Vestibular System.* Edited by G. Rasmussen and W. F. Windle. Chapter 14. Charles Thomas, Springfield.

Hubel, D. H. (1959). Single unit activity in striate cortex of unrestrained cats. *J. Physiol.* **147**: 226–238.

Hubel, D. H. (1960). Single unit activity in lateral geniculate body and optic tract of unrestrained cats. *J. Physiol.* **150**: 91–104.

Hubel, D. H. and Wiesel, T. N. (1959). Receptive fields of single neurones in the cat's striate cortex. *J. Physiol.* **148**: 574–591.

Hubel, D. H. and Wiesel, T. N. (1962). Receptive fields, binocular interaction and functional architecture in the cat's visual cortex. *J. Physiol.* **160**: 106–154.

Jabbur, S. J. and Towe, A. L. (1961). Cortical excitation of neurons in dorsal column nuclei of cat, including an analysis of pathways. *J. Neurophysiol.* **24**: 499–509.

Katsuki, Y. (1961). Neural mechanism of auditory sensation in cats. *Sensory Communication.* Edited by W. A. Rosenblith. Chapter 29. John Wiley and Sons, New York.

Landau, W. M. and Clare, M. H. (1956). A note on the characteristic response pattern in primary sensory projection cortex of the cat following a synchronous afferent volley. *Electroencephalog. Clin. Neurophysiol.* **8**: 457–464.

Lashley, K. S. (1942). The problem of cerebral organization in vision. *Biol. Symp.* **7**: 301–322.

LeGros Clark, W. F. (1940). Anatomical basis of color vision. *Nature* **146**: 558–559; and The laminar pattern of the lateral geniculate nucleus considered in relation to color vision. *Documenta Ophthalm.* **3**: 57–64 (1949).

Li, C. L., Cullen, C. and Jasper, H. H. (1956). Laminar microelectrode studies of specific somatosensory cortical potentials. *J. Neurophysiol.* **19**: 111–130.

Livingston, R. B. (1959). Central control of receptors and sensory transmission systems. *Handbook of Physiology—Neurophysiology*, Vol. 2, pp. 741–760. American Physiological Society, Washington, D.C.

Livingston, W. K. (1943). *Pain Mechanisms*. Macmillan, New York.

Lloyd, D. P. C. and McIntyre, A. K. (1950). Dorsal column conduction of Group I muscle afferent impulses and their relay through Clarke's column. *J. Neurophysiol.* **13**: 39–54.

Lorente de Nó, R. (1934). Studies on the structure of the cerebral cortex. II. Continuation of the study of the ammonic system. *J. Psychol. Neurol.*, Lpz. **46**: 113–177.

Lorente de Nó, R. (1953). Conduction of impulses in the neurons of the oculomotor nucleus. *The Spinal Cord.* Pp. 132–179. Ciba Foundation Symposium. Churchill, London.

MacKenzie, J. (1920). *Symptoms and Their Interpretation.* 4th Ed. Shaw and Sons, London.

Marshall, W. H. (1941). Observations on subcortical somatic sensory mechanisms of cats under nembutal anesthesia. *J. Neurophysiol.* **4**: 25–43.

Marshall, W. H. (1949). Excitability cycle and interaction in geniculate-striate system of cat. *J. Neurophysiol.* **4**: 277–288.

Marshall, W. H. (1950). The relation of dehydration of the brain to the spreading depression of Leão. *Electroencephalog. Clin. Neurophysiol.* **2**: 177–185.

Marshall, W. H. and Talbot, S. A. (1942). Recent evidence for neural mechanisms in vision leading to a general theory .of sensory activity. *Biol. Symp.* **7**: 117–164.

Marshall, W. H., Talbot, S. A. and Ades, H. W. (1943). Cortical response of the anesthetized cat to gross photic and electrical afferent stimulation. *J. Neurophysiol.* **6**: 1–15.

Maturana, H. R., Lettvin, J. Y., McCulloch, W. S. and Pitts, W. H. (1960). Anatomy and physiology of vision in the frog (*Rana pipiens*). *J. Gen. Physiol.* **43**: 129–176.

Minkowski, M. (1911). Zur physiologie der sehsphäre. *Pflugers Arch. Ges. Physiol.* **141**: 171–327.

Mountcastle, V. B. (1957). Modality and topographic properties of single neurons of cat's somatic sensory cortex. *J. Neurophysiol.* **20**: 408–434.

Mountcastle, V. B. (1961). Some functional properties of the somatic afferent system. *Sensory Communication.* Edited by W. Rosenblith. Chapter 22. John Wiley and Sons, New York.

Nakahama, H. (1959). Cerebral response of anterior sigmoid gyrus to ipsilateral posterior sigmoid stimulation in cat. *J. Neurophysiol.* **22**: 573–589.

Neff, W. D. (1960). Role of the auditory cortex in sound discrimination. *Neural Mechanisms of the Auditory and Vestibular Systems.* Edited by G. Rasmussen and W. F. Windle. Chapter 5. Charles Thomas, Springfield.

O'Leary, J. L. (1941). Structure of the area striata of the cat. *J. Comp. Neurol.* **75**: 131–164.

Penfield, W. and Jasper, H. H. (1954). *Epilepsy and the Functional Anatomy of the Human Brain.* Little, Brown & Co., Boston.

Penfield, W. and Roberts, L. (1959). *Speech and Brain Mechanisms.* Princeton University Press, Princeton.

Poggio, G. F. and Mountcastle, V. B. (1960). A study of the functional contributions of the lemniscal and spinothalamic systems to somatic sensibility. Central nervous mechanisms in pain. *Bull. Johns Hopkins Hosp.* **106**: 266–316.

Poljak, S. L. (1957). *The Vertebrate Visual System.* University of Chicago Press, Chicago.

Powell, T. P. S. and Mountcastle, V. B. (1959). Some aspects of the functional organization of the cortex of the post-central gyrus of the monkey: a correlation of findings obtained in a single-unit analysis with cytoarchitecture. *Bull. Johns Hopkins Hosp.* **105**: 133–162.

Putnam, T. J. and Liebman, S. (1942). Cortical representation of the macula lutea with special reference to the theory of bilateral representation. *Arch. Ophthal.* **28**: 415–443.

Rasmussen, G. L. (1960). Efferent fibers of the cochlear nerve and cochlear nucleus. *Neural Mechanisms of the Auditory and Vestibular Systems.* Edited by G. Rasmussen and W. F. Windle. Chapter 8. Charles Thomas, Springfield.

Rose, J. E. (1949). The cellular structure of the auditory region of the cat. *J. Comp. Neurol.* **91**: 409–439.

Rose, J. E. (1960). Organization of frequency sensitive neurons in the cochlear nuclear complex of the cat. *Neural Mechanisms of the Auditory and Vestibular Systems.* Edited by G. L. Rasmussen and W. F. Windle. Chapter 9. Charles Thomas, Springfield.

Rose, J. E. and Mountcastle, V. B. (1952). The thalamic tactile region in rabbit and cat. *J. Comp. Neurol.* **97**: 441–490.

Rose, J. E. and Mountcastle, V. B. (1959). Touch and kinesis. *Handbook of Physiology—Neurophysiology.* Vol. I, pp. 387–429. American Physiological Society, Washington, D.C.

Rose, J. E. and Woolsey, C. N. (1958). Cortical connections and functional organization of the thalamic auditory system of the cat. *Biological and Biochemical Basis of Behavior.* Edited by H. F. Harlow and C. N. Woolsey. Pp. 127–150. University of Wisconsin Press, Madison.

Suzuki, H. and Taira, N. (1961). Effect of reticular stimulation upon synaptic transmission in cat's lateral geniculate body. *Japan. J. Physiol.* **11**: 641–655.

Sweet, W. H. (1959). Pain. *Handbook of Physiology—Neurophysiology.* Vol. I, pp. 459–506. American Physiological Society, Washington, D.C.

Therman, P. O. (1941). Transmission of impulses through the Burdach nucleus. *J. Neurophysiol.* **4**: 153–166.

Thompson, R. F., Johnson, R. H. and Hoopes, J. J. (1963). Organization of auditory, somatic sensory, and visual projection to association fields of cerebral cortex in the cat. *J. Neurophysiol.* **26**: 343–364; and Auditory, somatic sensory, and visual response interactions in association and primary cortical fields of the cat. *Ibid.*, 365–378.

Towe, A. L. and Jabbur, S. L. (1961). Cortical inhibition of neurons in dorsal column nuclei of cat. *J. Neurophysiol.* **24**: 488–498.

Tunturi, A. R. (1950). Physiological determination of the arrangement of the afferent connections to the middle ectosylvian auditory area in the dog. *Am. J. Physiol.* **162**: 489–502.

Tunturi, A. R. (1960). Anatomy and physiology of the auditory cortex, *Neural Mechanisms of the Auditory and Vestibulary Systems.* Edited by G. Rasmussen and W. F. Windle. Chapter 13. Charles Thomas, Springfield.

Vastola, E. F. (1959). After-positivity in lateral geniculate body. *J. Neurophysiol.* **22**: 258–272.

von Euler, C. and Ricci, G. F. (1958). Cortical evoked responses in auditory area and significance of apical dendrites. *J. Neurophysiol.* **21**: 231–246.

Walker, A. E. (1943). Central representation of pain. *Assoc. Res. Nervous Mental Diseases* **23**: 63–85.

Wall, P. D. (1961). Two transmission systems for skin sensations. *Sensory Communication.* Edited by W. A. Rosenblith. John Wiley and Sons, New York.

Whitlock, D. G. and Perl, E. R. (1959). Afferent projections through ventrolateral funiculi to thalamus of cat. *J. Neurophysiol.* **22**: 133–148.

Wiersma, C. A. G. (1962). The organization of the arthropod central nervous system. *Am. Zool.* **2**: 67–78.

Woolsey, C. N. (1958). Organization of somatic sensory and motor areas of the cerebral cortex. *Biological and Biochemical Bases of Behavior.* Edited by H. F. Harlow and C. N. Woolsey. Pp. 63–81. University of Wisconsin Press, Madison.

Woolsey, C. N. (1960). Organization of cortical auditory system. A review and synthesis. *Neural Mechanisms of the Auditory and Vestibular Systems.* Edited by G. Rasmussen and W. F. Windle. Chapter 12. Charles Thomas, Springfield.

Woolsey, C. N., Marshall, W. H. and Bard, P. (1942). Representation of cutaneous tactile sensibility in the cerebral cortex of the monkey as indicated by evoked potentials. *Bull. Johns Hopkins Hosp.* **7**: 399–441.

22

Upper Motor Control and
Sensorimotor Organization

Motor areas in the cortex

Fritsch and Hitzig (1870) first showed that electrical stimulation of certain portions of the exposed cerebral cortex of animals gave rise to motor responses. On stimulating different regions, responses were found present either in the limbs, trunk or head muscles, depending on the site stimulated. In other words a *topographical* representation of various movements is present in the motor areas of the cortex (Ferrier, 1876). The representation of the peripheral musculature in the motor areas found for the chimpanzee is shown in Fig. 22.1. The somatotopic organization of the motor cortex of man (Fig. 22.2) is similar to that of the other primates. Motor responses which were elicited by stimulation of the brain of human patients under local anesthesia were not accompanied by a sense of willing the movements (Penfield and Jasper, 1954). Electrical stimulation of motor areas may make those muscles unavailable for voluntary movement. These results suggest that while volition for movement does not arise within the motor cortex (Walshe, 1947), voluntary control is mediated through the motor area.

The motor area which can be defined by electrical stimulation mainly corresponds with the cytoarchitectural area characterized by large pyramidal cells, the *Betz* cells found in area 4 of Brodmann's map (Chapter 21). The axons of these cells descend in the pyramidal tract of the spinal cord and terminate on the lower motor centers. This led to the concept that these large pyramidal cells were responsible for all the descending motor control of the various muscle groups. However, the number of Betz cells in the motor cortex are actually quite small compared to the total number of fibers within the pyramidal tract (Lassek, 1954). As will appear later on in this chapter, it is too simple a view of the motor cortex to consider the Betz cells as controlling the various muscle groups without taking into account the internal organization of the motor

493

cortex. To anticipate that discussion, analysis of normal and pathological alternations in the human shows that motor control is organized in terms of movements (Jackson, 1932; Walshe, 1947). For example, the movement of one digit is associated with patterns of inhibition and excitation in the other digits.

Area 6 of Brodmann just anterior to area 4 also gives rise to motor responses when stimulated. The motor responses excited from area

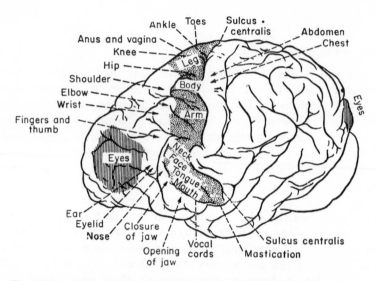

Fig. 22.1. Cortex of the chimpanzee showing regions in stippling which give rise on electrical stimulation to muscle responses in the various parts of the body indicated. The frontal eye field shown by vertical hatching is not the same in its reaction as other parts of the motor cortex and should, perhaps, not be considered the same. (Grunbaum and Sherrington, *Proc. Roy. Soc. B.* **72**: 152, 1903.)

6 have been described as qualitatively different from the motor responses obtained from area 4 (Fulton, 1949). The movements evoked from area 4 are mainly contralateral, simple, evoked in a few muscles and are blocked by pyramidal tract section. Movements elicited from stimulation of area 6 were characterized as slower and more complex, presumably involving more coordinating mechanisms. The rather sharp division of functions of areas 4 and 6 along cytoarchitectural lines is no longer considered significant as will be discussed in the following section.

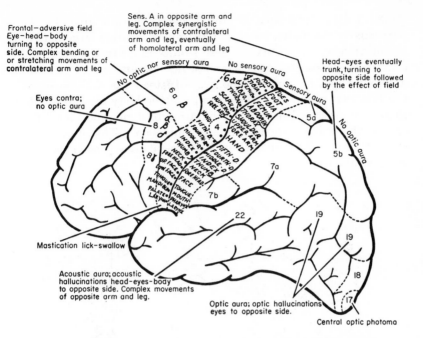

Fig. 22.2.   The motor area of man defined by electrical stimulation is seen lying mainly in region 4 in front of the central sulcus and is shown to be topographically similar in its relation to the various body musculatures as are the sensory areas 3, 1, 2 on the post-central gyrus to various regions on the surface of the skin.   (Bard, *Medical Physiology* (10th Ed.).   Mosby, 1956.)

Precentral and supplementary motor areas

In their detailed motor cortex studies, Woolsey, Meyer, Spencer, Hamuy and Travis (1952) examined animals several hours after induction of pentobarbital-anesthesia.   This simplifies and makes more regular the motor responses elicited by unipolar anodal stimulation.   A uniform procedure of stimulation was insured by using the minimal muscle contraction assessed by palpation of the muscles involved.   Figurines on the surface of the macaque's brain (Fig. 22.3) show the corresponding points on the cortex which have the lowest threshold for the activation of the various muscles indicated.   The correspondence of this *precentral motor* area with the cytoarchitectural regions identified as areas 4 and 6 is only approximate.   The rostral part of the precentral motor area lies mostly within area 6 where the larger muscle groups are situated (back, upper arm and head).   The muscle representation for lower arms, digits, tongue and face is found partly within area 4. These, particularly the digits, take up a disproportionately large part of the motor area of the cortex. These results indicate that under these conditions of study, areas 4 and 6 do not give rise to essentially different types of motor responses. Instead the differences reflect the fact that different muscle groups of the body are represented in these two areas. Muscle representation of digits and face falls into area 4 where finer movements are controlled. The more proximal musculature of the trunk falling into area 6 gives grosser movements when stimulated.

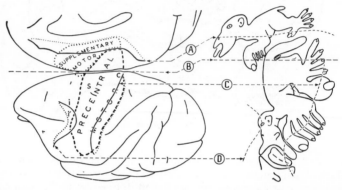

Fig. 22.3.   Motor figurine of the monkey brain shows where in the motor cortex the various musculatures of the body is controlled. The letters show the sulci indicating where the figurine falls on the precentral motor area of the brain surface.   Notice the proportionately large area controlling the tongue and digits, particularly the thumb and big toe areas.   The precentral motor area overlaps the central sulcus and also continues on to the medial surface of the brain shown above.   A second supplementary motor area is seen falling on the medial surface of the brain and is represented by a smaller figurine.   (From Woolsey, et al. 1952.)

Another smaller motor area was found medial and anterior to the precentral motor area (Fig. 22.3).   The figurine which represents this *supplementary* motor area is shown flattened out, most of it is turned around and hidden medially in the intercerebral cleft.   The supplementary motor area gives rise to motor responses which are slower than those obtained from the precentral motor 4 area (Penfield and Jasper, 1954).   Facilitation is more marked and limb positions are held for a longer time after excitation.   Ablation of the precentral motor cortex did not make any difference in the character of the motor responses obtained from the supplementary motor cortex indicating a separate downflow from each of these motor areas (Bertrand, 1956). The close relationship of the motor and sensory cortical areas is shown for a number of species in Fig. 22.4. In some species there is an overlap of sensory and motor areas.

The motor area has also been defined by antidromic stimulation of the pyramidal tract by recording the resulting responses in the

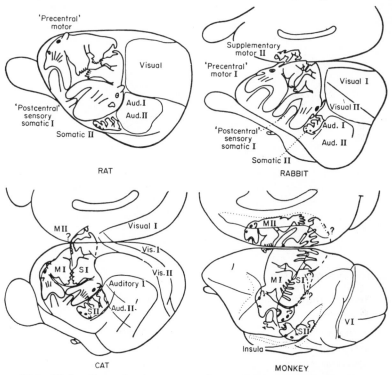

Fig. 22.4. Sensorimotor areas from different species, (rat, rabbit, cat and monkey) shows figurines representing the motor area anteriorly with the similar appearing sensory figurines located just posteriorly. (From Woolsey, *Biological and Biochemical Bases of Behavior.* Ed., Harlow and Woolsey. University of Wisconsin Press, 1958.)

cortex (Woolsey and Chang, 1948). The extent of the area excited antidromically is large (Fig. 22.5). Part of the reason for the large extent of the antidromic responses is that a fairly large area of the cortex sends fibers into the pyramidal tract. Also, when exciting the pyramidal tracts antidromically an adventitious spread of electrical current to the nearby ascending sensory tract often occurs unless special precautions are taken.

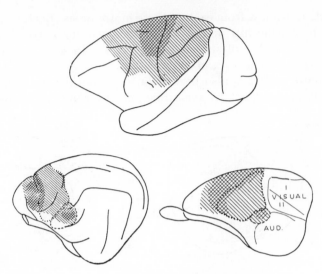

Fig. 22.5. Excitation of the medullary pyramidal tract of monkey (upper), cat (left) and rabbit (right), gives rise to antidromic
responses evoked in the sensorimotor cortex. The cortical region
giving rise to slow wave responses is indicated by slanted lines;
those in addition giving spike components by crossed-hatched lines.
(Woolsey and Chang, 1948.)

Intrinsic motor cortex organization

The lines of demarcation of the areas controlling various muscular
groups appear to be inexact and overlapping. How much of this
is due to the spread of electrical currents around the stimulating
electrodes and how much to an excitation of intracortical networks
and neuronal spread to distant pyramidal tract cells?

The concept of an intrinsic neuronal organization of motor
territories with overlapping effects was recognized by Leyton and
Sherrington (1917) in their studies of the motor cortex of the higher
primates. An 'instability' of a stimulated area was revealed by the
facilitation and the reversal of the effect of a stimulus upon repetition.
Also, instability was shown when the same response could be obtained
by successive lateral stimulations at points further and further away
from the site where it was originally evoked. Such instability and
the overlap of regions from which responses in different musculatures
could be obtained was also seen in the motor cortex of man (Penfield
and Boldrey, 1937). The effect of anesthesia on patterns of motor
responses was studied in animals with chronically implanted electrodes
(Lilly, Austin and Chambers, 1952). Using comparatively weak

stimuli in unanesthetized animals, movements were observed to involve wide areas of musculature. After pentobarbital-anesthesia was introduced, the same stimulation evoked responses from more discrete regions. The differences of motor responsivity found after anesthetization suggest that much of the variation of response is related to the nature of the intrinsic intracortical organization subserving motor control. Bubnoff and Heidenhain (1881) had earlier shown that a conditioning shock could change the effects of a later stimulation, and that these variations were eliminated when the cortex was removed and the underlying white matter stimulated. Dusser de Barenne and McCulloch (1939) studied the effects of conditioning shocks upon the motor cortex and further defined both facilitatory and inhibitory (*extinction*) effects following excitation. Facilitation accounts for the summating processes present in the cortex, indicated by the finding that single brief shocks are usually less effective to elicit motor responses than repetitive stimuli or single long duration pulses of 5 to 40 msec (Wyss and Obradoer, 1937).

A study of the factors controlling the extent of the cortical area from which a response of a given muscle could be obtained was made by Liddell and Phillips (1951). They used square-pulse stimulation and found that single shocks were effective at a pulse-duration of approximately 5 msec in a current range of several milliamperes. In the lightly anesthetized animal, a small movement such as a thumb-flick was elicited from the small circled area shown in A of Fig. 22.6. With increased strength of stimulating current, the area from which thumb movement was obtained became larger (B). At still greater strengths it increased further (C) and as shown by the upper circled area, a new response of muscles controlling the toe was evidenced. In D of Fig. 22.6, at still greater strength, the lower circled area represents the appearances of yet another new response, that of muscles controlling the mouth.

The extent of the thumb area was shown to be determined by spread of excitation in the cerebral cortex feeding into a smaller cortical region representing the muscle. When cuts were made between the central and outlying cortical sites the response was not blocked, showing that these various regions had separate fibers descending in the pyramidal tract to the lower motor centers.

The level of anesthesia was shown to control the size of the motor area determined by single pulses. A deepening of the anesthesia causes the motor areas to shrink or become unresponsive. Therefore, the cortical maps found in the moderately or lightly anesthetized animal is smaller than the normally larger area of motor control.

Some of the complexities of motor responses are due to the manner of stimulation. This was indicated by the use of a surface anodal electrode to stimulate the excitable motor area while recording the discharge in a single pyramidal tract fiber (Hern, Landgren and Phillips, 1962). There was an apparent difference when anodal currents were used to excite the pyramidal cell compared to cathodal currents. Anodal stimulation gave rise to little after-discharge while cathodal stimulation gave rise to a prolonged after-discharge. It would appear that the surface cathodal stimulation is effecting excitation of

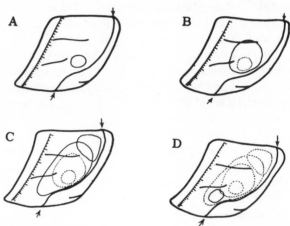

Fig. 22.6. (A) shows by the circle the region of the motor area of the monkey giving thumb and index finger responses to electrical stimulation. With an increased strength of stimulation (B), the size of the area becomes larger (continuous line). With still greater stimulating strength (C) an increase in the area occurs and, in addition, responses in the toe from the upper circled region. With still greater stimulation (D) a response in the mouth region appears as shown by the circled lower region. (From Liddell and Phillips, 1951.)

an intercortical network which results in facilitatory influences acting on pyramidal tract cells. Why anodal stimulation excites a simpler pyramidal cell discharge is unknown at present. Anodal currents could be exciting the lower layer pyramidal cell membranes directly. Consistent with this concept is the fact that with such stimulation the resulting pyramidal cell discharges have short latencies (Phillips, 1956; Li, 1963).

How much of the size of a motor area is due to current spread was further investigated (Landgren, Phillips and Porter, 1962). The excitable area is relatively large (in one case 8 × 2.5 mm), the motor cortex appearing to be composed of colonies of pyramidal cells which overlap widely. The complexity of the efferent cell population within the motor cortex can be appreciated from the estimate of Powell that within a column of cortex 1 mm² in cross-section and extending vertically from the underlying white matter to the surface there are 18,000 pyramidal cells, 90 of these are Betz cells.

Upon stimulation of the motor cortex while recording single fiber responses from the pyramidal tract with a microelectrode, Adrian and Moruzzi (1939) found that repetitive discharges were elicited in these pyramidal tract fibers along with associated movement of the

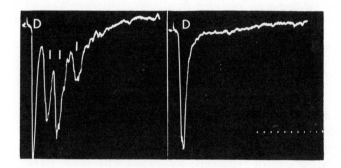

Fig. 22.7. Electrical stimulation of the sensorimotor area of the cortex gives rise to a first direct (D) response followed by a series of of smaller spike (I) responses recorded from the pyramidal tract (left). Stimulation of the underlying white matter of the brain (right) gives rise only to D response without the I responses. Timing dots 1 msec apart. (From Patton and Amassian, 1960.)

muscles. Paton and Amassian (1960) recorded pyramidal responses evoked by motor cortex stimulation and identified an early D wave and later I wave discharges, often of a repetitive nature (Fig. 22.7). The D wave has the short latency expected of a direct stimulation of Betz cells. The D wave is more resistant to anesthetics and will remain after spreading depression eliminates the following I waves. Also the D wave remains when the cortex is ablated and the underlying white matter stimulated as shown in Fig. 22.7. The I waves appear to be due to a second set of corticofugal fibers repetitively discharging. This is shown by the repetitive discharges obtained from a single pyramidal axon (Fig. 22.8). The intracortical cell giving rise to these I responses is excited after a latency of 2.0–2.5 msec. This delay is likely due to excitation of one or more

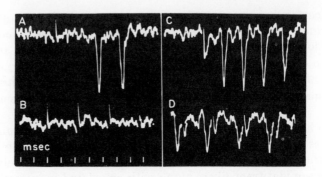

Fig. 22.8. Electrical stimulation of the sensorimotor cortex gives rise to discharges recorded from a single pyramidal tract fiber showing (A), two I discharges; (B), at a faster repetitive stimulation no responses; (C), using a stronger cortical stimulus than in A, a repetitive series of four I responses is seen. In D, repetitive stimulation at increased strength gives rise to short latency I responses. (From Patton and Amassian, *J. Neurophysiol.* **17**: 345, 1954.)

interneurons which in turn synapse on the pyramidal cell causing it to discharge rhythmically. Most likely the rhythm of the resulting discharge is controlled by the interneurons.

The larger size of Betz cells compared with other pyramidal cells is probably related to the large number of collaterals it has, as well as to the length of its axon coursing down the pyramidal tract. The relatively large soma permits a single-cell analysis to be made from these cells with intracellular microelectrodes. The pyramidal

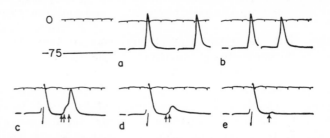

Fig. 22.9. Intracellular recording from a pyramidal cell of the cortex shows on antidromic stimulation of the pyramidal tract fiber an action potential with overshoot. (a) paired shocks at 4.4 msec, (b) with paired shocks at an interval of 2.8 msec, a break at the leading edge of the later response is seen. A fragmentation of the later response is seen in the record of paired responses in (c), (d), (e) at an interval of 1.8 msec. (From Phillips, 1959.)

tract fibers are excited in the medulla or *pes pedunculus* and identification of the unit recorded from within the motor cortex as a
Betz cell is made on the basis of the short latency of the antidromic
responses (Phillips, 1956, 1959). The antidromic response of the
Betz cell (Fig. 22.9) has a similarity to the antidromic responses of
spinal cord motoneurons (Chapter 16). Apparently the soma of the

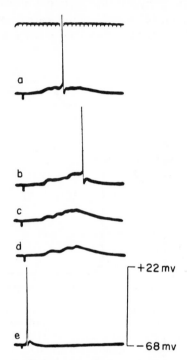

Fig. 22.10. Intracellular recording from a pyramidal cell
following stimulation of the pyramidal tract shows: (a) a prolonged
depolarizing synaptic potential before the spike; (b) a spike
appearing after a still longer synaptic response; (c) and (d)
synaptic potentials without a spike. An antidromic response (e)
has a briefer latency without a preceding synaptic potential.
(From Phillips, 1959.)

Betz cell also is a region of reduced excitability as shown by fragmentation into an IS-like spike by the use of paired shocks. When
stimulating the pyramidal tract to excite antidromic responses some
neurons of the cortex are found to be excited after a longer latency
preceded by a synaptic potential (Fig. 22.10). The depolarization
preceding the firing of the cell may be prolonged and irregular in

amplitude.   The critical level appears to be low—of the order of 5–8 mv.   These cells appear to be synaptically excited by the collaterals of antidromically fired Betz cells, possibly with an intervening interneuron, before terminating orthodromically on Betz cells as shown in Fig. 22.11.

In addition to evidence of EPSP activity in the cells excited by Betz cell collaterals, a hyperpolarizing potential with a prolonged time course is frequently seen in some cases without a preceding spike discharge (Fig. 22.12).   The long-lasting hyperpolarization is

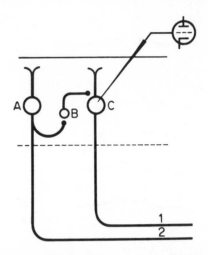

Fig. 22.11.   A microelectrode is diagrammatically shown inside a cell (C) which is excited to give an antidromic response by stimulation of its pyramidal tract fiber (1).   If pyramidal tract fiber (2) is excited by the stimulus, collateral fibers of the pyramidal cell A excites an interneuron B which in turn orthodromically fires cell C.   (Modified from Suzuki and Tukahara, 1963.)

associated with a prolonged inhibition as shown with paired shocks (Suzuki and Tukahara, 1963).

How is the discharge of Betz cells controlled?   Does it follow upon orthodromic activation of the apical dendrites?   Brookhart and Zanchetti (1956) have shown that the surface negative responses of the recruiting response were not associated with pyramidal tract firing, while firing was related to the positive phase of the augmenting response (Fig. 20.3).   In all probability part of the augmenting response is caused by the activity of specific sensory inputs to the cortex (Chapter 20) and we would expect that sensory nerve stimulation leading to somesthetic afferent excitation in the cortex could also drive Betz cells.   This was first shown by Adrian and Moruzzi (1939) who found in the excitable chloralose-anesthetized animals that touching the skin could excite a convulsive discharge.   This was seen as a high frequency burst of repetitive activity recorded in single pyramidal tract fibers.   More recently Li (1959, 1963) found that pyramidal tract cells were either facilitated or inhibited following sensory nerve stimulation.   Natural sensory stimulation can also drive pyramidal tract cells (Brooks, Rudomin and Slayman,

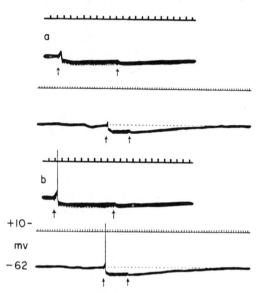

Fig. 22.12.   Intracellular hyperpolarizing responses in response to antidromic stimulations without (a) and with a spike (b).   Upper trace of each pair at a faster sweep—signals 100 cps.   (Phillips, 1959.)

1961).   The individual pyramidal tract cells respond to such specific modalities of sensory excitation as hair-bending, touch or pressure.

Quite possibly an intercortical system exists through which activation of sensory receptor neurons is relayed to the Betz cells.   Transmission via cortico-cortical fibers was considered to explain the results of spread of excitation from the somesthetic sensory area to the motor cortex of area 4 in humans by Foerster (1936).   The sensory and motor areas overlap (Penfield and Boldrey, 1937) or at least are very closely apposed (Woolsey, 1960).   This arrangement which is marked in some species appears to have its rationale in a unified or closely interconnected *sensorimotor control*, rather than as separate sensory and motor areas (Walshe, 1947). The placing and hopping reactions (Chapter 14) which have their localization in the sensorimotor areas of the cortex seem to be a prime example of such an intrinsic organization of sensory and motor components. There is also recent evidence that stretch receptors have cortical localization in this area.

Pyramidal and extrapyramidal corticofugal influences

Tower (1936, 1944) found that section of the pyramidal tract in the cat did not prevent complex motor behavior—running, jumping, etc. The outstanding effect of pyramidal tract section was *hypotonia*. An area 4 lesion also produces hypotonia. The effect of such motor cortex lesions is more pronounced in the higher primate where a larger cortical representation goes along with the greater importance in these species of fine control in the hands. This is even more so the case in man where at first the loss of cortical function is severely debilitating (Foerster, 1936).

The pyramidal tract has been considered to subserve fine coordinated activities while the grosser movements are subserved by the extrapyramidal outflow (Hines, 1944). Extirpation of the supplementary motor areas and clinical studies of lesions in this area show that its function is more closely related to more gross automatic movements which accompany the more highly specialized motor responses (Schneider and Crosby, 1960). However, a simple identification of specialized motor control with area 4 cannot be made because area 4 also supplies extrapyramidal fibers. These fibers descend along with the pyramidal tract fibers in the *internal capsule* to leave the pyramidal tract in the brain stem. The extrapyramidal fibers then terminate in the older motor nuclear groups, the *basal ganglia* (*vide infra*), and in the reticular formation. Very commonly a *stroke* occurs with a lesion in the internal capsule where both pyramidal and extrapyramidal fibers are present. The result is a marked *spasticity*. A lesion of the pyramidal tract at the level of the medulla, after most of the extrapyramidal fibers have left the tract, results in hypotonia, while a lesion in an extrapyramidal control site, in the supplementary motor area, gives rise to signs of spasticity (Travis, 1955). Therefore, capsular lesions giving rise to spasticity can be explained as an interruption of extrapyramidal tract fibers terminating in the reticular formation which are inhibitory in their function.

While a simple hypotonia is seen following an area 4 lesion, it may later change to a spasticity (Foerster, 1936). These later changes complicate the analysis of motor organization and will be discussed in a later section dealing with this problem of reorganization and compensation following a lesion.

Inhibition from the cortex

An inhibitory component arising from the cortex was indicated by paired shock stimulation. A reduction of motor responses to a second stimulus was seen following a strong one giving contraction (Bubnoff and Heidenhain, 1881). This *extinction* phenomenon was verified by Dusser de Barenne and McCullough (1939). Sherrington (1906) described inhibition of the biceps muscles with active contraction of the triceps upon cortical stimulation and considered the inhibition to be initiated from the lower motor centers.

However, it would appear that a more generalized non-reciprocal inhibitory mechanism may be excited in the cortex. Cortically induced inhibitory actions of two types were found by Tower (1936), i.e. inhibition of existing tone and an inhibition of ongoing movement. The inhibition of tone was demonstrated in preparations with the pyramidal tract cut. It was also seen in animals with an intact pyramidal tract if anesthesia was very light, the inhibition having a lower threshold than that for motor responses. The area giving inhibition of muscle tone was found present in the peri-cruciate cortex of the cat (the region usually considered the sensorimotor area) as well as in an anterior area found mainly on the anterior cruciate gyrus. Stimulation of this area gave rise to a widespread ipsilateral inhibition. Inhibition which was not on a reciprocal basis was also shown by the simultaneous inhibition found in both flexor and extensor limb muscles by Rioch and Rosenblueth (1935).

The inhibition of movement was characterized by Tower as an 'arrest of movement' or a 'quieting' influence on spontaneous movement. The movements appearing in light stages of anesthesia, such as swishing of the tail, striking or batting, pawing, placing movements of the forelegs or running movements, were inhibited by stimulation of frontal cortical fields in the gyrus proreus and cortical areas extending laterally over the auditory region. The inhibition is due to an excitation of corticofugal fibers as shown by elicitation of inhibition after removing the cortex and stimulating the underlying white matter.

To analyse the pathway of cortical inhibition, a continuous series of cortically evoked muscle responses was excited in order to test the inhibitory influence produced by stimulating other cortical areas. In such studies, Peacock (1954) found that inhibitory points were present in the motor cortex closely associated with the motor activation points and could be traced down into the internal capsule and the diencephalon. In similar experiments a myotatic reflex (knee-jerk) was used to test for inhibition within the sensorimotor cortex (Ochs, 1955). In both studies phasic and tonic effects were seen to be dissociated, suggesting separate mechanisms of control.

Motor control from the reticular formation and other brain stem regions

We have discussed the reticular formation from the point of view of its ascending action on the EEG and the conscious state. Historically, the control of reflex and motor functions in this region of the brain stem was investigated first. With stimulating electrodes placed within the medial part of the reticular formation of the medulla, Magoun and Rhines (1948) found an inhibition of cortically-elicited muscle responses (Fig. 22.13) and knee-jerk reflex responses. The inhibition had a rapid onset and responses returned rapidly without rebound when stimulation was stopped. A number of points within the medial part of the medulla of the brain stem were found to give the same inhibitory effect with both extensor and flexor reflexes inhibited. Therefore, the inhibition was characterized as 'global' (Magoun, 1950).

In the more anterior and lateral parts of the brain stem, stimulation of the reticular formation was found to give rise to facilitation (Fig. 22.14). An increase in the size of the knee-jerk reflex responses and motor responses was obtained when stimulating within this region.

The inhibitory and facilitatory regions of the reticular formation so demonstrated does not however exhaust all the potentialities of motor control present in this region. This is particularly true when barbiturate anesthesia is not used. Under this circumstance Gernandt and Thulin (1955) found both facilitatory and inhibitory points situated close together throughout both of these regions of the reticular formation. Also reciprocal actions on flexor and extensor muscles were found. When stimulating the reticular formation with implanted electrodes in the free moving animal, coordinated complex postural changes were elicited instead of pure facilitation or inhibition (Sprague and Chambers, 1954)

The distribution of mechanisms involved in tonic control in this brain stem region was studied by Peacock (1954) and Hankinson Namin and Ochs (1955). The tonic changes were traced stereoaxically from the upper cortex down into the tegmentum and then caudally from the region of the red nucleus.   The tonic patterns appeared to be part of the *tegmental response* (Ingram, Ranson, Hannett, Zeiss and Terwilliger, 1932).   In this response to stimulation of the tegmentum, the body curves toward the side stimu-

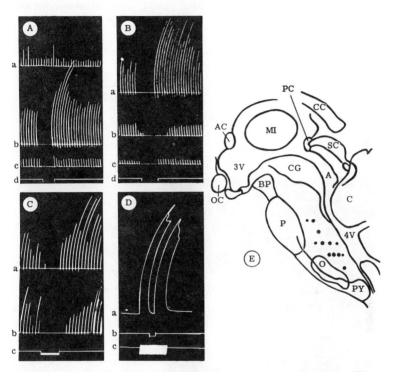

Fig. 22.13.   A diagram of the brain stem is shown at right, (E) with dots in regions of the medulla which on repetitive stimulation give rise to inhibitory effects on knee jerks.   The lower time signal in each of the records A–D show time of stimulation with inhibition of (a) flexor, (b) patellar and (c) blink responses in A and B and flexor responses in a and b of C.   D shows inhibitory effect on flexion (a) excited from internal capsule.   Signal on b line.
(From Magoun and Rhines, *J. Neurophysiol.* **9**: 165, 1946.)

ated, the legs are flexed on the ipsilateral side and extended on the contralateral side and the head is turned toward the stimulated side. A similar pattern of motor behavior is seen in the orienting reflex (Chapter 20).   Another region of motor control was one from which tremor was evoked on stimulation and designated by Jenkner and Ward (1953), the *tremorogenic zone* (Fig. 22.15).   In this connection,

the tremor seen in Parkinson's disease is of interest.   These patient
show an increase in muscle tonicity and a continual tremor of the
limbs and trunk.   The disease is believed due to an imbalanced
effect of the 'older motor' system.   This system is composed of
the corpus striatum (putamen and caudate) and the globus pallidu
(pallidum).   It has long been associated with motor control, but

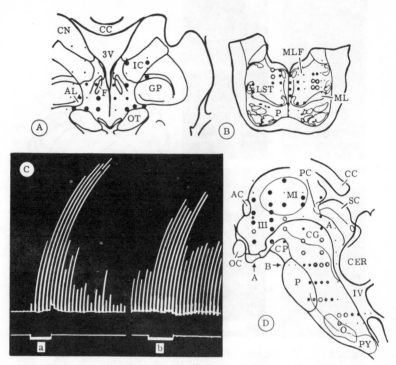

Fig. 22.14.   In diagrams of brain stem (A, B, D) the dots represent areas where a facilitation of cortically evoked motor responses and patellar reflexes can be obtained on stimulation.   In
record C cortical motor responses (a) are augmented during
brain stem stimulation at the time signal on lower line, and
patellar reflexes (b) augmented during the time signal.   (Rhines
and Magoun, *J. Neurophysiol.* **9**: 219, 1946.)

experimental studies have been conflicting (Mettler and Mettler
1942).   The evidence suggests that the basal ganglia act to coordinate
motor performance.   Disease of this system in man is characterized
by jerking, slow torsions or twistings of the limbs, head and body
In their review of this extrapyramidal motor system, Jung and
Hassler (1960) have presented evidence which suggests that the

substantia nigra is involved in Parkinson's disease and it is then the uncompensated effects of basal ganglionic outflow from the globus pallidus which brings about this state. Destruction of the neural outflow from the globus pallidus was shown to dramatically ameliorate the hypertonicity and tremor of Parkinson's disease (Cooper, 1961; Spiegel and Wycis, 1962).

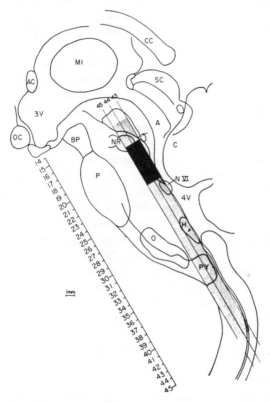

Fig. 22.15. Sagittal view of the monkey brain stem showing the regions which give rise to tremor on stimulation. Tremor was most marked in the black area and to a lesser degree was elicited from the grey area. (Jenkner and Ward, 1953.)

There is another set of special motor reactions obtained from subcortical centers. These have been studied in thalamic preparations after the cortex has been removed. These animals show *righting reactions* and are able to maintain a normal upright posture (Magnus, 1924, 1926). The righting reactions appear to occur in a sequence of reflexes as shown in high-speed photography. A cat is held upside down and then dropped.   As it falls the head turns, next the forelegs, the body, and thus the animal in short order can land on its feet.   These reactions occur in the normal animal with a speed and grace which is remarkable.   They are also seen in the decorticate preparation.

The labyrinths responding to gravity are the principal sensory organs by which the head righting reaction is initiated.   Visual clues are also important in higher animals.   In the case of an animal placed on its side, proprioceptive influences from the skin, joints and muscles are also important.   If an animal with its labyrinths destroyed is placed on its side blindfolded, it will attempt to right itself.   This is prevented by equalizing the tactile stimulation present in the skin by pressing a board down on its upper side.   A reaction seen in monkeys with large cortical ablations is the *grasp reflex* which appears to be a component of a body-righting mechanism (Bieber and Fulton, 1938).   The cortex-damaged monkey laid on its side will extend the lower arm, while its upper arm becomes flexed.   If the palm is touched by an object, the fingers of the hand will reflexly close over the object.   A similar reaction seen in the brain-damaged human is referred to as *forced grasping*.   The reaction is organized sub-cortically and was considered to be brought about by mechanisms in the thalamus.   However, a more caudal site of organization of this reflex in the brain stem was indicated by the excitation of a similar response from the tegmentum of the monkey.   The anencephalic human born without brain structure above the pons also shows it (Monnier, 1946).   Also, in the chronic midbrain cat preparation, after a few days a righting of the head and shoulders was seen.   After a week or two, the animals could right themselves and even walk about spontaneously (Bard and Macht, 1958).

Cerebellar control

The cerebellum or 'lesser' brain is situated over the medulla and pons, behind the cerebrum (Fig. 22.16).   It is composed of several developmentally distinct portions (Fig. 22.17).   The phylogenetically older *paleocerebellum* is found in the medially located anterior lobe of the cerebellum, and the flocullo-nodular portion of the posterior lobe with connections to vestibular receptors.   The phylogenetically newer *neocerebellar* portions of the cerebellum are found in the posterior lobe extending laterally as the cerebellar hemispheres.   One important input comes from the spindle receptors of muscles.   Fibers carrying discharges from the muscle sensory organs synapse on the large multipolar cells found in the dorsal

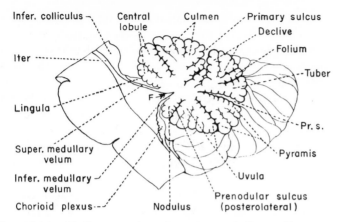

Fig. 22.16. Medium section through cerebellum. Pr.s., pre-pyramidal sulcus, F, fastigial recess of fourth ventricle. (After Strong and Elwyn, *Human Neuroanatomy*. Williams and Wilkins, 1943.)

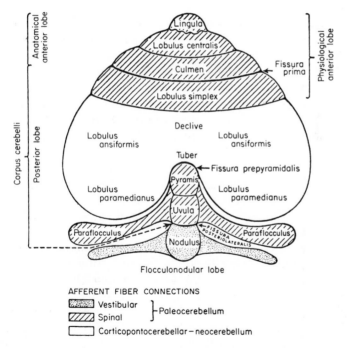

Fig. 22.17. Diagram of cerebellar cortex to show principal divisions. Paleocerebellum indicated by obliquely-hatched and stippled areas; neocerebellum by blank areas. (From Dow, after Fulton, *A Textbook of Physiology*, 17th Ed., Saunders, 1955.)

horn of the spinal cord, in Clarke's column. In turn axons pass across to the other side of the cord to ascend to the cerebellum as the dorsal spinocerebellar and ventral spinocerebellar tracts. Information from the muscle sense organs is integrated in the cerebellum with an input from the motor cortex and other motor regions so that the resultant movements are smoothly performed. Ablation of the cerebellum does not stop motor responses, but coordination of motor behavior is impaired. A decerebellated animal shows *ataxia*— defects of gait. It cannot make correct adjustments of limb movements so that over-shooting or under-shooting of an intended goal is seen—*dysmetria*. Instead of occurring smoothly, movements appear disjointed or jerky—*asynergia*. These maladjustments combine and lead to *intention tremor* which is seen when an object is reached for. Finally decerebellated animals appear to be weaker, and they are described as *hypotonic*. Removal of the cerebellum does not eliminate motor capabilities or result in an apparent defect of sensation, but as indicated, it interferes with the motor performance of the animal.

The type of movements made depends on the position maintained by an animal in space at any given moment. Impulses from the labyrinths reach the flocculo-nodular portions of the cerebellum. By this means the position of the head with relation to the earth and also of accelerations of the head become integrated in the cerebellum along with sensory inputs from joint, muscle, visual receptors, etc. The cerebellum acts as a *comparator* or overall motor feedback center. The somatopic projection of tactile and proprioceptor impulses from the body in the cerebellum (Fig. 22.18) as well as inputs from the sensorimotor cortex are certainly important for this comparator function of the cerebellum. In addition, the projection of auditory and visual sensory inputs onto the cerebellum (Fig. 22.19) points to highly complex integrations brought about in this part of the brain (Snider, 1952).

The cellular organization of the cerebellum appears suited for an integrative action (Fig. 22.20). Entering afferent fibers synapse with a number of granule cells which along with basket cells send axons up into the molecular layer to synapse on the profusely branched dendrites of the Purkinje cells. The axons of the Purkinje cells have collaterals which further spread activity within the cortex and its axons leave the cortex to terminate on cerebellar relay nuclei: the *fastigial* and *globose* nuclei medially and *dentate*, and *globiform* nuclei laterally. The largest bundle of efferent fibers from the cerebellum is contained in the brachium conjunctivum ascending to

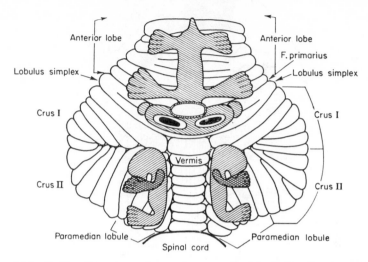

Fig. 22.18.   Figurines show the topographical distribution of tactile reception areas on the cerebellar surface.   An ipsilateral projection is present on the lobulus simplex and anterior lobe. Bilateral representations present in the paramedian lobes.   (Snider, 1952.)

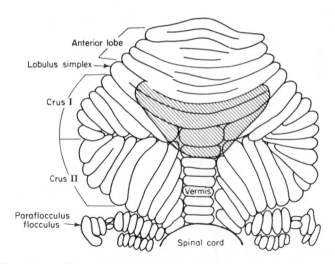

Fig. 22.19.   The obliquely hatched area shows the auditory and visual projections on the cerebellum, those giving responses to sound clicks and light flashes.   (Snider, 1952.)

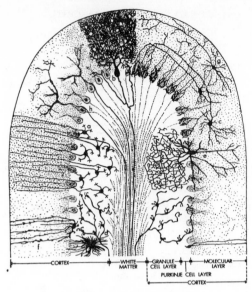

Fig. 22.20.   Cross-section of a cerebellar fold diagrammed to show main neuronal elements: Fibers entering the fold in the central white matter, dashed lines; (a), granule cells sending axons to outer (molecular) surface and receiving (d) mossy fibers and (e) Golgi type II cells; (b), Purkinje cell with great dendritic arborization receiving impulses from granule cells, from (h), climbing fibers, cells (g) and (f) of unknown function and (c) basket cells; axons of Purkinje cells leaving the fold in the white matter, solid lines.   (After Ramón y Cajal; from Snider, *Scient. Am.* **199**: No. 2, 84, 1958.)

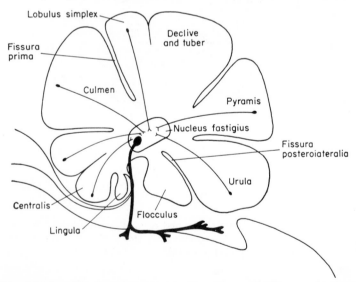

Fig. 22.21.   Cells from the paleocortex of the cerebellum send axons down to synapse on the fastigial nucleus.   Its fibers in turn terminate on the reticular formation and to spinal tracts to lower motor centers.

the thalamus where a principal motor regulating influence is exerted. Lesion of the dentate nucleus gives rise to severe and enduring defects of movements (*dyskinesia*) (Carpenter and Correl, 1961). Cutting the corticospinal tract was effective in blocking the dyskinesias so produced. Tonic control appears to be exerted through the fastigial nucleus (Fig. 22.21) and does not require the cortex. Stimulation of the anterior cerebellum acting through this relay nucleus gives rise to a powerful inhibitory effect. This was shown by Sherrington (1906) using decerebrate rigid animals. Stimulation of the anterior cerebellum causes a sudden melting of the rigidity. Conversely, an intensification of rigidity occurs with removal of the anterior cerebellum.

Upper motor control terminations in lower centers

Following section of the pyramidal tract, degenerating boutons terminating on the spinal cord motoneurons have been found (Hoff and Hoff, 1934). This is so only for the primates. The physiological investigations made in monkeys by Bernhard, Bohm and Petersén (1953), and Bernard and Bohm (1954) utilized local spinal monosynaptic reflex discharges to show the synaptic influence of the pyramidal tract fibers on motoneurons. Stimulation of pyramidal tract fibers resulted in a facilitation of the monosynaptic response. The latency of the facilitating effect would suggest that these corticospinal fibers synapse directly onto the motoneurons. However, unless repetitive stimulation of the cortex was used, the latency was longer than 0.8 msec which would arise if there were a termination of corticospinal fibers onto interneurons which in turn have such a facilitatory action on the motoneurons. A direct termination of pyramidal tract fibers onto motoneurons was confirmed by Preston and Whitlock (1960, 1961) with intracellular microelectrode recordings from spinal cord motoneurons. Pyramidal volleys were found to give EPSPs in the motoneurons with the short latencies expected of direct termination. Also, after an additional delay of 1.3 msec, IPSPs were recorded from some motoneurons. Landgren, Phillips and Porter (1962) employed intracellular recording from motoneurons to study the effect of anodal pulse excitation of Betz cells. Pulse durations of 5 msec were shown to produce a repetitive discharge in the motoneurons accounting for the efficacy of pulses of this duration in activating body movements (*vide supra*). The presence of EPSPs and IPSPs appearing in the motoneurons with both short and long latencies shows that a complex pattern of control is initiated from the pyramidal tract.

In lower species such as the cat there is no evidence of a direct activation of motoneurons, the pyramidal tract exerting its motor actions via interneurons (Lloyd, 1941a; Lundberg and Voorhoeve, 1961). Motor control systems present in the brain stem (vestibulo-spinal, reticulospinal and propriospinal tracts) were also shown by Lloyd (1941b) to have their earliest action on the interneurons in the lower motor centers in the spinal cord.

In addition to influences acting either directly on motoneurons (only in primates) or through interneurons, a termination of upper motor centers on fusimotor (gamma cell) motoneurons has been recognized. The effect of upper influences on them was shown by changes in the rate of efferent discharge recorded in gamma fibers isolated from a ventral root or motor nerve. Or, single fibers may be isolated from the dorsal root and identified as spindle afferents (Chapter 17), and the central changes of the fusimotor discharge may be determined indirectly by an increase or decrease in the discharge rate of the spindle afferent fiber. Control of a tonic fusimotor discharge by various brain regions was shown with this indirect method by Granit and Kaada (1952). A highly active system of control of spindle afferent discharge by the brain was further indicated by the experiments of Eldred, Granit and Merton (1953). Stimulation of the upper brain stem, particularly the reticular formation, was highly effective in increasing the activity of the fusimotor cells. Merton (1953) considers that these upper control mechanisms have a primary action on the fusimotor neurons. The increase of spindle discharge in turn activates the alpha moto-neurons and muscles. How far such a servo system of control may explain various types of upper control is at present speculative. Evidence of an increased discharge of fusimotor neurons in advance of alpha motoneuron activity was found in the decerebrate rigid animal (Granit, 1955, 1962). In Fig. 17.11 gamma discharge and muscle tension are shown recorded before, during and after a temporary increase of rigidity brought about by the anemic decere-bration technique of Pollock and Davis (1930). However, this technique of decerebration also damages the anterior cerebellum. As we have seen, the anterior cerebellum has a powerful effect on lower motor centers. Stimulation of the anterior cerebellum in decerebrate animals causes a dramatic reduction in the rigidity while interference with cerebellar outflow, either temporarily by cooling the anterior cerebellum or its destruction, will cause an increased limb rigidity. Therefore, the question arises as to whether the increased rigidity on destruction of the anterior cerebellum comes about through the same mechanism as does decerebrate rigidity. As previously noted (Chapter 14), decerebrate rigidity immediately abates and the limbs become flaccid when the dorsal roots are cut. The spindle afferent discharge is augmented by the increased fusimotor activity and this discharge acts to excite the alpha motoneurons. When, in addition, an anterior cerebellum lesion is produced and the dorsal roots cut, rigidity remains. Therefore it appears that the excitatory motor control exerted by the anterior cerebellum is on interneurons and motoneurons and not through the gamma loop (Granit, Holmgren and Merton, 1955).

From a comparison of reflex-tension curves obtained from decerebrate and decerebellated animals, Granit (1962) suggested that these two types of control, of the alpha (motoneuron) and of gamma (fusimotor) systems, are fundamental. The cerebellum may, as part of its coordinating function, switch from one type of control to the other.

Spinal shock

When the spinal cord of the vertebrate is transected there is an immediate decrease of most lower motor reflex activity; some reflexes remain. This state of *spinal shock* lasts for varied periods of time in different species. In the frog, a good return of reflexes may occur within approximately 5 minutes. In the dog and cat, a fair degree of reflex activity returns within several hours; but it may be weeks before a high degree of reflex activity recovers. In man, some reflexes may return only after weeks or months. Spinal shock is not an injury effect from the cut region. This was shown when, after recovery from spinal shock, a second cut was made below the original cut and a renewal of spinal shock did not ensue (Sherrington, 1906). The greater and longer-lasting loss of reflex activity in the higher species, i.e. longer in the monkey than in the cat and dog, and more marked in the latter than in the frog, exemplifies encephalization (Chapter 13). A phylogenetic transformation occurs during evolution with more and more of the higher motor control transferred to the upper brain centers. At the same time the lower spinal mechanisms become more dependent on higher mechanisms of control as indicated by the greater severity of spinal shock in the higher forms.

Spinal shock is also seen in autonomic motoneurons of the spinal cord. After transection, failure of micturition is regularly observed. The urinary bladder is under upper motor control so that the reflex mechanisms of micturition normally coming into play upon some level of bladder filling may be voluntarily inhibited. After spinal cord section, the loss of reflex excitability results in the bladder filling much beyond its normal size (Ruch, 1960). To prevent a shutdown of kidney function by accumulated urine backing up in the ureters, the urine must be manually expressed or drained from the bladder for the first days or weeks during spinal shock until the reflex threshold falls back toward normal levels. After recovery of excitability the bladder automatically voids when a certain level of filling has been attained and threshold is reached to excite the reflex—a condition referred to as an *automatic bladder*. Voluntary control is, of course, lost.

There are two main possibilities concerning the nature of spinal shock. In one view it is the loss of a preponderantly excitatory influence from upper centers acting to keep up a facilitatory background activity at the local spinal level (Creed *et al.*, 1932). Another concept is that spinal shock is caused by a loss of upper motor control which normally acts to inhibit local spinal inhibition. van Harreveld and Marmont (1939) have shown that an increased reflex activity may be realized in an animal in spinal shock if the spinal cord is asphyxiated for a period of 30–60 minutes. Such asphyxiation produces a spastic state. The permanent rigidity produced in the isolated spinal cord by partial asphyxiation has recently been reinvestigated by Biersteker and van Harreveld (1963) who found that the increase in tone after asphyxiation is reflex in origin as shown by its decrease on cutting the dorsal roots. The spasticity also appears to be due to a greater excitability of the motor cells (Gelfan and Tarlov, 1959). This apparently accounts for the later increases in tone which are observed days and weeks later after asphyxiation.

Reorganization (compensation)

Logically, by studying an animal after part of the nervous system is removed we should be able to analyse the neural mechanism by the deficiency in behavior produced by that removal. However, the nervous system is difficult to analyse in such simple fashion because there is a reorganization of the remaining parts so that the original functions are resumed, a process referred to as *compensation*. This was noted after lesions of the sensorimotor cortex where motor area lesions at first may give rise to hypotonia and then later be followed by spasticity (Foerster, 1936) or recovery with no apparent signs of deficiency (Glees and Cole, 1950). The depth of the cortical layers involved by lesions appears to be crucial with respect to the endurance of the effect. Dusser de Barenne (1934) used a heat coagulation technique to produce destruction of the motor arm area of monkeys throughout the cortical depth or of the upper cortical layers only. Destruction of upper layers produced only transient effects lasting an hour at most. Following destruction of all the cortex, paralysis on the contralateral side was seen lasting for a few days; this gradually subsided until after several weeks there was no sign of paralysis remaining.

If the decerebrate animal is kept alive for extended periods of time, this preparation shows a progressively richer and more varied complement of behavior (Bard and Macht, 1958). The chronic midbrain animal can then show a good return of righting movements and even spontaneous walking. Such behaviors have usually been considered (from acute decerebration studies) to have their mechanisms above this level of transection (*vide supra*).

In the spinal dog and cat reflex excitability may progressively increase, and 4 weeks after spinal transection there is an increase of muscle tone. Similar changes may appear in man some time after recovery from spinal shock. A touch or other mild stimulus may excite spasms of the limbs and signs of autonomic discharge such as profuse sweating and flushing, the *mass discharge*.

The reorganization underlying these changes is at present little understood. An increased sensitivity to synaptic neurotransmitter substances may be involved (Stavraky, 1961). Such an effect is similar to the denervation hypersensitization found for the neuromuscular junction and autonomic ganglia (Chapters 9, 11). Another possibility is that there is an increased sprouting and regrowth of the presynaptic fibers to effect new synaptic unions (McCouch, Austin, Liu and Liu, 1958). Support for a massive non-specific sprouting was not found after cutting the dorsal root fibers central to the ganglia in kittens (Eccles, Eccles and Shealy, 1962). However, a small but significant degree of specific regrowth of neurons to the appropriate denervated motoneurons on a myoptic or chemotropic basis appeared to be present (Eccles, Eccles, Shealy and Willis, 1962).

In the reorganization following a destruction of part of the nervous system, a fundamental biological problem exists. After an ablation of sensory afferents motor behavior is appropriate if some sensory information is left remaining (Adrian, 1947). Some underlying direction of reorganization appears to be present in the nervous system. It is not possible to frame the concept of this hypothetical underlying 'directive' pattern in more precise fashion. Presumably the mechanisms would be similar to those controlling growth and connectivity during development and which still remains present in lower animals (Chapter 8). The identification and control of these forces would have the greatest significance.

REFERENCES

Adrian, E. D. (1947). General principles of nervous activity. *Brain* **70**: 1–17.

Adrian, E. D. and Moruzzi, G. (1939). Impulses in the pyramidal tract. *J. Physiol.* **97**: 153–199.

Bard, P. and Macht, M. B. (1958). The behavior of chronically decerebrate cats. *Neurological Basis of Behavior*. Pp. 55–75. Ciba Foundation Symposium. Churchill, London.

Bernhard, C. G. and Bohm, E. (1954). Monosynaptic corticospinal activation of forelimb motoneurones in monkeys (*Macaca mulatta*). *Acta Physiol. Scand.* **31**: 104–112; Cortical representation and functional significance of the corticomotoneuronal system. *Arch. Neurol. Psychiat.*, **72**: 473–502.

Bernhard, C. G., Bohm, E. and Petersén, I. (1953). Investigations on the organisation of the corticospinal system in monkeys. *Acta Physiol. Scand.* **29**: *Suppl.* **106**, 79–105.

Bertrand, G. (1956). Spinal efferent pathways from the supplementary motor area. *Brain* **79**: 461–473.

Bieber, I. and Fulton, J. F. (1938). The relation of the cerebral cortex to the grasp reflex and to the postural and righting reflexes. *Arch. Neurol. Psychiat.* **39**: 435–454.

Biersteker, P. A. and van Harreveld, A. (1963). The nature of rigidity caused by spinal cord asphyxiation. *J. Physiol.* **166**: 382–394.

Brookhart, J. M. and Zanchetti, A. (1956). The relation between electrocortical waves and responsiveness of the cortico-spinal system. *Electroencephalog. Clin. Neurophysiol.* **8**: 427–444.

Brooks, V. B., Rudomin, P. and Slayman, C. L. (1961). Sensory activation of neurons in the cat's cerebral cortex. *J. Neurophysiol.* **24**: 286–325.

Bubnoff, N. and Heidenhain, R. (1881). Ueber Erregungs- und Hemmungsvorgänge innerhalb der motorischen Hirncentren. *Arch. ges. Physiol.* **26**: 137–200. (English transl.); Excitatory and inhibitory processes. *The Pre-Central Motor Cortex* (1944). Chapter 7. Edited by P. C. Bucy. University of Illinois Press, Urbana.

Carpenter, M. B. and Correll, J. W. (1961). Spinal pathways mediating cerebellar dyskinesia in Rhesus monkey. *J. Neurophysiol.* **24**: 534–551.

Cooper, I. S. (1961). *Parkinsonism. Its Medical and Surgical Therapy.* Charles C. Thomas, Springfield.

Creed, R. S., Denny-Brown, D., Eccles, J. C., Liddell, E. G. T. and Sherrington, C. S. (1932). *Reflex Activity of the Spinal Cord.* Oxford University Press, Oxford.

Dusser de Barenne, J. G. (1934). The disturbances after laminar thermocoagulation of the motor cerebral cortex. *Brain* **57**: 517–526.

Dusser de Barenne, J. G. and McCulloch, W. S. (1939). Factors for facilitation and extinction. *J. Neurophysiol.* **2**: 319–355.

Eccles, J. C., Eccles, R. M. and Shealy, C. N. (1962). An investigation into the effect of degenerating primary afferent fibers on the monosynaptic innervation of motoneurons. *J. Neurophysiol.* **25**: 544–558.

Eccles, J. C., Eccles, R. M., Shealy, C. N. and Willis, W. D. (1962). Experiments utilizing monosynaptic excitatory action on motoneurons for testing hypotheses relating to specificity of neuronal connections. *J. Neurophysiol.* **25**: 559–580.

Eldred, E., Granit, R. and Merton, P. A. (1953). Supraspinal control of the muscle spindles and its significance. *J. Physiol.* **122**: 498–523.

Ferrier, D. (1876). *The Functions of the Brain.* Smith Elder, London.

Foerster, O. (1936). The motor cortex in the light of Hughlings Jackson's doctrines. *Brain* **59**: 135–159.

Fritsch, G. and Hitzig, E. (1870). Uber die electrische Erregbarkeit des Grosshirns. *Arch. Anat. Physiol. Wiss. Med.* **37**: 300–332.

Fulton, J. F. (1949). *Physiology of the Nervous System.* 3rd Ed. Oxford University Press, Oxford.

Gelfan, S. and Tarlov, I. M. (1959). Interneurones and rigidity of spinal origin. *J. Physiol.* **146**: 594–617.

Gernandt, B. E. and Thulin, C. A. (1955). Reciprocal effects upon spinal motoneurons from stimulation of bulbar reticular formation. *J. Neurophysiol.* **18**: 113–129.

Glees, P. and Cole, J. (1950). Recovery of skilled motor functions after small repeated lesions in motor cortex in macaque. *J. Neurophysiol.* **13**: 137–148.

Granit, R. (1955). *Receptors and Sensory Perception.* Yale University Press, New Haven.

Granit, R. (1962). Muscle tone and postural regulation. *Muscle as a Tissue.* Edited by K. Rodahl and S. M. Hovarth. Chapter 10. McGraw-Hill, New York.

Granit, R. and Kaada, B. R. (1952). Influence of stimulation of central nervous structures on muscle spindles in cat. *Acta Physiol. Scand.* **27**: 130–160.

Granit, R., Holmgren, B. and Merton, P. A. (1955). The two routes for excitation of muscle and their subservience to the cerebellum. *J. Physiol.* **130**: 213–224.

Hankinson, J., Namin, P. and Ochs, S. (1955). Cortical and subcortical systems inhibiting the knee-jerk in the cat. *Brain* **78**: 133–147.

Hern, J. E. C., Landgren, S. and Phillips, C. G. (1962). Selective excitation of corticofugal neurones by surface-anodal stimulation of the baboon's motor cortex. *J. Physiol.* **161**: 73–90.

Hines, M. (1944). Significance of the precentral motor cortex. *The Precentral Motor Cortex.* Chapter 18. Edited by P. C. Bucy. University of Illinois Press, Urbana.

Hoff, E. C. and Hoff, H. E. (1934). Spinal terminations of the projection fibres from the motor cortex of primates. *Brain* **57**: 454–474.

Ingram, W. R., Ranson, S. W., Hannett, F. I., Zeiss, F. R. and Terwilliger, E. H. (1932). Results of stimulation of the tegmentum with the Horsley-Clarke stereotaxic instrument. *Arch. Neurol. Psychiat.* **28**: 513–541.

Jackson, J. H. (1932). *Selected Writings of John Hughlings Jackson.* Edited by J. Taylor. Hodder and Stoughton, London.
Jenkner, F. L. and Ward, A. A., Jr. (1953). Bulbar reticular formation and tremor. *Arch. Neurol. Psychiat.* **70**: 489–502.
Jung, R. and Hassler, R. (1960). The extrapyramidal motor system. *Handbook of Physiology—Neurophysiology.* Vol. 2, pp. 863–927. American Physiological Society, Washington, D.C.
Landgren, S., Phillips, C. G. and Porter, R. (1962). Cortical fields of origin of the monosynaptic pyramidal pathways to some alpha motoneurones of the baboon's hand and forearm. *J. Physiol.* **161**: 112–125.
Lassek, A. M. (1954). *The Pyramidal Tract: Its Status in Medicine.* Charles C. Thomas, Springfield.
Leyton, A. S. F. and Sherrington, C. S. (1917). Observations on the excitable cortex of the chimpanzee, orangutan and gorilla. *Quart. J. Exptl. Physiol.* **11**: 135–222.
Li, C. L. (1959). Some properties of pyramidal neurones in motor cortex with particular reference to sensory stimulation. *J. Neurophysiol.* **22**: 385–394.
Li, C. L. (1963). Cortical intracellular synaptic potentials in response to thalamic stimulation. *J. Cell. Comp. Physiol.* **61**: 165–179.
Liddell, E. G. T. and Phillips, C. G. (1951). Overlapping areas in the motor cortex of the baboon. *J. Physiol.* **112**: 392–399.
Lilly, J. C., Austin, G. M. and Chambers, W. W. (1952). Threshold movements produced by excitation of cerebral cortex and efferent fibers with some parametric regions of rectangular current pulses (cat and monkeys). *J. Neurophysiol.* **15**: 319–341.
Lloyd, D. P. C. (1941a). Activity in neurons of the bulbospinal correlation system. *J. Neurophysiol.* **4**: 115–134.
Lloyd, D. P. C. (1941b). The spinal mechanism of the pyramidal system in cats. *J. Neurophysiol.* **4**: 525–546.
Lundberg, A. and Voorhoeve, P. E. (1961). Pyramidal activation of various spinal reflex arcs in the cat. *Experientia* **17**: 46–47.
Magnus, R. (1924). *Körperstellung.* Springer, Berlin.
Magnus, R. (1926). Some results of studies in the physiology of posture. *Lancet* **2**: 531–536; 585–588.
Magoun, H. W. (1950). Caudal and cephalic influences of the brain stem reticular formation. *Physiol. Rev.* **30**: 459–474.
Magoun, H. W. and Rhines, R. (1948). *Spasticity: The Stretch Reflex and Extrapyramidal Systems.* Charles C. Thomas, Springfield.
McCouch, G. P., Austin, G. M., Liu, C. N. and Liu, C. Y. (1958). Sprouting as a cause of spasticity. *J. Neurophysiol.* **21**: 205–216.
Merton, P. A. (1953). Speculations on the servo-control of movement. *The Spinal Cord.* Ciba Foundation Symposium. Churchill, London.
Mettler, C. L. and Mettler, F. A. (1942). The effects of striatal injury. *Brain* **65**: 242–255.
Monnier, M. (1946). L'organization des fonctions motrices chez les primates. *Schweiz. Arch. Neurol. Psychiat.* **56**: 233–238; *ibid.*, **57**: 325–349.
Ochs, S. (1955). The origin of inhibition from the motor cortex. *Am. J. Physiol.* **182**: 411–414.

Patton, H. D. and Amassian, V. B. (1960). The pyramidal tract: its excitation and functions. *Handbook of Physiology—Neurophysiology*. Vol. 2, pp. 837–861. American Physiological Society, Washington, D.C.

Peacock, S. M., Jr. (1954). Studies on subcortical motor activity. I. Motor activity and inhibition from identical anatomical points. *J. Neurophysiol.* **17**: 144–156.

Penfield, W. G. and Boldrey, E. (1937). Somatic motor and sensory representation in the cerebral cortex of man studied by electrical stimulation. *Brain* **60**: 389–443.

Penfield, W. and Jasper, H. H. (1954). *Epilepsy and the Functional Anatomy of the Human Brain*. Little Brown and Company, Boston.

Phillips, C. G. (1956). Cortical motor threshold and the thresholds and distribution of excited Betz cells in the cat. *Quart. J. Exptl. Physiol.* **41**: 70–84.

Phillips, C. G. (1959). Actions of pyramidal volleys on single Betz cells in the cat. *Quart. J. Exptl. Physiol.* **44**: 1–25.

Pollock, L. J. and Davis, L. E. (1930). The reflex activities of a decerebrate animal. *J. Comp. Neurol.* **50**: 377–411.

Preston, J. B. and Whitlock, D. G. (1960). Precentral facilitation and inhibition of spinal motoneurones. *J. Neurophysiol.* **23**: 154–170.

Preston, J. B. and Whitlock, D. G. (1961). Intracellular potentials recorded from motoneurons following precentral gyrus stimulation in primate. *J. Neurophysiol.* **24**: 91–100.

Rioch, D. McK. and Rosenblueth, A. (1935). Inhibition from the cerebral cortex. *Am. J. Physiol.* **113**: 663–676.

Ruch, T. C. (1960). The urinary bladder. *Medical Physiology and Biophysics*. Edited by T. C. Ruch and J. F. Fulton. Chapter 47. Saunders, Philadelphia.

Schneider, R. C. and Crosby, E. C. (1960). A study of tonus and motor dysfunctions from brain lesions in primates. *Structure and Function of the Cerebral Cortex*. Edited by D. B. Tower and J. P. Schadé. Pp. 104–115. Elsevier, New York.

Sherrington, C. S. (1906). *The Integrative Action of the Nervous System*. Yale University Press, New Haven. Rev. Ed. (1947). Cambridge University Press, Cambridge.

Snider, R. S. (1952). Interrelations of cerebellum and brain stem. *Proc. Assoc. Res. Nervous Mental Disease* **30**: 267–281.

Spiegel, E. A. and Wycis, H. T. (1962). *Stereoencephalotomy. Part II. Clinical and Physiological Applications*. Grune and Stratton, New York.

Sprague, J. M. and Chambers, W. W. (1954). Control of posture by reticular formation and cerebellum in the intact anesthetized and unanesthetized and in the decerebrated cat. *Am. J. Physiol.* **176**: 52–64.

Stavraky, G. W. (1961). *Supersensitivity Following Lesions of the Nervous System*. University of Toronto Press, Toronto.

Suzuki, H. and Tukahara, Y. (1963). Recurrent inhibition of the Betz cell. *Japan. J. Physiol.* **13**: 386–398.

Tower, S. S. (1936). Extrapyramidal action from the cat's cerebral cortex: Motor and inhibitory. *J. Physiol.* **59**: 408–444.

Tower, S. S. (1944). The pyramidal tract. *The Precentral Motor Cortex*. Chapter 6. Edited by P. C. Bucy. University of Illinois Press, Urbana.

Travis, A. M. (1955).   Neurological deficiencies following motor area lesions in *Macaca mulatta*.   *Brain* **78**: 174–198.

van Harreveld, A. and Marmont, G. (1939).   The course of recovery of the spinal cord from asphyxia.   *J. Neurophysiol.* **2**: 101–111.

Walshe, F. M. R. (1947).   On the role of the pyramidal tract in willed movements.   *Brain* **70**: 329–354.

Woolsey, C. N. (1960).   Some observations on brain fissuration in relation to cortical localization of function.   *Structure and Function of the Cerebral Cortex*.   Edited by D. B. Tower and J. P. Schadé.   Pp. 64–68. Elsevier, New York.

Woolsey, C. N. and Chang, H-T. (1948).   Activation of the cerebral cortex by antidromic volleys in the pyramidal tract.   *Res. Publ. Assoc. Nervous Mental Disease* **27**: 146–161.

Woolsey, C. N., Meyer, D. R., Settlage, P. H., Meyer, D. R., Spencer, W., Hamuy, T. P. and Travis, A. M. (1952).   Patterns of localization in precentral and 'supplementary' motor areas and their relation to the concept of a premotor area.   *Res. Publ. Assoc. Nervous Mental Disease* **30**: 238–264.

Wyss, O. A. M. and Obrador, S. (1937).   Adequate shape and rate of stimuli in electrical stimulation of the cerebral motor cortex.   *Am. J. Physiol.* **120**: 42–51.

23

Higher Visceral Centers

The autonomic reflex mechanisms of the spinal cord (Chapter 10) have upper control centers located in the brain. Cardiovascular, respiration and temperature regulation centers are found in the reticular formation of the brain stem and in the hypothalamus. The nuclei of the hypothalamus are found in the walls of the third

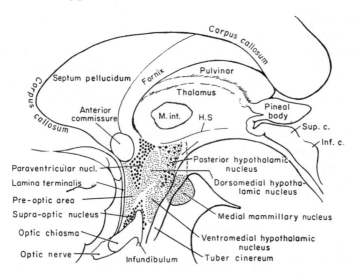

Fig. 23.1. Ventricular surface of human diencephalon in sagittal section with hypothalamic nuclei given by the various sized stippling; paraventricular, preoptic, supraoptic, dorsomedial, posterior, ventromedial and medial mammillary nuclei. Just below is the hypophysis. Posteriorly is the midbrain, superiorly the thalamus and the cerebrum. (Strong and Elwyn, *Human Neuro-anatomy*. Williams and Wilkins, Baltimore, 1943.)

ventricle at the base of the brain (Fig. 23.1). The hypothalamus is a visceral control center receiving influences from other parts of the brain (particularly the limbic system to be described in Chapter 24), the cortex and reticular formation. In turn, the hypothalamus sends impulses back to the cortex and down to the autonomic centers in the brain stem and spinal cord.   The hypothalamus also influences the hormonal output of the pituitary gland (hypophysis) which is found just below it at the base of the brain.   The hypophysis has been called the 'master' endocrine gland.   It secretes hormones which in turn control the function of other endocrine glands. Therefore, such important functions as those relating to water and electrolyte balance, food intake, growth and development, sexual activity and reactions to stress are controlled by the hypophysis. The relation of the hypothalamus to some of these pituitary controls will be discussed in a later section.   Emotional reactions which are a concomitant of visceral reactions, especially those related to feeding and sexual activity, will be discussed separately in Chapter 24.

Respiratory control

Respiration is the utilization of O_2 from the inspired air.   In the vertebrates breathing mechanisms have evolved to take O_2 into the body and remove CO_2.   In breathing the lungs are relatively passive. As the diaphragmatic and/or costal muscles contract, the thoracic volume is increased and air enters.   The muscles then relax.   This is followed by an elastic recoil of the lungs and the lung air is expired.

The cyclic alteration of inspiration and expiration in normal (*eupnic*) respiration shows much similarity to reflex action.   This cyclic pattern occurs with no conscious attention during sleep and yet it is readily interrupted at will, for example, when speaking, swimming, etc.

That a control region for respiration is present in the medulla was demonstrated when transection of the brain stem at successively more caudal levels did not interrupt the rhythm of respiration until the medulla was reached—an observation made by Legallois in the early part of the 19th century.

Pitts, Magoun and Ranson (1939) used the stereotaxic technique to apply electrical stimuli at different places within this region of the medulla.   They found a maintained inspiration for as long as stimulation was continued within the *inspiratory region* (Fig. 23.2). Somewhat more rostrally and dorsally placed in the medulla is a region which on stimulation caused an arrest of inspiration and, with an increase of stimulus strength, an expiration which could be maintained as long as stimulation continued—the *expiratory region.*

The neurons of the two respiratory centers were considered to be reciprocally connected with activity of inspiratory neurons acting to inhibit that of the expiratory neurons.   At the end of inspiration the inspiratory neurons decrease their discharge and the expiratory neurons become excited to inhibit the inspiratory cell activity, etc. The rhythmicity of respiration is therefore on this hypothesis an autorhythmicity intrinsically present in the medulla.

Another theory of rhythmicity is that impulses from the stretch receptors of the lung act to inhibit the inspiratory center. At a sufficient degree of inflation the inhibitory effect is maximal and then the expiratory neurons are excited. The evidence for this concept is that an inflation of the lungs can terminate inspiration, the *Hering–Breur reflex*. However, if the vagus nerves carrying impulses from these stretch afferents are cut in a preparation where

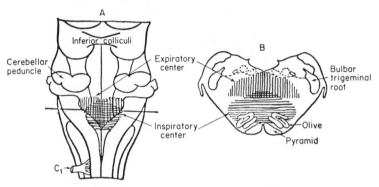

Fig. 23.2. (A) location of respiratory centers of the cat shown in dorsal view of the brain stem. (B) transverse section of the medulla at the horizontal line of A. Expiratory center shown by vertical and inspiratory center by horizontal lines. C_1, first cervical root. (From Pitts, Magoun and Ransom; after Fulton, 1955.)

the brain stem has been transected above the medulla, respiratory rhythmicity persists, showing that an autorhythmic mechanism is present in the medulla.

Electrical recordings from the medulla made by Gesell *et al.* (1936) showed periodic bursts of neuron potentials associated with inspiration and with expiration. More recently single-unit studies made by Cohen and Wang (1959) and by Salmoiraghi and Burns (1960) of neurons in this region have shown that some cells discharge at a high rate during expiration (Fig. 23.3), others at a high rate during inspiration (Fig. 23.4). The intracellular recordings made of these respiratory cells by Salmoiraghi and von Baumgarten (1961) indicate that the excitation and discharge rate is related to slow changes in polarization and firing level during the respiratory

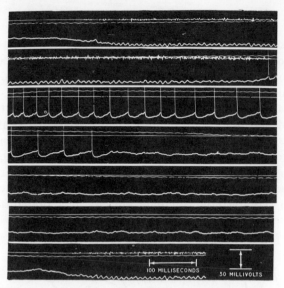

Fig. 23.3. A single-cell recording from an expiratory neuron in the respiratory center is shown during one respiratory cycle. Upper trace in each set of three records shows diaphragmatic motor units; middle trace, tracheal pressure (inflation upward deflection); lower trace, the intracellular recording of steady and spike potentials. Continuous record from top to bottom. (Salmoiraghi and von Baumgarten, 1961.)

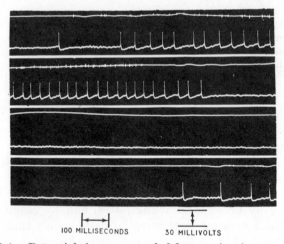

Fig. 23.4. Potential changes recorded from an inspiratory neuron during one respiratory cycle. Upper trace in each set of records, diaphragmatic motor units; lower trace, intracellular potentials. Continuous record from top to bottom. (Salmoiraghi and von Baumgarten, 1961.)

cycle.   There appears to be a reciprocal action between the inspiratory and expiratory neurons in the respiratory center.

The factors controlling the buildup of depolarization are not entirely understood.   One of the functions of respiration is the removal of CO_2 from the blood.   An increase of CO_2 causes an increase in respiration rate and depth.   Microinjection of a bicarbonate–CO_2 solution into this medullary region was found to be stimulatory to respiration (Comroe, 1943).   Yet, pH changes may also be involved and, as well, neural impulses from the reticular formation of the pons and upper brain stem (Hoff and Breckenridge, 1955).

The character of the respiratory rhythm in the isolated medulla is gasping (Wang and Ngai, 1963).   This differs from the smooth rhythm of normal respiration.   In the pons an *apneustic* center is considered to interact with the inspiratory and expiratory medullary centers to smooth the cyclic interaction.   Apparently, however, the degree of smoothness of respiratory rhythm obtained from an isolated medulla varies in different species (Hoff and Breckenridge, 1955).   Possibly centers of the brain stem rostral to the medulla serve to introduce modulating changes in expiration and inspiration.   These mechanisms would come into play during a number of acts requiring interruption of the respiratory rhythm such as occurs in coughing, sneezing, the abeyance of respiration in swallowing and the series of delicate and complex patterns of respiratory movements required of speech.

Cardiovascular control

Regions within the medulla controlling heart rate and the degree of tonic vessel constriction required to keep up blood pressure were inferred from the fact that lesions in this site (with artificial respiration given) produce a slowing of the heart rate and a fall in blood pressure.   Alexander (1946) recorded a tonic neural discharge from the cardiac nerves of decerebrate animals.   Transection of the medulla (at level II, Fig. 23.5) reduced the rate of tonic outflow, the tonic discharges decreasing along with blood pressure as most of this *pressor region* was removed.   The finding that some increase in rate was found on a still more distant section (level III, Fig. 23.5) suggested the presence of an inhibitory or depressor region in the lower medulla.   Stimulation with electrodes using a stereotaxic apparatus has shown that the pressor region is present laterally in the rostral part of the medulla.   A *depressor region* was found more medially in the caudal part of the medulla.

Areas in more forward parts of the brain have been found to exert pressor and depressor effects. One of the earlier studies showing this was made with the use of chloroform which has as a side effect, a sensitization of the heart muscle so that adrenalin when present can cause such irregularities of heart rhythm as extrasystoles and fibrillation. Stimulation of the sympathetic nerves innervating the heart can by the release of adrenalin cause this effect in the

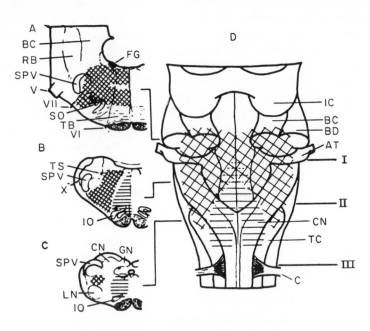

Fig. 23.5. Vasomotor regions in the medulla are shown in the diagram of D by cross-hatching and horizontal lines. At the different levels shown in D, A–C show by cross-hatching the pressor region; horizontal hatching, the depressor region. (Alexander, 1946.)

chloroformed animal (Beattie, Brow and Long, 1930). The cardiac irregularity was abolished in different animals by cutting the sympathetic nerves to the heart and as well by making lesions successively higher into the brain stem until the posterior hypothalamus was reached. This indicated the existence of a path of cardiovascular control from the hypothalamus down the brain stem and into the cardiac nerves. Pitts, Larrabee and Bronk (1941) recorded action potentials from the inferior cardiac and cervical sympathetic nerves, and found that hypothalamic stimulation increased the rate of

sympathetic nerve outflow.   Stimulation on one side of the hypothalamus gave rise to increased discharges on both sides.   By use of
stereotaxic technique of stimulation, a tract of fibers which produced
increases in heart rate and blood pressure was followed from the
hypothalamus down into the medullary reticular formation (Ranson
and Magoun, 1939).   Stimulation within the hypothalamus has also
been shown to give rise to depressor effects such as vasodilation of
blood vessels in skeletal muscles.   The center giving rise to such
depressor actions appears to be restricted to a small area in the medial
hypothalamus (Uvnäs, 1954).

Cardiovascular effects are also elicited by stimulation of other
regions of the limbic brain (Chapter 24).   Stimulation of the cingulate gyrus causes a rise in blood pressure (Kaada, 1951).   Both
pressor and depressor areas have been found within the rostral part
of the limbic system by Löfving (1961).   Stimulation of the sensorimotor cortex not only gives rise to motor movements but also to
vasomotor changes.   The result may be a vasodilation of vessels in
skeletal muscle (Green and Hoff, 1937) as well as a constriction
(Hoff, Kell and Carroll, 1963).   With electrodes chronically implanted
in the cortex, Delgado (1960) found quite specific cardiovascular
responses from points located in the frontal cortex, motor areas, the
anterior temporal cortex and the cingulate cortex of the limbic
brain.   The stability of the responses found with repeated stimulations for a period of months was noteworthy.   It is possible to obtain
pressor responses and cardiac arrhythmias on cortical stimulation
and chronic cortical stimulation has been reported to produce
pathological changes in the cardiovascular system (Hoff, Kell and
Carroll, 1963).

Temperature regulation

The normal mammalian body temperature shows a remarkable
constancy in the face of widely varying external heat and cold loads;
the mammal has a *homeothermic* type of temperature regulation.
A *poikilothermic* animal such as the reptile suffers a change in
body temperature as the external temperature changes; it must
protect itself from extreme heat, and in the cold it is sluggish and
can more easily fall victim to predators.   Mechanisms of heat
control in the mammal depend in large part on vascular adjustments.
Rodbard (1948) has suggested that mechanisms of temperature
regulation were developed within the hypothalamus from the circulatory control centers in the course of evolution from the
reptile to the mammal.   Mammals lose body temperature by

dilation of surface blood vessels which increases heat convection and radiation from the blood to the external environment (Hardy, 1961). Sweat is secreted as an additional mechanism of cooling by evaporation. In some species such as the dog a considerable loss of heat by evaporation is produced from the mouth by panting. To conserve body heat, surface blood vessels constrict. In hairy animals piloerection causes the hairs to stand out and this helps contain body heat. In addition, muscular activity, especially shivering, increases the metabolic rate and in turn the body temperature.

The site of temperature regulatory mechanisms in the hypothalamus was shown by brain stem transection made at different levels. If the brain anterior to the hypothalamus is removed, little effect is seen on temperature control. However, if the hypothalamus is destroyed, the animal becomes poikilothermic (Barbour, 1921). With a lesion placed just behind the hypothalamus the animal shows a loss of temperature regulation (Keller, 1950). An animal so prepared and placed in a cold room will show a fall in its internal or *core temperature* with a poor return to its original level when the cold load is relieved (Fig. 23.6). A similar loss of temperature regulating functions in the face of an increased heat load was also shown by the body temperature remaining high after an increased external temperature load was reduced to a lower level (Fig. 23.6). Temperature regulation is mediated by the hypothalamus in response to changes in blood temperature. In addition, sensory impulses from the skin on cooling can act via the hypothalamic mechanisms to increase body heat (through shivering, piloerection and vasoconstriction of skin vessels). Both these control mechanisms are depressed by barbiturate anesthesia.

The presence of heat-sensitive receptors in the hypothalamus was shown by localized stimulation of this region with heated wires or by electrical pulses (Magoun, Harrison, Brobeck and Ranson, 1938; Ström, 1950). The increased heat is the stimulus for exciting mechanisms which result in a heat loss. Such a heat-loss center was found in the anterior hypothalamus. A comparable heat-producing center in the posterior hypothalamus was suggested by the finding that animals with anterior hypothalamic lesions can still shiver when cooled, thereby increasing heat production, but do not shiver when the posterior hypothalamus is removed. The results of localized stimulation experiments within the posterior hypothalamus to demonstrate such a heat-producing region have been conflicting. Ranson and Magoun (1939) did not find heat production (shivering) on electrical stimulation of the posterior hypothalamus, nor did local cooling of the posterior hypothalamus cause a heat rise (Ström, 1950). However, such apparent failures were considered by Hardy (1961) to be due to the cool environment during those experiments and an already present vasoconstriction. Considering this factor Hammel, Hardy and Fusco (1960) obtained shivering on localized cooling in the hypothalamus. Stuart, Kawamura and Hemingway (1961) using electrical stimulation found that stimulation of the posterior hypothalamus was effective in exciting shivering. This occurred some time after anesthesia had worn off. The point

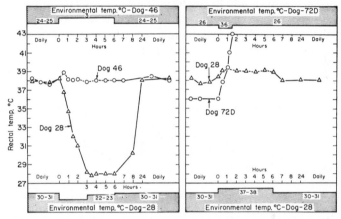

Fig. 23.6. Regulation of normal animal's body temperature shown at left by curve (dog 46) during lowered environmental temperature and maintained body temperature contrasted with an animal (dog 28) with a large lesion in the posterior hypothalamus where a large fall in body temperature occurs. Shown at right, this animal's regulation against a heat load is normal. This is in contrast to another animal (dog 72D) with a lesion in the heat-loss center and where body temperature rose markedly with increased environmental temperature. (Keller, 1950.)

was made that previous studies did not reveal the mechanism because the level of anesthesia was too deep. The concept of a heat-loss center in the anterior hypothalamus and a heat-producing center in the posterior hypothalamus therefore seems to be valid.

Certain bacteria release *endotoxins* which cause fever, and such *pyrogenic* substances have been extracted from white blood cells. It would appear that many clinical cases of fever can be explained by the release of pyrogenic substances from the injured cells of the host (Atkins, 1960). Little is known concerning the way the pyrogens act on the heat-regulating mechanisms of the hypothalamus.

Feeding and satiety centers

A center for food control located in the hypothalamus was indicated by the clinical syndrome described by Fröhlich (1910). This condition, found usually among pre-adolescent boys, is characterized by overeating, obesity and somnolence, resembling in the two latter respects the fat boy of Dickens' *Pickwick Papers*. Lesions were found in the hypothalamus in cases of Fröhlich's syndrome implicating this region and the pituitary gland. The relation of the hypothalamus to food intake was studied experimentally in animals by means of stereotaxic lesions made in the hypothalamus by Hetherington and Ranson (1942). *Hyperphagia*, an increased intake of food leading to obesity was caused by lesions made in the medial hypothalamic region. Brobeck, Tepperman and Long (1943) showed that the

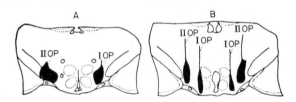

Fig. 23.7. (A) Lesions shown by the black regions in the lateral hypothalamus in transverse section of the rat brain stem, first operation I OP, no effect but after the second lesion was made, II OP, complete absence of feeding. (B) Bilateral lesions of the ventromedial nuclei in a first operation (I OP) caused hyperphagia and obesity. Lesions made subsequently (II OP) in the lateral hypothalamic nuclei caused aphagia. (Anand and Brobeck, 1951.)

body metabolism *per se* was not altered; the defect produced is a deranged regulation of food intake. Bilateral lesions made in the lateral hypothalamus (Fig. 23.7) cause animals to reduce food intake, to become *hypophagic*, or they may even stop eating, becoming *aphagic* (Anand and Brobeck, 1951). Therefore, a *feeding* center appears to be present in the lateral hypothalamus; its destruction leads to aphagia. A *satiety* center is present in the *ventromedial* nuclei of the hypothalamus; its destruction results in increased food intake. The aphagia seen with lateral nuclear lesions has some resemblance to *anorexia nervosa*, a clinical condition in which there is a refusal or rejection of food.

Further support for two such separate centers controlling feeding comes from electrical stimulation of these regions in animals with chronically implanted electrodes. Stimulation of the lateral nuclear area will cause excessive eating, even when the animal has just eaten. Electrical stimulation of the ventromedial nuclear areas will cause cessation of eating even in a starved animal (Anand, 1961). Most likely the two centers are reciprocally related as in the respiratory and temperature regulation centers previously described. As feeding progresses, the satiety center inhibits the feeding center. Later, the activity of the satiety center is lower and hunger increases. It is noteworthy that the general level of motor activity of the hungry animal is also increased, as would be expected of free-moving animals which have to hunt or search for food (Chapter 13).

What is the signal for an increased activity of the feeding center? An earlier theory of food intake regulation was that periodic contractions of the stomach increased during hunger and the hunger contractions by their neural impulses could trigger the feeding center. However, denervation of the gastrointestinal tract does not block hunger sensations. In the *glucostatic* theory of Mayer (1955) the signal for increased activity of the feeding center and/or decreased activity of the satiety center is a decreased level of glucose in the blood reaching the brain. It may be that the absolute level of glucose is not the important factor but rather the arterio-venous difference in the glucose supply passing to the brain (Anand, 1961). Evidence for the glucostatic theory in this modified form was given by Anand, Dua and Singh (1961). Electrodes were implanted in both the ventromedial hypothalamic satiety center and the lateral hypothalamic feeding center, and the electrical activity of these centers recorded while the blood glucose levels were varied. With increased glucose administration, activity of the satiety center increased. With decreased blood glucose levels, there was a decreased activity of the satiety center and some increase in the feeding center. Another line of evidence came from the action of gold thioglucose, a substance with a chemical structure similar to glucose. When administered to mice, gold thioglucose produces hyperphagia and obesity (Mayer, 1955). It appears that gold thioglucose competes with glucose in the ventromedial nuclear center where gold thioglucose has been shown to accumulate (Debons et al., 1962).

An interesting responsivity of the lateral hypothalamic nuclei to autonomic transmitter substances has been shown by Grossman (Miller, 1961). Stimulation of the lateral nucleus with adrenalin and other adrenergic substances via chronically implanted cannulae caused rats, even when satiated, to eat or perform learned responses (Chapter 25) for food. Intraperitoneal injection of the adrenergic blocking substance ethoxybutamoxane prevents this action.   In contrast to adrenergic substances, injection of ACh and other cholinergic substances causes drinking (*vide infra*).

In addition to this type of short-term regulation of feeding, note must be taken of another type of regulation.   Food intake may be greater or less than the metabolic needs required for a short-term period, but it must somehow become adjusted to the general level of expenditure of metabolic energy over long-term periods as indicated by the relative constancy of body weight.

Hypothalamic–hypophysial transport mechanisms

In the Fröhlich syndrome described in the preceding section, a sexual disturbance shown by infantilism is observed in addition to feeding disturbances and obesity.   In the attempt to initiate the syndrome experimentally there was historically some confusion as to whether the hypothalamus or the pituitary gland was involved. This problem became resolved when the close interrelationship of the hypothalamus to the hypophysis was appreciated.   Before discussing the visceral control systems to be described in the following sections, it will be of advantage to show first their anatomical interrelationships.

In the supraoptic and paraventricular regions of the hypothalamus, Scharrer and Scharrer (1940) described neurons with large cell bodies and an appearance typical of secretory cells.   These neurons were found to have axons leading into the posterior part of the pituitary gland (Fig. 23.8), forming the hypothalamic–hypophysial tract. Transport of the hormonal substances or their precursors from these cells of the hypothalamus down through these axons into the posterior hypophysis occurs by means of axoplasmic flow (Chapter 8).

Another type of transport mechanism occurs with respect to the anterior pituitary (Fig. 23.9).   Blood vessels in the vicinity of the hypothalamic nuclei join with a *portal system* of blood vessels. These portal blood vessels pass down into the anterior lobe of the pituitary where they supply the cells in this part of the gland. Special humoral substances (*vide infra*) are carried by the portal vessels to influence hormonal production in the anterior pituitary gland.   The different areas in the hypothalamus where small lesions have been found to interfere with hormonal production or release of individual hypophysial hormones into the blood stream are shown in Fig. 23.10.   These regions and the hormones with which they are associated are further discussed in the next three sections.

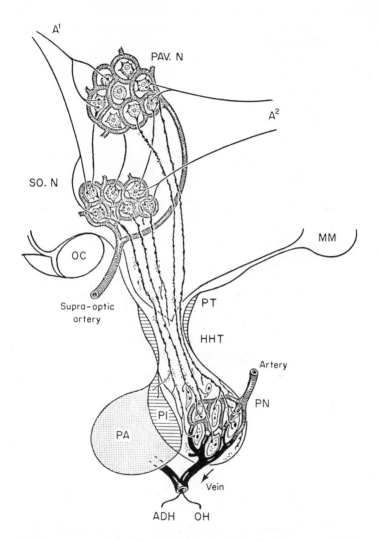

Fig. 23.8.   Diagram of hypothalamic nuclei and the hypothalamic–hypophysial tract (HHT) showing transport of materials to the posterior lobe.   The neural control of these centers is suggested by arrows indicating stimuli from higher (A¹) and peripheral pathways (A²).   (ADH), antidiuretic hormone; (MM), mammillary nuclei; (OC), optic chiasm; (OH), oxytocic hormone; (PA), pars anterior; (PAV.N) paraventricular nucleus; (PI), pars intermedia; (PN), pars neuralis; (PT), pars tuberalis; (SO.N) supraoptic nucleus.   (Brooks *et al.*, 1962.)

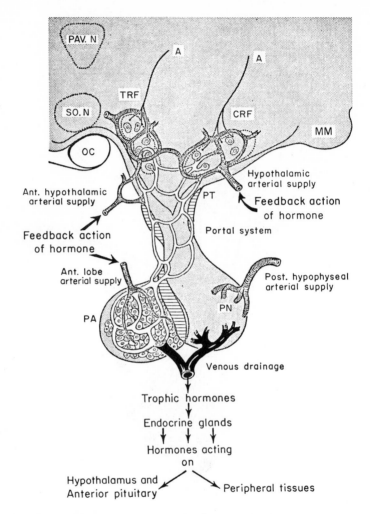

Fig. 23.9.   Diagram of hypothalamic–hypophysial portal system
which is presumed to transport corticotrophin-releasing factor
(CRF) and thyrotrophic-hormone releasing factor (TRF) from
special areas of the hypothalamus to the anterior lobe.   The proposed feedback effects of various hormones on the anterior lobe and
hypothalamus are shown.   (A) Neurally conducted stimuli which
initiate reactions.   (MM) mammillary nuclei; (OC) optic chiasma;
(PA) pars anterior; (PN) pars neuralis; (PT) pars tuberalis;
(PAV.N) paraventricular nucleus; (SO.N) supraoptic nucleus.
(Brooks et al., 1962.)

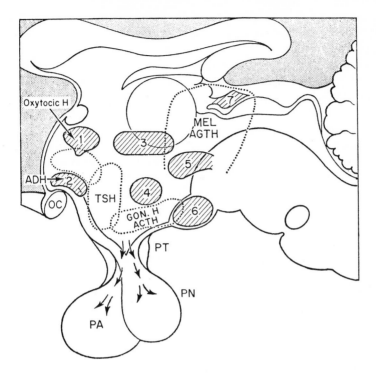

Fig. 23.10. Diagram of hypothalamic regions of the brain showing areas from which specific materials are liberated or hormonal controls are exerted. (1) paraventricular n.; (2) supraoptic n.; (3) dorsomedian n.; (4) ventromedian n.; (5) post hypoth. n.; (6) mammillary n.; (7) pineal; (AGTH) adrenoglomerultrophic hormone; (ADH) antidiuretic hormone; (GON.H) gonadotrophic hormone; (LH) luteinizing hormone; (MEL) melantonin; (TSH) thyrotrophic hormone; (ACTH) adrenocorticotrophic hormone. (Brooks *et al.*, 1962.)

Regulation of body water and electrolytes

Lesions within the hypothalamus which interfere with the supraoptic nucleus or with their fibers in the stalk leading to the posterior pituitary cause *diabetes insipidus*. In this condition copious quantities of water are consumed and lost in the urine. A patient may take in and eliminate as much as 10 gallons of water a day. Produced in the posterior hypophysis is an *antidiuretic hormone (ADH)*. This hormone normally acts on the kidney to reabsorb most of the water from the tubules leading to a concentrated urine output.

The loss of ADH through an interference with its synthesis, transport, storage or release from the posterior hypophysis will result in diabetes insipidus.

The water content of the body is closely regulated by the changing levels of ADH in response to too much or too little water in the diet. Verney (1948) has suggested that certain vesicular structures present in the hypothalamus are sensitive to changes in the osmotic pressure of the blood. These *osmoreceptors* could signal the degree of concentration or dilution of the blood and thereby lead to changes in the output of ADH. By use of microelectrode recording from cells in the supraoptic nuclei, Cross and Green (1959) were able to show that injections of hypertonic solutions into the blood passing to the brain caused increased firing of the cells. This was confirmed by Sundsten and Sawyer (1961) who found in addition that these responses could be obtained from isolated islands of hypothalamus containing the supraoptic nuclei. Another control of body water levels is accomplished by water intake. A drinking center similar to a feeding center has been located in the hypothalamus. Lesions in the lateral hypothalamus not only cause aphagia but also *adipsia*, a decreased water intake. Some investigators have supposed that a common center for eating and drinking is involved, others that drinking and feeding centers are separate (Anand, 1961). A drinking center in the goat was shown to be present in the hypothalamus. Andersson, Jewell and Larsson (1958) found that electrical stimulation of this region could cause such copious drinking that the animals drink as much as 30% of their body weight. Stimulation of the drinking center could cause the goats to drink acidic or bitter solutions which the animals would ordinarily reject. Already mentioned above were the experiments of Grossman showing that stimulation of the lateral hypothalamic areas with ACh (or other cholinergic substances) led to excessive drinking. This response is blocked if the cholinergic blocking agent atropine had been injected systemically beforehand.

Closely related to water balance is the intake of salt. The electrolytes Na^+ and K^+ are of particular importance. It has recently been shown that the regulation of Na^+ and K^+ levels of the blood is controlled by the hormone *aldosterone* which is produced in the adrenal cortex. Aldosterone output is regulated by a hormone which appears to be released from some part of the brain stem (Farrell, 1958). Hypophysectomy does not lead to a decreased output, but large lesions in the caudal diencephalon and rostral midbrain reticular formation suppress the release of aldosterone.

Stress

The animal exposed to danger or seeking its prey shows widespread changes of the autonomic nervous system—the fight or flight pattern (Chapter 10)—with the release of adrenalin. In addition the cortex of the adrenal gland is excited to release a number of corticosteroids which have important actions on body cells. The removal of the adrenals leads to a weakening of the organism and death. Similar effects of adrenal insufficiency are seen in the condition known as *Addison's disease*. The anterior pituitary produces *adrenocorticotrophic hormone* (*ACTH*), which stimulates the release of adrenal corticosteroids. The anterior pituitary releases ACTH in response to a wide variety of stress-producing situations, i.e., cold, high temperature, painful trauma, ether anesthesia, and anxiety. Stress agents via the CNS increase the activity of the hypothalamus where a hormone, corticotrophin-releasing factor (CRF) (Fig. 23.9), is released in the portal circulation to gain entrance to the anterior pituitary and in turn release ACTH. Lesions in the part of the ventral hypothalamus shown in Fig. 23.11 interfere with the release of ACTH following a stress stimulation (McCann, 1953). An interaction of the sympathetic nervous system and mechanisms controlling ACTH is accomplished by the adrenalin released in the blood during stress. The adrenalin excites the activating mechanisms of the reticular formation (Chapter 20) and this activation in turn leads to hypothalamic stimulation and the release of ACTH from the pituitary. Porter (1953) has shown that low concentrations of adrenalin injected into the blood supply of the brain can excite increased electrical activity in the posterior hypothalamus, and direct electrical stimulation of this region causes ACTH release (Porter, 1954).

While a decrease of adrenal corticosteroids leads to weakness and death, a continued overproduction also causes diseases. A number of these have been characterized by Selye (1950) as the 'adaptation syndrome.' French, Longmire, Porter and Movius (1953) have shown that stimulation of the posterior hypothalamus causes gastric secretion of HCl and continued stimulation of this part of the brain for periods of one to three months can cause gastric ulcers. The mechanism involved appears to be an increased release of ACTH leading to an overproduction of adrenal steroids and, in turn an increase in the amount of gastric acid produced. This observation is of interest with respect to the belief that states of anxiety can produce ulcers (cf. Brady, 1958).

A long period of stress may not be required to produce long-lasting alterations in this system. Richter (1958) has shown that a severe stress in rats such as forcing them to swim to save themselves from drowning or savage fighting can cause marked and long-lasting changes in hypothalamic function.

Another hormone related to stress is *thyroxin* which is secreted by the thyroid gland. A deficiency of thyroxin leads to the low metabolic rate and the sluggish condition of *myxedema*. Conversely, an increased output of thyroxin is seen in the hyperthyroidism of *Graves disease* with a state of overactivity or agitation. The thyroxin output of the thyroid gland is controlled by the *thyroid-stimulating hormone* (*TSH*) which is released from the anterior hypophysis. In turn, TSH output is controlled by a substance released from the hypothalamus into the portal circulation, the thyrotrophic-releasing factor (TRF) (Fig. 23.9). Lesions in the region shown in Fig. 23.10 interfere with the release of TSH in response to the stress produced by restraint, i.e. by tying an animal to a board, or to the stress produced by exposure to cold. Electrical stimulation within this area also gives rise to an increased output of TSH. A negative feedback regulation is afforded by the action of thyroid hormone on hypothalamic centers to decrease production of TSH and possibly a direct action on the anterior hypophysis (Bozdanove and Crabill, 1961).

Sexual functions

In the female the ovarian hormone, *estrogen*, is required for maturation and development of secondary sex characteristics. In the mature female the periodic increase and decrease of estrogen and progesterone from the follicles of the ovary in the menstrual cycle is controlled by two anterior hypophysial hormones. These hormones are the *follicle stimulating hormone* (*FSH*) and the *luteinizing hormone* (*LH*) (Brooks, Gilbert, Levey and Curtis, 1962). These hormones are neurally controlled by centers in the hypothalamus (Everett, 1964).

A lesion made in the hypothalamic area shown in Fig. 23.10 will prevent the release of substances into the portal circuit which in turn releases the sex-controlling hormones (the gonadotrophins) from the anterior pituitary. A feedback effect of gonadal hormones to control the hypophysis is also present (Harris, 1962). In a number of lower animals there is a periodic increase of estrogen release in the sex cycle. During the release of estrogen, there is a receptivity to the male. This mating behavior is due to the activity of estrogen on the hypothalamus (Harris, 1962). This was shown by Harris, Michael and Scott (1958) using ovariectomized cats. These animals do not display the usual sexual behavior of normal cats and their secondary sexual organs are atrophied; for example, the vaginal epithelium is not developed. The estrogenic substance, stilbesterol, was introduced into the hypothalamus of these ovariectomized cats by means of chronically implanted hypodermic tubing. The animals then showed normal sexual behavior with ready acceptance of the male, although histological examination revealed that the epithelial development of the vagina and uterus remained subnormal. This showed that circulated estrogen was not the cause of the altered behavior; the estrogenic substance was acting locally in the hypothalamus.

In the male, secondary sexual characteristics are determined by *testosterone*, which is produced in the testes. Removal in puberty leads to infantile male characteristics and feminization—eunuchism. The production of testosterone is controlled by gonadotrophic hormone produced in the hypophysis. In turn the gonadotrophic hormone is controlled by the hypothalamus. Stimulation of the region of the hypothalamus shown in Fig. 23.10 gives rise to an increased output of gonadotrophic hormone.

Other pituitary hormones

A number of other hormones of the pituitary are involved in mechanisms similar to those described above. *Pitocin*, the oxytocic factor involved in the maternal functions of milk-ejection and parturition, has a hypothalamic–hypophysial pattern of control similar to that of ADH. Vasopressin which acts on blood vessels has a different control pattern. Normal growth requires growth hormones supplied by the pituitary in addition to the gonadotrophic hormones. Reference to these and other hormones involved will be found in the review by Brooks, Gilbert, Levey and Curtis (1962).

REFERENCES

Alexander, R. S. (1946). Tonic and reflex functions of medullary sympathetic cardiovascular centers. *J. Neurophysiol.* **9**: 205–217.

Anand, B. K. (1961). Nervous regulation of food intake. *Physiol. Rev.* **41**: 677–708.

Anand, B. K. and Brobeck, J. R. (1951). Hypothalamic control of food intake in rats and cats. *Yale J. Biol. Med.* **24**: 123–140.

Anand, B. K., Dua, S. and Singh, B. (1961). Electrical activity of the hypothalamic 'feeding centers' under the effect of changes in blood chemistry. *Electroencephalog. Clin. Neurophysiol.* **13**: 54–59.

Andersson, B., Jewell, P. A. and Larsson, S. (1958).   An appraisal of the effects of diencephalic stimulation of conscious animals in terms of normal behavior.   *Neurological Basis of Behavior.*   Pp. 76–89.   Ciba Foundation Symposium.   Churchill, London.

Atkins, E. (1960).   Pathogenesis of fever.   *Physiol. Rev.* **40**: 580–646.

Barbour, H. G. (1921).   The heat-regulating mechanism of the body.   *Physiol. Rev.* **1**: 295–326.

Beattie, J., Brow, G. R. and Long, C. N. H. (1930).   The hypothalamus and the sympathetic nervous system.   I. The dependence of the extrasystolic arrhythmia of the heart produced by chloroform, upon the integrity of the sympathetic nervous system; and the use of this arrhythmia as an indicator of sympathetic activity.   *Res. Publ. Assoc. Mental Nervous Disease.* **9**: 249–294; II. The higher connections of the sympathetic nervous system as studied by experimental lesions of the hypothalamus. *Ibid.,* 295–316.

Bozdanove, E. M. and Crabill, E. V. (1961).   Thyroid-pituitary feedback: direct or indirect?   A comparison of the effects of intrahypothalamic and intrapituitary thyroid autotransplants on pituitary thyroidectomy reactions in the rat.   *Endocrinology* **69**: 581–595.

Brady, J. V. (1958).   Ulcers in 'executive' monkeys.   *Scient. Am.* 95–98.

Brobeck, J. R., Tepperman, J. and Long, C. N. H. (1943).   Experimental hypothalamic hyperphagia in the albino rat.   *Yale J. Biol. Med.* **15**: 831–853.

Brooks, C. McC., Gilbert, J. L., Levey, H. A. and Curtis, D. R. (1962).   *Humors, Hormones, and Neurosecretion.*   State University of New York, New York.

Cohen, M. I. and Wang, S. C. (1959).   Respiratory neuronal activity in pons of cat.   *J. Neurophysiol.* **22**: 33–50.

Comroe, J. H., Jr. (1943).   Effects of direct chemical and electrical stimulation of respiratory center in cat.   *Am. J. Physiol.* **139**: 490–497.

Cross, B. A. and Green, J. D. (1959).   Activity of single neurones in the hypothalamus: effect of osmotic and other stimuli.   *J. Physiol.* **148**: 554–569.

Debons, A. F., Silver, L., Cronkite, E. P., Johnson, H. A., Brecher, G., Tenzer, D. and Schwartz, I. L. (1962).   Localization of gold in mouse brain in relation to gold thioglucose obesity.   *Am. J. Physiol.* **202**: 743–750.

Delgado, J. M. R. (1960).   Circulatory effects of cortical stimulation.   *Physiol. Rev.* **40**: *Suppl.* **4**: 146–171.

Everett, J. W. (1964).   Central neural control of reproductive functions.   *Physiol. Rev.* **44**: 373–431.

Farrell, G. (1958).   Regulation of aldosterone secretion.   *Physiol. Rev.* **38**: 709–728.

French, J. D., Longmire, R. L., Porter, R. W. and Movius, H. J. (1953).   Extra-vagal influences and gastric hydrochloric acid secretion induced by stress stimuli.   *Surgery* **34**: 621–632.

Fröhlich, A. (1901).   Ein Fall von Tumor der Hypophsis cerebri ohne Akromegalie.   *Wien. klin. Rdsch,* **15**: 883–6; *Res. Publ. Assoc. Nervous Mental Disease* **20**: xvi–xxvii (1940).

Gesell, R., Bricker J. and Conway, M. (1936).   Structural and functional organization of the central mechanisms controlling breathing.   *Am. J. Physiol.* **117**: 423–452.

Green, H. D. and Hoff, E. C. (1937). Effects of faradic stimulation of the cerebral cortex on limb and renal volumes in the cat and monkey. *Am. J. Physiol.* **118**: 641–658.

Hammel, H. T., Hardy, J. D. and Fusco, M. M. (1960). Thermo-regulatory responses to hypothalamic cooling in unanesthetized dogs. *Am. J. Physiol.* **198**: 481–486.

Hardy, J. D. (1961). Physiology of temperature regulation. *Physiol. Rev.* **41**: 521–606.

Harris, G. W. (1962). The development of neuroendocrinology. *Frontiers in Brain Research.* Edited by J. D. French. Pp. 191–241. Columbia University Press, New York.

Harris, G. W., Michael, R. P. and Scott, P. (1958). Neurological site of action of stilbestrol in eliciting sexual behavior. *Neurological Basis of Behavior* Pp. 236–254. Ciba Foundation Symposium. Churchill, London.

Hetherington, A. W. and Ranson, S. W. (1942). The relation of various hypothalamic lesions to adiposity in the rat. *J. Comp. Neurol.* **76**: 475–499; and Effect of early hypophysectomy on hypothalamic obesity. *Endocrinology* **31**: 30–41.

Hoff, E. C., Kell, J. F., Jr. and Carroll, M. N., Jr. (1963). Effects of cortical stimulation and lesions of cardiovascular function. *Physiol. Rev.* **43**: 68–114.

Hoff, H. E. and Breckenridge, C. G. (1955). The neurogenesis of respiration. *A Textbook of Physiology.* Edited by J. F. Fulton. Chapter 42. 17th Ed. Saunders Co.

Kaada, B. R. (1951). Somato-motor, autonomic and electrocorticographic responses to electrical stimulation of 'rhinencephalic' and other structures in primates, cat and dog. (Study of responses from limbic, subcallosal, orbito-insular, piriform and temporal cortex, hippocampus-fornix and amygdala.) *Acta. Physiol. Scand.* **24** *Suppl.* **83**: 1–285.

Keller, A. D. (1950). The role of circulation in the physiology of heat regulation. *Phys. Therapy Rev.* **30**: 511–519.

Löfving, B. (1961). Cardiovascular adjustments induced from the rostral cingulate gyrus, with special reference to sympatho-inhibitory mechanisms. *Acta Physiol. Scand.* **53** *Suppl.* **184**: 1–82.

Magoun, H. W., Harrison, F., Brobeck, J. R. and Ranson, S. W. (1938). Activation of heat loss mechanisms by local heating of the brain. *J. Neurophysiol.* **1**: 101–114.

Mayer, J. (1955). Regulation of energy intake and the body weight: the glucostatic theory and the lipostatic theory. *Ann. N. Y. Acad. Sci.* **63**: 15–43.

McCann, S. M. (1953). Effect of hypothalamic lesions on the adrenal response to stress in the rat. *Am. J. Physiol.* **175**: 13–20.

Miller, N. E. (1961). Analytical studies of drive and reward. *Am. Psychol.* **16**: 739–754.

Pitts, R. F., Larrabee, M. G. and Bronk, D. W. (1941). An analysis of hypothalamic cardiovascular control. *Am. J. Physiol.* **134**: 359–383.

Pitts, R. F., Magoun, H. W. and Ranson, J. W. (1939). Localization of the medullary respiratory centers in the cat. *Am. J. Physiol.* **126**: 673–688; and Interrelations of the respiratory centers in the cat. *Ibid.*, 689–707.

Porter, R. W. (1953). Hypothalamic involvement in the pituitary-adreno-cortical response to stress stimuli. *Am. J. Physiol.* **172**: 515–519.

Porter, R. W. (1954). The central nervous system and stress-induced eosinopenia. *Recent. Progr. Hormone Res.* **10**: 1–27.

Ranson, S. W. and Magoun, H. W. (1939). The hypothalamus. *Ergeb. Physiol.* **41**: 56–163.

Richter, C. P. (1958). Neurological basis of responses to stress. *Neurological Basis of Behavior.* Pp. 204–221. Ciba Foundation Symposium. Churchill, London.

Rodbard, S. (1948). Body temperature, blood pressure, and hypothalamus. *Science* **108**: 413–415.

Salmoiraghi, G. C. and Burns, B. D. (1960). Localization and patterns of discharge of respiratory neurones in brain-stem of cat. *J. Neurophysiol.* **23**: 2–13; and Notes on mechanism of rhythmic respiration. *Ibid.,* 14–26.

Salmoiraghi, G. C. and von Baumgarten, R. (1961). Intracellular potentials from respiratory neurones in the brain-stem of cat and mechanism of rhythmic respiration. *J. Neurophysiol.* **24**: 203–218.

Scharrer, E. and Scharrer, B. (1940). Secretory cells within the hypothalamus. *Assoc. Res. Nervous Mental Disease* **20**: 170–194.

Selye, H. (1950). *The Physiology and Pathology of Exposure to Stress.* (A treatise based on the concepts of the general-adaptation syndrome and the diseases of adaptation.) Acta, Montreal.

Ström, G. (1950). Influence of local thermal stimulation of the hypothalamus of the cat on cutaneous blood flow and respiratory rate. *Acta Physiol. Scand.* **20**: *Suppl.* **70**: 47–76; and Effect of hypothalamic cooling on cutaneous blood flow in the unanesthetized dog. *Acta Physiol. Scand.* **21**: 271–277.

Stuart, D. G., Kawamura, Y. and Hemingway, A. (1961). Activation and suppression of shivering during septal and hypothalamic shivering. *Exptl. Neurol.* **4**: 485–506.

Sundsten, J. W. and Sawyer, C. H. (1961). Osmotic activation of neuro-hypophysial hormone release in rabbits with hypothalamic islands. *Exptl. Neurol.* **4**: 548–561.

Uvnäs, B. (1954). Sympathetic vasodilator outflow. *Physiol. Rev.* **34**: 608–618.

Verney, E. B. (1948). The antidiuretic hormone and the factors which determine its release. *Proc. Roy. Soc. B* **135**: 25–106.

Wang, S. C. and Ngai, S. H. (1963). Respiration coordinating mechanism of the brain stem—a few controversial points. *Ann. N. Y. Acad. Sci.* **109**: 550–560.

24

Emotion

The particular pattern of motor, autonomic and endocrine changes during fight or flight (Chapter 10) is of fundamental importance for an animal living as prey and/or predator in nature. The effectiveness with which an appropriate response may be mobilized will determine whether it will survive. Emotional states are also involved. A cat prepared to fight and showing rage has extended claws, raised hair, dilated pupils, its jaws open and it is tensed to leap, claw and bite. The biological usefulness of this reaction is evident (Sherrington, 1906). This *rage reaction* is to be contrasted to the placid behavior a cat may show on other occasions; reactions which we may term as loving, playful or friendly. It then purrs, rubs against our legs, curls up on a chair, etc. In their appearance when mating, hunting for food, their contented appearance after eating—in all these it is difficult not to believe that animals have in addition to the external display of emotion some subjective awareness similar to those we as humans experience.

In our human existence we are aware that the subjective aspect of emotions can often be strong and long-lasting or at times sudden and almost reflex-like—shocks, throbs, thrills, etc. Emotions may appear without conscious prompting and even in ancient Greek psychological writings emotions have been separated from the intellect. However, there are interactions between these categories. It is often our intellectual appreciation (or possibly lack of appreciation) which leads to emotional states. The problems of alcohol addiction and widespread use of tranquilizers indicate the prevalence of disagreeable emotions present in modern existence. On the other hand, the pleasures of life are strong emotions. As will be discussed later in this chapter, rage and pleasure mechanisms have been opened to neurophysiological investigation.

Two aspects of emotion must be considered. One is the performatory or expressive aspect already discussed. The other is the 'motive' aspect—a *drive* which makes an animal search for gratification of that emotion or move away from disagreeable situations. We may call these drives *positive* when the animal moves towards rewarding (*reinforcing*) or gratifying sources; *negative* when avoidance of disagreeable sources is involved. The emotions related to drive are *appetitive*; those involved in the gratification of the drives are *consummatory*. The visceral centers discussed in Chapter 23 can be considered as the origin of appetitive drive states, and emotions considered as augmentation mechanisms intensifying the drives and leading to a satisfaction of those primary needs. It is not therefore surprising that the emotional mechanisms are closely connected with visceral centers. The neural connections between higher visceral centers in the hypothalamus and the limbic brain structures related to emotions will be discussed in the next section. Connections between these systems and the cortex, which is involved with higher functions (Chapter 25), are also present.

Instead of emotional states arising from the internal activities of brain centers, in an older theory, the *James–Lange theory*, conscious awareness of an emotion is due to activity of visceral organs. A perception results in a motor nerve discharge to one or other of the peripheral visceral organs causing palpitation of the heart, a spasm of the gut, etc. In turn, this peripheral change excites sensory receptors leading back to the central nervous system and as a result of these sensory discharges, emotions are experienced.

Sherrington (1906) attempted to experimentally determine the validity of the theory. A dog's spinal cord was cut below the exit of respiratory nerves and the vagus nerves were also transected. By means of these sections a large part of the periphery was prevented from influencing the brain. The animal selected for this operation was previously known to show joyful responses to some persons and angry responses to others. After the operative sections, the animal showed these same emotional responses. Noted also were unimpaired sexual responses to the male during estrus. This experiment then indicated that emotional states occurred without the intervention of a feedback from visceral organs of the periphery. After accidental spinal transections or vagotomy, humans do not lose their capacity for emotional response. More direct evidence has since been obtained of emotional centers within the brain by the effects of direct localized stimulations and recordings. We shall first describe the anatomical structures and some neural properties of those parts of the brain which have been found to be critically involved in emotion.

The limbic system and electrophysiology of the hippocampus

Around the medial aspect to the brain and at its base (Fig. 24.1) are found a number of brain structures which Broca (1878) has considered a basic system found in all mammals, namely, the *limbic brain* or *limbic system*. Another term sometimes applied to it is the *visceral brain*. The limbic system appear to be an interconnected group of nuclei and fiber tracts as shown by recent anatomical and physiological investigations (Fig. 24.2). Several of these structures, such as the *hippocampus*, have long been considered to be part of the higher center for the sense of smell. For this reason these structures have been referred to as *rhinencephalic*. However, Brodal's (1947) critical review of the evidence on which this hypothesis was based showed that it was erroneous, and suggested that the hippocampus might have some function other than an olfactory one.

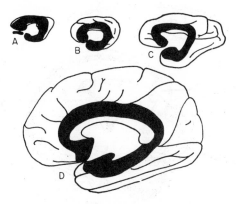

Fig. 24.1. The limbic lobe shown in black on the medial surface of the brain of the rabbit (A); cat (B); monkey (C); and man (D). (From MacLean, modified by Russell, 1961.)

Papez (1937) gathering together what was known of these limbic brain structures considered them to constitute an interconnected system for the elaboration and experience of emotion. He emphasized the numerous interconnections which exist between parts of the limbic brain structures and the hypothalamus. In Papez's theory, sensory pathways diverge at the thalamus, one path leading to the cortex for perception, the other path passing to the hippocampus. From here impulses are carried in fibers of the *fornix* to the mammillary bodies of the hypothalamus, thence via the mammillo-thalamus tract to the anterior thalamus. In turn, connections pass to the *cingulate cortex* where connections are made with other cortical areas. By this means the subjective experience of emotion is supposedly appreciated. Interconnections back to the hippocampus were considered as part of the elaboration of emotional states in these structures.   More recent anatomical studies which served to fill in the number of interconnections between these regions have been described by Russell (1961).   The connections of the *amygdaloid nuclei* to the limbic brain was recognized after the study of Klüver and Bucy (1939) on bitemporal ablations in monkeys and the subsequent emotional changes, to be described below.   For the most part, the effects were due to damage of the amygdaloid nuclei, these nuclei having important connections with other limbic brain structures.   Some of the connections the amygdala makes with the septum and from that region to other limbic brain regions and

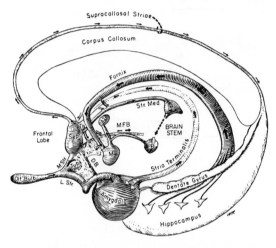

Fig. 24.2.   Diagrammatic representation of parts of the limbic system designated as follows: A.T., anterior thalamic nucleus; D.B., diagonal band; H, habenula; I.P., interpeduncular nucleus; L.Str., lateral olfactory stria; M, mammillary body; M.F.B., medial forebrain bundle; M.Str., medial olfactory stria; Olf. Bulb, olfactory bulb; Sep., septal region; Str. Med., stria medullaris; Tub., olfactory tubercle.   (From Krieg; modified by MacLean, *Psychosom. Med.* **11**: 338, 1949.)

the cortex are shown in Fig. 24.3.   A number of interconnections of the limbic brain with other regions are made by fibers in the *medial forebrain bundle* connecting this region with hypothalamic structures.   Other important connections extend back into the reticular formation of the brain stem.

The hippocampus is an important limbic system structure which has received much study.   In the remainder of this section its anatomical and electrophysiological properties will be briefly

described.   The hippocampus is composed of a relatively simple
structure compared to the cortex.   Of interest is the inverted
position of pyramidal cells (Fig. 24.4).   The apical dendrites of the
pyramidal cells extend down into the gray matter while the surface
white matter of the hippocampus is composed of axons (Ramón y
Cajal, 1955).   The fornix and fibria mainly contain efferent fibers
from the hippocampus.   Afferent excitation comes from the subiculum.   Stimulation of these pathways evokes slow negative

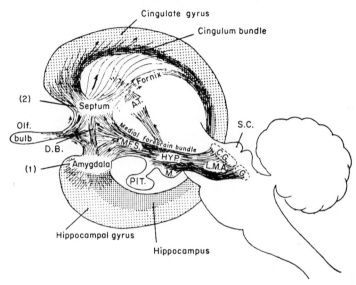

Fig. 24.3.   The medial forebrain bundle is shown to be an important
pathway communicating with various limbic brain structures and
the hypothalamus and midbrain.   A strong interconnection is
seen between the amygdala (1) and the septum (2) where there are
important connections with the olfactory bulb (Olf. bulb) and
posteriorly with the hypothalamus and limbic midbrain area
(L.M.A.).   Other abbreviations: S.C., superior colliculus; C.G.,
central gray of midbrain; G., nucleus of Gudden.   Also, cf. Fig.
24.2.   (MacLean, *Am. J. Med.* **25**: 611, 1958.)

responses from the surface of the hippocampus.   The surface negative wave response arising from the apical dendrites in deeper levels
becomes inverted on laminar recording below the surface (Eidelberg, 1961).   Paired shocks showed that a refractory period is present,
evidence that these slow potentials are not EPSPs (cf. Chapter 18).
Kandel, Spencer and Brinley (1961) have investigated the properties
of hippocampal pyramidal cells with intracellular microelectrodes.
On stimulating the fornix or fibria, antidromic responses with small

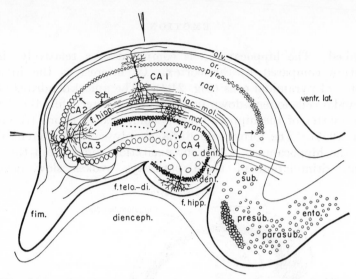

Fig. 24.4.   A sagittal section of the rabbit hippocampus 3 mm from the midline is shown diagrammatically.   Hippocampal pyramidal cells are oriented with their apical dendrites pointed down from the surface.   Fibers passing from the subiculum (sub.) synapse orthodromically on the apical dendrites.   The area labelled CA1 is the most dorsal; CA2, CA3, CA4 are other areas.   Layers indicated are: alv., alveus; or., stratum oriens; pyr., pyramidal; rad., stratum radiatum; lac.-mol., stratum lacunosum-moleculare; mol., stratum moleculare; gran., granular layer of dentate area.   Other abbreviations: fim., fimbria; a. dent., dentate area; ento., entorhinal area; presub., presubiculum; parasub., parasubiculum; Sch., Schaffer collaterals; ventr. lat., ventrolateral direction.
Andersen, *Acta Physiol. Scand.* **47**: 63, 1959.)

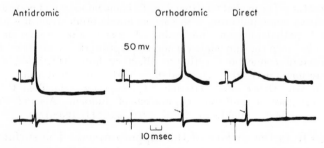

Fig. 24.5.   Intracellular recording from hippocampal pyramidal cells shows upon antidromic stimulation via the fornix a response with large after-positivity.   Stimulation via the subiculum gives rise to an orthodromic response which has a preceding synaptic potential.   Direct stimulation of the cell was accomplished by passing current through the electrode tip.   Lower records show electrically differentiated response with an inflection indicated by the arrow on the rising phase.   (Kandel, Spencer and Brinley, 1961.)

latencies were found (Fig. 24.5). Orthodromic stimulation via the subiculum gave rise to EPSPs exciting spike potentials after long latencies. Unlike motoneurons, these pyramidal cells showed brief bursts of repetitive firing (Fig. 24.6). During arousal when the cortical rhythm is decreased in amplitude, 4–7/sec waves of large amplitude (*theta rhythm*) appear in the hippocampus (Fig. 24.7) (Liberson and Cadhilac, 1953; Green and Arduini, 1954). This theta rhythm precedes the appearance of cortical arousal. Like

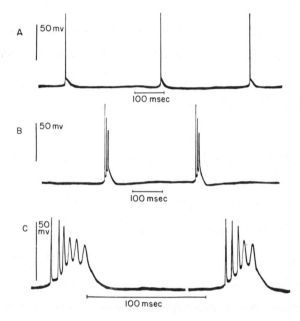

Fig. 24.6.   Spontaneous firing patterns of hippocampal pyramidal cells shows A, solitary spikes; B, brief bursts; C, on an expanded sweep, moderate duration bursts showing large negative shift and decreased amplitudes of later spikes in burst.   Gap in baseline of record C indicates a lapse of 200 msec.   (Kandel and Spencer, *J. Neurophysiol.* **24**: 243, 1961.)

arousal, the theta rhythm can be excited from various afferent sources as shown in Fig. 24.8. Spontaneous theta rhythms are also found. An augmentation of theta rhythmic activity is also found in the hippocampus early in conditioned learning (Chapter 25). As will be discussed, learning appears to have sub-cortical components, and emotional mechanisms present in the hippocampus are involved in the early stages of learning. Either or both of these functions may be related to the theta activity in the hippocampus.

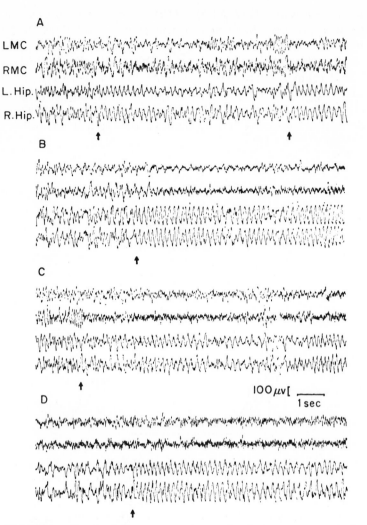

Fig. 24.7. In the upper traces A, at the first arrow a sound stimulus gives rise to a brief period of increased amplitude slow waves in the hippocampal records (L.Hip. and R.Hip.) with little change in cortical leads (LMC, RMC). At the second arrow a louder sound stimulus gives rise to more pronounced slow waves in the hippocampus and to arousal in the cortical traces. In B, at the arrow, sound stimulation causes a pronounced hippocampal arousal which precedes a cortical arousal. C, cortical arousal precedes the hippocampal change (an unusual case). In D, hippocampal arousal to the stimulus appears, while the cortex is in a continuous state of arousal. (Green and Arduini, 1954.)

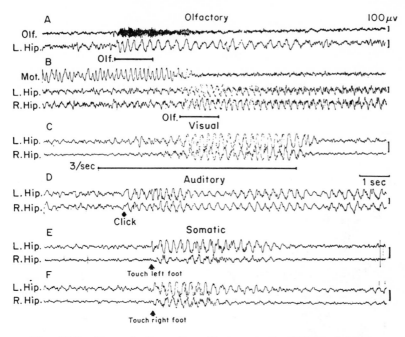

Fig. 24.8. Records from the olfactory bulb (Olf.) and hippocampus (L.Hip. R.Hip.) show in A, an olfactory stimulus (Olf.) at
the time represented by bar causing a discharge in the olfactory bulb
and hippocampal arousal. B, olfactory stimulation causes arousal
in motor cortex (Mot.) along with hippocampal arousal. C, visual
stimulation causes hippocampal arousal. D, an auditory stimulation by a click causes arousal. In E touch of the left foot
causes by this somatic stimulation, a larger arousal in the left
hippocampus. In F, touch of right foot causes a larger right
hippocampal arousal. (Green and Arduini, 1954.)

Localization in limbic brain of centers for feeding and sex

The obtaining of food and sexual activity are both emotionally charged
activities of an organism. It is, therefore, of interest that lesions
or stimulations in these regions produce changes in emotional
behavior relating to these activities.

A very curious type of oral behavior was found in monkeys as
part of the *Klüver–Bucy syndrome* seen after bilateral temporal
lobectomy which includes the amygdaloid nuclei (*vide supra*).
These temporal lobe damaged animals would pick up and place in
their mouths any conceivable object. This 'mouth exploratory'
process might include strange things like bolts, string, etc., and
even such things as a snake which the animal would normally be

afraid of.   The behavior was very much as if manipulation of the object by the lips was the means of recognizing it.   Inedible objects such as nails, marbles, etc., were spit out and only food objects were eaten.   The incessant picking up and placing all available objects in the mouth, often over and over after spitting them out, was described as a combination of 'oral tendencies' and lack of visual recognition—'agnosia' (Klüver, 1958).   Some of the associated alterations of higher function found in these temporal lobe damaged animals will be discussed in Chapter 25.

Morgane and Kosman (1959) made lesions directly in the amygdaloid nuclei of cats (Fig 24.9) and found a relatively steady increase

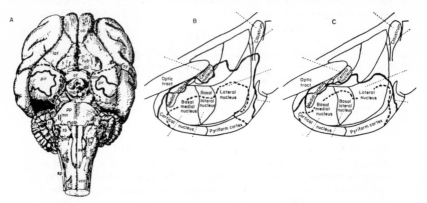

Fig. 24.9.   A, base of the brain showing the extent of lesions made in the pyriform–amygdaloid region (pir).   B and C frontal cross-sections through the amygdaloid complex showing by the dashed lines the extent of these lesions in relation to these groups (cf. Fig. 24.10).   (Morgane and Kosman, 1959.)

in food intake leading to obesity in these animals.   Lesions made in many parts of the limbic brain produce alterations in types of behavior closely connected with feeding such as sniffing, licking, salivating, chewing and swallowing.   Such reactions were also prominent on electrical stimulation within the amygdaloid nuclei (Fig. 24.10) (MacLean and Delgado, 1953).

The importance of the limbic brain with regard to sexual mechanism was also seen as part of the temporal lobe syndrome of Klüver and Bucy.   These animals show hypersexuality, attempting to take as partners animals of the same gender or even those of other species (Schreiner and Kling, 1953).   Green, Clemente and de Groot (1957) showed that hypersexual behavior occurred when lesions were made in the pyriform cortex beneath the basal and lateral amygdala.

Another reaction relating limbic structures to sexual mechanisms is the penile erection in the male upon stimulation within the hippocampus, medial forebrain bundle, cingulate cortex and nearby neocortex (MacLean, 1959). In the female rat, lesions made within regions analogous to the cingular cortex in higher animals caused

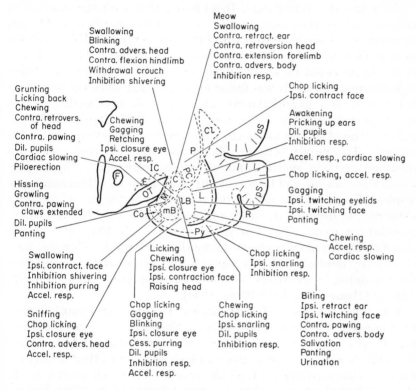

Fig. 24.10. The various major nuclear groups of the amygdala are shown where stimulation results in alimentary, defensive and combative elements of behavior; lB and mB, lateral and medial parts of basal nuclei of amygdala; C, central nucleus; L, lateral nucleus; Py, pyriform cortex. (MacLean and Delgado, 1953.)

hypersexuality and also defects in maternal behavior. Following lesions in this region mother rats would not make proper nests for litters, nor would they nurse or retrieve pups from danger as do normal mother rats (Stamm, 1955).

Alarm, aggression and rage

Timorous or aggressive behavior is in part determined by individual experiences, and in part it is genetically determined. The difference in behavior between the naturally wild and the laboratory tamed mouse or rat or the differences in temperament noted between different strains of dogs is apparent. A genetically aggressive and tame behavior is shown by mating wild and tame strains; these traits appear in the offspring in a Mendelian distribution (Hall, 1951).

Early investigators (Goltz, 1892) found that with the removal of various parts of the brain, animals became emotionally unstable and more prone to snap and growl with little provocation. This result led to experiments directed to determine how much of the rostral part of the brain could be progressively ablated and yet produce these rage-like responses. It was found in the cat that when the brain just anterior to the hypothalamus was removed, a remarkable rage behavior was shown (Cannon and Britton, 1925; Bard and Rioch, 1937). The attack would begin with a widespread sympathetic discharge. The pupils became dilated hair bristled and claws unsheathed; spitting, snarling and tail-lashing were seen. This display would then subside and later recur in cyclic fashion. This automatic display of rage and its undirected nature led to the use of the term *sham-rage* to describe it. If the hypothalamus was removed sham-rage did not occur. The central importance of the hypothalamus for this display of rage was shown in another way when electrodes were chronically implanted in this region. The hypothalamus could then be stimulated by electrical currents with a resulting immediate rage display (Masserman, 1943; Hess, 1954).

Yet, not all aspects of rage display require the hypothalamus. In studies of the decerebrate animal, Sherrington (1906) described *pseudo-affective* states. These are anger simulating responses; the decerebrate animals growl, hiss, tail-lash and show other displays of anger. This capacity for rage-like reactions is much greater in the chronic decerebrate cat where a greater degree of growling, hissing, tail-lashing and thrashing movements of the fore-legs was observed some days and weeks after decerebration (Bard and Macht, 1958). Hunsperger (1956) used chronically implanted electrodes to stimulate various brain stem regions and showed that *affective reactions*— hissing, laying back of the ears, hunching of the back, pupillary dilation and piloerection—could be obtained from the hypothalamus and from an area reaching back down into the central gray of the brain stem, the *affective region* delineated by Fernandez de Molina and Hunsperger (1959). From the outward behavior of the animal upon chronic stimulation in these areas, Roberts (1958) suggested that 'alarm' points are widely distributed in the midbrain and diencephalon, and 'flight' reactions are elicited from a small area in the vicinity of the posterior hypothalamus and also from the amygdala.

An effect noted by Klüver and Bucy, in their bitemporal lobectomized animals where the amygdala was destroyed, was the taming produced by these lesions. A series of investigations made on localized amygdala destruction has given somewhat varied results. Taming was reported by Schreiner and Kling (1953). A different result was obtained by Bard and Mountcastle (1947) who compared neocortical ablations with lesions of the limbic brain of cats. Removal of the neocortex alone produced placidity. The behavior of the animals was mild and calm when subjected to such provocation as tying down the animal in dorsal decubitus, shaking, pinching or crushing, and tetanic skin stimulation. But if its limbic brain structures were subsequently removed, then the animal's placid state was converted to a ferocious one. Structures included in such removals were: the cingulate cortex, post-subicular, pyriform and peri-amygdaloid complex. Their result would indicate that lowered thresholds to rage follows damage to the temporal lobe (amygdaloid and peri-amygdaloid) structures connected with the limbic brain.

Electrical stimulation of the pyriform cortex, amygdala and hippocampus of cats and squirrel monkeys produced directed attack by the animal (MacLean and Delgado, 1953). Shealy and Peele (1957) also found that stimulation of the amygdaloid nuclei in cats gave rise to rage, but that it was not directed towards the source of provocation. Ablation of these structures tamed the animals. The use of the normally wild marsupial, the phlanger, is of interest in this connection. Adey (1959) found that destruction of the amygdaloid tamed these naturally wild animals. It would appear that an increase in ferocity or tameness will follow lesions made in this part of the brain depending on the temperament of the animal. Some of the discordant results of destruction and stimulation may also be due to different degrees of involvement of the various amygdaloid nuclear groups (Fig. 24.10) which appear to have antagonistic interactions.

Limbic structures which perform complex and opposing functions may give rise to various emotional behaviors. Fiber tract connections just forward to the hypothalamus seem to constitute an inhibiting mechanism for rage. A cut in this area just anterior to the hypothalamus (area 14 in the medial orbital gyrus) created an animal so ferocious as to be considered a veritable machine of destruction (Fulton, 1949). The rage released was dangerous because

the attacks were directed toward the provocating source. Similar
ferocious states are produced by small lesions made in parts of the
hypothalamus.

In a number of other limbic system regions, changes of mood and
'social behavior' have been described following localized destructions.
Lesions of the cingulate cortex cause monkeys to lose their shyness
and fear of man. They showed no affection, hostility or signs of
anxiety (Ward, 1948).

One of the lines of evidence used by Papez to connect emotional
states with the hippocampus is the localization of the virus of
rabies in the negri bodies in this part of the brain. Rabies is characterized by excitement, emotional instability, and in an attack, a
ferocious rage-like state. However, stimulation or ablation of the
hippocampus usually appears to have little effect. One notable
exception is an experiment of Bureš (1959) using spreading depression (Chapter 18) to suppress the activity of the hippocampus.
Cannulae were implanted down to the surface of the hippocampus
and KCl introduced. By this means a long-lasting state of spreading
depression was produced in the two hippocampi without a spread
to the neocortex. Two rats so prepared, when placed together,
faced each other in a typical aggressive display, with fore-legs
extended and noses touching.

Self-stimulation—pleasure mechanisms

A new approach to behavioral study of the nervous system has been
discovered (Olds and Milner, 1954; Olds, 1962). Stimulating electrodes were chronically inserted into sub-cortical structures and
connected by a thin flexible cable to a source of stimulating current
which could be controlled by a bar placed within the animal's cage.
When the animal presses the bar, it permits a flow of stimulating
current to excite its own brain structures (Fig. 24.11). With the
electrode tips chronically implanted into a *positive rewarding site*,
the animal will repeatedly strike the bar to administer *self-stimulations*. The cumulative record (Fig. 24.12) shows the rate of this responding by the slope of the line (the pen returns to the bottom of the
page at intervals giving rise to the saw-tooth appearance). To be
noted is the very long length of each of the daily self-stimulations;
the peaks represent one hour intervals. Also to be noted is
the steady high rate of bar-pressing—as high as 5000/hr. The
regions in which electrode insertions gave the highest positive
reinforcing responses were those located in the basal and medial parts
of the brain with the most powerful reinforcements found in the

medial forebrain bundle. Other limbic system structures also are highly reinforcing (Fig. 24.13). In addition to the positive rewarding areas shown in this figure by the dark shaded area, negative reinforcing areas are shown by the stippling. When electrodes were placed in these areas, the animal will not bar-press and will actively work to prevent stimulation of this area. In addition, there are ambivalent areas where both positive and negative types of response are found. Brady (1961) finds that reinforcing regions can be arranged in the following order of preference: hypothalamus,

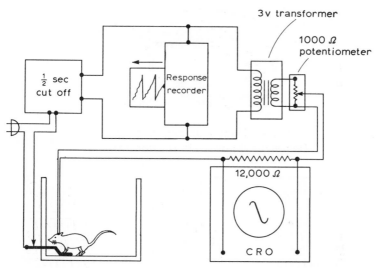

Fig. 24.11. A rat is shown pressing a bar-lever controlling a switch which turns on a brief electrical current led in via electrodes to cause self-stimulation of its own brain. The responses to pressing (its rate of bar-pressing) is recorded in the response recorder and the stimulus strength is measured with an oscilloscope. (Olds and Peretz, *Electroencephalog. Clin. Neurophysiol.* **12**: 445, 1960.)

anterior medial forebrain bundle, orbitofrontal cortex, amygdala, enterorhinal cortex. The septal area was neutral and the fornix was negative in its reinforcing value.

Can the animal be experiencing pleasure when bar-pressing in a positive reinforcing site? There is a reluctance by some to relate the bar-pressing of animals to pleasure. However, it is only by behavior that we characterize snarling and biting as rage, cowering or whining with fear. We are obviously unable to know the subjective state of an animal. A qualitative answer comes from stimulations of analogous brain regions in the conscious human which have been

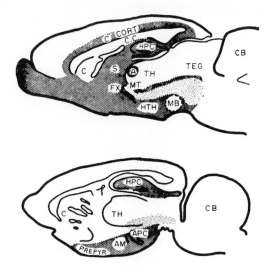

Fifteen days of responding
Posterior hypothalmic electrode

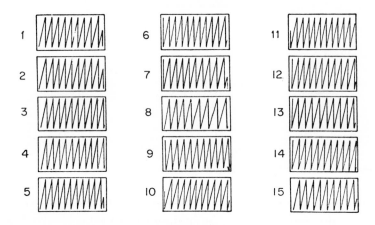

Fig. 24.12. The slant-lined regions of the sagittal sections of the rat brain above show where chronically implanted electrodes were found to give high rates of self-stimulation. The lower graphs show 15 consecutive days of cumulative recording of an animal's bar-pressing responses. Each peak of the record indicates the end of an hour of continuous self-stimulation. The slope gives the rate which could reach 5000 bar-presses an hour. (From Olds, *Science* **127**: 315, 1958.)

made in the course of neurosurgical intervention by Sem-Jacobsen and Torkildsen (1960). Reports included feelings of joy and satisfaction and experiences of tickling and fluttering of muscles in the pelvic region which were pleasurable. Given a key to control the stimulus, patients would eagerly respond by self-stimulation. In the rat self-stimulation studies, Olds found that these animals will stay awake to bar-press and will self-stimulate to the point of physical exhaustion. Animals will also prefer self-stimulation to food, to mating, and will even undergo a painful experience in order to reach the bar for self-stimulation (Olds, 1958).

In view of the similar experiences found in humans and the demonstrable drive of animals to self-stimulate analogous regions, there seems little reason to withhold the appelation of *pleasure sites* to the

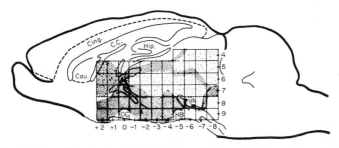

Fig. 24.13. The dark shaded region of the sagittal section of the rat brain shows those regions where an implanted electrode gives a strong self-stimulation though with moderately high threshold. A thalamic system (light shading) gives mild self-stimulation, but often with very low thresholds. Many points in stippled area produce escape behavior. Abbreviations: Cing., cingulate; c.c., corpus callosum; cau., caudate; Hip., hippocampus. (Olds and Peretz, *Electroencephalog. Clin. Neurophysiol.* **12**: 445, 1960.)

regions from which positive self-stimulating reinforcement can be obtained. The problem arises as to where the sensations are subjectively appreciated. Is it the cingulate cortex as postulated by Papez or are impulses projected to the neocortex for subjective appreciation? This problem will be discussed in Chapter 25.

REFERENCES

Adey, W. R. (1959). Recent studies of the rhinencephalon in relation to temporal lobe epilepsy and behavior disorders. *Intern. Rev. Neurobiol.* **1**: 1–46.

Bard, P. and Macht, M. B. (1958). The behavior of chronically decerebrated cats. *Neurological Basis of Behavior*. Pp. 55–75. Ciba Foundation Symposium. Churchill, London.

Bard, P. and Mountcastle, V. B. (1947). Some forebrain mechanisms involved in expression of rage with special reference to suppression of angry behavior. *Res. Pub. Assoc. Nervous Mental Disease* **27**: 362–404.

Bard, P. and Rioch, D. McK. (1937). A study of four cats deprived of neocortex and additional portions of the forebrain. *Bull. Johns Hopkins Hosp.* **60**: 73–157.

Brady, J. V. (1961). Motivational-emotional factors and intracranial self-stimulation. *Electrical Stimulation of the Brain.* Edited by D. E. Sheer. Chapter 30. University of Texas Press, Austin.

Broca, P. (1878). Anatomie comparée des circonvolutions cérébrales. Le grand lobe limbique et la scissure limbique dans la série des mammiferes. *Rev. Anthropol.* **1**: 385–498.

Brodal, A. (1947). The hippocampus and the sense of smell. A review. *Brain* **70**: 179–222.

Bureš, J. (1959). Reversible decortication and behavior. *The Central Nervous System and Behavior.* Edited by M. A. B. Brazier. Pp. 207–248. Second Conference. Macy Foundation, New York.

Cannon, W. B. and Britton, S. W. (1925). Studies on the conditions of activity in endocrine glands XV. Pseudoaffective medulliadrenal secretion. *Am. J. Physiol.* **72**: 283–294.

Eidelberg, E. (1961). Hippocampal 'dendritic' responses in rabbits. *J. Neurophysiol.* **24**: 521–533.

Fernandez de Molina, A. and Hunsperger, R. W. (1959). Central representation of affective reactions in forebrain and brain stem: electrical stimulation of amygdala, stria terminalis, and adjacent structures. *J. Physiol.* **145**: 251–265.

Fulton, J. F. (1949). *Functional Localization in the Frontal Lobes and Cerebellum.* Clarendon Press, Oxford.

Goltz, F. (1892). Der Hund ohne grosshirne. *Pfluger's Arch. Ges. Physiol.* **51**: 570–614.

Green, J. D. and Arduini, A. (1954). Hippocampal electrical activity in arousal. *J. Neurophysiol.* **17**: 533–557.

Green, J. D., Clemente, C. D. and de Groot, J. (1957). Rhinencephalic lesions and behavior in cat. *J. Comp. Neurol.* **108**: 505–545.

Hall, C. S. (1951). The genetics of behavior. *Handbook of Experimental Psychology.* Chapter 9. John Wiley & Sons, New York.

Hess, W. R. (1954). *Diencephalon, Autonomic and Extrapyramidal Functions.* Grune and Stratton, New York.

Hunsperger, R. W. (1956). Affektreaktionen auf elektrische Reizung im Hirnstamm der Katze. *Helvet. Physiol. Acta.* **14**: 70–92.

Kandel, E. R., Spencer, W. A. and Brinley, F. J., Jr. (1961). Electrophysiology of hippocampal neurons. *J. Neurophysiol.* **24**: 225–242.

Klüver, H. (1958). The temporal lobe syndrome produced by bilateral ablations. *Neurological Basis of Behavior.* Pp. 175–186. Ciba Foundation Symposium. Churchill, London.

Klüver, H. and Bucy, P. C. (1939). Preliminary analysis of functions of the temporal lobes in monkeys. *Arch. Neurol. Psychiat.* **42**: 979–1000.

Liberson, W. T. and Cadhilac, J. G. (1953). Electroshock and rhinencephalic seizure states. *Conf. Neurol.* **13**: 278–286.

MacLean, P. D. (1959). The limbic system with respect to two basic life principles. *The Central Nervous System and Behavior. Transactions of the Second Conference.* Pp. 31–118. Edited by M. A. B. Brazier. Macy Foundation, New York.

MacLean, P. D. and Delgado, J. M. R. (1953). Electrical and chemical stimulation of frontotemporal portion of the limbic system in the waking animal. *Electroencephalog. Clin. Neurophysiol.* **5**: 91–100.

Masserman, J. H. (1943). *Behavior and Neurosis.* University of Chicago Press, Chicago.

Morgane, P. J. and Kosman, A. J. (1959). A rhinencephalic feeding center in the cat. *Am. J. Physiol.* **197**: 158–162.

Olds, J. (1958). Selective effects of drives and drugs on "reward" systems of the brain. *Neurological Basis of Behavior.* Pp. 124–148. Ciba Foundation Symposium. Little, Brown and Co., Boston.

Olds, J. (1962). Hypothalamic substrates of reward. *Physiol. Revs.* **42**: 554–604.

Olds, J. and Milner, P. (1954). Positive reinforcement produced by electrical stimulation of septal area and other regions of rat brain. *J. Comp. Physiol. Psychol.* **47**: 419–427.

Papez, J. W. (1937). A proposed mechanism of emotion. *Arch. Neurol. Psychiat.* **38**: 725–745.

Ramón y Cajal, S. (1955). *Studies on the Cerebral Cortex (Limbic Structures).* Translated by L. M. Kraft. Lloyd-Luke Ltd., London.

Roberts, W. W. (1958). Rapid escape learning without avoidance learning motivated by hypothalamic stimulation in cats. *J. Comp. Physiol. Psychol.* **51**: 400–407.

Russell, G. V. (1961). Interrelationships within the limbic and centrencephalic systems. *Electrical Stimulation of the Brain.* Chapter 15. Edited by D. E. Sheer. University of Texas Press, Austin.

Schreiner, L. and Kling, A. (1953). Behavioral changes following rhinencephalic injury in the cat. *J. Neurophysiol.* **16**: 643–659.

Sem-Jacobsen, C. W. and Torkildsen, A. (1960). Depth recording and electrical stimulation in the human brain. *Electrical Studies on the Unanesthetized Brain.* Pp. 275. Edited by E. R. Ramey and D. S. O'Doherty. Hoeber, New York.

Shealy, C. N. and Peele, T. L. (1957). Studies on amygdaloid nucleus of cat. *J. Neurophysiol.* **20**: 125–139.

Sherrington, C. S. (1906). *Integrative Action of the Nervous System.* Yale University Press, New Haven. Rev. Ed. (1947). Cambridge University Press, Cambridge.

Stamm, J. S. (1955). The function of the median cerebral cortex in maternal behavior of rats. *J. Comp. Physiol. Psychol.* **48**: 347–356.

Ward, A. A., Jr. (1948). The cingular gyrus: area 24. *J. Neurophysiol.* **11**: 13–23.

25

Higher Functions of the Nervous System

Behavior was previously analysed in terms of innate characteristic responses, the reflexes (Chapter 13). However, inborn reflexes cannot explain all the behavior observed in the higher forms. The acquisition of experience leading to new ways of behaving soon separates the behavior of one individual from others of his species. Consideration must be given to this *plasticity* of the nervous system in addition to the stability afforded by its genetic endowments. The modification of performance by experience is *learning*, and our problem is to relate learning to the operation of the nervous system. We must consider the relation of mind or *mentation* to the nervous system. Classically this is the *mind–body problem*. Here 'body' refers to the neural machinery of the nervous system controlling the external motor performances of the organism. One form of the problem is the elementary question—how is it that when I will to move my finger I can do so, and when I am stuck with a pin I feel pain? Or, when I look at an object how do I recognize it as such? In other words, how is it that from the multitude of sensory impressions we can identify some of these as constituting separate objects and *perceive* objects as such.

The problem of perception is viewed differently by 'atomistic' and 'molar' psychologists. According to the former, a perception is pieced together from the individual sensory elements: tones, points of light, etc. According to the molar or holistic viewpoint of Gestalt psychology, perception comes as a whole and missing parts of a whole figure may be supplied by the viewing organism. The problem has been investigated experimentally by Pritchard (1961). It has been known that in normal vision, small tremors and shifts of the eyeball cause an image to be distributed over different areas of the retina. By means of a miniature projector fixed to a contact lens and placed over the eyeball, an image can be projected onto a fixed region of retinal cells. When a projected figure with such retinally stabilized images was viewed, portions of the figure were seen to fade and then reappear. The portions of the figure which were seen were those which had meaning for the subject. For example, if the figure of a head is viewed, the portions seen were the face, brow, hair, etc., and if these portions were left out, the figure still appeared complete in the perception. These results fit with Hebb's (1949) theory of perception where a group of 'perceiving neurons' act as a *cell-assembly*. When a part of the whole becomes activated, the remainder also becomes active (*vide infra*).

The perception of sensory fragments and their joining into a complete figure appears to take place in the cortex as suggested by the reverse phenomenon where cortical lesions produce agnosias (Chapter 22). A patient with a parietal lesion may be asked to identify by touch a key placed in his hand. He may feel the key as having smooth and rough parts, being warm or cold, and identify parts but not the key as an object until he looks at it whereupon he immediately recognizes it as a key. A patient with an occipital lesion in the visual area may be asked to draw an object. Even when looking at the object to be copied he cannot connect the individual elements into a representation of the object.

Perception requires not only mechanisms of coherence but also memory mechanisms. Memory here is defined as a previous conscious awareness of the object which results in an enduring change in the neural apparatus. The possible molecular basis of storage of memories (*retention*) will be discussed in a later section. Behaviorally, memory is demonstrated by recognition of previous events and by their recall. Recognition is the matching of an object which is being perceived at the time to a memory of its previous perception. It is a commonplace observation that animals do learn to recognize objects. Is some form of consciousness present (perhaps in a more obscure form) in the lower animals to account for their remembrances? Herrick (1924) expressed this when he wrote that consciousness (mindness) is a factor to be dealt with at all levels of the nervous system and it is present to some extent in all forms of life. As computers approach closely in their abilities those of humans in problem-solving, the making of 'strategic' decisions, etc., a question first proposed humorously became seriously considered, namely, at what stage of development of computer complexity could we consider it to have a mind (Hook, 1961)? Such a question brings out the basic problem of consciousness. It has been the custom of some behavioral psychologists not to consider mentation, regarding rather the behavior of organisms as a complete description. In this sense, the strict behaviorist would properly ascribe consciousness to the workings of a sufficiently complex computer. Opposed to his *monistic* position is the *dualistic* concept that there are two types of substance, of mind and material objects (neurons) which can interact. Perhaps more commonly held is the notion that mind is an *epiphenomenon*, a product in some sense of the operation of the neural machinery. Another view is that consciousness and mentation can be considered as the function of neurons. Our individual experiences are to be *identified* with the activities of certain neuronal assemblies. Accepting this position, the problem is to determine where in the brain the cell-assemblies related to consciousness, perception, ideation, etc., are located and what kinds of activity occur in them.

In the preceding chapter emotion was considered as biologically important in the satisfaction of visceral needs. In the same biological sense we can consider the development of a mind as the appearance of neural mechanisms which will insure that future actions will satisfy those goals. Judgment and planning, in short, *ideation*, have their origin in this need. The arousal of anticipation of eating by the sight of food, the 'cephalic' phase of eating, would be a low-order expression of this idea. More to the point is the working for wages to buy food next week, next month, etc. Some behaviors in lower animals which appear to suggest long-range planning are more likely instinctive reflex-like behaviors as discussed in Chapter 13. The autumnal hoarding of winter food by the squirrel is an example. The hoarding of non-edible and evidently useless objects by other species shows this instinctive behavior in exaggerated form. In order to determine whether animals do have higher functions, special experimental procedures must be used to distinguish learned from instinctive and reflex behavior. In the next sections an outline of some techniques will be described to serve as a basis for a discussion of their use in investigations into these higher mechanisms.

Learning procedures

The various psychological procedures used for behavioral studies may be broadly grouped as *classical conditioning* (*respondent*) or *operant conditioning* (*instrumental*) (Keller and Schoenfeld, 1950).

In classical conditioning an originally neutral stimulus becomes a signal for some normal type of reflex response, a study first developed by Pavlov (1927) and his fellow workers. In the classical studies of conditioned reflexes a cannula is put into the duct of the exteriorized parotid gland of dogs so that the amount of saliva produced can be measured (Fig. 25.1(a)). Meat juices or dilute acids could be injected into the mouth by means of another tube. The animal is placed in a harness and all extraneous sounds and sights are eliminated.   Procedures are controlled and responses recorded by means of apparatus placed in another room.   At the onset there was little salivary output.   However, the flow of saliva was increased if meat juice was injected into the mouth of a hungry dog. In this case the taste of the meat juice is a normal stimulus to the hungry animal and it produces a salivary reflex response. If an originally neutral stimulus such as a click or a tone signal is sounded just before the meat juice is given and this pairing of a sound with an injection of meat juice is repeated a number of times, a salivary reflex response develops to the sound stimulus alone.   Salivation

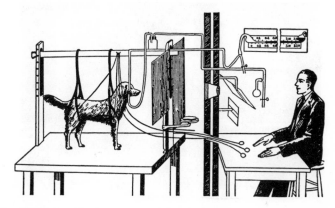

Fig. 25.1(a).   To demonstrate classical (Pavlovian) conditioning, a dog is placed in a harness with cannulae surgically implanted into the mouth so that acid can be injected and the flow of saliva measured by the scale above the head of the experimenter who is in a separate room.   With the keys on the table the experimenter can mechanically stimulate the skin at two points.   (From Pavlov, *Lectures on Conditioned Reflexes*, Lawrence and Wishart, London, 1928.)

in response to the sound is then called a *conditioned reflex* (conditional on the presence of the sound stimulus).   The meat juice which stimulates the taste receptors is called the *unconditioned stimulus*; the sound stimulus is called the *conditioned stimulus*.   Salivation to meat juice is an *unconditioned response*, while salivation to the sound stimulus after conditioning has occurred is a *conditioned response*.   The paired presentation of the conditioned stimulus and the unconditioned stimulus is called *reinforcement*.   If the conditioned stimulus is presented without reinforcing at intervals, *extinction* occurs, i.e. salivary flow in response to the conditioned stimulus becomes gradually diminished and eventually no response occurs. It will, however, spontaneously recur after a rest period.

In operant conditioning the response of an animal is rewarded by food, water, etc., the reinforcement *strengthens* or increases the probability of a similar behavior (Keller, 1954). A type of operant conditioning which has come into wide use in recent years utilizes a box containing a bar switch which the animal can press. Upon the appropriate bar-pressing behavior, reinforcement can be automatically delivered (Skinner, 1938) (Fig. 25.1(b)). When placed in the box

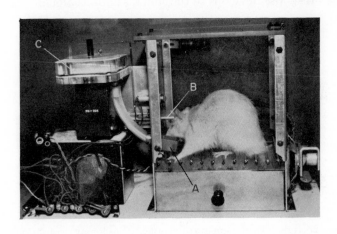

Fig. 25.1(b). An example of a Skinner box for operant conditioning shown with a rat inside a box constructed of plexiglass and viewed from the side. The bar (B) it presses to receive a food reinforcement is just in front of the head. Food pellets fall via a chute into the food trough (A) directly in front of the animal. The pellet is ejected from the pellet supply (C) outside the box. Some of the control mechanisms are shown outside the box at left.

the rat will accidentally hit the projecting bar. Sooner or later the animal learns that pressing the bar causes the delivery of a small pellet of food. Once such learning has begun, the experimenter can arrange for reinforcement after 1, 2, 3 . . . up to a hundred or more bar-presses (Ferster and Skinner, 1958). In the theory of operant behavior the animal will make a number of different responses as part of its innate repertoire of behavior. Those responses which are reinforced are the ones which are augmented; the unreinforced responses are extinguished. If a learned response is not reinforced, an extinction curve of decreased bar-pressing is obtained just as it is in classical conditioning.

Negative as well as positive reinforcement occurs in both operant and classical conditioning.   An animal can learn to press a bar to prevent being painfully shocked in the *avoidance response* procedure of Sidman (1953).   This is somewhat related to *avoidance conditioning* where the animal learns to respond in a selected way to a sensory stimulus to avert a shock.   For example, a dog might be taught to lift its leg when a tone is sounded to avoid getting an electrical shock to its paws or to the skin of its flank.   Another type of avoidance arrangement is to place an animal in a box with a metal grid floor, the box divided into two compartments by a low wall or a wall with a door.   Upon a signal such as a light or buzzer, the animal must move to the other compartment or receive a painful electrical shock from the floor grid.   These are examples of *active avoidance* where the animal must learn to make a specified response to avoid a painful shock.   *Passive avoidance* takes place when an animal learns not to respond, for example, not to approach and eat from a food trough after previously experiencing one or several painful electrical shocks at the trough when it begins to feed.

Another type of instrumental learning is shown by *maze* learning. An animal is put into a set of narrow passages which connect in various ways.   At the end of the maze is a goal, such as food or a sexually receptive mate, etc.   The time of running such a maze is a function of taking the correct path among several alternative paths at each of the several *choice-points*.   Learning is indicated when, on repeated trials, the shortest path is taken in the shortest time. Some other learning techniques used for specific neurophysiological problems will be described in later sections.

Learning in lower animals and relation to the CNS

Is a nervous system required for learning?   We have discussed the neuroidal system of control present in some unicellular organisms (Chapter 13).   Do single-celled organisms show learning?   Some evidence (Jennings, 1905) suggests that these organisms without nervous systems may show a primitive type of learning known as *habituation*.   A stimulus which causes some type of reflex response such as a movement is used.   Repetition of the stimulus gradually becomes less and less effective, but a novel stimulation is immediately responded to by the organism.   More recently Gelber (1952) has indicated that conditioning could occur in *Paramecium* although this has not been well established.   In view of the theoretical importance of learning behavior in single-celled organisms, this area of study should be re-explored. (Cf. Katz and Deterline, 1958.)

Adaptive learning has been shown with respect to complex feeding patterns in the *coelenterate*, such as the hydra which uses its tentacles to put food objects into its oral cavity. If the animal is repeatedly presented with food to the tentacles on one side, and is prevented from eating it, it eventually becomes unresponsive to the food objects presented to those tentacles. Thereafter, when food was presented to the tentacles on the other side, the food objects were readily taken (Parker, 1919). A similar habituation is also seen in the brain of higher organisms; this will be discussed in a later section.

Wells (1962) has reviewed studies on the learning abilities of the highest forms of radially organized animals, the *cephalopods*. Some common species found in this group are the squid, sepia and octopus. Most attention was paid to learning in the octopus where both visual and tactile discriminations can be conditioned. One part of the brain, the vertical lobe, is of particular interest with regard to higher functions. When it is removed, animals forget and relearn only slowly (Boycott and Young, 1955, 1957). Young (1961) suggested that *generalization* (the 'recognition' of the same object when falling on different places in the retina) takes place in this part of the brain. One remarkable feature is that the learning shown by these radially-organized animals appears to be similar to that of vertebrates in spite of their fundamentally different body plan.

The relation of 'brain' structures to learning is shown in the lowest of the linearly-organized forms. Earthworms may be conditioned in a T-shaped passageway constructed with a piece of rough sandpaper at the entrance to one part of the T (Yerkes, 1912). When the animal moved over the sandpaper to that side, it was given an electrical shock. After 20–100 trials the animal learned to avoid turning to that side, and thus avoided the electrical shock. When the habit was acquired, the brain was amputated along with the anterior five segments. Later the worm was tested in the maze and it made the right responses. Two months later, after a new brain was regenerated, the habit was lost (Herrick, 1924). In recent years the flat worm *Planaria* has been used in similar experiments (McConnell, Jacobson and Kimble, 1959; Best, 1963). *Planaria* could be conditioned to a light stimulus as the conditioned stimulus and a nociceptive electrical shock as the unconditioned stimulus. If cut in half, each half of the worm regenerates into a complete worm. When conditioned worms were cut in half, both regenerated worms showed retention of the con-

ditioned behavior.   The participation of nucleic acids in the retention of the conditioning in the body halves was indicated.   However,
further studies will be required because of some of the difficulties
found in the study of the conditioned responses in these lower
forms.   (Cf. Hartry and Keith-Lee, 1964.)

When higher animal forms are studied, conditioning cannot be
readily obtained without the brain present.   Even animals as low
as amphibia which have survived brain destruction are not readily
conditioned.   We consider that the function of learning and also of
memory storage resides somewhere in the brain and, as will be shown
in the next section, the cerebral cortex plays an important role.

Cerebral cortex and learned responses

Using classical conditioning methods, it was shown that the decorticate animal can be conditioned, though with difficulty.   This
does not apply to all types of conditioning.   *Escape conditioning*
where an animal learns to jump over a wall upon nociceptive stimulation through the floor grid is not much interfered with by cortical
ablation.   Classical conditioned avoidance responses to a light,
touch or sound signal are impaired but can be learned in the decorticated animal.   Pavlov (1927) stressed the role of the cortex in
learning and considered that new neuronal connections were made
between the unconditioned and conditioned signals within the
cortex.   Gastaut (1958) on the other hand, considers that a classical
conditioning takes place in sub-cortical centers.

In an attempt to study this problem Lashley (1929, 1950) using a
variety of tests found a definite cortical participation in operant
conditioning.   In one such test of visual discrimination, the
animal is placed on a platform and is confronted with two different
geometric shapes, one placed over each of two doors.   The animal
is forced to leap from the platform to one or another of these doors.
For a wrong choice the animal is punished by bumping itself against a
solid front.   The correct choice leads the animal past the door into a
compartment where a reinforcement is present.   By using this and
other visual discrimination tests followed by ablation of cortical areas
and observing of the retention of learning, Lashley concluded that the
associational areas were not specifically involved in retention.   Instead
it appeared that the amount of cortex ablated was the important
variable in both the learning and the retention of the conditioned
behavior.   The sensory areas were necessary for discriminations but
not all of the area was required.   Discriminations could be made if
a small part of the primary receptor area was left intact (Chapter 21).

As a procedure to study the relation of the cortex to other parts of the brain, ablation has certain disadvantages.   The animal cannot be adequately tested until it has recovered from the non-specific trauma of ablation.   Also, during the prolonged times required for recovery from surgery, plasticity may be observed, i.e. other regions may gradually take over functions of those parts removed by the ablation (Chapter 22).   For this reason, the recent use of spreading depression as a means of temporary decortication (Bureš, 1959) is of considerable importance.   In the work of Bureš and his collabora-

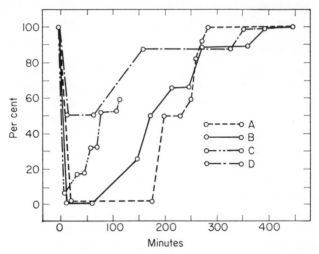

Fig. 25.2.   Effect of spreading depression on alimentary (A) and avoidance (B) conditioned reflexes, escape reactions (C) and EEG amplitude (D) are expressed as percentage of the initial amplitude.   Time in minutes on abscissa after the application of KCl to induce spreading depression.   A decrease in all these parameters with gradual recovery over a period of hours is shown. (Bureš, Burešová and Záhorová, *J. Comp. Physiol. Psychol.*, **51**: 263, 1958.)

tors, rats were prepared with burr holes through the skull so that both cortices could be depressed by application of small amounts of KCl.   When this is done, a series of waves of SD are initiated from this locus at intervals of 5–15 minutes, essentially keeping the cortex functionally depressed for periods as long as 4 hours.   The simple escape behaviors were not seriously affected by SD, but the conditioned avoidance responses were completely blocked (Fig. 25.2).

Some of the psychological test procedures used to assess brain function and the ability of monkeys to make discriminations were described by Harlow (1958). One such test uses a tray device (Fig. 25.3) where pellets of food are offered in wells covered with special cups. These cups function as stimuli. In any one set of experiments they may have different geometrical shapes, colors or design symbols painted on them. The animal learns to pick the right stimulus in order to receive the food reinforcement. In the *delayed-response* test, two covers are used as the stimuli. Food is placed in one well in full view of the animal, the stimulus covers placed over both wells; then, a screen is lowered between the animal and the wells. After an interval the screen is raised and the monkey is allowed to choose one or the other stimuli to get food reinforcement. In the *delayed alternation* test, the

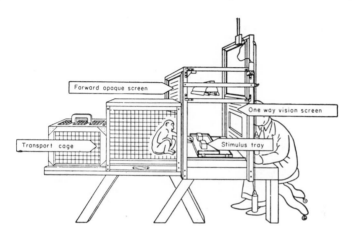

Fig. 25.3. A delayed response trial is shown with a monkey in a cage able to reach its arm toward a tray where pieces of food are hidden by covers of various shapes and colors. The food is placed under one of these stimulus covers out of reach as the animal watches. It is then moved toward the animal to allow it to pick the stimulus over the food. (Harlow, 1958.)

reward is placed first under one cover, then under the other, etc. Learning was indicated by a high percentage of correct responses on successive trial days. Using such tests as this, Pribram (1958) ablated the infero-temporal cortex, the associational cortex near the visual area, and found that it had an effect on learned visual discriminations. Other association areas near the somesthetic area had an effect on tactile discriminations, and those near the auditory cortex on audition. Pribram used the term 'intrinsic sector' to refer to these associational brain areas (Fig. 25.4).

Chow (1961) compared the learning abilities of animals with ablations leaving only the visual area intact and those in which a larger area around the visual area was left intact.   In animals with just the visual area remaining, simple pattern discriminations could be learned.   However, the nearby temporal cortex was required for the animal to learn to make a series of connected learned discriminations, a *learning-set* (Harlow, 1958).   Therefore, the associational

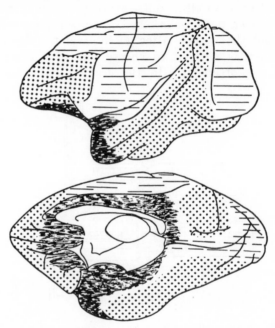

Fig. 25.4.   Lateral surface of the monkey brain shown above and medial surface below.   Lined area indicates extrinsic (sensory) cortex; dotted area, the intrinsic (associative) cortex; shaded area, the limbic brain regions.   (Pribram, 1958.)

regions present near the primary areas appear to be required for higher-order types of learned behavior which are more complex than simple recognition.

One associational region which has long been considered important for higher functions is that present in the frontal lobes of the brain. It is defined as the region receiving projections from the dorsomedial and anteromedial nuclei of the thalamus (Rose and Woolsey, 1948). Its main afferent inputs and efferent projections are shown in Fig. 25.5.   Ablation of the frontal lobes produces a learning defect as shown by a variety of tests.   A normal chimpanzee in a cage can use a stick to bring in a food object out of its reach, while an animal with bilateral frontal lobotomy does not do so. Simple latch box problems can be solved after frontal lobe ablation but not more complicated problems. The delayed response is seriously depressed by such lesions (Jacobsen, 1936). The effect of disrupting the

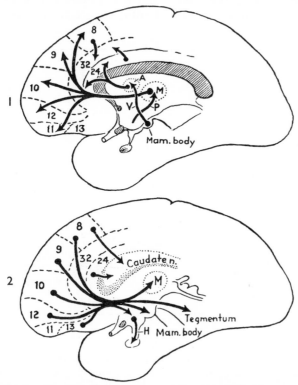

Fig. 25.5. Medial aspect of the cerebral hemisphere shown with its main afferent connections in the upper diagram (1) and efferent connections in the lower (2): A, anterior nucleus of thalamus; H, hypophysis; Mam. body, mammillary body; M, dorsomedial nucleus; P, periventricular system extending from hypothalamus to dorsomedial nucleus; and V, mammillothalamic tract. Numbers on cortex are Brodmann's cytoarchitectural areas. (Le Gros Clark, *Lancet* 1: 353, 1948.)

organized activity of the frontal lobes was studied using alumina cream to produce a chronic state of localized convulsive activity in the frontal lobes (Stamm and Pribram, 1960). After evidence of convulsive activity was obtained by EEG recordings, the ability to learn or retain a delayed alternation was tested. Monkeys with epileptic seizures in the frontal lobes took longer to learn than did normal control animals (Fig. 25.6). In contrast to this difference in *learning rate*, the presence in this region of epileptic discharges apparently had no effect on the retention of a previously learned alternation task. This difference between learning and retention was also shown by Stamm (1961) using repetitive electrical stimulation via electrodes chronically implanted over the frontal cortex to disrupt function.

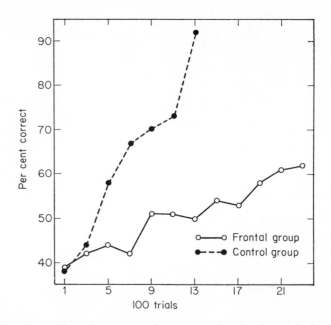

Fig. 25.6. Learning curve of a group of animals made locally epileptic in the frontal cortex and of a control group of normal animals. Groups of 100 trials of delayed alternation given on the abscissa with percent correct responses shown on the ordinate. A marked deficiency in the learning by the epileptoid group is indicated (Stamm and Pribram).

The learning of an alternation discrimination was depressed. Pribram (1958) believes that this frontal association area is involved in those kinds of learning where a comparison must be made between a stimulus which is present and one which has to be recalled. There appears to be no difficulty in learning a discrimination task when the two patterns to be discriminated are presented simultaneously in the visual field.

The connections of the frontal cortex made with the cingulate cortex and other limbic brain structures suggest that the frontal lobes have some relation to emotion. Frontal lobotomy, which has been used as a treatment for certain mental disease, does not appear to cause changes in intelligence so much as a change in emotional reactivity (Fulton, 1951). Problems may not be readily solved after frontal lobe ablation because of distraction. The emotional mechanisms normally are presumed to channel attention and keep the intellect focussed on the problem until the emotional drive is satisfied.

Is the cingulate necessary for the awareness of emotion? Ablation of the cingulate cortex does not eliminate the retention of a conditioned avoidance response in the cat (McLeary, 1961). The animals were conditioned by allowing them to approach a feeding trough and on touching the food an electrical circuit was completed, and they received a strong electrical shock. The animals learned not to approach the feeding trough after one or two trials. After cingulate ablation they still did not approach the trough. On the other hand, ablation of another cortical area more forwardly placed in the medial subcallosal region eliminated this learned avoidance. The cats would return to the feed trough soon after receiving shocks.

Electrical changes associated with learning

A primitive type of learning is habituation, the decreased responsitivity to repetitive presentation of the same stimulus. This process was shown to occur in the brain using arousal of the EEG on presenting a brief sensory stimulation such as a click or flash of light (Sharpless and Jasper, 1956). As expected, a click excites an EEG arousal which is relatively long-lasting, one having a duration of scores of seconds (Fig. 25.7). Repeated stimulations produce progressively shorter periods of arousal until when habituation was complete, no EEG arousal was seen at all. Arousal is a response to a novel stimulus (Chapter 20) and habituation is a learned discrimination to that stimulus. If the signal which produces adaptation is changed (Fig. 25.8) from 500 cps to 100 cps, or to 1000 cps, then arousal is once again seen to these tones but not to the 500 cps tone. The presence of a different stimulus, such as a sudden puff of air produced just before a 500 cps tone to which the animal is habituated, will cause a loss of habituation, a *dishabituation*.

Habituation of a sensory-evoked response was shown by Hernández-Peón, Jouvet and Scherrer (1957) using cochlear nucleus responses to clicks. Auditory-evoked responses recorded from the cortex showed a faster habituation than lower parts of the auditory system (Hernández-Peón, 1960). Habituation of evoked responses recorded in the cortex to light, olfactory and tactile stimulation were also described by Hernández-Peón. Variation in the stimulus leads to the process of dishabituation, the novel stimulus again exciting the arousal mechanism and the orienting reflex. Habituation of evoked responses in sub-cortical relay stations can be seen after decortication, indicating that non-specific thalamic and reticular formation mechanisms are involved in habituation and dishabituation.

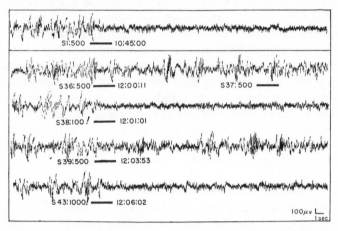

Fig. 25.7. EEG records taken from the suprasylvian gyrus of a cat showing habituation. An arousal to a 500 cps tone indicated by the bar occurs in the uppermost trace. In the second trace the 36th trial shows a brief period of arousal just afterwards; at the 37th trial, no arousal at all—habituation has been achieved. In the third trace (38th trial) the use of a novel stimulus, a tone of 100 cps, again causes arousal. Repetition of a 500 cps note in the 4th trace on the 39th trial again shows habituation. Another novel tone in the last trace at the 43rd trial; a tone of 1000 cps again gives arousal. (After Sharpless and Jasper, 1956.)

Durup and Fessard (1935), and Jasper and Shagass (1941) found that the EEG arousal reaction could be classically conditioned. A weak sound stimulus, one too low to cause arousal, or a stimulus to which an animal has been habituated was presented shortly before or concurrently with a visual stimulus which blocks the alpha rhythm. After a number of pairings of these stimuli, conditioning occurs, the sound stimulus alone producing alpha blocking. An example of EEG conditioning taken from a human subject is shown in Fig. 25.8. A long pulse of continuous light was used as the unconditioned visual stimulus. In the second line of the figure alpha blocking is shown to occur to the light. In C on the third line a tone signal to which the subject was habituated was ineffective. Later, as shown in D, after conditioning had occurred, EEG blocking occurred at the time of the conditioning tone signal and *before* the onset of the unconditioned light signal (Morell and Jasper, 1956; Morell, 1958).

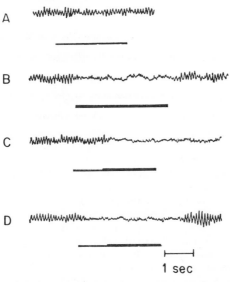

Fig. 25.8. Conditioning of the human EEG is shown. In A, no arousal in response to a tone signal given at the time shown by the thickened line underneath. The subject had been habituated to the tone signal. In B, arousal in response to a light stimulus at the time shown by the thick line under the EEG record. In C, the tone signal precedes the light stimulus before conditioning has occurred and arousal occurs at the time of the light stimulus (thick part of line). In D, after conditioning took place, arousal occurs at the time of the conditioning sound (thin line). (Morell, *Neurology* **6**: 327, 1956.)

The use of a flashing light as the unconditioned stimulus reveals an interesting characteristic of conditioning (Yoshii and Hockaday, 1958). As shown in A of Fig. 25.9, before conditioning light flashes at 7.5/sec gave rise to repetitive evoked responses in the parietal temporal areas. At first no response occurred to the tone signal which preceded the flashing light. After conditioning occurred, repetitive conditioned responses with a rate of approximately 7.5/sec were found in the different EEG leads in response to the

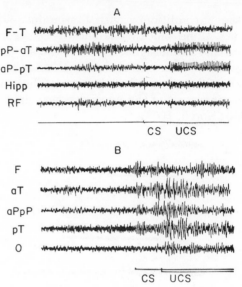

A

F–T

pP–aT

aP–pT

Hipp

RF

CS   UCS

B

F

aT

aPpP

pT

O

CS   UCS

Fig. 25.9. In A, a 7.5 per sec flashing light is used as the unconditioned stimulus (UCS) giving rise in the EEG to a repetitive
evoked response at this frequency in various cortical regions:
F, frontal; P, parietal; T, temporal; O, occipital; Hipp, hippocampal; RF, reticular formation. No conditioning has occurred
in response to the conditioned stimulus (CS) tone signal preceding
the unconditioned light stimulus. In B, following a number of
pairings of CS and UCS conditioning has occurred and 7.5 per sec
responses are obtained from a number of different cortical areas.
Conditioning is shown by the occurrence of the responses at the
onset of the CS tone stimulus and before the unconditioned light
stimulus. (From Yoshii and Hockaday, 1958.)

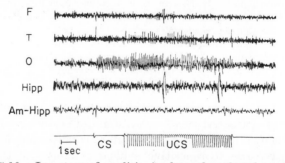

F

T

O

Hipp

Am–Hipp

1 sec   CS   UCS

Fig. 25.10. In a stage of conditioning later than that shown in Fig.
25.9, the frequency-specific conditioned response which precedes
the unconditioned light stimulus becomes restricted to the visual
area (O) of the cortex. Symbols as in Fig. 25.9 and Am, amygdala. (Yoshii and Hockaday, 1958.)

tone signal.   Later in conditioning, the conditioned 7.5/sec rhythm was found restricted to the visual area as shown by the conditioned repetitive responses found only in the occipital lead (O of Fig. 25.10). The rate of conditioned repetitive responses had the same frequency as the unconditioned light flashes if a low rate was used; a sub-harmonic if a higher frequency was used (Morrell, 1958).   The restriction of the conditioned response to the region of the un-conditioned primary receptor area suggests a discrimination pro-cess taking place there during conditioning.   John and Killam (1959) used the appearance of a repetitive conditioned response as a 'tracer' to indicate which parts of the brain were involved in conditioning.   Early in conditioning they found repetitive responses in the reticular formation and hippocampus.   Later in conditioning repetitive responses were localized in visual system structures.

The conditioning process was further studied by recording single-cell activity in the unanesthetized animal (Jasper, Ricci and Doane, 1960).   Cells in the motor area were found to increase their rate of discharge in response to a photic conditioning stimulus while other units were inhibited during this time (Fig. 25.11).   These effects occurred before the unconditioned motor response (an avoidance withdrawal to nociceptive stimulus to the hand).   Conditioning of the rate of discharge of single units was also found in units located in the non-motor areas, i.e., in the parietal cortex.

Single cells could also be conditioned with an operant technique (Olds and Olds, 1961).   Animals were prepared with self-stimulating electrodes chronically implanted in a region giving a high rate of positive self-stimulation (Chapter 24).   Then later, in an acute experiment, microelectrodes were placed near neurons in various sub-cortical brain areas to record their unit discharges.   A unit was found which fired intermittently.   When it began to fire, this neuron was 'rewarded' by stimulation of the electrodes in the posi-tive rewarding site.   This 'reinforced' the firing of the unit dis-charges until firing occurred at high rates.   While the 'conditioned' cell fired at these high rates, other cells nearby showed unchanged rates of firing, indicating that a general increase in cell activity was not taking place.   The conditioned cell also showed extinction when reinforcement was discontinued.

The electrical changes in the EEG found after conditioning do not however mediate behavior.   This was shown in cats when the EEG activity was conditioned to repetitive light flashes and then to an avoidance behavior using a tone signal.   The same EEG changes were established to the tone but the avoidance behavior was not produced by the tone (Chow, Dement and John, 1957). The electrical changes found in conditioning are therefore correlative events. In any case further investigation of these responses during different types of learning procedures holds promise of revealing which brain regions are involved and how they act in the learning process.

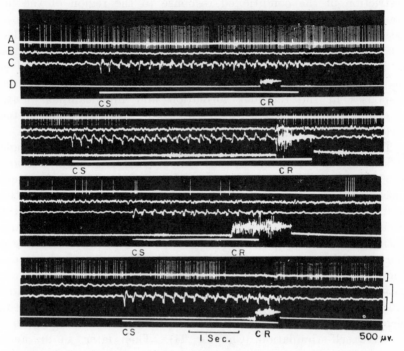

Fig. 25.11. Pattern of firing of units in motor cortex: (A) microelectrode, (B) surface recording motor cortex, (C) surface occipital area, (D) electromyogram from arm performing conditioned response (CR) avoidance act indicated by upward trace (D) in response to conditioning stimulus (CS). Four different patterns shown top to bottom: acceleration of unit discharge preceding and outlasting movement; arrest of unit discharge at beginning of CS and return just after CR; a brief burst at onset of CS; and arrest at CS and for some time before CR. No change in firing pattern found in 25–30% of units. (Jasper *et al.*, 1960.)

Site of conditioned learning

Two different theories are considered with regard to conditioning. According to Pavlov (1927), conditioning is a cortico-cortical interaction with new neuronal connections made in the cortex.

Much recent neurophysiological information (John, 1961) suggests another theory, that 'closure' between conditioning and unconditioning activities takes place in a sub-cortical region, possibly in the non-specific regions of the thalamus (Gastaut, 1958). The cortex participates in conditioning via corticopetal fibers passing information to it and corticofugal fibers sending impulses back down to these lower centers. This concept has some relationship to the *centrencephalic theory* of Penfield and Jasper (1954). This theory was based on the evidence that abnormal triggering activity from the non-specific thalamus gives rise to the generalized convulsive wave activity of Petit Mal epilepsy where interruption of consciousness is the chief defect (Chapter 18). Animals in which electrodes were chronically implanted in this region showed upon stimulation an 'arrest' behavior (Hunter and Jasper, 1949) which Jasper has likened to an aphasia or a disruption of pattern activity. Jasper (1954) has emphasized that in the non-specific thalamic nuclei different mechanisms must be present to account for the discriminations required in conditioning and other types of learning.

A participation of the cortex in learning conditioned responses was shown by use of direct stimulation of the cortex via chronically implanted electrodes to condition an avoidance response (Doty, Rutledge and Larsen, 1956; Doty, 1961). It was also possible to use cortical stimulation for both conditioned and unconditioned stimuli. Motor responses were produced by stimulation of the motor cortex and this unconditioned response became conditioned by pairing it with cortical stimulation elsewhere, for example, in the visual area (Doty and Giurgea, 1961).

It appears to be difficult, though perhaps not impossible (Doty, 1961) to condition sub-cortical sites. Masserman (1943) stimulated the hypothalamus to get rage responses (Chapter 24). Using hypothalamic stimulation as the unconditioned stimulus, conditioning was not obtained. However, Cohen, Brown and Brown (1957) conditioned sham-rage, produced by electrical stimulation of the hypothalamus, with a tone signal. Doty and Giurgea (1961) also reported some successes. Unsuccessful were attempts to condition water intake by hypothalamic stimulation in the drinking area of goats (Andersson and Larsson, 1956; Andersson, Jewell and Larsson, 1958).

Memory—the site of the engram

Memories may be permanent though we are not always conscious of them. Under hypnosis detailed information which was believed long forgotten can be recalled. Even the motor patterns are 'remembered' as demonstrated by the childish writing elicited during hypnotic age regression. This and other properties of memory have made the *trace theory* of memory generally accepted (Gomulicki, 1953). Some enduring change has been produced in the brain of which we are unconscious; on proper evocation of the trace, it becomes a conscious memory. We may liken these memories (*engrams*) to a magnetic tape which can be played back at later times.

However, a trace theory of memory requires a number of mechanisms. There is the complex wholeness of a memory to consider. Is each memory retained as a whole or are various parts of memories distributed in several types of memory 'stores'? Is there also a memory store of generalized concepts, those which relate to the idea of objects, dogs, stones, etc., as well as those universal terms required of conceptual thought? If memories are distributed to different sensory stores, then some 'selector' must pick these up and some process must join them at the time of remembering.

Experimental evidence has been obtained suggesting that memories are present in an integrated form. Penfield (1958) electrically stimulated the temporal lobe of patients brought to surgery for removal of scars and tumors from this region. An hallucinatory-like evocation of memories was found. The patients may upon temporal lobe stimulation report seeing a brother or child in the operating room; a whole complicated memory could unfold, complete with sights and sounds. Electrical stimulation of this region most likely triggers a memory store present in some deeper centers. This was in fact shown when stimulation of the fibers just under the cortex excited these memories.

Problems of learning and memory storage have been studied by use of the *split-brain preparation*. Visual information may be channeled to one cerebral hemisphere by cutting the optic chiasm antero-posteriorly in the mid-line and also other mid-line fiber tracts, particularly the corpus callosum (Fig. 25.12). Myers (1959, 1962) used this preparation to train cats with a visual pattern presented to one eye with the other eye masked. The side which was masked during training remained untrained as shown by the 'naive' performance of the animal when the masked eye was uncovered for testing while the eye originally open in training was covered. In another group, animals were prepared by cutting the optic chiasm as before, but with the corpus callosum uncut. Training of one eye with the other eye masked was done as before. But when the masked eye was then uncovered for testing and the eye originally open in training covered, the animal showed learned

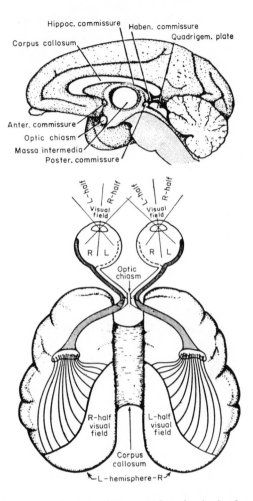

Fig. 25.12. Sagittal view of the monkey brain is shown in the upper figure with the major interhemispheric connecting tracts; corpus collosum, massa intermedia, anterior and posterior commissures. In the lower figure the optic chiasm is cut through in the anterior-posterior direction so that visual information by one eye is channelled to the visual cortex on that side. The corpus collosum is either cut or left uncut to demonstrate unilateral training or transfer in the split-brain preparations. (Sperry, 1961.)

responses.   The conclusion from these two sets of experiments was
that the visual discrimination acquired on the one side could be
transmitted to the other side via corpus callosum fibers.   In some
fashion the cortex participates in the retention of the engram or at
least functions in its dissemination.   A similar one-sided lateralization of a somesthetic discrimination habit on one side of a split-brain

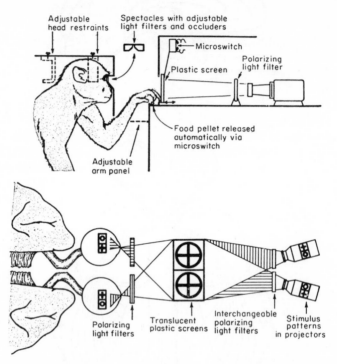

Fig. 25.13.   In the upper diagram the arrangement of the
monkey's head in a set of constricting eye ports is shown with
various visual stimuli projected onto a plastic screen in front of
each eye.   In the lower diagram the use of filters and stimulator
projections are shown with the representation of the projected
images to each eye of the split-brain preparation.   (From
Trevarthin; Sperry, 1961.)

preparation was shown by Stamm and Sperry (1957).   In animals
with the callosum uncut, transfer via the corpus callosum from one
side to the other was shown.   Transfer also occurs in monkeys via
the anterior commissure (Downer, 1962).

Each half of the split-brain preparation appears to have a relatively
independent action (Sperry, 1961).   In monkeys with a split brain,

an apparatus was devised so that a visual discrimination pattern could be presented to each eye separately (Fig. 15.13).   On the one side the animal could be trained to respond to one pattern, e.g., a cross, by pressing the bar to receive a food pellet as reinforcement. Presentation of a circle was a negative visual stimulus to which the animal was trained not to respond.   Conversely, with the other eye and that half of the brain, the animal was trained positively to press the bar on presentation of the circle and not to respond to the cross. There was no conflict in learning these two opposing types of trained responses presented to each half of the split-brain preparation.   What happens when the crosses are presented simultaneously to both sides? In that case there appears to be little conflict, the animal responds either positively or negatively.   It would appear that the engram of one side gains ascendancy and activity is controlled by it while the response to the other stimulus is suppressed (Sperry, 1961).

Bureš (1959) used SD to localize a conditioned response to one hemisphere, by this means creating a preparation in some respects like the split-brain animal.   A small amount of 25% KCl was placed through a trephine hole onto one cortex.   This produces recurring waves of SD which effectively block cortical function in that hemisphere for 3 to 4 hours.   The other hemisphere remains unaffected.   During the time when the cortex on one side was depressed, the animal was trained to a conditioned response. When cortical function returned later that day or on the next day, SD was initiated in the opposite hemisphere.   The animal then responded as a 'naive' animal would as shown by the number of trials required for conditioning (Fig. 25.14).   These results showed that the habit could be localized in one hemisphere.   Lateralization of an engram was also found using operant conditioning (Russell and Ochs, 1963).   Animals were given daily training sessions while SD was present in one hemisphere to temporarily suppress its activity. After a number of days a suitable level of bar-pressing performance was reached, and the opposite hemisphere was then depressed. Responses fell to 'naive' levels.   Switching back to depress the originally depressed side showed that the engram was localized in, or controlled from, one side (Fig. 25.15).

The engram present in one side is not spontaneously transferred to the other side after recovery from the effects of SD even though the corpus callosum and other interhemispheric interconnections are intact.   Transfer however was shown to occur after training one side if the animals were allowed to respond without SD present in an 'open' interval.   Transfer was shown by then

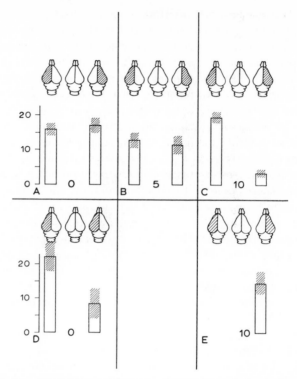

Fig. 25.14.   Unilateral conditioning and interhemispheric transfer.
The rat's hemisphere is unilaterally depressed (slanted shading)
and the number of conditioning trials to criterion shown in the
bar graph below.   SD was produced by 25% KCl applied to the
left hemisphere (A) and 15 trials were required for the rat to reach
criterion.   Then, next day the same number of trials was required
when SD was initiated in the other cortex.   In D, however, when
SD was introduced on the same side, the next day the number of
trials required to reach criterion was diminished.   Learning had
occurred on the undepressed side.   When 5 trials were permitted
without SD (B) this had no effect on the next day's test.   However,
10 trials with both sides open (C) did cause transfer as shown
when the trained side was depressed and fewer trials were required.
E, as a control, shows effect of SD without training when the other
        hemisphere was previously depressed.   (From Bureš, 1959.)

depressing the trained side and obtaining a trained type of
performance with the untrained side.   This is indicated in C of
Fig. 24.14.   After training on the left side the animal was allowed
to give conditioned responses in an open period with both cortices
undepressed.   On then testing the untrained side very few trials

were required, indicating transfer of the engram (cf. C and E of Fig. 25.14). Transfer occurs when the same conditions are present in the open period as in the original training of the first side. This was further indicated in studies of transfer using operant conditioning (Russell and Ochs, 1963) where, because the animal was trained to press the bar to receive one pellet,

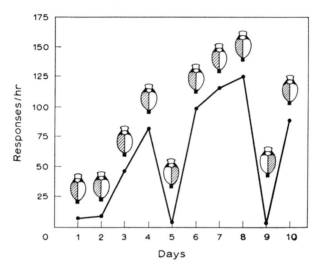

Fig. 25.15. Unilateral engram obtained with SD in chronic studies. The rat was prepared with cup inserts so that SD could be induced on one side for a number of days. The animal was put in the box for 1-hour sessions with one side (shaded) depressed with 25% KCl. The animal is hungry and pressing the lever will give one food pellet. On days 1 and 2 the animal makes only a few accidental bar-presses; on days 3 and 4 learning has occurred as indicated by the higher bar-press rates for food reinforcement. On day 5 the trained side was depressed and the rate fell to low levels. On days 6, 7, 8, the original side was again functional and a return to high rates of bar-pressing seen. On day 9 the untrained side was tested and few responses were seen. On day 10 after return to the original side the rate was high. (Russell and Ochs, *Science* **133**: 1077, 1961.)

such a performance in the open interval led to a one-trial transfer (Fig. 25.16). A similar one-trial transfer using SD in rats was shown by Ray and Emley (1964) with a visual discrimination maze type of learning. They found that when the trained side was depressed 10 seconds after exposure in the open period, transfer from the trained to the untrained side did not occur. If 10 minutes were allowed, transfer did take place. This fits with other studies showing that a certain period of time is required for learning to take place. In the following section this consolidation of memory will be discussed in further detail.

The experiments made with the split-brain preparations and with SD show that the cortex is involved in some way with regard to an engram controlling conditioned response behavior. However, a sub-cortical site for such an engram is not excluded and it is likely that at least some of the engrams are stored in a sub-cortical site. Sub-cortical components have been suggested by recent studies of the split-brain preparation (Sperry, 1962). An interesting study is one presented by Downer (1962). As previously noted in Chapter 24, bilateral temporal ablations lead to the Klüver–Bucy syndrome. In addition to the peculiar reactions to food and inedible objects treated as food by these preparations, the temporal-ablated animals lose their fear and aggressive reactions. In split-brain monkeys Downer found that a unilateral temporal lobectomy which included removal of the amygdala would bring on the Klüver–Bucy syndrome with tameness when the eye on the side of the lesion was open and the other eye closed. However, when the eye on the side of the lesion was closed and the other eye open the animal exhibited its normal aggressive behavior. This alteration of tameness and aggression could be switched on and off depending on which eye was open and the change was a stable one; it was possible to alter the behavior in this fashion for a period of months.

Consolidation and the molecular basis of memory

Memory mechanisms wherever located in the brain appear to entail two different phases or processes. One is an early type of memory process lasting up to approximately one hour and it is labile. Electrical shocks given to rats within an hour after a training experience were found to interfere with the retention of learning while shocks given an hour after a learning experience had little effect (Duncan, 1948). A similar effect was found if an anesthetic agent was given at various times up to an hour after a learning session (Abt, Essman and Jarvik, 1961). This early period represents a process of specific neuronal activity required for the *consolidation* of a memory. Thereafter, changes in neuronal activity have little effect. Electroconvulsive activation anesthesia or low temperature cooling in hibernating animals to the point of very low EEG activity, do not affect these consolidated permanent memories (Gerard, 1961).   Humans suffering temporary loss of blood flow to the brain which lasts much beyond the time of EEG depression (though no longer than 5 minutes (Chapters 18, 19)) can upon recovery retain most if not all their previous memories. The lability of recent memories is shown by the phenomenon of *retrograde amnesia*.   After a head concussion, events occurring a short time before the injury are not remembered.   However, there is much variability in the duration of completeness of retrograde amnesia in the reported clinical cases (Russell, 1959).

How are the traces formed?   On the basis of information theory, our memories are composed of so many 'bits' of information.   A tiny part of a patch of light within one visual field is a bit.   The image is composed of many thousands of bits.   Considering all the bits stored within our memory to account for all the scenes, sounds, smells, etc. of our memories indicates that theoretically there are not enough neurons available in the brain to hold all the bits of information (Schmitt, 1962).   Some comparatively larger numbers of sub-cellular elements must be permanently modified to enable us to contain as much information as is present in our memory stores.   A permanent change in synapses has been suggested for such sub-cellular units by Konorski (1948) among others.   More recently Hydén (1959) developed a theory of memories based on the ribonucleic acid (RNA) control of protein production in nerve cells (Chapters 1, 8).   In the theory, neuronal events cause changes in RNA molecules, leading to the production of 'coded' proteins.   These coded proteins continually synthesized in the cell constitute the engrams.   There is little doubt that the informational content of nucleic acid and proteins is sufficiently large to account for all the bits of information required for a large memory store (Schmitt, 1962).   There are also the suggestive results obtained with drugs which modify the RNA levels of neural tissue correlated with changes in learning in the rat (Chamberlain, Rothschild and Gerard, 1963).   An important problem yet to be resolved was mentioned by Dingman and Sporn (1964).   They point out that changes in RNA would, due to its control of protein synthesis, be expected to cause general neuronal alterations without being necessarily related to those specific changes in molecular configurations required by the molecular theory of memory.   In any case, there is difficulty in imagining the translation of excitation changes in the neuron membrane to a related specific sub-cellular RNA change.   There is also the correlative difficulty of envisioning how the information stored in proteins could be retranslated back into neuron activity.

According to our present concepts of nerve activity this would occur via control of synaptic transmitter release at the axon terminations. In spite of the theoretical difficulties with respect to how RNA storage of memories may come about, it would appear that some such sub-cellular basis for the engram is required. It is hoped that future studies will clarify this obscure yet important problem.

REFERENCES

Abt, J. P., Essman, W. B. and Jarvik, M. E. (1961). Ether-induced retrograde amnesia for one-trial conditioning in mice. *Science* **133**: 1477–1478.
Andersson, B., Jewell, P. A. and Larsson, S. (1958). An appraisal of the effects of diencephalic stimulation of conscious animals in terms of normal behavior. *Neurological Basis of Behavior*. Pp. 76–89. Ciba Foundation Symposium. Churchill, London.
Andersson, B. and Larsson, S. (1956). An attempt to condition hypothalamic polydipsia. *Acta Physiol. Scand.* **36**: 377–382.
Best, J. B. (1963). Protophsychology. *Scient. Am.* **208**: 54–62.
Boycott, B. B. and Young, J. Z. (1955). A memory system in *Octopus vulgaris* Lamarck. *Proc. Roy. Soc. B*, **143**: 449–480.
Boycott, B. B. and Young, J. Z. (1957). Effects of interference with the vertical lobe on visual discriminations in *Octopus vulgaris* Lamarck. *Proc. Roy. Soc. B*, **146**: 539–459.
Bureš, J. (1959). Reversible decortication and behavior. *The Central Nervous System and Behavior*. Pp. 207–248. Edited by M. A. B. Brazier. Second Conference. Macy Foundation, New York.
Chamberlain, T. J., Rothschild, G. H. and Gerard, R. W. (1963). Drugs affecting RNA and learning. *Proc. Natl. Acad. Sci.* **49**: 918–924.
Chow, K. L. (1961). Anatomical and electrographical analysis of temporal neocortex in relation to visual discrimination learning in monkeys. *Brain Mechanisms and Learning*. Pp. 507–525. Edited by A. Fessard, R. W. Gerard and J. Konorski. Charles C. Thomas, Springfield.
Chow, K. L., Dement, W. C. and John, E. R. (1957). Conditioned electrocorticographic potentials and behavioral avoidance response in cats. *J. Neurophysiol.* **20**: 482–493.
Cohen, B. D., Brown, G. W. and Brown, M. L. (1957). Avoidance learning motivated by hypothalamic stimulation. *J. Exptl. Psychol.* **53**: 228–233.
Dingman, W. and Sporn, M. B. (1964). Molecular theories of memory. *Science* **144**: 26–29.
Doty, R. (1961). Conditioned reflexes formed and evoked by brain stimulation. *Electrical Stimulation of the Brain*. Chapter 29. Edited by D. E. Sheer. University of Texas Press, Austin.
Doty, R. and Giurgea, C. (1961). Conditioned reflexes established by coupling electrical excitations of two cortical areas. *Brain Mechanisms and Learning*. Pp. 133–151. Edited by A. Fessard, R. W. Gerard and J. Konorski. Charles C. Thomas, Springfield.

Doty, R. W., Rutledge, L. T., Jr. and Larsen, R. M. (1956). Conditioned reflexes established to electrical stimulation of cat cerebral cortex. *J. Neurophysiol.* **19**: 401–415.

Downer, John, L. de C. (1962). Interhemispheric integration in the visual system. *Interhemispheric Relations and Cerebral Dominance.* Chapter 6. Edited by V. B. Mountcastle. Johns Hopkins Press, Baltimore.

Duncan, C. P. (1948). The retroactive effect of electroshock on learning in rats. *J. Comp. Physiol. Psychol.* **42**: 32–44.

Durup, G. and Fessard, A. (1935). L'electroencephalogramme de l'homme. *Ann. Psychol.* **36**: 1–32.

Ferster, C. B. and Skinner, B. F. (1957). *Schedules of Reinforcement.* Appleton-Century-Crofts, Inc., New York.

Fulton, J. F. (1951), *Frontal Lobotomy and Affective Behavior; a Neurophysiological Analysis.* Norton, New York.

Gastaut, H. (1958). Some aspects of the neurophysiological basis of conditioned reflexes and behavior. *Neurological Basis of Behavior.* Ciba Foundation Symposium, Churchill, London.

Gelber, B. (1952). Investigations of the behavior of *Paramecium aurelia*: I. Modification of behavior after training with reinforcement. *J. Comp. Physiol. Psychol.* **45**: 58–65.

Gerard, R. W. (1961). The fixation of experience. *Brain Mechanisms and Learning.* Pp. 21–35. Edited by A. Fessard, R. W. Gerard and J. Konorski. Charles C. Thomas, Springfield.

Gomulicki, B. R. (1953). *The Development and Present Status of the Trace Theory of Memory.* Cambridge University Press, Cambridge.

Harlow, H. F. (1958). Behavioral contributions to interdisciplinary research. *Biological and Biochemical Bases of Behavior.* Pp. 3–23. Edited by H. F. Harlow and C. N. Woolsey. University of Wisconsin Press, Madison.

Hartry, A. L. and Keith-Lee, P. (1964). *Planaria*: memory transfer through cannabalism re-examined. *Science* **146**: 274–275.

Hebb, D. O. (1949). *The Organization of Behavior.* John Wiley & Sons, Inc., New York.

Hernández-Peón, R. (1960). Neurophysiological correlates of habituation and other manifestations of plastic inhibition. *The Moscow Colloquium on Electroencephalography of Higher Nervous Activity.* Edited by H. H. Jasper and G. D. Smirnov. *Electroencephalog. Clin. Neurophysiol. Suppl.* **13**: 101–114.

Hernández-Peón, R., Jouvet, M. and Scherrer, H. (1957). Auditory potentials at cochlear nucleus during acoustic habituation. *Acta Neurol. Latinoamer.* **3**: 144–156.

Herrick, C. J. (1924). *Neurological Foundations of Animal Behavior.* Henry Holt and Company, New York.

Hook, W. (1961). (Editor) *Dimensions of Mind. A Symposium.* Collier Books, New York.

Hunter, J. and Jasper, H. H. (1949). Effects of the thalamic stimulation in unanesthetized animals; arrest reaction and petit-mal seizures, activation patterns and generalized convulsions. *Electroencephalog. Clin. Neurophysiol.* **1**: 305–324.

Hydén, H. (1959).   Biochemical changes in glial cells and nerve cells at varying activity.   *Biochemistry of the Nervous System*.   Edited by F. Brucke.   Pergamon Press, New York.

Jacobsen, C. F. (1936).   Studies of cerebral function in primates.   I. The functions of the frontal association areas in monkeys.   *Comp. Psychol. Monograph*. **13**: 3–60.

Jasper, H. H. (1954).   Functional properties of the thalamic reticular system. *Brain Mechanisms and Consciousness*.   *A Symposium*.   Pp. 374–401. Edited by E. D. Adrian, F. Bremer and H. H. Jasper.   Blackwell, Oxford.

Jasper, H. H., Ricci, G. and Doane, B. (1960).   Microelectrode analysis of cortical cell discharge during avoidance conditioning in the monkey.   *The Moscow Colloquium on Electroencephalography of Higher Nervous Activity*.   *Electroencephalog. Clin. Neurophysiol*.   *Suppl*. **13**: pp. 137–155.

Jasper, H. H. and Shagass, C. (1941).   Conditioning the occipital alpha rhythm in man.   *J. Exptl. Psychol*. **28**: 373–388.

Jennings, H. S. (1905).   *Behavior of Lower Organisms*.   Reprinted 1962, with introduction by D. D. Jensen.   Indiana University Press, Bloomington.

John, E. R. (1962).   Higher nervous functions: brain structures and learning. *Ann. Rev. Physiol*. **23**: 451–458.

John, E. R. and Killam, K. F. (1959).   Electrophysiological correlates of avoidance conditioning in the cat.   *J. Pharmacol. Exptl. Therap*. **125**: 252–274.

Katz, M. S. and Deterline, W. A. (1958).   Apparent learning in the *Paramecium*.   *J. Comp. Physiol. Psychol*. **51**: 243–247.

Keller, F. S. (1954).   *Learning Reinforcement Theory*.   Random House, New York.

Keller, F. S. and Schoenfeld, W. N. (1950).   *Principles of Psychology*. Appleton-Century-Crofts, Inc., New York.

Kimble, G. A. (1961).   *Hilgard and Marquis' Conditioning and Learning*. Second Ed.   Appleton-Century-Crofts, Inc., New York.

Klüver, H. (1941).   Visual functions after removal of the occipital lobes. *J. Psychol*. **11**: 23–45.

Konorski, J. (1948).   *Conditioned Reflexes and Neuron Organization*.   Cambridge University Press, Cambridge.

Konorski, J. (1961).   The physiological approach to the problem of recent memory.   *Brain Mechanisms and Learning*.   Pp. 115–132.   Edited by A. Fessard, R. W. Gerard and J. Konorski.   Charles C. Thomas, Springfield.

Lashley, K. S. (1929).   *Brain Mechanisms and Intelligence*.   University of Chicago Press, Chicago.

Lashley, K. S. (1950).   In search of the engram.   *Soc. Exptl. Biol*. **4**: 454–482.

Masserman, J. H. (1941).   Is the hypothalamus a center of emotion ?   *Psychosom. Med*. **3**: 3–25.

McCleary, R. A. (1961).   Response specificity in the behavioral effects of limbic system lesions in the cat.   *J. Comp. Physiol. Psychol*. **54**: 605–613.

McConnell, J. V., Jacobson, A. L. and Kimble, D. P. (1959).   The effects of regeneration upon retention of a conditioned response in the *Planarian*. *J. Comp. Physiol. Psychol*. **52**: 1–5.

Morrell, F. (1958).   Some electrical events involved in the formation of temporary connection.   *Reticular Formation of the Brain. An International Symposium.*   Little, Brown and Co., Boston.

Morrell, F. and Jasper, H. H. (1956).   Electrographic studies of the formation of temporary connections in the brain.   *Electroenceph. Clin. Neurophysiol.* **8**: 201-215.

Myers, R. E. (1962).   Transmission of visual information within and between the hemispheres: a behavioral study.   *Interhemispheric Relations and Cerebral Dominance.*   Chapter 4.   Edited by V. B. Mountcastle.   Johns Hopkins Press, Baltimore.

Myers, R. E. (1959).   Function of corpus callosum in interocular transfer.   *Brain* **79**: 358–363.

Olds, J. and Olds, M. E. (1961).   Interference and learning in palaeocortical systems.   *Brain Mechanisms and Learning.*   Pp. 153–187.   Edited by A. Fessard, R. W. Gerard and J. Konorski.   Charles C. Thomas, Springfield.

Parker, G. H. (1919).   *The Elementary Nervous System.*   J. B. Lippincott Co., Philadelphia.

Pavlov, I. P. (1927).   *Conditioned Reflexes.*   Translated and Edited by G. V. Anrep.   (Republished, 1960.)   Dover Publications, Inc., New York.

Penfield, W. (1958).   The role of the temporal cortex in recall of past experience and interpretation of the present.   *Neurological Basis of Behavior.*   Pp. 149–174.   Ciba Foundation Symposium.   Churchill, London.

Penfield, W. and Jasper, H. H. (1954).   *Epilepsy and Functional Anatomy of the Human Brain.*   Little, Brown and Co., Boston.

Pribram, K. H. (1958).   Neocortical function in behavior.   *Biological and Biochemical Bases of Behavior.*   Pp. 151–172.   Edited by H. F. Harlow and C. N. Woolsey.   University of Wisconsin Press, Madison.

Pritchard, R. M. (1961).   Stabilized images on the retina.   *Scient. Am.* **204**: 72–78.

Ray, O. S. and Emley, G. (1964).   Time factors in interhemispheric transfer of learning.   *Science* **144**: 76–78.

Rose, J. E. and Woolsey, C. N. (1948).   The orbitofrontal cortex and its connections with the medio-dorsal nucleus in rabbit, sheep and cat.   *Res. Publ. Assoc. Nervous Mental Disease* **27**: 210–232.

Russell, W. R. (1959).   *Brain, Memory, Learning. A Neurologist's View.*   Clarendon Press, Oxford.

Russell, I. S. and Ochs, S. (1963).   Localization of a memory trace in one cortical hemisphere and transfer to the other hemisphere.   *Brain* **86**: 37–54.

Schmitt, F. O. (1962).   (Ed.) *Macromolecular Specificity and Biological Memory.*   M.I.T. Press, Cambridge.

Sharpless, S. and Jasper, H. H. (1956).   Habituation of the arousal reaction.   *Brain* **79**: 655–680.

Sidman, M. (1953).   Avoidance conditioning with brief shock and no exteroceptive warning signal.   *Science* **118**: 157–158.

Skinner, B. F. (1938).   *The Behavior of Organisms.*   Appleton-Century-Crofts, Inc., New York.

Sperry, R. W. (1961).   Cerebral organization and behavior.   *Science* **133**: 1749–1757.

Sperry, R. W. (1962). Some general aspects of interhemispheric integration. *Interhemispheric Relations and Cerebral Dominance.* Chapter 3. Edited by V. B. Mountcastle. Johns Hopkins Press, Baltimore.

Stamm, J. S. (1961). Electrical stimulation of frontal cortex in monkeys during learning of an alternation task. *J. Neurophysiol.* **24**:414–426.

Stamm, J. S. and Pribram, K. H. (1960). Effects of epileptogenic lesions in frontal cortex on learning and retention in monkeys. *J. Neurophysiol.* **23**: 552–563.

Stamm, J. S. and Sperry, R. W. (1957). Function of corpus callosum in contralateral transfer of somesthetic discrimination in cats. *J. Comp. Physiol. Psychol.* **50**: 138–143.

Wells, M. J. (1962). Brain and behavior in cephalopods. Stanford University Press, Stanford.

Yerkes, R. M. (1912). The intelligence of earthworms. *J. Animal Behav.* **2**: 332–352.

Yoshii, N. and Hockaday, W. J. (1958). Conditioning of frequency characteristic repetitive EEG response with intermittent photic stimulation. *Electroencephalog. Clin. Neurophysiol.* **10**: 487–502.

Young, J. Z. (1961). Learning and discrimination in the octopus. *Biol. Rev.* **36**: 32–96.

Index